# INSTRUCTOR'S MANUAL WITH TEST BANK

*to accompany*

# CALCULUS

SINGLE AND MULTIVARIABLE                SECOND EDITION

**Deborah Hughes-Hallett**
*Harvard University*

**Andrew M. Gleason**
*Harvard University*

**William G. McCallum**
*University of Arizona*

**et al.**

| | | |
|---|---|---|
| Prepared by: | Frank Avenoso | Karen R. Thrash |
| | *Nassau Community College* | *University of Southern Mississippi* |
| | Philip Cheifetz | Joe Watkins |
| | *Nassau Community College* | *University of Arizona* |
| | Brad G. Osgood | Eric K. Wepsic |
| | *Stanford University* | *Harvard University* |
| | Jeff Tecosky-Feldman | Millie Johnson |
| | *Haverford College* | *Western Washington University* |
| With the assistance of: | Bill Dunn | Barbara Shipman |
| | *Montgomery College* | *University of Arizona* |
| Compiled by : | Srdjan Divac | Denise C. Todd |
| | *Harvard University* | *University of Arizona* |

**John Wiley & Sons, Inc.**
**New York • Chichester • Weinheim • Brisbane • Singapore • Toronto**

This project was supported, in part,
by the
**National Science Foundation**
Opinions expressed are those of the authors
and not necessarily those of the Foundation
Grant No. DUE-9352905

# PREFACE

The best way to get a feel for what we have done, and to get excited about it, is to read the book; above all to read and try the problems. But if you are the sort of person who always reads the manual first, here it is. It is organized into several parts, starting with The Book and The Chapters. Read the first part to get a general idea of our approach. Then, as you read through the text, refer to the second part for comments on particular chapters. When you are preparing individual classes, you may want to look back at the second part for tips on each section and comments about specific problems. Additional parts of the manual contain sample syllabi, masters for overhead transparencies, calculator programs, sample exam questions and gateway tests.

# Table of Contents

# PART I

# THE BOOK

## A New Curriculum With a Variety of Options

The first edition of this book was the work of faculty at a consortium of eleven institutions, supported by the National Science Foundation. It represents the first consensus between such a diverse group of research mathematicians and instructors to have shaped a mainstream calculus text. The second edition has the same vision as the first edition and provides instructors with additional choices through the *Focus On* sections. Instructors can select a focus for their course which reflects their interests and the needs of their students. In particular:

- All *Focus On* sections are optional.
- Chapter 3 (the definite integral) may be covered immediately before Chapter 6 (the antiderivative).
- In Chapters 5 and 8, instructors may select the sections relevant to their students.
- Chapters 9 and 10 may be covered in either order.

## The Development of Mathematical Thinking

The first stage in the development of mathematical thinking is the acquisition of a clear intuitive picture of the central ideas. In the next stage, the student learns to reason with the intuitive ideas and explain the reasoning clearly in plain English. After this foundation has been laid, there is a choice of direction. Some students, for example mathematics majors, may benefit from a more theoretical approach, while others, for example science and engineering majors, may benefit from a further exploration of modeling. Supplementary sections, *Focus on Theory* and *Focus on Modeling*, provide material to support either choice.

### Focus on Theory

Calculus as a logical structure of theorem and proof is a masterpiece of mathematics. Its beauty attracts mathematically inclined students to their vocation. In the *Focus on Theory* sections we have chosen a few topics to cover in depth. We show how axioms, definitions, and theorems are formulated, and how proofs are constructed. Since we believe that to understand and appreciate this material students must work with it themselves, we have included challenging exercises that guide students to construct definitions and proofs on their own.

### Focus on Modeling

Calculus is a powerful tool for analyzing the real world. Students gain an understanding of the power of calculus by focusing on its use in an extended problem. The *Focus on Modeling* sections explore selected applications of calculus in depth.

## The Development of Mathematical Skills

To use calculus effectively, students need skill in both symbolic manipulation and the use of technology. The exact proportions of each may vary widely, depending on the preparation of the student and the wishes of the instructor. The book is adaptable to many different combinations.

### Focus on Practice

These new sections increase students' skills in the mechanics of differentiation and integration.

### Technology

The book does not require any specific software or technology. It has been used with graphing calculators, graphing software, and computer algebra systems. Any technology with the ability to graph functions and perform numerical integration will suffice. Students are expected to use their own judgement to determine where technology is useful.

## The Rule of Four

The Rule of Four means that, where appropriate, concepts should be introduced graphically, numerically, analytically, and verbally. This means giving equal time to all four components of understanding. It means expecting and accepting geometric or verbal explanations: for example, giving full credit to a student who can give a clear graphical or verbal explanation of why $f'' > 0$ means the graph of $f$ is concave up. It means giving at least partial credit for a correct numerical estimate of an answer, such as

$$\frac{d}{dx}(x^x)\Big|_{x=2} \approx \frac{2.01^{2.01} - 2^2}{0.01} \approx 6.8.$$

The Rule of Four means teaching in such a way that students are encouraged to make such approximations. We often give real numbers as approximations in this text: 3.63, not $\pi^2/e$. This is because decimals are closer to everyday experience: when you measure a board, your tape measure reads 3.63, not $\pi^2/e$. We want to encourage students to apply their common sense.

## The Problems

The problems are the heart of the text. Assign fewer of them than you normally would, and give the students more time. Many require thought and the ability to write clearly. There are some essay questions, questions that require graphical and numerical work rather than algebra, and questions that require use of a calculator or computer program.

Verbal explanations are an essential part of the course. Composing written answers helps students clarify their own understanding and reading these explanations will provide you with valuable insight into students' thinking processes.

Many of the problems in the text do not have unique answers. If you plan to use student graders or lab assistants, urge them to be open to a variety of interpretations and explanations. Be flexible. Any reasonable answer (with reasonable justification) should be accepted.

Although many of the problems are not difficult, students are not accustomed to reading and interpreting math problems. They expect to see problems which mimic the examples in the text—and have unique answers in the back of the book. The initial shock (perhaps even hostility) at finding these conditions changed needs to be dealt with. You may need to reassure students frequently that these problems are indeed different, but that their efforts to deal with them will pay off in the end. More detailed comments on some of the problems are included in the second part of this guide.

## Technology

If you mistrust technology, listen to this student, who started out the same way:

Using computers is strange, but surprisingly beneficial, and in my opinion is what leads to success in this class. I have difficulty visualizing graphs in my head, and this has always led to my downfall in calculus. With the assistance of the computers, that stress was no longer a factor, and I was able to concentrate on the concepts behind the shapes of the graphs, and since these became gradually more clear, I got increasingly better at picturing what the graphs should look like. It's the old story of not being able to get a job without previous experience, but not being able to get experience without a job. Relying on the computer to help me avoid graphing, I was tricked into focusing on what the graphs meant instead of how to make them look right, and what graphs symbolize is the fundamental basis of this class. By being able to see what I was trying to describe and learn from, I could understand a lot more about the concepts, because I could change the conditions and see the results. For the first time, I was able to see how everything works together . . . .

That was a student at the University of Arizona who took calculus in Fall 1990, the first time we used the text. She was terrified of calculus, got a C on her first test, but finished with an A for the course.

The text assumes the students have access to a computer program or calculator that:

- finds roots of equations,
- draws graphs of functions,
- integrates functions numerically.

In addition, for the chapter on differential equations it is helpful (but not essential) for the students to have access to a computer or calculator that

- draws slope fields,
- computes numerically and graphs solutions to differential equations.

## Calculator Programs

Calculator programs for several types of calculators are provided on page 121 of this manual.

## A Book to be Read as a Book

This book is an account of the basic ideas of calculus. It is not a reference book nor an encyclopedia; the writing is informal because we want students to read it. However, we have intentionally made it difficult for students to do what they normally do, which is to look first at the homework problems, then to look for a worked example that fits the template, and only as a last resort to read the pieces of text between the examples.

## Overview of Book: What's in Each Chapter

- **Chapter 1: A Library of Functions.** This chapter introduces all the elementary functions to be used in the book. Although the functions are probably familiar, the graphical, numerical, verbal, and modeling approach to them is likely to be new. We introduce exponential functions at the earliest possible stage, since they are fundamental to the understanding of real-world processes.
- **Chapter 2: Key Concept—The Derivative.** The purpose of this chapter is to give the student a practical understanding of the definition of the derivative and its interpretation as an instantaneous rate of change. The power rule is introduced; other rules are introduced in Chapter 4.
- **Chapter 3: Key Concept—The Definite Integral.** The purpose of this chapter is to give the student a practical understanding of the definite integral as a limit of Riemann sums and to bring out the connection between the derivative and the definite integral in the Fundamental Theorem of Calculus. Some instructors using the first edition of the book have delayed covering Chapter 3 until after Chapter 5 without any difficulty.
- **Chapter 4: Short-Cuts to Differentiation.** The derivatives of all the functions in Chapter 1 are introduced, as well as the rules for differentiating products, quotients, and composite functions.
- **Chapter 5: Using the Derivative.** The aim of this chapter is to enable the student to use the derivative in solving problems, including optimization and graphing. It is not necessary to cover all the sections.
- **Chapter 6: Constructing Antiderivatives.** This chapter focuses on going backward from a derivative to the original function, first graphically and numerically, then analytically. It introduces the Second Fundamental Theorem of Calculus and the concept of a differential equation.
- **Chapter 7: Integration.** This chapter includes several techniques of integration; others are included in the table of integrals. There is a discussion of numerical methods and of improper integrals.

- **Chapter 8: Using the Definite Integral.** This chapter emphasizes the idea of subdividing a quantity to produce Riemann sums which, in the limit, yield a definite integral. It shows how the integral is used in geometry, physics, and economics; it is not necessary to cover all the sections.

- **Chapter 9: Approximations and Series.** This chapter introduces Taylor Series and Fourier series via the idea of approximating functions with simpler functions. Geometric series, the ratio test, the harmonic series, and alternating series are discussed.

- **Chapter 10: Differential Equations.** This chapter introduces differential equations. The emphasis is on qualitative solutions, modeling, and interpretation.

- **Chapter 11: Functions of Many Variables.** Functions of many variables are introduced using formulas, surface graphs, contour diagrams, and tables. Attention is paid to the idea of a cross-section of a function, obtained by varying one variable independently of the others, as this notion helps students understand partial derivatives.

- **Chapter 12: A Fundamental Tool: Vectors.** Vectors are defined as geometric objects having direction and magnitude and then are represented in terms of coordinates. Equivalent geometric and algebraic definitions of the dot and cross products are given.

- **Chapter 13: Differentiating Functions of Many Variables.** This chapter introduces the notions of partial derivative, directional derivative, gradient, and differential. Local linearity is used to introduce differentiability and the multivariable chain rule. Higher order partial derivatives and their application to quadratic Taylor approximations are discussed.

- **Chapter 14: Optimization.** The ideas of the previous chapter are applied to optimization problems, both constrained and unconstrained. The section on constrained optimization discusses Lagrange multipliers, equality and inequality constraints.

- **Chapter 15: Integrating Functions of Many Variables.** The multivariable definite integral is introduced graphically using a density function. Double and triple integrals in Cartesian, polar, spherical, and cylindrical coordinates are discussed.

- **Chapter 16: Parametric Curves.** This chapter starts by representing curves parametrically, and then uses parametric representations to describe motion and to analyze velocity and acceleration.

- **Chapter 17: Vector Fields.** Vector fields are introduced in this chapter and the foundation is laid for the geometric approach in Chapters 18, 19, and 20 to line integrals, flux integrals, divergence, and curl.

- **Chapter 18: Line Integrals.** A coordinate-free definition of line integrals is presented, and then line integrals are calculated using parameterizations. Path independent, or conservative fields, gradient fields, the Fundamental Theorem of Calculus for Line Integrals, and Green's Theorem are discussed.

- **Chapter 19: Flux Integrals.** The flux integral of a vector field through a surface is introduced in the same way as line integrals. First a coordinate-free definition is given, then flux integrals are calculated over surface graphs, portions of cylinders, and portions of spheres.

- **Chapter 20: Calculus of Vector Fields.** The divergence and curl are introduced in a coordinate-free way; the divergence in terms of flux density, and curl in terms of circulation density. The formulas in Cartesian coordinates are then given. The Divergence Theorem and Stokes' Theorem are explained geometrically.

- **Appendices:** Polar coordinates, complex numbers, determinants, and some additional projects.

## The First Three Chapters and Chapter Eleven

If you have taught calculus frequently, you may be tempted to go too fast through these chapters. We know from experience how important it is for the students to have a thorough grasp of the material in Chapter 1. Although much of this material should be familiar to the students, it is presented in a sufficiently different manner that most will find it quite new. It is crucial that students get comfortable with graphical and numerical work early on. The idea of Chapter 1 is to make the students thoroughly familiar with functions from all points of view. For example, we want students to be able to recognize that a function is linear from a table of its values, or to understand in graphical terms the relative growth rates of functions.

Chapters 2 and 3 introduce the key concepts of derivative and definite integral one after the other, in order to show clearly the relation between them. It is only after this introduction that we get into the techniques and formulas for differentiation and integration. Chapters 2 and 3 are important to the spirit of the book. You should cover them slowly enough for the students to think about what the key concepts really mean.

It is equally important for the students to have a thorough grasp of the material in Chapter 11. Students need to be comfortable with the many different ways of representing functions of many variables and with three-dimensional visualization. For example, we want students to be able to recognize that a function is linear from a table of its values, from its graph, and from its contour diagram.

## "Focus On" Sections

These sections are optional.

## A Few Warnings: What Students Find Difficult

Students are often reasonably proficient at using rules to manipulate formulas. They are much less proficient at understanding and interpreting mathematics critically, as well as applying it to practical situations. This means that many students initially find the material in this book difficult. In particular, if you have students who have previously done well in courses emphasizing manipulation, both you and they may be surprised at the difficulty they have. Dealing with their apprehension will probably require your repeated reassurance, particularly early on.

Students have more difficulty with tables and graphs than they do with formulas. They confuse functions with their formulas, the rules that generate them. Tables are usually foreign to them; they need time and practice to get used to them. Graphs can also be difficult; while most students will have seen graphs before, they may not be used to interpreting them. For example, many students will have difficulty interpreting a graph of distance versus time, often confusing it with a trajectory. A graph of velocity versus time can also cause them trouble. This difficulty with interpretation is one of the reasons for our emphasis on interpreting the derivative and the definite integral.

Students often have considerable difficulty thinking geometrically. Many, for example, cannot read the slope of a line from its graph. Try to wean them away from depending on formulas to estimate such quantities. They may also have problems interpreting geometric objects: many confuse the secant line itself with the average rate of change (which is the slope of the secant line), and may confuse the tangent line with the derivative (which is the slope of the tangent line).

Many students have difficulty with basic material, such as exponential functions and logarithms, or even percents or fractions. We suggest that you not spend too much time at the beginning of the course going over manipulative rules but instead review as you go along whenever there is difficulty or confusion.

Students may also misinterpret results on their graphing calculators or computers. This is often due to the computer's tendency to deal badly with the very large (say, near an asymptote) and the very small (roundoff error). Finding an appropriate viewing region for a graph can be difficult for students as well. They often give up too easily when graphing to find points of intersection, especially when very large values are involved (for example, $y = e^x$ and $y = 2 + 1000x^8$). Students sometimes also assume that if the cursor is on top of the point of intersection then the $(x, y)$ values are exact, whereas these values can actually be off by large amounts, depending on the window settings.

## Teaching Style

In the spirit of the book, try to make your class interactive: make it a class rather than a lecture. Since many of the problems can be done by several different methods, a useful class discussion can result from having students explain to the rest of the class what method they used and why. As you develop new ideas, ask questions to the class (and give them time to answer) to get students into the habit of thinking ahead and of asking themselves "what if."

# PART II

# THE CHAPTERS

In this part of the manual, we give more detailed information about each chapter and section of the book. However, there are many different teaching styles. If you have your own ideas on how to teach a particular section, by all means try them out (and let us know how they work). On the other hand, if you have trouble knowing what to do with a particular section, or what the main point is supposed to be, look at the information on that section. There you will find information on timing (assuming 50-minute classes), as well as suggestions on how to introduce the topic, some extra examples, tips on what the students find particularly hard, or ideas for a computer lab.

In addition, we briefly discuss the problems for each section. The suggested problems were selected to reflect the Rule of Four, wherever possible. We are *not* recommending that you assign all the suggested problems. You may need to adjust the number of problems up or down depending upon the needs of your class and the speed at which you intend to cover the material.

# CHAPTER ONE

## Overview

This chapter was the most difficult to write and is probably the hardest to teach. The differences in students' backgrounds and the universal resistance to being asked to think about math in new ways can be frustrating for you and your students. Try not to get bogged down on any particular section; keep the flow as fast-paced and lively as possible. The time needed to cover the material in the first eleven sections can range from around eight to twelve 50-minute class meetings. An extremely fast class for well-prepared students might cover the material in as few as six meetings. Be assured (and assure your class) that the time spent on these sections will pay off later on.

All the elementary functions to be used in the book are introduced in this chapter. Although the functions are probably familiar, the graphical, numerical, and modeling approach to them is probably new. Our purpose is to acquaint the student with each function's individuality (the shape of its graph, characteristic properties, comparative growth rates, and general uses), to give the student the skill to read graphs and think graphically, to read tables and think numerically, and to apply these skills, along with their algebraic skills, to modeling the real world. Further attention is given to constructing new functions from old ones—how to shift, flip and stretch the graph of any basic function into a new, related function.

The section on inverse functions (Section 1.5) may be omitted or covered later in the course. The rest of the first eleven sections of this chapter are fundamental to this course.

### Changes from the First Edition

Compound interest moved to the appendix; introduction to continuity moved in from the appendix; optional Focus on Theory sections.

## 1.1   WHAT'S A FUNCTION?

**Class Time:** One half to one class

## Key points

The Rule of Four: representing functions by tables, graphs, formulas, and words.

## Ideas for the class

Start with the concept of function. Emphasize from the outset that a function is nothing but a rule that uniquely assigns to one number some other number: this rule is not necessarily a "math formula." Students often believe functions and formulas are one and the same, so lead off with examples that deemphasize formulas in favor of tables, graphs, and verbal descriptions.

To start the ball rolling, describe a situation familiar to the students. For example:

- the height above the ground of an object dropped from a ledge or a plane, as a function of time,
- the value of a computer or a car over time,
- the number of minutes it takes water to come to a boil as a function of altitude,
- the efficiency (mpg) of an auto with respect to speed (mph).

The options are many. Have students draw a graph depicting the situation and justify the shape of their graph. Ask for reasonable data and put the data in a table. Or, describe a situation, ask for data, and then plot the graph.

Try to include the terminology from the text (domain/range, continuous/discrete, increasing/decreasing), and to discuss the merits of each method of representation. (Graphs give a good picture of the global behavior; tables are often the way functions originate – as from measurements of a physical quantity.)

If you have chosen a situation for which a formula is reasonable (e.g., a falling object or straight-line depreciation), you can take the final step in the Rule of Four. If not, fine. Most of the problems deal with words, graphs and tables.

**New:** Interval notation is introduced.

## Problems

1, 2, 3, 13, 14, 15, 24 — are the first of many requests for a written explanation or story. Be flexible in accepting varied answers, but stick to your guns from the beginning on the need to explain.

8–12 — require a graphical representation of a story. Assign a couple of these. Problems 6 and 9 are particularly good for class discussion, before or after they are assigned.

4–7 — ask for formula representations using direct/inverse proportion.

16–23 — ask for the domain and range from graphs and formulas.

24 — an example which shows how early thinkers struggled with ideas that are now used by scientists everyday. This problem could serve as a lead-in for the discussion on lines in the next section or as an example for that section.

**Suggested Problems:** 2, 3, 5, 9, 12, 13, 17.

**Problems Requiring Substantial Use of Algebra:** 22, 23.

## 1.2  LINEAR FUNCTIONS

**Class Time:** One half to one class

## Key points

Linear functions are fundamental by virtue of the property that characterizes them: the value of the function changes by equal amounts over equal intervals. In other words, as the independent variable changes by a fixed amount, a constant amount is added to (or subtracted from) the value of the function.

**New:** Δ-notation introduced; "budget constraint" example removed.

## Ideas for the class

Follow the Rule of Four. Start with a table of values of a linear function, and ask the students to give you the slope or the formula. It's a good idea to use a real life example such as the Olympic pole vault (page 7) or the success of search and rescue teams (page 9). Otherwise students will think that you are simply trying to torture them by making a table, then hiding the equation that produced it. You want the class to focus on how the formula is deduced from the table, not on how the table is made from the formula. Students will have trouble at first realizing that they can see the slope (or rate of change) of such a function by looking at the ratio between an increment in $y$ and the corresponding increment in $x$. (It's important to give some tables whose $x$-values aren't evenly spaced.)

Also, give the students a verbal description of a linear function and ask them to write down its equation. For example: The cost of a case of apples fresh from the orchard is $20, but it drops by 35¢ a day; write a formula for a function that gives the cost of a case which has been sitting in the store for $t$ days. Again emphasize that the characteristic property of a linear function was embodied in this verbal description in the constant rate of decrease in the price.

Students should be able to see from a graph that a slope is approximately 2 or approximately $-1/2$ without computing the slope from two points. (You might be surprised how many students can't do this.) If you want to calculate some slopes from points, have different students pick different pairs of points to do so. Point out that a characteristic property of linear functions is that the slope is the same regardless of the points chosen.

The terms increasing and decreasing are introduced in this section. Be sure to stress that these definitions apply as the independent variable goes from left to right. Some students are confused about this—they say, for example, that $f(x) = x^2$ increases for negative $x$; after all, the curve is going up from the origin. It's only natural to make this sort of mistake at first.

Students find it difficult to think of linear functions as functions rather than as straight lines. They find it difficult to recognize linearity from a table of values. They also find it quite difficult to make a mathematical model; it is worth going over one of the examples from the text in detail.

## Problems

Nearly all of the problems for this section involve a formula at some point; equations of lines are important. Assign problems that reflect a variety of graphical, numerical and verbal representations.

7–9 — involve properties of parallel and perpendicular lines.

10, 11, 19, 20 — graphical interpretation. Students will find these more difficult than you'd think.

12 — requires the distance formula.

14 — excellent problem. This simple-looking problem will point out which students are reading the problems and which are not. [Many students will graph a straight line increasing from the origin.]

15–22 — multi-step problems, good for discussion (preferably after assigned). Some are hard for students because they involve literal constants rather than numbers.

23–24 — similar ideas. If you pick just one, try the yam (23), as yams become quite famous (perhaps infamous) in the text.

**Suggested Problems:** 2, 6, 8, 11, 14, 16, 18, 23.

## 1.3  EXPONENTIAL FUNCTIONS

**Class Time:** One or two classes

## Key points

Exponential functions are characterized by a simple property: the value of the function changes by equal ratios over equal intervals. In other words, as the independent variable changes by a fixed amount, the value of the function changes by a constant factor. (Contrast with the way in which linear functions change.)

**New:** Expanded discussion of asymptotes.

## Ideas for the class

Start with a table of values of $2^t$ at $t = 0, 1, 2, \ldots$. This could be the population of a colony of bacteria that is doubling every hour. Point out that the $y$-values double every time, hence the 2 in the base of the exponential function. Now give a table of values of, say, $2 \cdot (1.1)^t$ for the same $t$-values, but without the formula. Ask the students how they would decide if this is also an exponential function (answer: take ratios of successive values to see if they are the same each time). One can see that the constant in front is 2 by looking at the value at $t = 0$. (Note: students have particular trouble coming up with a formula from a table when the value at $t = 0$ is not given, and if you have time you may want to do such an example.) Again, an example using real data always helps: perhaps population projections for a local community.

Point out that given a table of values for a mystery function (with equally spaced $x$-values), you can test it for linearity by subtracting successive $y$-values, while you can test to see if it is an exponential function by taking ratios of successive $y$-values. Demonstrate the explosive growth of exponential functions both by tabulating values and by examining graphs on different scales using a graphing program. Practice deriving the formula from a table, or from particular values. Be sure to also give examples of exponential functions which are decreasing and ones that increase to a horizontal asymptote.

Concavity is introduced in this section. Give examples of increasing and decreasing functions of all possible concavities (up, down, and straight lines). Connect concavity with increasing/decreasing rates of change (this function is "increasing at an increasing rate"), but don't get too technical.

Students often find this material surprisingly hard. They have had little experience with exponential functions, and are often not comfortable with percents, which are important here. In particular, they find the formula for exponential functions (on page 17) difficult.

## Problems

1–6 — straightforward interpretations of the terminology from the text.

7–9, 24–25 — involve tables. In 24, students do not need to find a formula; they just need to compare the ways in which the data are increasing.

10–13 — more graphs to draw from stories. 12 is particularly good because it combines a line and an exponential.

14–17 — explore asymptotic behavior.

18, 19 — provide data in the form of function notation.

20–23 — assign at least a couple. Students may need some help getting started. [For 23 refer to the drug build-up example of the text.]

26–32 — assign at most a couple, as these take time. On 26, students are expected to use trial and error, as logarithms have not been discussed yet. Problems 27–29 demonstrate that these questions can be answered without knowing an initial quantity (a frightening idea to students). 32 introduces the idea of fitting different models to data, which is good for discussion afterwards.

**Suggested Problems:** 7-9, 10, 11, 16, 19, 20, 22, 28, 30.

**Problems Requiring Substantial Use of Algebra:** 18–19, 21–23, 27-30.

## 1.4  POWER FUNCTIONS

**Class Time:** Half a class or a whole computer lab

## Key points

How different powers compare on large and small scales; Basic shapes of graphs of power functions. Increasing exponential functions grow more quickly than power functions.

## Ideas for the class

Ideally, this is a class in which to draw lots of graphs on the computer or the graphing calculator. For example, graph $x$, $x^2$, $x^3$, and $x^4$ on scales $[-5, 5]$ by $[-10, 10]$ (to illustrate the general shapes and the behavior of even versus odd exponents), then on $[0, 1.2]$ by $[0, 2]$ (to illustrate small scale behavior), then on $[0, 10]$ by $[0, 10^n]$ for $n = 1, 2, 3, 4$ (to illustrate large scale behavior). If you are doing this in the classroom, get the students to suggest a $y$-scale that will clearly distinguish between the various powers. Don't be afraid of being too elementary; you would be amazed at the trouble students have picturing even simple functions like power functions. Briefly review odd and even integral powers as well as zero and negative powers and fractional powers.

Even better, if you have the facilities, devote the entire class to a computer lab, where you walk around looking over the students' shoulders and get them to do the work. For example, get them to do the problem on choosing different viewing rectangles to get different pictures of $x^4$ and $3^x$ (see Problem 25). Students find it quite hard to understand the way the choice of scale affects the dominance of one function over another; they are used to thinking of functions in terms of a single picture. Demonstrate, that for large $x$, $2^x$ will overwhelm $x^n$ for all $n$. Help students select appropriate window settings early on. Don't underestimate how difficult it can be for students to choose a good window on a computer or calculator.

Unfortunately, you may not have the facilities for this kind of lab. If not, the graphs in the text are good and fairly easy to reconstruct on the blackboard or overheads. You might prepare transparencies with the graphs of $x^3$ and $2^x$ on $[0, 10]$ by $[0, 10]$, $[0, 10]$ by $[0, 100]$, and $[0, 10]$ by $[0, 1000]$. For each picture, ask the students which graph *looks* like it will ultimately dominate. Use a final picture of the two functions on $[0, 20]$ by $[0, 10,000]$ to show that $2^x$ ultimately dominates, although it doesn't look like it on a small scale.

## Problems

1–8 — simplifying using the rules of exponents.

9–14 — students should be encouraged to recognize long-term behavior from the formula rather than resorting to technology here. Some of these would be good for in-class examples.

15–16, 25 — are all meant to be worked using graphing technology.

19–22 — applications. Assign one or two of these.

23–24 — assign at least one of these. Students feel at a loss as to how to begin at first. Good for class discussion after students have thought about the problem.

**Suggested Problems:** 3, 4, 6, 8, 10, 18, 19, 22, 24, 25.

**Problems Requiring Substantial Use of Algebra:** 1–8, 19.

## 1.5  NOTES ON INVERSE FUNCTIONS

**Class Time:** One class, or omit

## Key points

The concept of an inverse function.

## Ideas for the class

Too often students have a purely algebraic understanding of inverse functions: they know how to solve an equation for $x$ then swap $x$ and $y$, but they don't know why they are doing this. There are several ways to get around this. Application problems can be particularly useful in getting students to think about what an inverse function tells you. The beginning of the section, which gives times for Arturo Barrios's world record 10 kilometer run is a case in point. Distance (in meters) in the original function gives elapsed time (in seconds); in the inverse, the elapsed time yields the distance run.

Inverses lend themselves beautifully to the Rule of Four. Draw the graph of a function on the board (but give no formula) and ask for, say, $f^{-1}(5)$ or $f^{-1}(2)$. Then show that since the point $(1, 5)$ is on the graph of $f$, the point $(5, 1)$ is on the graph of $f^{-1}$. Use this reasoning to sketch the function $f^{-1}$, and then draw the reflecting line $y = x$. This will show that the graph of $f$ determines the graph of $f^{-1}$, even without a formula. This same interpretation can also be made numerically by simply writing out $f$ and $f^{-1}$ in tabular form, as in the Barrios example in the text (page 31, Tables 1.19 and 1.20), and noting that the table for $f^{-1}$ is obtained from that of $f$ by reversing the $x$ and $y$ columns.

Another way to describe the inverse function is in purely operational terms: the inverse function to $f$ is the function that undoes whatever $f$ does. For example, if $f$ transforms a frog into a prince, then $f^{-1}$ would begin with the prince and return the frog. For a more mathematical example, let $f(x) = 1/(x + 1)$, and determine the inverse verbally without doing any algebra. Just say out loud what $f$ does: it adds 1 to $x$ then takes the reciprocal of the result. So the inverse function must take the reciprocal first, then subtract 1; i.e., the inverse function is $g(x) = (1/x) - 1$. Note that this process requires students to decompose functions. The more practice they get doing this, the better—they'll need it for the chain rule.

## Problems

Nearly all of the problems for this section require students to write an explanation. These are very important—a few short sentences will tell you (and your students) a lot about their understanding of concepts.

12 — only assign if graphing technology is available.

14 — many students will put the 2.2 on the wrong side of the equation.

**Suggested Problems:** 2, 4, 10, 11, 12, 13, 17.

## 1.6  LOGARITHMS

**Class Time:** One class

## Key points

The logarithm as the inverse of the exponential; Using the logarithm to solve equations involving exponentials; Getting practice using the calculator to solve equations which can't be solved analytically.

**New:** Problems and examples asking to solve for intersections have been removed. Technology which does this is assumed.

## Ideas for the class

Many students come into the course with little or no understanding of logarithms. Define $\log_{10} x$, both symbolically and in words. Draw a graph of $10^x$ and read off the values of $\log_{10} x$. Discuss how the slow growth of $\log_{10} x$ follows from the rapid growth of $10^x$; illustrate this by asking how large $x$ needs to be to get $10^x$ equal to a thousand, a million, a billion, etc. Emphasize the inverse relation between the exponential and the logarithm. Compare their graphs and explain why they are symmetrical about the line $y = x$. Make sure that students have a basic picture in their minds of the graph of the logarithm, and compare it with power functions and exponentials. They should be building up a catalog of graphs to go with their library of functions.

Students sometimes have difficulty deciding whether a graph represents an exponential or a logarithmic function. You can give them the following rule of thumb: an exponential function has a horizontal asymptote, and a logarithmic function has a vertical asymptote. (This will help students who have trouble telling apart $y = 1 - 10^{-x}$ and $y = \log x$, for example.) Make sure you ask students why this rule of thumb is true.

Do a number of examples using the logarithm to solve for an exponent (e.g. "How long will it be until the population reaches. . . ?") It's always worth using real data on the population of countries or cities that the students are familiar with.

## Problems

If your students are weak (or rusty) on the rules of logarithms, there is no harm in assigning all or part of problems 2–17 to be worked as needed—and providing a key for students to check their own work. It is not necessarily beneficial to spend a lot of class time reviewing logarithm rules at this time, so try not to get bogged down here. Pick a few of the other problems to give some practice using logs. Students' abilities to interpret graphs are generally weak regardless of their manipulative skills. They may have problems finding the slope and intercept from the graph for 22, but it is an excellent problem to assign. Students generally like real world applications such as Problems 23–28.

**Suggested Problems:** 20, 21, 24, 25, 27, plus 2-17, as needed.

**Problems Requiring Substantial Use of Algebra:** 2–17, 23–27, 29.

## 1.7  THE NUMBER $e$ AND NATURAL LOGARITHMS

**Class Time:** Half to one class

## Key points

The base $e$ is just another number; its naturalness as a base for exponentials will become clear in Chapter 4. By varying the constant $k$ in $e^{kt}$, any exponential can be expressed with base $e$. The inverse of $e^x$ is the natural logarithm.

**New:** The time constant, often used in engineering instead of half-life, is introduced in Example 5.

## Ideas for the class

A practical way of introducing $e^x$ is to point out that it has its own button on the student's calculator. Be honest that there is no great justification *yet* for singling out $e$ as a base and calling it natural, but point out that the justification will be given in Chapter 4. A good in-class exercise is to have students find (by trial and error) the approximate value of $k$ that makes $e^k = 2$. (Determine $k$ to at least four decimal places. This won't take long.) Then have students use graphing technology to match the graphs of $e^{kt}$ and $2^t$. Finally, find $k$ using the natural logarithm. Approximating $k$ numerically and graphically first can help make the number given by the calculator for $\ln 2$ seem less mysterious.

Work some examples (like Example 3) with the function expressed both in base $a$ and base $e$.

## Problems

2–23 — involve rules of exponents and logarithms. Once again, you may want to assign some of these and give out a key for students to check their own work. Students with weak algebra skills will have trouble with some.

32 — algebraically difficult for many students.

33–46 — plenty of applications. Choose some to assign. Most are straightforward uses of the formulas on page 41, but 36 is similar to the drug buildup example in Section 1.3.

**Suggested Problems:** (Some from 2–23, as needed), 34, 40, 42, 44, 45.

**Problems Requiring Substantial Use of Algebra:** 2–27, 29–32, 34–35, 37–46.

## 1.8  NEW FUNCTIONS FROM OLD

**Class Time:** One class, or use part of a class now and then review this material as you teach later sections

## Key points

Graphical interpretation of linear combinations of functions; Modeling interpretation of composition of functions; Basic manipulations of graphs, including shifts, flips, and stretches; Odd and even functions.

## Ideas for the class

It's very important for students to recognize basic manipulations of the functions in their library. They should be comfortable with the following facts and know how to use them: $f(x) + k$ and $f(x + k)$ represent vertical and horizontal shifts, respectively; $-f(x)$ and $f(-x)$ represent vertical and horizontal flips; $kf(x)$ and $f(kx)$ represent vertical and horizontal distortions, either "stretches" or "shrinks" depending on the magnitude of $k$. You can use the Rule of Four to demonstrate these. Starting with a table of values for $f(x)$, make new tables of $f(x + 1)$, $f(x) + 1$, $-f(x)$, $f(-x)$, etc. Compare the ensuing graphs, and discuss. Then give a formula for $f$ and derive formulas for related functions. (This also gives a good review of function notation.) A function like $f(x) = x^2 - 4x + 7$ is a good example, as it is a parabola with vertex $(2, 3)$ and thus undergoes obvious changes when flipped or shifted. Trigonometric functions can also be used, but as they won't have been covered yet, you may have to rely on calculators to graph $\sin x$.

Have students identify (by eye!) where the functions being studied are concave up or down.

## Problems

3–11, 22–25 — provide a variety of composition exercises and also present numerous opportunities for algebraic errors. Beware of improper simplifications.

18–21 — answers are not unique.

26–28 — require graphing technology.

12–15 and 37–40 — assign some of these. Students still need to be weaned from reliance on formulas. 40 may be difficult, as the text does not discuss reciprocals.

30–35 — are difficult but worthwhile because they require that students think about the meaning of composition. Suggest that students make tables for 33–35 (see solution manual).

29 and 41 — good, but hard for some students.

**Suggested Problems:** 1, 3, 4, 6, 9, 18, 27, 31, 32, 33, 41.

**Problems Requiring Substantial Use of Algebra:** 3–11, 22–25.

## 1.9   THE TRIGONOMETRIC FUNCTIONS

**Class Time:** One class

### Key points

The basic picture of a sine curve as an infinitely repeating wave; its use to represent periodic phenomena; Amplitude, period, and radians.

### Ideas for the class

Work entirely in radians: make sure that students' calculators are set to radians.

Start by drawing the graph of $\sin x$ on the blackboard. Point out its amplitude (1) and its period ($2\pi$). Then ask what you need to do to its equation to, say, double its amplitude or halve its period. Move on from there to examples where you draw a sine curve on the blackboard and ask your students to write down its equation (similar to 21–28). Or, give a table of values of a sine function and ask for the approximate amplitude and phase shift; get the students to make conjectures on what the function is and then check the answers on a calculator. Or, ask for the periods of various real-life phenomena (see 25). For a computer demonstration on composition of functions, compare the graphs of $\sin(e^x)$ and $e^{\sin x}$, and explain their shape in terms of the basic properties of the sine and the exponential: $\sin(e^x)$ is the sine of something which increases more and more rapidly, hence it oscillates faster and faster; $e^{\sin x}$ is the exponential of something which oscillates regularly between 1 and $-1$, hence it oscillates regularly between $e$ and $e^{-1}$. Discuss inverse trig functions and range restrictions. If you have time, show some graphs like the damped oscillation in Example 6.

### Problems

1–13 — provide opportunities for review of trigonometry. Use as needed.

14 — you may want to use in class to go with Example 3.

20–28, 31 — involve graphs. Students still have trouble finding formulas when the graph is given. Remind graders that answers can vary on these.

33–36 — require a graphing calculator. Be sure to require an explanation.

29–30, 32, 37–38 — assign at least one of these application problems.

**Suggested Problems:** 6, 8, 11, 18, 20, 23, 26, 28, 30, 32.

## 1.10   POLYNOMIALS AND RATIONAL FUNCTIONS

**Class Time:** Half to most of a class. Rational functions can be omitted

## Key points

Flexibility of polynomial graphs on a small scale; basic resemblance to power functions on a large scale; Varying the coefficients to produce particular graphs; Rational functions and horizontal and vertical asymptotes.

## Ideas for the class

Polynomials are useful for representing shapes because they are so flexible; you might mention that bits of cubic polynomials form the basic drawing elements in many computer drafting programs. (Curves pieced together from bits of cubics are called *cubic splines*.)

Do examples where coefficients have to be varied to fit a quadratic or cubic to a particular situation. For example: say you have a parabolic mirror which is 2 meters wide and 5 cm deep at its center; write down a quadratic polynomial whose graph gives the cross section of the mirror. This is a good problem because the students have to set up the coordinate axes themselves.

You will probably find the students are not very familiar with altering the coefficients to produce a polynomial with a given shape. They are used to being asked "What is the shape of $y = -x^2$," but they are not used to being asked "How do you make an upside-down parabola?" They may not understand the effect varying the leading coefficient has on the width of the parabola; explain this numerically: if the leading coefficient is large, then only a small $x$-value is required to produce a large $y$-value, so the parabola is narrow.

To show that on a large scale polynomials look like their leading terms, get the students to do a computer or calculator lab where they compare the two on various scales. First, give them $f(x) = x^3 - x + 83$ and $g(x) = x^3$ to plot on $[-10, 10]$, by $[-100, 100]$ and then on $[-50, 50]$ by $[-10{,}000, 10{,}000]$. Then give them a different polynomial, and ask them to identify the leading term. Giving a polynomial with the terms out of order, so that the leading term is in the middle, helps get the point across. Ask students to plot the two polynomials on the same set of axes and to determine two appropriate viewing windows, one where the graphs are separated and one where they appear the same.

Note that many calculators and computer programs give confusing results when asked to graph a rational function with vertical asymptotes. (They might connect the two branches of the curve, for example.) If students are using a machine to try to produce something like Figure 1.86, page 64, be aware of, and be sure to discuss, the limitations of their technology.

Again, have students identify (by eye!) regions where the functions studied are increasing, decreasing, and concave up or down.

## Problems

1–8 — these should be somewhat familiar to students from previous courses, but can be hard for some.

9–12 — rational functions are also hard. Be certain students can interpret asymptotic behavior on the calculator or computer. The graph for 11 crosses its horizontal asymptote (sometimes a surprise to students), and 9 has an oblique asymptote.

13–15 — involve interpretation of quadratic functions. Problem 13 is hardest because answers are in terms of $v_0$ and $g$.

16–23 — more formulas from graphs. For 18–21, ask students whether the leading coefficient is positive or negative.

24–30 — applications. Assign some of these. Problems 24 and 25 can be difficult, once again because they are literal, involving constants rather than numbers.

**Suggested Problems:** 2, 4, 10, 12, 15, 16, 20, 26, 27.

**Problems Requiring Substantial Use of Algebra:** 14, 15.

## 1.11  INTRODUCTION TO CONTINUITY

**Class Time:** One-half class or assign for reading

## Key points

An understanding of what the concept of continuity means graphically and numerically.

## Ideas for the class

This is a brief, intuitive introduction to continuity. The emphasis here is on continuity on an interval rather than continuity at a point. Continuity at a point is postponed until the Focus on Theory section at the end of Chapter 2, because it requires the notion of a limit. The notion of continuity on an interval is represented by a graph without holes or jumps. Point out that many well-known functions (positive powers, exponentials, sines and cosines) are continuous.

Do mention the numerical point of view, that small changes in values of the independent variable produce small changes in values of the dependent variable; think about turning a dimmer switch on a light, or a volume control on a radio, for example. (It's true that this is getting close to continuity at a point, but don't push that now.)

As an example, graph the function given by

$$f(x) = \begin{cases} x & \text{for } x < 2 \\ x^2 & \text{for } x \geq 2. \end{cases}$$

Point out that the function is not continuous on any interval containing $x = 2$. Then ask students what value of $k$ makes the following function continuous:

$$g(x) = \begin{cases} x + k & \text{for } x < 2 \\ x^2 & \text{for } x \geq 2. \end{cases}$$

## Problems

**Suggested Problems:** 1, 3, 5, 7, 8, 9, 11.

## FOCUS ON THEORY

This is the first of several sections in the book devoted to the more theoretical aspects of calculus. They appear between chapters, supporting and elaborating on the material just covered. They are appropriate for supplementary reading or for incorporating into the regular class sessions, as time permits. These *Focus on Theory* sections are optional.

If you intend to cover the later theory sections, or assign them as reading, be sure the students have gone through the section on the completeness of the real numbers. This property lies at the heart of the rigorous foundations of calculus and is used, one way or another, in many proofs.

Whatever you decide, have students read the opening section on *Underpinnings of Calculus*. It's a brief account, starting with Euclid, of the subtleties and difficulties in what constitutes rigor and proof.

## FOCUS ON THEORY: THE BINOMIAL THEOREM

**Class Time:** One class

### Key points

Binomial expansion and binomial coefficients; Pascal's triangle; Proof by induction.

### Ideas for the class

The emphasis should be placed on the steps leading to the formulation of the theorem and on its proof, rather than on the properties of Pascal's triangle. As examples of what we want to emphasize, namely the progression from pattern recognition to conjecture to proof, you could use the binomial theorem itself or the fact that $1 + 2 + 3 + \cdots + n = n(n+1)/2$.

Students often have trouble with the abstract formulation of the induction principle, and in particular with the induction step. One way to make the induction principle clearer is by analogy: To prove that all houses on a certain street are white, it is sufficient to show that the whiteness of one house implies the whiteness of the next house, and that the first house is white.

### Problems

1,2 — ask for proofs of properties of binomial coefficients.

3 — explores a property of Pascal's triangle.

## FOCUS ON THEORY: COMPLETENESS OF THE REAL NUMBERS

**Class Time:** One class

### Key points

Least upper bound; Completeness; Intermediate Value Theorem.

### Ideas for the class

You may motivate the discussion by searching for roots of a function by zooming in. Call attention to the fact that on a calculator or computer, visual accuracy is limited by pixel size, and that completeness is precisely the abstract property of the set of real numbers which ensures that ideal graphical representations of (continuous) functions are not jagged.

Mention that the Nested Interval Theorem is used widely in proofs of many important theorems (and in many problems in this book). Its proof can be presented as an application of completeness.

Students generally find the Intermediate Value Theorem intuitive but the fact that it is a statement of the existence of a special point, rather than an algorithm for finding it, needs stressing. As a way of involving students, ask them to provide examples showing why both the continuity of a function and a closed interval are necessary hypotheses. As such examples you can eventually offer:

$$f(x) = \begin{cases} 0 & 0 \le x \le \frac{1}{2} \\ 1 & \frac{1}{2} < x \le 1 \end{cases}$$

and

$$g(x) = \begin{cases} 1 - 2x^2 & 0 \le x < \frac{1}{2} \\ 1 - x & \frac{1}{2} < x \le 1 \end{cases}$$

In the case of $f(x)$, the conclusion of the Intermediate Value Theorem fails because $f$ is not continuous. In the case of $g$ it fails because $g$ is not defined at all points in the interval [0,1]. (Note that $g$ is continuous at all points in its domain.)

### Problems

3 — a nice application of completeness to the infinite decimal expansion of a real number.

# CHAPTER TWO

## Overview

The purpose of this chapter is to give the student a practical understanding of the limit definition of the derivative and its interpretation as an instantaneous rate of change. By the end of this chapter, students should be able to find derivatives numerically by taking arbitrarily fine difference quotients, to visualize derivatives graphically as the slope of the graph when you zoom in (using a calculator), and to interpret the meaning of first and second derivatives in various applications.

The first five sections form a coherent account of the key concept, and are crucial. In Section 2.1 we show how to capture the concept of instantaneous velocity as a limit of average velocities. Then we formalize this into the definition of the derivative in Section 2.2 and interpret it as a general rate of change and as a slope. We give examples of computing the derivative numerically, estimating it graphically, and deriving it algebraically. In Section 2.3 we introduce the derivative function, and relate the global behavior of the derivative to the global behavior of the function; students should certainly understand that

$$f' > 0 \text{ on an interval} \Rightarrow f \text{ is sloping upward in that interval}$$

$$f' < 0 \text{ on an interval} \Rightarrow f \text{ is sloping downward in that interval}.$$

We discuss the standard interpretations of the derivative in Section 2.4, but also give examples of how to interpret it in non-standard situations. Leibniz notation, $dy/dx$, is introduced and we discuss the value of that notation in thinking about what the derivative means. This section flows into Section 2.5, where we discuss the second derivative and concavity.

The optional Focus on Theory sections present the definition of limit and continuity and analyze the connection between differentiability and local linearity.

### Changes from the First Edition

The derivatives of constant and linear functions and the statement of the power rule are given in Section 2.3. Local linearity and the former "Notes on" sections are a part of the new Focus on Theory sections.

## 2.1 HOW DO WE MEASURE SPEED?

**Class Time:** One class

## Key points

Instantaneous velocity as a limit of average velocities, and as a slope on the position-versus-time graph.
**New:** Slightly expanded discussion of limit.

## Ideas for the class

Focus solely on measuring velocity in this class.

If you want an interesting problem around which to build a discussion, try the following idea. There is a Dover book of the first "motion pictures" ever of animals in motion, by Edward Muybridge. Each page has a series of frames from a movie of an animal running against a grid background, so that you can measure their progress from frame to frame. Make an overhead slide of one of these pages and ask your students how fast the animal is moving in a given frame. It immediately becomes clear that you need *two* frames to get a velocity, and it is natural to choose two adjacent frames.

An easier example is that of something being thrown straight up in the air. The text uses a grapefruit, and asks how fast it is moving at different times. When you plot your data (height above ground as a function of time), explain the graph very carefully. Some students will believe that you have drawn the trajectory of the grapefruit—i.e., its path through physical space. They're (not unreasonably) assuming that the horizontal axis is spatial. Make sure that you convince them that the actual trajectory of the grapefruit is straight up and down, not arch-shaped. (Perhaps use a real grapefruit.) Mark units on the axes, and ask if the units are realistic; get students to read from the graph how high the object went, how fast it was thrown, if the height and velocity fit their experience and are consistent with each other.

You should probably work with a table of data without using any formula. If you use a formula, students may resort to short cuts—applying the rules of differentiation some of them may have memorized in a previous class. There is also the danger that you could end up spending a lot of time trying to justify the formula.

Compute various average velocities on the board, or have students work them out on their calculators, before you get to the idea of instantaneous velocity. Explain to your students why the slope of the secant line on your graph represents the average velocity of the grapefruit for some given interval of time. This is not obvious to students. They sometimes identify the average velocity with the secant line itself, rather than with its slope. Of course, this doesn't make sense, but you may often find that students need help in separating one feature of a graph from all the others. Emphasize that the secant line segment represents how the grapefruit would be moving if its velocity were constant over some interval, and that the slope represents this constant velocity.

When you begin to discuss instantaneous velocity, make the argument that looking at the function over smaller and smaller intervals reveals an increasingly linear curve, one that resembles more and more its own tangent line. Here, if you have the technology, it might be useful to have students zoom in on various curved functions on their calculators until they look linear.

Be sure to state explicitly that the difference quotient is just a disguised version of the slope formula they've always known, $\Delta y / \Delta x$. Taking the limit is necessary only because the slope being measured is at a point on a curve and not of a straight line.

In a discussion section, it may be fun to spend some time discussing the paradox of the notion of instantaneous velocity.

## Problems

1–3 — should be intuitive, but students can still have difficulty with these.

4–8 — good problems. Assign at least one.

9–22 — numerical approximations of limits. Watch for students that choose $h$ *too* small and get an answer of zero when it is not appropriate. Stress the idea of watching for a pattern as $h$ approaches zero through both positive and negative values.

**Suggested Problems:** 2, 4, 5, 6, 7, 10, 12.

## 2.2  THE DERIVATIVE AT A POINT

**Class Time:** One class

## Key points

Practical understanding of the limit definition of the derivative.

## Ideas for the class

It is important to spend time on the idea of the derivative, and to do lots of examples—numerical, graphical, and algebraic—along the same lines as the ones given in the text. Begin by reviewing the difference quotient, the secant line, and the idea of rate of change of a function. When you define the derivative of $f(x)$ at $a$, make sure you emphasize that the definition applies at a point, so that the derivative is just a number. If you have the technology, zoom in on a graph until it becomes straight; the slope of this line is the derivative. Calculate a few derivatives this way.

Your students who have had calculus before will begin to feel at sea. They will want to know when you are going to start teaching them "real" calculus. Most of the ones with calculus experience will be accustomed to thinking of the derivative as a function of $x$. Some may be able to find derivatives of very complicated functions analytically and yet be unable to explain clearly what the derivative of a function at a point means. The important thing is not to do everything for them; get them to answer questions. If it takes time, allow the time. Above all, make sure they understand that the derivative is approximated by a difference quotient, and that it represents a slope.

Ask your students for the derivative of $x^x$ at $x = 2$. The ones who have had calculus before may say $4 \, (= 2 \cdot 2^{2-1})$. Find the derivative numerically by calculating the difference quotient

$$\frac{2.001^{2.001} - 2^2}{0.001} \approx 6.779.$$

Compute derivatives of other functions numerically. Try to avoid functions like $x^2$ if possible, as this will confirm the prejudices of the experienced students, who will just scream out, "$2x$!"

Hand out photocopies of a graph drawn on graph paper (for example, $\sin(x^2)$), and ask your students for the value of the derivative at various points, or at what points the derivative is $-1$. Or combine the graphical and numerical approaches: draw the graph of $e^{-x}$ on the blackboard, and ask what you can say about the derivative of $e^{-x}$ at $x = 0$ just from the graph. (Answer: it is negative, and is about $-1$). Then compute some difference quotients, with $h = \pm 0.1, \pm 0.01, \dots$.

If you are using graphing technology, zoom in on $e^{ax}$ at $x = 0$ for various values of $a$. Have the students make a conjecture of what the derivative is at $x = 0$. (An instructive mistake that can be made in this problem is to fail to observe that the scales on the $x$ and $y$ axes need to be different.)

Of course, you should do some simple algebraic examples as well. When going through the examples, and when assigning homework, be sure to remind students that derivatives should be found without short cuts, at least for the time being.

In this class, you should consider functions whose rates of change *aren't* velocities. See Example 1, page 96, and Example 2, page 97. You should not assume that by the end of the class students completely understand the idea of the derivative. It will need to be repeated many times throughout the course.

## Problems

5–6 — assign one and/or discuss in class.

4, 7–10 — make good in-class examples or could serve to stimulate a follow-up discussion after students have tried the problems. 10 brings up an interesting graphical interpretation used by economists. This idea is used again in Section 5.4, so you may want to assign or discuss the problem.

13–24 — algebra weaknesses can surface here.

27 — requires graphing calculator or computer.

**Suggested Problems:** 2, 4, 5, 8, 10, 14, 17, 20 (uses 14), 28.

**Problems Requiring Substantial Use of Algebra:** 13–24.

## 2.3  THE DERIVATIVE FUNCTION

**Class Time:** One class

## Key points

Understanding the derivative function. Sketching the graph of the derivative from the graph of the function. Seeing how the shape of the graph of a function affects the shape of the graph of its derivative.

**New:** Derivatives of constant and linear functions and statement of the power rule have been moved to this section.

## Ideas for the class

Hand out photocopies of a graph (for example, a generic cubic) and ask your students to figure out the general shape of its derivative function. Most students will need a lot of practice moving from point to point along the curve, sketching small tangent lines, estimating their slope, and plotting them on the graph of $f'$. Each time you plot a point, point out that the derivative graph is above the axis where the function is increasing, below it where the function is decreasing, and crosses it in between, where the function changes direction (from increasing to decreasing or vice-versa). It is also helpful to point out that the slope is steepest (positively and negatively) where the concavity changes. Don't be surprised if you get questions about how one knows the concavity of the derivative graph. (The answer is you don't know, because one can't "see" the third derivative on the graph of the original function.)

Since it takes quite some time for students to come to terms with the graph of the derivative function, resist the temptation to make too many connections for them at this point. For example, unless someone in class points out the relation between zeros of the derivative and extrema of the original function, or between the extrema of the derivative and the critical points of the original function, don't do so yourself. If these issues do arise, don't let them overtake the discussion. Chalk them up as perceptive observations that merit future consideration, and then move on.

Sketch the graph of $\tan^{-1} x$ and its derivative on the same axes, without identifying the functions, and ask them which function is the derivative of which. The way to see the answer is to observe that exactly one of these functions is always increasing, and exactly one of them is always positive. Or, present the graph of a sine curve as the derivative of a mystery function, and ask what it tells about the graph of the original function; then give the same graph shifted up so that it never dips below the $x$-axis. Ideally (but this may be difficult) you want to wean students away from a point by point approach to a global approach; you want them to look at the second graph and say: "Well, whatever else is going on, the function is always increasing because the derivative is always positive." Try the same sort of thing with tables of values; again, you want students to be able to look for global properties, such as regions where the function is increasing or decreasing.

Cover the derivatives of constant and linear functions. Then find the formula for the derivative of $f(x) = x^2$ quickly; either algebraically, or by making a table of $f'$ at different values of $x$ and looking for the pattern. For the sake of students who already know the shortcuts, point out that the way you prove that the shortcuts work is to use difference quotients. It's worth making this point because some students have had the shortcuts hammered so forcefully into their heads that they believe such shortcuts are the definition of the derivative.

If you have time, talk the students through the power rule for $n$ an integer, using the binomial theorem. In any case, state that the power rule works for all real $n$.

Students find graphical differentiation quite difficult. One way of giving them some practice is to ask each student to draw the graph of a function on a piece of paper, put his or her name on it, and pass it to a neighbor. The neighbor draws the graph of the derivative on a different piece of paper, copying the name of the first person on it. The derivative graph is passed to a third student, while the original graph is passed back to its author. The third student sketches a graph of the original function from the derivative, and then compares it with the original; they should be the same shape. (This is a problem which may be used later in the semester for review; even at the end of the term it will not be easy for many.) This activity produces a lot of noise, but also a lot of useful mathematical discussion.

## Problems

Graphing problems (like 1 through 10 and 23 through 28) are difficult for students but well worth the effort. If many of your students have had calculus before, assign the "less obvious" graphs (like 7 or 9). Some students with previous calculus experience, when asked to explain their graph of $f'(x)$ for Problem 2, may say "The derivative of a quadratic is a line." The same students may spend time trying to find a formula for functions like those in 4 or 6 so they can use the differentiation rules to find the derivative. (Wean them from these approaches!)

Problems 17, 18 and 29 are good problems to check understanding (and proper interpretation) of notation. It takes lots of practice for students to learn to shift from $f$ to $f'$ and vice-versa.

Once again, remind the grader, or students with access to solutions, that many of the answers in this section will vary, as they are approximations.

**Suggested Problems:** 5, 8, 12, 13, 17, 26, 31, 32.

## 2.4  INTERPRETATIONS OF THE DERIVATIVE

**Class Time:** Half a class or assign for reading, then assign relevant homework problems, then spend a class going over the homework

### Key points

Using the difference quotient to interpret the meaning of the derivative.
**New:** Discussion of acceleration is now in Section 2.5.

### Ideas for the class

This section can be difficult for the students. They may not have trouble understanding various interpretations of the derivative once you have explained them, but they can find it very difficult to come up with their own interpretations. For example, consider Problem 13: If $g(v)$ is the fuel efficiency of a car going at $v$ miles per hour, what is the practical meaning of the statement

$$g'(55) = -0.54?$$

We would like the students to be able to seize on the negative sign as the key part of the right hand side of this equation, but they are sometimes so alarmed by the numbers that they don't even notice the negative. Help students think about what the units of the derivative can tell them.

The students are probably not going to get much out of a class on this section if they haven't done some work on it previously. One possibility is to assign the section for reading, and then get the students to discuss the examples in the text and air their misunderstandings. Another is to go over some of the examples, then save most of the talking until after the students have struggled with some of the key problems, such as Problems 9 and 10. (Make sure you have struggled with them yourself first.)

The mathematical content of this class should be nearly identical to the content of the last class; only the examples used should be different. The $dy/dx$ notation is useful in this section. Emphasize that although the notation looks like a fraction, it isn't; canceling the $d$'s makes no sense.

## Problems

Nearly every problem in this section requires a written explanation. Assign only a few problems at first. (You may want to return to others after the first assignment has been discussed.) Be picky about explanations. When students can articulate their answers to these types of problems they will begin to understand the *concept* of a rate of change.

**Suggested Problems:** [Warning: These should be spread over two or more assignments or else pared down considerably!] 2, 4, 6, 7, 10, 12, 15.

## 2.5  THE SECOND DERIVATIVE

**Class Time:** One class

## Key points

Interpretation of the second derivative as concavity and as acceleration.

## Ideas for the class

The explanation of why the sign of the second derivative gives the concavity is fun to give and worth going over carefully. Let students write out (in clear, concise English) their own explanation of what the second derivative tells them about concavity. Mention that a straight line is neither concave up nor concave down, and has second derivative zero.

Draw two possible position versus time graphs of an accelerating car: both increasing and starting from zero, but one concave up and one concave down. Ask which is correct. Answer: the concave up one, since the acceleration is positive. The other one illustrates a car that starts with a positive velocity and brakes.

Provide a table of velocity as a function of time, and have students find the average change in velocity over given intervals. Be very careful when you graph your data, because this may be the first graph students have seen of velocity versus time. They may confuse it with plots of distance versus time or with trajectories.

Keep in mind that students can easily confuse *increasing first derivative* with *first derivative of increasing magnitude*. They tend to associate any graph which gets "steeper and steeper" with an increasing first derivative, even if the first derivative is negative and decreasing(for example, the graph of $y = -e^x$). They also sometimes think that decreasing functions can't have increasing first derivatives, so show them $e^{-x}$ and discuss. If the confusion persists, convince them that it makes sense to say that the sequence $\{-1, -2, -3, \ldots\}$ is decreasing while the sequence $\{-5, -4, -3, \ldots\}$ is increasing; it can help if you draw a vertical number line (like a thermometer) as a reference. Do some examples like Example 1; look at an example in which the acceleration isn't constant (e.g., Example 4).

## Problems

1–6, 15–17 — Students *should* be getting better at the graphical interpretations. Stress that 16 shows the graph of the *derivative* function. Also, ask for an explanation on 16. It is possible to get the right answer for the wrong reasons!

8–13 — more explanations. Keep requiring these!

7, 14 — back to numerical estimation.

**Suggested Problems:** 4–6, 8, 10, 11, 15, 16, 18.

# FOCUS ON THEORY

This is a substantial section. It covers the formal $\epsilon$, $\delta$ definition of the limit, continuity, the limit theorems, and concludes with the relationship between differentiability and local linearity. There's enough flexibility in the arrangement of the topics, examples, and problems to allow you to be more or less detailed, as you choose. Part of the discussion of the error term in the linear approximation uses the precise definition of the limit, but students can still get the essential ideas (very worthwhile) without a lot of previous practice with deltas and epsilons.

# FOCUS ON THEORY: LIMITS AND CONTINUITY

**Class Time:** One class

## Key points

Epsilon-delta definition of limit; continuity at a point.

## Ideas for the class

To motivate the discussion, you can ask the students to decide if

$$\lim_{x \to 0} x \sin \frac{1}{x} = 0.$$

Once you state the formal definition of the limit, you can make it palpable by following the graphical approach used in Example 1. Make sure you stress the relationship between the viewing window's length and height, and $\delta$ and $\epsilon$, respectively. You need not spend time proving the properties of limits. Most of the proofs are just one step removed from the definition of limit and can be assigned as homework.

It might be worth stressing that the two-sided nature of limits is a direct consequence of the definition. As an illustration, compare limits at 0, of $f(x) = x/x$ and $g(x) = x/|x|$.

To motivate the discussion of continuity, you can ask the students to pick $a$ so that

$$g(x) = \begin{cases} x \sin \left(\frac{1}{x}\right) & \text{if } x \neq 0 \\ a & \text{if } x = 0 \end{cases}$$

is continuous at $x = 0$. Do point out that the intuitive notion of "no skips, jumps, or gaps" is an adequate description of continuity in most cases we encounter.

It is important to emphasize that the definition of continuity at a point assumes that the function is defined at that point. So, for instance, one would not say that $f(x) = \sin x/x$, $x \neq 0$, is continuous at 0 since it is undefined at zero. On the other hand the function $g(x) = \sin x/x$ for $x \neq 0$ and $g(0) = 1$ *is* continuous at $x = 0$. This point is made in Problem 2.

## Problems:

Proofs of the basic properties of limits are in Problems 13–17. Problems 26 and 27 are proofs using the Nested Interval Theorem of finding a root by zooming and of the Intermediate Value Theorem.

**Suggested problems:** 1, 3, 9, any of 11, 12, 19, 26, 27.

**Problems Requiring Substantial Use of Algebra:** 12.

# FOCUS ON THEORY: DIFFERENTIABILITY AND LINEAR APPROXIMATION

**Class Time:** One-half to one class

## Key points

Differentiability and its graphical interpretation; Linear approximation; error in linear approximation.

## Ideas for the class

The first part of the section discusses differentiability and nondifferentiability in terms of corners and vertical tangent lines. You could start by asking the class whether the following function is differentiable everywhere:

$$f(x) = \begin{cases} x & \text{for } x < 1 \\ x^2 & \text{for } x \geq 1. \end{cases}$$

Then consider what values of $a$ and $b$ make the following function both continuous and differentiable everywhere.

$$g(x) = \begin{cases} ax + 2 & \text{for } x < 0 \\ b(x-1)^2 & \text{for } x \geq 0. \end{cases}$$

The main part of the section is on the error in the tangent line approximation to a differentiable function. By now, students are used to observing on their graphing calculator that a graph and its tangent line are virtually indistinguishable on a small scale. Raise explicitly the question of *why* the graph of a differentiable function looks like a straight line on a small scale and *why* the the tangent line is the "best linear approximation." These questions are addressed in this section.

The important phenomenon in the linear approximation to a differentiable function $f(x)$ at a point $x = a$ is that the error $E(x)$ is "small compared to $|x - a|$." This is expressed precisely as $\lim_{x \to a} E(x)/(x - a) = 0$. (The error $E(x)$ is identically zero when the function $f$ is linear. That's worth mentioning.) However, comparing the size of two functions is not an easy thing. It's illuminating to look at this numerically. For example, take $f(x) = x^2$ and its linear approximation $L(x) = 2x - 1$ at the point $a = 1$. Then the error in the linear approximation is $E(x) = f(x) - L(x) = x^2 - (2x - 1) = (x - 1)^2$. So if $h = x - 1$, or $x = 1 + h$, then the error is $h^2$. Be explicit about what this means numerically: if we're $h = 0.1$ away from the point 1 then the error in the linear approximation is $(0.1)^2 = 0.01$, if we're $h = 0.01$ away then the error is $0.0001$, etc. You can also do some extra numerical work on the example in the text of the error in the linear approximation of $\sin x$ at 0. In that case $E(x) = \sin x - x$. The algebra isn't there to help this time, but a calculator gives $E(0.1) = -0.000166583$ and $E(0.01) = -1.6666 \times 10^{-7}$. Even after doing these examples, it's still important to repeat that it's not only that the error is small, it's small relative to $|x - a|$.

## Problems

There are a number of pure and applied problems in this section. Problem 2 looks at (non)-corners in a graph and the limits of a calculator's display. Problems 6, 7, 8, and 10 look at continuity and differentiability for functions coming from physics. Problem 15 concerns why the tangent line approximation is the best linear approximation (or the only "good" linear approximation).

**Suggested problems:** 2, 3, 5, any of 6, 7, 8, and 10, 14, 15.

# CHAPTER THREE

## Overview

The purpose of this chapter is to give the student a practical understanding of the definite integral as a limit of Riemann sums, and to bring out the connection between the derivative and the definite integral in the Fundamental Theorem of Calculus. We use the same method as in Chapter 2, introducing the fundamental concept in depth without going into technique. The motivating problem is computing the total distance traveled from the velocity function. The student should finish the chapter with a good grasp of the definite integral as a limit of Riemann sums, the ability to compute it numerically, and an understanding of how to interpret the definite integral in various contexts. Note the parallel between the development here and the development in Chapter 2. In Section 3.1 we introduce the thought experiment of estimating total distance traveled from velocity measurements, the reverse of Section 2.1. This leads very naturally to left and right hand sums, and even to accuracy estimates when the velocity function is monotonic. In Section 3.2 we define the definite integral using left and right hand sums and give the standard interpretation of the definite integral as area. We discuss average value of a function, units, and other interpretations of the definite integral in Section 3.3. In Section 3.4 we give the Fundamental Theorem of Calculus in the weak form: If $F'(x) = f(x)$, then

$$\int_a^b f(x)\,dx = F(b) - F(a).$$

This is almost a tautology, given our distance interpretation of the definite integral. The optional Focus on Theory section explores the formal definition of the definite integral using upper and lower sums.

### Changes from the First Edition

Discussion of numerical techniques using increased numbers of subdivisions for Riemann sums has been reduced. (Technology to approximate the definite integral is assumed.) The area interpretation of the definite integral has moved from Section 3.3 to Section 3.2. Material formerly in Sections 6.1 and 6.2 has been moved to this chapter. Focus on Theory section has replaced the former Notes on the Limit.

## 3.1  HOW DO WE MEASURE DISTANCE TRAVELED?

**Class Time:** One class

## Key points

To calculate total distance traveled, given the velocity function, add estimates of distance traveled over small time intervals. This leads to the idea of a Riemann sum as an approximation for the exact distance, and eventually to a precise formula in terms of a limit of Riemann sums.

## Ideas for the class

Go over the thought experiment in the text, but using different numbers. Better still, have the students try a problem or two for homework, before you talk about it. Start with a table of velocities—don't use graphs at first. Have students give lower and upper bounds for distance traveled, using what we call left and right hand sums. Demonstrate that more data (intermediate velocities) will make the lower and upper bounds closer together. As much as possible, elicit the answers from the students themselves; get them to give the initial distance estimates.

After students have given upper and lower estimates, show how they are represented on a graph. Spend some time leading them to the realization that the difference between the left and right sums is $(f(b) - f(a))\Delta x$; this makes it clear that the left and right sums (which bracket the true distance if the velocity function is monotonic) are converging to a common limit.

Above all, don't rush. Students may have trouble reading such formulas as

$$\text{Total distance traveled between A and B} \approx f(t_0)\Delta t + f(t_1)\Delta t + f(t_2)\Delta t + \cdots + f(t_{n-1})\Delta t$$

unless you are quite patient. Don't introduce $\sum$ notation yet. Make sure that the connection between whatever formalism you introduce and the thought experiment is as obvious as possible: draw lots of graphs. As always, don't get bogged down in limits.

Explicitly point out the parallel between this section and Section 2.1. Consider only monotonic increasing (or decreasing) functions for now.

When you make a graph of velocity versus time, be alert for confusion. Students are accustomed to graphs of distance versus time and will be prone to treat the new graph as such. Even those who understand what the axes mean may be confused by the fact that an *area* under a graph is now representing a *distance*. While they may be used to the idea of letting a length represent any number of quantities, they don't have much experience letting an area represent anything other than area. It helps to remind them that on such a graph vertical length represents velocity, whereas horizontal length represents time. For a somewhat more sophisticated introduction to the ideas of this section, you could use the following example in class instead of a velocity example.

---

*Example 1*    Suppose oil is leaking out of a container at a decreasing rate. The rate is measured at hourly intervals and given in Table 3.1.1.

**TABLE 3.1.1**    *Rate at which oil is leaking*

| Time (hours) | 0 | 1 | 2 | 3 | 4 |
|---|---|---|---|---|---|
| Rate (liters/hour) | 35 | 30 | 26 | 23 | 21 |

We want to estimate the total amount of oil that has leaked out of the container during the time shown. Answering these questions will show you how to set about making such an estimate.

(a)    What is the maximum amount of oil that could have leaked out during the first hour? The minimum?

(b)    What is the maximum amount of oil that could have leaked out during the second hour (i.e between $t = 1$ and $t = 2$)? The minimum? How about during the third and fourth hours?

(c)    During the entire four-hour interval from $t = 0$ to $t = 4$, what is the maximum amount of oil that could have leaked out? The minimum? Explain where you used the assumption that the rate at which the oil was leaking was decreasing.

(d)    If you had to guess how much oil actually leaked in the four-hour interval, what would be your guess? What is the maximum possible error in your guess? (In other words, what is the maximum possible difference between your guess and the true value?)

Suppose additional readings are obtained, and compiled in Table 3.1.2.

**TABLE 3.1.2**    *Rate at which oil is leaking*

| Time (hours) | 0.5 | 1.5 | 2.5 | 3.5 |
|---|---|---|---|---|
| Rate (liters/hour) | 33 | 27 | 24 | 22 |

5   Is the second set of information consistent with the first? In what interval would the rate at 0.5 hours have to be to be consistent?

(a)   Recalculate the upper and lower estimates in light of this new information. Make a new guess for the total amount of oil which has leaked out in the four-hour interval, and estimate the maximum possible error in your guess.

(b)   If readings of the rate were obtained for every 1/10 hour, by how much would your upper estimate exceed your lower? What if readings were obtained for every 1/100 hour?

(c)   Explain why you can calculate the total amount of oil that has leaked out to any desired degree of accuracy if you have access to readings of the rate at every instant during the four-hour interval.

*Solution*   You could first do this problem numerically; then, graph the rate oil is leaking and show the sum graphically.

_____

## Problems

Once again, watch out for students who have had calculus before. For example, these students might immediately resort to the Fundamental Theorem on Problem 5, get the correct answer, but be unable to interpret. Steer those students toward problems without formulas, but where a quantity must be obtained graphically or approximated numerically.

**Suggested Problems:** 2, 3, 4, 6, 9, 11.

## 3.2  THE DEFINITE INTEGRAL

**Class Time:** One class

## Key points

The definite integral as a limit of Riemann sums; interpretation as an area.
**New:** Numerical approximations de-emphasized; area moved from former 3.3.

## Ideas for the class

Since you'll need $\sum$ notation, it's a good idea to introduce it at the start of class. Practice it in some context other than integration (evaluate a few finite sums, for example). Once students are comfortable with the notation, return to integration.

Write out the formulas you obtained during the last class for left- and right-hand sums and help students figure out how to express these using the $\sum$ notation. Make sure they understand what the subscript on the variable $t$ means in the expression $\sum_{i=0}^{n-1} f(t_i)\Delta t$, but try not to lose sight of the forest for the trees: the goal is not the notation but understanding integration.

Start off by computing a Riemann sum by hand: for example, compute $\int_0^1 e^{-x^2}\,dx$ by making a table of values of the function for $x = 0, 0.1, 0.2, \ldots, 1$, adding up all values but the last one, multiply by $\Delta x = 0.1$; similarly for the right sum. For a good estimate, take the average of the left and right sums. Students should understand this method without the need for a special integration program. Make sure you do an example where $\Delta x \neq 1$, such as with $\int_1^3 \left((\sin x)/x\right)\,dx$. (A common mistake is to always multiply by 1, or to forget the $\Delta x$ altogether.) Emphasize that the definite integral is a number (the above examples will help). Some students think that it is an antiderivative; many others think that $\int_a^b f(x)\,dx$ is *defined* to be $F(b) - F(a)$.

Some students will have had calculus and will want to know why you aren't doing integrals "the easy way," i.e., using the Fundamental Theorem. The previous example can't be done this way, since the integrand does not have an elementary antiderivative. However, there is no need to go overboard with such examples; do a simple one like $\int_0^1 x^2\, dx$ also.

If the issue of convergence for non-monotonic functions arises, convince students that any definite integral can be evaluated by first breaking the domain into intervals on which $f$ is monotonic and working on these smaller intervals.

The area interpretation of the integral follows directly from the idea of summing thinner and thinner rectangles. However, be careful with the case where $f(x) < 0$. When students learn that the definite integral gives the negative of the area in such cases, some begin to think that they must insert a negative sign any time the integral gives a negative value. Stress that the definite integral is a number and that area is only one of many interpretations of the integral. Example 4 of the text or problems similar to 19 of this section should help to minimize this confusion.

## Problems

Students need a programmable calculator or computer to do some of these exercises.

Problems 5 and 7 provide opportunities to discuss functions that are not monotonic over the chosen interval. If you have time, have students split the interval on one of these problems so that the function is monotonic over each subinterval.

Problems 3–8 ask for a program that allows students to enter the number of subdivisions.

Problems 15–18 extend the area interpretation beyond the discussion in the text but should be intuitive for most students.

If you assign 9, 22, or 28, remind students of the formula in Section 3.1 on page 149.

**Suggested Problems:** 1, 2, 4, 10, 14, 16, 20, 23, 24.

## 3.3  INTERPRETATIONS OF THE DEFINITE INTEGRAL

**Class Time:** One class

## Key points

Interpretations of the definite integral as area and average value; Using the notation to interpret the definite integral.
**New:** Applications of the definite integral using area moved from former 6.1.

## Ideas for the class

Average value makes sense to students who grasp the concept of the integral as a limit of sums. Confusion is more likely to arise among students who have had calculus before, and who have a fixed image of the integral as an antiderivative. Introducing average value before the Fundamental Theorem can help to build up the intuitive concept of the definite integral that such students may be missing.

The discussion of units and notation for the definite integral corresponds to the discussion in Section 2.4 where the Leibniz notation $dy/dx$ was introduced for the derivative. An understanding of how units can be used to make interpretations will be extremely helpful for the applications of the definite integral in Chapter 8.

The last part of this section asks students to use the area interpretation of the definite integral. A similar problem, which usually generates an excellent class discussion, follows.

*Example 1*   Below is the graph[1] of the rate $r$ (in arrivals per hour) at which patrons arrive at the theater in order to get rush seats for the evening performance. The first people arrive at 8 am and the ticket windows open at 9 am. Suppose that once the windows open, people can be served at an (average) rate of 200 per hour.

Use the graph to find or provide an estimate of:

(a)   The length of the line at 9 am when the windows open.
(b)   The length of the line at 10 am.
(c)   The length of the line at 11 am.
(d)   The rate at which the line is growing in length at 10 am.
(e)   The time at which the length of the line is maximum.
(f)   The length of time a person who arrives at 9 am has to stand in line.
(g)   The time at which the line disappears.
(h)   Suppose you were given a formula for $r$ in terms of $t$. Explain how you would answer the above questions.

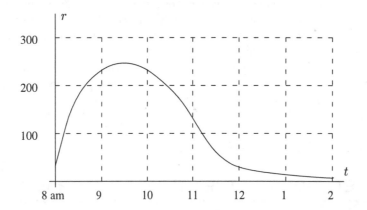

## Problems

4–6 — interpretations using units. Excellent—assign all three or use for class discussion.

1–3, 10–11 — all involve area. Students will need to use numerical approximations or geometric interpretations. Allow for variation in answers.

8–21 — average value. Problems 19–21 are good application problems.

24, 25 — get students to think about properties of the definite integral which are not explicitly discussed until Section 3.4. The problems are reasonably straightforward graphical interpretations, but you may need to work one (or part of one) first so students understand the expected format of the answers.

**Suggested Problems:** 2, 3, 6, 17, 21 25.

## 3.4  THEOREMS ABOUT DEFINITE INTEGRALS

**Class Time:** One class

[1]From *Calculus: The Analysis of Functions*, by Peter D. Taylor (Toronto: Wall & Emerson, Inc., 1992). Reprinted with permission of the publisher.

## Key points

The definite integral of a rate of change as the total change in the original function; the Fundamental Theorem of Calculus.
**New:** Properties of the definite integral and comparison of integrals moved from former Section 6.2.

## Ideas for the class

The interpretation of the definite integral as total change is essential. The Fundamental Theorem of Calculus, as we present it, is a simple extension of this interpretation. There is, however, an important new element. In stating the theorem, we introduce parameters $a$ and $b$ for the endpoints. Later this will become extremely important, as we allow $b$ to vary in order to construct antiderivatives using the definite integral. So it is a good idea to do some examples now where various choices of $a$ and $b$ are used with a fixed integrand. (See Problem 3 of this section.) Note that the presentation of the Fundamental Theorem comes well before the notation for the indefinite integral is introduced.

Some students make the initial mistake of thinking the Fundamental Theorem says

$$\int_a^b f(x)\, dx = f(b) - f(a).$$

You need to drive the point home that the theorem involves a function *and* its derivative. To illustrate the theorem, write down a function $F$, give the students the formula for its derivative, compute a definite integral of the derivative using Riemann sums, and then compute $F(b) - F(a)$.

## Problems

1–3 — involve graphical interpretations. They are excellent for checking understanding.

4–5, 10–13, — perhaps more difficult interpretations at this time, but any are excellent to test understanding. Remind students to be very careful to note *which* graph (i.e., $f$ or $f'$) they are viewing before attempting a problem. Let students wrestle with these on their own before discussion in class.

6–8 — involve numerical integration techniques.

14–19, 24 — use the properties of definite integrals.

20 — remind students that the table values have already been divided by $\sqrt{2\pi}$.

**Suggested Problems:** 1, 4, 5, 8, 9, 15, 17, 19, 21.

# FOCUS ON THEORY: THE DEFINITE INTEGRAL

**Class Time:** One Class

## Key points

Upper and lower sums; General Riemann sums; The definition of the definite integral; Theorem on existence of the integral of a continuous function. (These topics can also be covered after Chapters 6 or 7.)

## Ideas for the class

Start by recalling the way we defined the definite integral for monotonic functions. Make sure that students understand that for this case, the left and right hand sums bracket the integral and it is possible to estimate directly how far apart the sums are. These are the features that we want in a more general definition of the definite integral. There are two obstacles to overcome. First, how do we bracket the integral (yet to be defined) between two approximating sums, although the function is not monotonic? Second, how do we get better and better approximations—what is the limiting process?

The solution to the first problem is to introduce the upper and lower sums. We haven't said what the integral *is* yet, but we know what we're aiming for, and the upper and lower sums are a natural way to bracket what we want.

To see why general partitions are needed, consider the function

$$f(x) = \begin{cases} 1 & \text{if } x \text{ is a rational number} \\ 0 & \text{if } x \text{ is an irrational number.} \end{cases}$$

If we only used the left and right hand sums with equal subdivisions then we would have the nonsensical result that

$$\int_0^1 f(x)\, dx = 1 \quad and \quad \int_0^{\sqrt{2}} f(x)\, dx = 0,$$

since for the first integral all the endpoints would be rational numbers, and for the second integral all but the first are irrational. The definition using general Riemann sums gives the correct result: neither integral exists.

How do we get better and better approximations? This is the question of how to take the limit when working with upper and lower sums. It's tricky. The limit is hidden in an appeal to completeness of the real numbers by considering the least upper bound of the lower sums and the greatest lower bound of the upper sums. You can suggest, with pictures, that what's going on is that for finer and finer partitions the lower sums are increasing and the upper sums are decreasing. This is the limiting process. (Some computational details of this process are provided in Problems 13–15.) If the least upper bound and greatest lower bounds are equal, the function is integrable and the common value is the value of the integral; that's the ultimate definition.

The basic theorem says that a continuous function is integrable. We point out a few features of the proof. We have to find a way of controlling the difference between the upper and lower sums. While this was easy to do in the case of monotonic functions over the entire interval of integration (the simple model case), here the main issue is to find a subdivision of the interval so that the function varies by at most $\epsilon$ on each subinterval (the same $\epsilon$ for all subintervals). We give an indirect proof of this based on the Nested Interval Theorem. This is somewhat unusual but it provides a way of getting the desired estimates without explicitly bringing in uniform continuity.

General Riemann sums, where one evaluates the function at an arbitrary point in each subinterval of a partition, can be discussed briefly.

## Problems

**Suggested problems:** 1, 2, 5, 12, 13–18, 20.

# CHAPTER FOUR

## Overview

The title is intended to remind the student that the basic differentiation formulas are not the definition of the derivative. We find the derivatives of all the functions introduced in Chapter 1 as well as the rules for differentiating the combinations discussed in Chapter 1. Implicit differentiation is introduced and used to find derivatives of several basic functions. We give informal but mathematically sound justifications, introducing graphical and numerical reasoning where appropriate. The student should finish this chapter with basic proficiency in differentiation and an understanding, in terms of the definition, of why the various differentiation rules are true.

For additional drill, see the Focus on Practice section.

### Changes from the First Edition

The chapter essentially begins with former 4.2. The derivatives of constant, linear and power functions are now given in Chapter 2. New Section 4.8 on linear approximations and limits includes l'Hopital's Rule, justified at $a$, and stated for other cases.

## 4.1  POWERS AND POLYNOMIALS

**Class Time:** One class

## Key points

The section begins with $d[cf(x)]/dx$, covers derivatives of sums and differences, justification of power rule for $n$ a positive integer. Don't neglect to draw graphs and use geometric arguments where possible.

## Ideas for the class

This is all quite straightforward and your students (and you too, maybe!) will be relieved to have come to the easy stuff. However, remember that some of them may be seeing it for the first time. It is always worthwhile to use a geometric argument if there is one; for example, to explore graphically the rule for the derivative of a constant multiple. Whenever you compute a derivative from a formula by using the definition, draw a graph first and ask what the answer ought to look like before computing it.

Since derivatives of power functions have been covered, you can show how to get the derivative of a polynomial as an application of the rules for sums and multiples, and then say that these rules work for any functions, not just power functions.

## Problems

1–3 — Problems 1 and 2 confirm the rules from this section using the definition of the derivative. Problem 3 looks at composition of linear functions. If you assign Problem 3 you will be able to refer back to it when you get to Section 4.4.

4–24 — very standard.

25 — only discussed briefly in the text where a derivative is undefined (see Example 5 (c) in Section 4.1). You may need to discuss this problem further if it is assigned.

26–34 — assign only before covering the next sections (otherwise they are not useful). Many students don't like to be asked to identify problems they *can't* work, but being able to do this is an important mathematical skill.

36–52 — take more time, so only pick a few of these.

36–39 — involve using or analyzing the derivative; students may have trouble with inequalities, as in 36–38 .

44 — involves a differential equation

45 — may seem difficult to some students.

46 — a variation on a standard problem that students with previous calculus experience will have seen before.

47, 48, 52 — difficult because they involve the general case.

48–51 — all require an explanation. These might seem difficult, but are good for discussion. Students may not recognize surface area in 51.

**Suggested Problems:** 6, 7, 10, 11, 18, 19, 22, 24, 30, 34, 36, 38, 48.

## 4.2  THE EXPONENTIAL FUNCTION

**Class Time:** One class

## Key points

To understand that the derivative of an exponential is a constant times that exponential. The significance of the constant $e$.

## Ideas for the class

Start by drawing the graph of an exponential function and pointing out that its derivative shows much the same behavior as the function: it starts out small and gets larger and larger faster and faster.

The justification that the derivative is a constant times the original function is well worth the time and effort. Students find it quite difficult to understand that in the calculation

$$\lim_{h \to 0} \frac{a^{x+h} - a^x}{h} = \left( \lim_{h \to 0} \frac{a^h - 1}{h} \right) a^x$$

the second limit is—for a particular $a$—just a constant (independent of $x$), and needs to be evaluated only once for a particular $a$.

If you have not shown the class before, you may want to introduce ways to graph the derivative of a function using a graphing calculator or computer program. Most calculators or software programs have a built-in command which can be used to graph the derivative (e.g., NDERIV on TI models). However, students can graph $(f(x+0.0001) - f(x))/0.0001$ to get a similar result. Use one of these methods to graph $a^x$ and the derivative of $a^x$ for various values of $a$. Have the students find a value for $a$ that makes the two graphs look identical. Or, if you have a computer lab, use a spreadsheet to produce values of $a^x$ and its derivative by computing $(a^{(x+0.001)} - a^x)/0.001$. Vary the value of $a$ until the two columns are the same.

If technology is unavailable for your class, all of the graphs and data are in the text. However, the result that $e^x$ is its own derivative is much more exciting to *discover* than to read about!

## Problems

1–21 — assign enough to get plenty of practice. Be certain that students rewrite 11–13, because these do not fit the rules of the section in the format given. Also, watch for incorrect simplification on 17.

22–30 — good problems asking whether the differentiation rules so far apply. Some difficult ones here, particularly 26 and 27.

31–34 — reminders that the derivative represents a rate of change. Assign at least one.

37 — a step beyond the idea of the linear approximation towards using Taylor polynomials to approximate functions (see Chapter 9).

34, 38, 39 — require explanations. Look at the solution manual for a good discussion of 39. Might make a good classroom discussion.

**Suggested Problems:** 5, 6, 12, 16, 21, 25, 30, 32, 34, 36, 37.

**Problems Requiring Substantial Use of Algebra:** 35–37.

## 4.3  THE PRODUCT AND QUOTIENT RULES

**Class Time:** One class

## Key points

Make sure the students understand when and how to use these rules.

## Ideas for the class

A large part of this class should be spent going over examples to make sure that the students become proficient at using these rules. However, try to give some intuitive understanding of why these rules are true, and some examples to convince students that the rules they might expect to be true are not (e.g. $(fg)' \neq f'g'$). Here are a couple of ideas on how to do this through numerical examples.

For the product rule, you may want to give an intuitive or geometrical explanation (see the text) of why you'd expect the derivative to have this form. Alternatively, if you have done enough on local linearization, you can do the following as a preliminary exercise for the product rule. Derive the product rule in a particular case, e.g. $f(x) = x^2 + 2x + 1$, $g(x) = e^x$, by writing down the local linearizations near $x = 0$:

$$e^x \approx 1 + x,$$
$$x^2 + 2x + 1 \approx 2x + 1.$$

Multiply them together, so

$$e^x(x^2 + 2x + 1) \approx (1+x)(2x+1) = 2x^2 + 3x + 1,$$

and the derivative of the right-hand side is 3 at $x = 0$. Therefore, the derivative of $e^x(x^2 + 2x + 1)$ should be approximately 3 at $x = 0$. You can then use a numerical derivative program to calculate the approximate value of the derivative of $e^x(x^2 + 2x + 12)$ at $x = 0$; you will find it is about 3. Note that $f'(0) \cdot g'(0) = 2$, so this shows that $(fg)' \neq f'g'$.

## Problems

1–24 — students need *lots* of practice on these rules. You may want to give students a key to these problems and have them be responsible for their own work.

27–30 — are heading toward the chain rule.

31, 32, 42, 43 — looking for patterns.

35 — a good type of problem to demonstrate understanding of rules. Other problems of this type occur in the next few sections.

37–40 — applications reminiscent of Chapter 2 and looking toward Chapter 5. Look for explanations, when requested.

39 — involves compound interest, rather difficult.

41 — requires a short proof.

**Suggested Problems:** 2, 4, 9, 12, 14, 19, 25, 34, 35, 40.

## 4.4 THE CHAIN RULE

**Class Time:** One class

## Key points

When and how to use the chain rule.

## Ideas for the class

Problem 3 of Section 4.1 provided students with a conjecture about the derivative of a composition of linear functions. To extend beyond linear functions, let $g(x) = x^2$, $f(x) = 3^x$, and $h(x) = f(g(x)) = 3^{x^2}$. Using the fact that $g'(x) = 2x$ and $f'(x) = 3^x \ln 3$, ask students to make a conjecture about $h'(2)$. Construct a table to approximate $h'(2)$ numerically by taking

$$\frac{f(g(2+h)) - f(g(2))}{h} = \frac{3^{(2+h)^2} - 3^4}{h} \quad \text{for } h = 0.01, 0.001, 0.0001, \text{ etc.}$$

If students have guessed that since $g'(2) = 4$, and $f'(2) = 9 \cdot \ln 3 \approx 9.8875$, therefore $h'(2) = g'(2) \cdot f'(2) \approx 39.55$, the fact that the numerical approximations for $h'(2)$ are approaching 356 will demonstrate that the derivative of a composition is more complicated than the linear example led them to believe.

Example 1 in Section 4.4 is a good example to get students to think about what the derivative of a composite function should be. Explain the chain rule using expansion factors: if $y = f(t)$, then $dy/dt$ is the factor by which the function $f$ expands changes in $t$ to give changes in $y$, and so on. Cover the general case in the text and return to the example of $h(x) = f(g(x)) = 3^{x^2}$ to verify that $h'(2) \approx 355.95$.

The notation $\dfrac{d}{dx} f(g(x)) = f'(g(x))g'(x)$ is difficult for many students. In particular, the symbol $f'(g(x))$ can be hard to interpret. It helps to provide a version of the chain rule in English, writing something like: "Take the derivative of the outside function without changing the inside, and then multiply this result by the derivative of the inside."

Another approach is to motivate the chain rule graphically, using the numerical derivative function found on most calculators. For example, on a TI graphing calculator, if a function is stored as $y1$, then enter $y2 =$ nDERIV$(y1, x, x)$ on the TI-82 and TI-83, or $y2 =$ nDer$(y1, x, x)$ on the TI-85 and TI-86. This yields the numerical derivative of $y1$ with respect to $x$ evaluated at the variable point $x$. When graphed, this produces the graph of the derivative of the function $y1$. An example of this activity using trigonometric functions is given in the ideas for Section 4.5.

## Problems

1–30 — students need lots of practice on these rules.

32 — difficult inequality.

34–37 — good problems to demonstrate understanding of the rules.

38 — involves a differential equation.

41–44 — applications of the chain rule; problem 43 involves compound interest.

45–46 — more difficult. 47 involves time constant (see Section 1.7, Example 1).

**Suggested Problems:** 2, 8, 12, 16, 18, 27, 30, 34, 35, 36, 39, 42.

## 4.5  THE TRIGONOMETRIC FUNCTIONS

**Class Time:** One-half to one class

## Key points

Graphical understanding the derivatives of trigonometric functions; using these derivatives with other derivative rules.

## Ideas for the class

Graphically show that the derivative formulas for sine, cosine, and tangent are reasonable. Start the class by drawing a graph of $\sin x$ and asking what its derivative ought to look like: positive where $\sin x$ is increasing, negative where $\sin x$ is decreasing, repeating with the same period as $\sin x$. This sort of reasoning produces a cosine-like graph. Alternatively, graph $\left((\sin x + 0.01) - \sin x\right)/0.01$ and then to superimpose the graph of $\cos x$.

Compute the derivative of $\tan x$ using the quotient rule. Note that this derivative is given as $1/\cos^2 x$ since we did not introduce the secant. Then do lots of examples involving the chain rule, as well as some with the product and quotient rules.

Remind students that these derivative formulas are only valid when the units are in radians. Students often reset their calculators in degrees, so be sure to have them verify that their settings are correct.

To encourage students to reflect on the chain rule, try the following activity. Graph the function $f(x) = \sin x$ and its derivative for $0 \le x \le 3$ and $-1 \le y \le 1$ using the numerical differentiation routine on a calculator. Make sure that the students understand the kinds of graphs being displayed.

Now consider the function $f(x) = \sin 2x$. The product rule and the trigonometric identity $\sin(2x) = 2\sin x \cos x$ can be used to derive the formula

$$\frac{d(\sin 2x)}{dx} = 2\cos 2x,$$

but graphs are useful to explain why there is an extra factor of 2 in front of $\cos 2x$. Graph the function $f(x) = \sin 2x$ along with its derivative for $0 \le x \le 3$ and $-2 \le y \le 2$. Since the sinusoid now completes two full cycles between 0 and $2\pi$, it is easy to see that $f(x)$ is changing twice as fast as $f(x) = \sin x$ and so its derivative will be twice as large at each point; the graph of the derivative bears this out. (You can check this at particular points by approximating the value of the derivative numerically there.) More importantly, this argument explains where the extra factor of 2 comes from.

Now consider the function $f(x) = \sin(x^2)$ for $-5 \le x \le 5$ and $-10 \le y \le 10$. From the graph, it is apparent that the function changes ever faster as $x$ increases. What about its derivative? The faster that the function changes, the larger the size of the derivative, so the derivative is an oscillatory function whose amplitude grows with $x$. This is borne out by the graphs of the function and its derivative. What is the formula for the derivative? It looks like a non-constant multiple of $\cos(x^2)$. To determine what that multiple should be, trace the derivative function to estimate the height of $f'(x)$ at different points and compare them to the values of $f(x)$. This is quite effective for integer values of $x$. Also, suppose you add two extra functions to the graph: $y3 = 2x$ and $y4 = -2x$. The two lines envelop the derivative function. This suggests that formula of the derivative of $\sin(x^2)$ might be

$$\frac{d(\sin x^2)}{dx} = 2x\cos x^2.$$

The class can be wrapped up by graphing $y = 2x\cos(x^2)$ and observing how closely it matches the numerical derivative.

## Problems

2–29 — as in the last two sections, students may need to work a lot of these.

32–38 — any of these could make good in-class discussion problems.

35 — quite difficult.

36 — problem is easy but explanation isn't.

39, 40 — provide more rigorous derivations of the derivatives of the trigonometric functions, which you could use in class.

**Suggested Problems:** 4, 6, 9, 12, 14, 16, 23, 25, 32, 33, 34.

**Problems Requiring Substantial Use of Algebra:** 35–36.

## 4.6 APPLICATIONS OF THE CHAIN RULE

**Class Time:** One half to one class

## Key points

The chain rule is used to find derivatives of various inverse functions (for example, $\sqrt{x}$, $\ln x$, $\arctan x$).

## Ideas for the class

The arguments used here are similar to those used in the next section on implicit differentiation since in both cases the derivative is obtained from the chain rule.

It is worthwhile to do some of the calculations in more than one way. For example, if $f(x) = x^{1/2}$, then $f'(x)$ can be found using the chain rule (as is done in the text). But it can also be found using the product rule:

$$(f(x) \cdot f(x))' = x' = 1$$
$$f(x) \cdot f'(x) + f'(x) \cdot f(x) = 1$$
$$2f'(x) \cdot f(x) = 1$$
$$f'(x) = \frac{1}{2f(x)} = \frac{1}{2}x^{-1/2}.$$

In the derivation of $(\arctan x)' = 1/(1 + x^2)$, use is made of the identity $1 + \tan^2\theta = 1/\cos^2\theta$ to simplify the expression $\cos^2(\arctan x)$. The same expression can be simplified without using the identity by drawing a right triangle with legs 1 and $x$ so that the hypotenuse is $\sqrt{1 + x^2}$. By choosing $\theta$ so that $\tan\theta = x$, it follows that $\arctan x$ is $\theta$, and from this that $\cos^2(\arctan x) = \cos^2\theta = 1/(1+x^2)$. For some reason, many students think that this triangle derivation is obvious, while the derivation using the identity is tricky. A similar construction shows that $\cos(\arcsin x) = \sqrt{1 - x^2}$ is used in deriving $d[\arcsin x]/dx$.

## Problems

1–17 — this may be the first time since Chapter 1 that some of the algebraic properties of logs and exponential functions have been encountered. Students may still have trouble with these.

24–25 — good for in-class examples.

28 — a great problem which takes time, so be sure to allow for that in your assignment. (Students may also need a hint on how to start.) Review Problem 5 is a similar problem. If you assign group work or projects, the two problems go well together. Either can serve as a basis for in-class discussion if you have the time.

30–31 — The two problems here compare linear with second-order approximations—ideas revisited in Chapter 9. Problem 31 is like 37 in Section 4.2. You may need to give the additional instructions if you did not assign the problem in Section 4.2.

36 — is *very* difficult for most students to set up *and* to work.

**Suggested Problems:** 3, 4, 8, 10, 16, 18, 20, 23, 27, 31, 35.

**Problems Requiring Substantial Use of Algebra:** 30–36.

## 4.7  IMPLICIT FUNCTIONS

**Class Time:** A half to a whole class

## Key points

Implicit differentiation as another application of the chain rule.

## Ideas for the class

First define an implicit function, as many students do not know the difference between implicit and explicit functions. Show the class that many implicit functions cannot be solved for either variable in terms of the other.

It is worth going over some examples in class; the main point to keep in mind is that we are only using the chain rule. Where possible, draw graphs of the functions and their derivatives and check that the derivatives make sense graphically.

You can start with the circle when you introduce implicit functions, since everyone should be familiar with it, and find $dy/dx$ implicitly as is done in the text. Having found $dy/dx$, you can also find it directly for the upper half-circle given by $y = \sqrt{1 - x^2}$ and show that the results are the same. Point out the difference between the two formulas: $x^2 + y^2 = 1$ gives the whole circle and is implicit, while $y = \sqrt{1 - x^2}$ gives only a semicircle and is explicit.

Having done this, you should discuss Figure 4.28. Drawing tangent lines to the circle in all four quadrants to verify that the formula

$$\frac{dy}{dx} = -\frac{x}{y}$$

is very helpful. Organize relevant information in a table. Many students will (understandably) have trouble with the notation

$$\frac{d}{dx}(x^2) + \frac{d}{dx}(y^2) = 0.$$

Some will think $\frac{d}{dx}(y^2)$ should be zero, since $y$ looks like a constant; others will think $\frac{d}{dx}(y^2) = 2y$. Emphasize that $y$ depends on $x$, so $y$ must change when $x$ does.

Next, cover something like Example 1, which considers $y^3 - xy = -6$. Convince students that they cannot solve for $y$ (although they can solve for $x$!). Show them the graph (Figure 4.29), and admit that it isn't the graph of a function in the usual sense, since it fails the vertical line test. (The circle has the same problem.) Point out that the graph does have a tangent line and a slope at (almost) every point. The purpose of implicit differentiation is to find this slope. Again, as you differentiate the function, keep in mind that students need to be taken slowly through statements like

$$\frac{d}{dx}(xy) = y + x\frac{dy}{dx}.$$

Emphasize that you are using the product rule and the chain rule, since $y$ is (implicitly) a function of $x$. It can be helpful to write $y(x)$ instead of $y$. Some instructors go so far as to write $y = k(x)$, telling the class that while we can't solve for the function $k$, we use it as a reminder (when applying the chain or product rule) that $y$ depends on $x$. In this case, the equation

$$\frac{d}{dx}(y^3) - \frac{d}{dx}(xy) = 0$$

becomes

$$\frac{d}{dx}(k(x)^3) - \frac{d}{dx}(xk(x)) = 0,$$

an equation which shows the need for the chain and product rules. If you have time, Example 2 is a good follow-up to Example 1.

## Problems

1–16 — these problems involve implicit differentiation (which is difficult for students), as well as considerable algebra.

**Suggested Problems:** 2, 6, 7, 8, 14, 20.

**Problems Requiring Substantial Use of Algebra:** 1–22.

## 4.8  LINEAR APPROXIMATIONS AND LIMITS

**Class Time:** Part of a class

## Key points

L'Hopital's rule is explained for $\lim_{x \to a}$ when $f(a) = g(a) = 0$ and $a$ is finite. The rule is stated for $a = \pm\infty$ and when limits of $f$ and $g$ tend to $\pm\infty$.

## Ideas for the class

Start with an example which demonstrates the case when $a$ is finite and $f(a) = g(a) = 0$, for example

$$\lim_{x \to 0} \frac{\sin(2x)}{3x}.$$

Approximate the limit graphically and numerically. Show that these functions satisfy the condition $f(a) = g(a) = 0$. Graph $y = f(x)$ and $y = g(x)$ and the tangent line approximations for $f$ and $g$ on the same axes and give a graphical explanation of the rule in this case. Then use l'Hopital's rule to evaluate the limit.

Students are inclined to misuse l'Hopital's rule once they've seen it. Stress that the appropriate conditions must be met in order to apply the rule. For example, take

$$\lim_{x \to 1} \frac{\sin 2x}{3x}$$

and show that the rule doesn't apply or work.

Discuss the other cases in the section and work some examples such as

$$\lim_{x \to \infty} \frac{t^2}{e^t}$$

where you will need to use the rule twice.

## Problems

6–17 — should be straightforward.

18 — assign or use for in-class discussion.

13–15 — useful techniques for evaluation of improper integrals and series.

**Suggested Problems:** 8, 9, 10, 12, 15, 17, 18.

**Problems Requiring Substantial Use of Algebra:** 20.

## FOCUS ON PRACTICE: DIFFERENTIATION

There are many problems on which students can practice their skills. These are a good preparation for gateway tests which are available later in this manual.

# CHAPTER FIVE

## Overview

The aim of this chapter is to enable the student to use the derivative in solving problems, rather than to learn a catalog of application templates. It is not meant to be comprehensive, and it is not necessary to cover all the sections. The student should finish this chapter with the experience of having successfully tackled a few problems that required sustained thought over more than one session.

### Changes from the First Edition

Newton's method moved to the appendix; new section (optional) on hyperbolic functions; material reorganized.

## 5.1   USING FIRST AND SECOND DERIVATIVES

**Class Time:** One class

## Key points

If the derivative is positive, the function is increasing; if negative, decreasing. Second derivative indicates concavity. Critical points; inflection points; the first and second derivative tests for local extrema.
**New:** Local extrema can occur at critical points and at endpoints. First and second derivative tests are both included. Global extrema moved to Section 5.3.

## Ideas for the class

By now, most students should know the correspondence between the sign of the derivative and the function's behavior, but they don't necessarily know how to put this information to use. Some elementary curve sketching is in order here before going on to anything more difficult. Sketch a simple cubic equation, or $e^{-x^2}$, or $\tan^{-1} x$, or some function where you can see quickly and easily how the derivative is behaving, where there is a chance of seeing as a whole the relation between the derivative and the shape of the function.

Illustrate the power of the result that if $f' > 0$ on an interval, then $f$ is increasing there. For example, after explaining this result, write down on the board the two cubics $x^3 - x^2 + x - 1$ and $x^3 - x^2 - x - 1$. Only one of them is always increasing: which is it? (If you are using a graphing program, draw the graphs, and then ask: how could we have known which it was going to be?) Answer: the derivatives are $3x^2 - 2x + 1$ and $3x^2 - 2x - 1$, and the quadratic formula tells us that the first has no real roots, the second has two. So the first function is always increasing, as its derivative is always positive.

Define critical points and use the first derivative test to check for local extrema on one of the functions you picked to begin the class. Notice that a local maximum or minimum can be at a critical point or an endpoint.

Use the same example to discuss concavity, the role of the second derivative, and to introduce and use the second derivative test. Define inflection points and ask students where they would expect to find an inflection point on your example function. Then use the second derivative to find the point(s). Some students have trouble with inflection points at first, because they they are less straightforward than maxima and minima. Spend some time on simple examples. Watch out for students who think that an inflection point always occurs where the second derivative is zero rather than where the concavity changes.

A particularly good example is $e^{-x^2}$; since it has a maximum of 1 at $x = 0$ and is asymptotic to the $x$-axis, it must have at least two inflection points. Ask if it is possible to have a function which approaches a horizontal asymptote from above and stays concave down. (Answer: no, because a concave down function has to stay below its tangent line, and the tangent line at some point will be pointing down, hence it will cross the asymptote.)

Despite all the calculations necessary, keep the discussion primarily focused on graphs.

## Problems

2, 3, 5, 6 — students need to notice whether they are looking at the graph of $f'$, $f''$ or $f$.

8–17, 26 — require access to graphing technology.

18–20, 22 — good problem to investigate understanding of concepts.

21 — good problem. Require the explanation.

24, 25 — look different, but note that the information which can be obtained from the pictures is very similar!

27–32 — assign at least a few of these. They shouldn't be terribly hard, but may seem difficult to some students. Be careful of 30 and 32 if you've skipped the Differentiability section. You may want to do one of those in class.

33 — difficult because it's different (i.e., deals with the reciprocal).

**Suggested Problems:** 2, 3, 5, 10, 14, 16, 18, 20, 21, 27, 30.

## 5.2  FAMILIES OF CURVES: A QUALITATIVE STUDY

**Class Time:** One class or a computer lab

## Key points

Calculus is most useful when applied to the graphs of families of functions rather than to graphing specific functions. The latter can be analyzed individually using a calculator or computer; to understand dependence on parameters, calculus is required.

## Ideas for the class

When you begin to look at families of functions, you can point out to students that they are already familiar with several important families including linear functions and trigonometric functions. Remind them of some of the effects that various parameters have on the graph of a general function (e.g., $f(x+a)$ represents a horizontal shift of $f$ while $f(x)+b$ represents a vertical shift). Emphasize that with calculus, families of functions can be studied in greater detail than previously possible.

It is helpful to have a graphing calculator or computer program (like TWIDDLE, University of Arizona Software) which allows you to enter parameterized families and then vary the parameters. Most calculators will accept parameterized families and allow several functions to be sketched in the same viewing window. You might want to break the class into groups and have each group investigate and report back on various families.

The students find the idea of functions with parameters in them quite hard, so it is worth spending some time on this. After students get the idea from the graphs, you can start doing analysis using critical points, etc., as in the text. Notice that for problems of this type, it is helpful to break each question into several very specific smaller parts. Possible examples[1] to use in class are

$$y = ax + \frac{b}{x} \quad \text{or} \quad y = axe^{-bx} \quad \text{or} \quad y = x + k\sin x$$

## Problems

Students find this section difficult. Assign fewer problems and plan to discuss them after assigned.

1, 2 — go together and are straightforward.

3, 15 — are really Chapter 1 type problems. Students should be able to answer these easily and explain their answers using the ideas of calculus.

7 — long, but not really hard.

4, 5, 16, 17 — all are related to an example from the text. You might refer students back to the appropriate discussion, if assigned, or use one of these to expand on in-class discussion.

**Suggested Problems:** 1, 2, 5, 6, 10, 11, 17.

**Problems Requiring Substantial Use of Algebra:** 1–7, 12–14, 18.

## 5.3 OPTIMIZATION

**Class Time:** One to two classes

## Key points

The derivative provides a simple criterion for optimization: find critical points by looking at points where the derivative is zero and check end points and critical points to find the global optimum. **New:** Global extrema now introduced in this section.

## Ideas for the class

This is another class where you should get the students to try some examples before you talk too much; perhaps just do a couple of examples (one graphical), assign homework (not too many), and return to the homework later. The graphical examples are excellent. The section on gasoline consumption (including Example 3) is particularly challenging and very fruitful for students. It's also a lot of fun! Walk students through the units—they may not be used to using them.

Try not to reduce the solution of the algebraic examples to rules, and in grading homework be open to unconventional approaches. Since the emphasis is on problem solving, you should work the same problem in different ways in class.

## Problems

6–8 — excellent problems to check understanding.

23–26 — beautiful problems for in-class discussions. Perhaps assign one or two for students to think about, then discuss.

**Suggested Problems:** 2, 4, 6, 12, 22, 26.

**Problems Requiring Substantial Use of Algebra:** 11–16.

---

[1] $y = x + k\sin x$ suggested by Paul Zorn.

## 5.4  APPLICATIONS TO MARGINALITY

**Class Time:** One class or skip entirely

## Key points

Use of differentiation in qualitative, graphical reasoning. Representation of economic ideas graphically, including cost, revenue, profit, and marginality.

## Ideas for the class

The reasoning in this section is largely graphical. Some students will feel uncomfortable with the lack of formulas here and will try to make up formulas of their own. Others may be helped by putting (made up) units on the axes, to help them see where the derivative is increasing and where it is decreasing. A good kickoff is to draw a cost function and ask the students what its slope and concavity mean. Discuss why the cost and revenue functions aren't necessarily linear, and discuss why most revenue functions are concave down. A good problem on interpreting the derivative is to write down a difference quotient with $h = 1$ to show that the derivative is approximately the cost of an extra item. From there you can go on to analyze profit, cost, and revenue.

When working a problem like Example 2, explain why a company should increase production if marginal revenue exceeds marginal cost. Keep in mind that there are several ways to attack many of these problems, all of them worthwhile. In Example 4, for example, the book gives two arguments to show that profit is maximized when marginal cost equals marginal revenue The first is graphical: when the vertical distance between cost and revenue curve is maximized, profit (or loss!) is maximized. The second is analytical. Since

$$\pi(q) = R(q) - C(q),$$

where $\pi$ represents the profit, profit is maximized when $\pi'(q) = R'(q) - C'(q) = 0$, that is, when $R'(q) = C'(q)$. This solution also has a graphic interpretation (parallel tangents). In keeping with the Rule of Four, you can make a table of marginal revenue and marginal cost at different quantities. You can include marginal profit and also total profit, which is cumulative. From the table, it'll be clear that if marginal revenue exceeds marginal cost, marginal profit is positive and total profit is therefore increasing. This example brings a lot of concepts together for students.

You might want to point out that the domains and ranges of these functions are discrete (units sold, price in cents) but that it makes sense to pretend that the curves are smooth and defined for all $q > 0$. You may also wonder why the symbol "$\pi$" is used for profit. The answer is that economists, having used $p$ for price, use $\pi$ for profit.

## Problems

1–3 — problems go well together as they emphasize graphical interpretation.

5, 7, 10 — will seem easiest because there are formulas with numbers.

6, 11 — look difficult but really aren't; perhaps use for class discussion.

**Suggested Problems:** 1, 4, 5, 9, 10.

## 5.5  MORE OPTIMIZATION: INTRODUCTION TO MODELING

**Class Time:** One class, or assign for reading and homework or skip entirely

## Key points

Using functions to construct models and techniques of differentiation to find optima.

## Ideas for Class

This is a hard section!

Focus solely on specific examples. Example 1 explores how to select optimum dimensions to minimize metal for a can of given volume. Students often don't know where to begin this sort of question: it's not immediately clear what to do. Remind them that the quantity to be optimized should be given as a function of quantities they can vary. Decide what the relevant variables are. Discuss the importance of constraints here. Go over Figure 5.62, justifying the curve's shape. (Too small a radius yields a very tall can; too large a radius gives a very large top and bottom.) If you have time, bring in a real soda can. It will be taller than predicted. Ask why! (Answer: Taller containers look like they hold more and are easy to carry in one hand; moreover, the top and bottom actually have thicker walls—ask the class how that will affect their answer.)

If you work carefully through examples, you probably won't have time to do more than a couple of problems. Don't assign many homework problems. Encourage students to write down as much information as they can about their efforts, even if they can't give complete solutions.

## Problems

1–15 — similar to problems you have probably seen before, but they are hard for students.

18 — looks harder than it is.

19, 20 — may require some help with the trig.

**Suggested Problems:** 2, 4, 5, 10, 14.

**Problems Requiring Substantial Use of Algebra:** 1–17.

## 5.6  HYPERBOLIC FUNCTIONS

**Class Time:** Part of a class or skip

## Key points

Definition and properties of hyperbolic functions.

## Ideas for the class

Define the hyperbolic sine and cosine, and show their graphs. It is useful to demonstrate some of the properties or identities in the text, as students may be rusty on the algebra or exponential rules involved. If you plan to spend an entire class on the section, problems like 13–15 are good opportunities for group-work.

## Problems

Assign just a few. Be alert for algebra errors.

**Suggested Problems:** 4, 6, 8, 14.

**Problems Requiring Substantial Use of Algebra:** 1–6, 13–14, 16.

# FOCUS ON THEORY: CONTINUOUS AND DIFFERENTIABLE FUNCTIONS

**Class Time:** One class

## Key Points

Extreme Value Theorem; Mean Value Theorem; Race Track principle.

## Ideas for the class

You may want to precede the statement of the Extreme Value Theorem by drawing a whole series of graphs such as

$$f(x) = x^2$$

$$g(x) = \frac{1}{x}$$

$$h(x) = \begin{cases} x & \text{if } 0 \leq x \leq 1/2 \\ 0 & \text{if } 1/2 \leq x \leq 1 \end{cases}$$

$$k(x) = \sin x, \ 0 \leq x \leq 3\pi/4$$
$$m(x) = 1 - |x|, \ -1 \leq x \leq 1/2$$

in order to formulate the set of requirements which would guarantee the existence of both global extrema. The functions $h$ and $g$ can be used as examples which illustrate why continuity and closure of the interval of domain are required as hypotheses for the theorem to hold. You can point out that the above graphs suggest that global extrema can be found at the endpoints or at critical points inside the appropriate interval. When discussing the theorem on local extrema and critical points, point out that its use is limited to identifying potential global extrema of differentiable functions.

For the Mean Value Theorem, stress the picture that illustrates its statement. To motivate its statement, you may ask your students to decide whether the fact that a car covers a certain distance at an average velocity of 60 mph necessarily implies that at some point in time the car's velocity was *exactly* 60 mph.

To justify the two hypotheses of the Mean Value Theorem, you may offer

$$f(x) = \begin{cases} 1 - x^2 & \text{if } -1 \leq x \leq 1, \ x \neq 0 \\ 0 & \text{if } x = 0 \end{cases}$$

and

$$g(x) = 1 - |x|, \ -1 \leq x \leq 1.$$

Point out that the Mean Value Theorem relates a local property (derivative at a point) to a global property (average rate of change) of a function which satisfies the requirements of the theorem. Problems 18 and 19 present a proof of the Mean Value Theorem via Rolle's Theorem.

Illustrate the Race Track Principle with pictures. Point out that its proof is a direct application of the Increasing Function Theorem. Problems 1–4 illustrate the basic uses of the Race Track Principle.

## Problems

Selected problems are discussed above.

**Suggested Problems:** 1–4, 11, 16, 17, 18, 19.

# CHAPTER SIX

## Overview

This chapter focuses on the three ways (graphical, numerical, and analytic) of going backwards from a derivative to the original function. The chapter starts with reconstructing the original function from the derivative graphically and numerically. The indefinite integral is introduced in Section 6.2, along with antiderivatives of simple elementary functions. There is a brief introduction to differential equations (Section 6.3), and the chapter culminates with the Construction Theorem for Antiderivatives and the Second Fundamental Theorem of Calculus.

### Changes from the First Edition

This chapter needs to be covered in its entirety. It no longer begins with a review of Chapter 3. Material formerly in 6.1 and 6.2 has been moved to Chapter 3. The Construction Theorem, or Second Fundamental Theorem of Calculus (now in 6.4) was formerly in Chapter 7.

## 6.1 ANTIDERIVATIVES GRAPHICALLY AND NUMERICALLY

**Class Time:** One class

## Key points

The graph of $f'$ tells us where $f$ is increasing and where $f$ is decreasing. The Fundamental Theorem tells us exactly how much $f$ increases and exactly how much $f$ decreases.

## Ideas for the class

Start with a graph of $f'$ (no formula) and ask students for a possible sketch of $f$. (It's probably best to choose $f(0) = 0$.) Make sure the class remembers that

$$f' > 0 \quad \text{on an interval} \quad \Rightarrow \quad f \quad \text{is increasing there}$$
$$f' < 0 \quad \text{on an interval} \quad \Rightarrow \quad f \quad \text{is decreasing there.}$$

Thus, if $f' > 0$, the graph of $f$ will climb until $f'$ crosses the $x$-axis. To find out how far it climbs, we can estimate the area under the curve using the Fundamental Theorem.

## Problems

1–9 — students beginning this course with Chapter 6 will have difficulty with these at first, but all students will need plenty of practice with this type of problem.

10–17 — more involved than the previous problems but excellent for demonstration of understanding. Assign at least a couple of these.

**Suggested Problems:** 1, 6, 8, 12, 13, 16.

## 6.2  CONSTRUCTING ANTIDERIVATIVES ANALYTICALLY

**Class Time:** One or two classes

## Key points

Indefinite integral notation; basic antiderivatives; antiderivatives of sums; differences and constant multiples of functions.

## Ideas for the class

Emphasize the distinction between the definite integral (a number computed by limits of sums) and the indefinite integral (the general antiderivative, which happens to be useful in computing definite integrals). You will have to do this again and again throughout this chapter; because the notations are so similar, the students are likely to confuse the two ideas.

Explain the sum and constant multiple rules as reversals of the corresponding rules for derivatives; set up the theme of reversing rules of differentiation, with the warning that it won't be so easy for the chain and product rules.

Spend time using the sum and constant multiple rules to find antiderivatives, e.g.

$$\int \left(\frac{1}{x} + \frac{1}{x^2}\right) dx, \quad \int \pi x^3 \, dx, \quad \int (2\cos x - 5\sin x) \, dx.$$

Include some examples where the constant is in the denominator, e.g.

$$\int \frac{e^x}{5} \, dx.$$

Some students may need to be reminded that in this case the integrand is just $(1/5)e^x$.

Make sure students can do definite integrals using the Fundamental Theorem, e.g., $\int_2^3 (1/x^2 + 3x) \, dx$, $\int_0^{\pi/2} \cos x \, dx$. Include examples where the answer can be expressed both symbolically and numerically, e.g.,

$$\int_2^3 \frac{1}{2x} \, dx = \frac{1}{2}(\ln 3 - \ln 2) = 0.2027.$$

If you have time, do an example that requires thinking about whether the answers mechanically obtained make sense; for example, ask your students to decide which is bigger, $\int_0^1 x^2 \, dx$ or $\int_0^1 x^3 \, dx$, just using their knowledge of the graphs of the integrands; then calculate the integrals to confirm their choice. Or, ask them to guess the order of magnitude of $\int_2^3 e^x \, dx$ and $\int_2^3 e^{-x} \, dx$, and then calculate the answer. Or, ask them to decide from the graph whether $\int_{0.5}^{1.5} (x^2 - 1) \, dx$ is positive or negative, and then calculate the answer.

Here, and in the next few sections, include some application problems in each homework you assign.

## Problems

1–28, 37–61 — Students are asked to find antiderivatives by inspection and some of the problems will involve very careful inspection (and careful checking). Emphasize the need to check. (The hints will help on the tricky ones and will help prepare students for substitution.)

22–29 — ask for specific antiderivatives. 29 is the only one with $C \neq 0$. You might want to include it for that reason.

46–55 — here to emphasize the difference between the definite and indefinite integrals.

56–59 — area problems. 57 and 58 involve area between two curves.

60, 61 — involve average value (and a little algebra in 60).

62, 63 — straightforward applications; assign at least one of these. 62 may be difficult for some students to set up properly unless they are familiar with the material from Section 5.4.

**Suggested Problems:** 6, 12, 16, 25, 34, 36, 43, 48, 58, 60, 62.

**Problems Requiring Substantial Use of Algebra:** 56, 59–60.

## 6.3 DIFFERENTIAL EQUATIONS

**Class Time:** One class

## Key points

Concept of differential equation, parameterized family of solutions, initial conditions.

## Ideas for the class

This section forms a brief introduction to differential equations. Emphasize the idea of a family of solutions, and choosing a particular solution using initial or other values.

Focus on antidifferentiation as a process of "working backward." Emphasize that though the antiderivatives of a function form a family, when one additional condition is imposed, there is a unique antiderivative. One such situation is in describing an object thrown in the air. Starting with its initial velocity, we need one additional constraint—its initial height—to find its position. Starting with its acceleration (that due to gravity) you need two additional pieces of information—the initial velocity and position.

A fun thing to do with velocity and acceleration is to ask the students to guess how fast they can throw a ball in the air. One way to get a feel for the accuracy of the guess is to see how high a ball thrown that fast would go, and ask them if they think they can really throw a ball that high.

## Problems

1–4 — straightforward.

5–9 — initial value problems.

13–22 — velocity/acceleration applications. Problems are not difficult.

**Suggested Problems:** 2, 4, 6, 8, 11, 15, 16, 20.

## 6.4 SECOND FUNDAMENTAL THEOREM OF CALCULUS

**Class Time:** One class

## Key points

Construction theorem for antiderivatives; Second Fundamental Theorem of Calculus.

## Ideas for the class

Emphasize that many functions do not have elementary function antiderivatives. The construction theorem allows us to define and analyze an antiderivative function.

Students find this idea mysterious, so be sure to tell them through the graphical justification and the "squeeze theorem." (If this chapter begins a new semester for your class, you may want to refer students back to Section 3.4 for preparation for these ideas.)

Extend the examples on $\text{Si}(x)$ by using problems 7 or 13 of the text, or use the error function (defined and used in Problems 16–19). Students find it interesting that these functions don't have elementary antiderivatives but *do* have names. It is also useful to use the construction theorem on a function that does antidifferentiate easily (e.g., problem 15) to show that the answers agree.

**New:** This material was formerly in Chapter 7, combined with slope fields. This section is done without slope fields. They will be introduced in the projects at the end of Chapter 7 and then in Chapter 10.

## Problems

2, 6, 7 — similar to Example 5, Section 6.1.

8–15 — very good for checking understanding. 13 involves the chain rule.

16–19 — involve $\text{erf}(x)$, defined in the problems.

**Suggested Problems:** 1, 4, 6, 7, 12, 13, 16.

# FOCUS ON MODELING: THE EQUATIONS OF MOTION

**Class Time:** One class or part of a class

## Key points

Historical development of the equations of motion.

## Ideas for the class

This section will appeal to students with a particular interest in the history and philosophy of physics. During the class point out the central role of acceleration in describing the motion of a body moving under gravity. Derive the laws of motion, starting with Newton's Second Law and the Inverse Square Law of Gravitation.

## Problems

5–7 — challenging problems that require interpretation of passages from Galileo's writings

# CHAPTER SEVEN

## Overview

We treat standard substitutions in Section 7.1, and less obvious substitution techniques in Section 7.2, where we also discuss how to change the limits of integration in a definite integral. Section 7.3 covers integration by parts. Section 7.4 shows how to use a table of integrals, with examples of how the formulas in such tables are obtained, and introduces partial fractions.

In Section 7.5 we introduce the simpler numerical methods for computing definite integrals; in Section 7.6 we analyze the errors in these methods, and use this analysis to derive Simpson's Rule. Sections 7.7 and 7.8 are on improper integrals. In Section 7.7, antiderivatives are found explicitly; in Section 7.8, convergence is determined by comparison.

### Changes from the First Edition

Basic antiderivatives, formerly in Section 7.1, have been moved to Chapter 6. This chapter starts with substitution. Additional problems for skill practice are included in the new Focus on Practice section.

## 7.1  INTEGRATION BY SUBSTITUTION: PART I

**Class Time:** One class

## Key points

Simple substitutions where only a constant factor must be introduced.

## Ideas for the class

Explain that the basic idea behind the substitution method is to find a way of reversing the chain rule.

Start with an easy example such as $\int 2x \cos(x^2)\, dx$. Possibly introduce this integral by writing $\int \cos(x^2)\, dx$ first, showing how the obvious guess, $\sin(x^2)$, does not work because of the chain rule, and then point out that if the $2x$ from the chain rule had been there in the first place you could have done the integral. This gets the point across that integrands have to be in a rather special shape to be integrated using substitution, a point that you will need to come back to again and again. Then go on to do $\int t^2 e^{5t^3}\, dt$ and $\int \cos x \sqrt{\sin x + 1}\, dx$ by the guess-and-check method. If the last one is too difficult to guess, it can be replaced by a simpler example such as $\int x^3 \sqrt{2 + x^4}\, dx$. However, working through the difficulty leads naturally to the quest for a more systematic method, namely the $w$-substitution. (We use $w$ instead of the more traditional $u$ to distinguish it from the $u$, $v$ of integration by parts.)

Once you have introduced the $w$-substitution, go back and do the same examples you did before. Remind students that this method grew out of looking for the end products of the chain rule; therefore, you are looking for an inside function whose derivative is somewhere outside, and when you have found it you want to put $w$ equal to the inside function. This makes the tricky ones such as $\int \cos x \sqrt{\sin x + 1}\, dx$ easier, since once you have decided to put $w = \sin x + 1$ the rest is mechanical. Students should also see an example where the outside function and the inside function are hard to recognize, for example $\int x/(1 + x^2)\, dx$ (let $w = 1 + x^2$) or $\int x/(1 + x^4)\, dx$ (let $w = x^2$). Be prepared for questions about what $dx$ means or where $dw$ came from.

Encourage your students not to rely too much on the mechanics of substitution; do examples to convince them that they really can guess-and-check in simple cases; encourage them to look for patterns. For example, $\int \cos(2x)\,dx = \frac{1}{2}\sin(2x)$, $\int e^{3x}\,dx = \frac{1}{3}e^{3x}$, $\int (5x-1)^3\,dx = \frac{1}{20}(5x-1)^4$ can all be done without formal substitution, if you point out the patterns to students. Always emphasize the reversal of differentiation; they are familiar with a constant coming out the front when they differentiate; so, when it is absent, you first have to divide by the constant.

An interesting example is $\int 1/(2x)\,dx$. The answer is either $\frac{1}{2}\ln x + C$ or $\frac{1}{2}\ln(2x) + C$ (using $w = 2x$). Show that the two antiderivatives differ only by a constant.

## Problems

1–41 — Although the emphasis of this course is not on drill problems, students do need plenty of practice on the techniques of this chapter. Assign as many of these problems as you feel are appropriate. It is a good idea to mix in some that do not work with the techniques of this section (e.g., 18, 35, 39) and some which should be rewritten first (e.g. 29, 41).

43 — a problem where the antiderivatives are different – with a chance to require an explanation.

44–46 — application problems. 45 will seem much harder for students (since it involves all letters, no numbers).

**Suggested Problems:** 4, 7, 10, evens 12–40, 41, 43, 44.

**Problems Requiring Substantial Use of Algebra:** 41–42.

## 7.2  INTEGRATION BY SUBSTITUTION: PART II

**Class Time:** A half to a whole class

## Key points

Substitutions in definite integrals; less obvious substitutions.

## Ideas for the class

Calculate a definite integral, say $\int_1^2 x \sin(x^2)\,dx$ or $\int_0^1 x^2/(1 + x^3)\,dx$, in two ways: by evaluating the indefinite integral first (using a substitution) and by changing the limits of integration when you make the substitution. Students may prefer the first way, even though it is often more laborious. You need to explain changing the limits of integration quite carefully; many students have trouble with it. This is partly because they have never appreciated the significance of the $dx$ and $dw$ in the integral (in fact many of them leave it out; this is a good place to remind them of its usefulness). Choose another example, similar to the first one you do, where a substitution does not work, and point out that it must be done numerically. For the two above, you could choose $\int_1^2 \sin(x^2)\,dx$ and $\int_0^1 x^2/(1 + x^4)\,dx$ (which in fact can be done in elementary, but complicated, terms). They should see an example like Example 4; a simpler one you can do in class is $\int x\sqrt{x - 1}\,dx$ (let $w = x - 1$).

The text does not give a list of special substitutions but rather the suggestion that sometimes it can be helpful to substitute $w$ for a complex part of the integrand and see what happens. The philosophy taken by the text is that students ought to be able to perform simple substitutions accurately and quickly; more complicated integrands should be antidifferentiated using tables or a computer algebra system.

A nice digression showing the usefulness of the substitution method in transforming integrals is to demonstrate the formula for the area of a circle $A = \pi r^2$. Start by expressing the area as an integral

$$A = 2\int_{-r}^{r} \sqrt{r^2 - x^2}\,dx.$$

Now suggest that students try the substitution $w = x/r$. This has the effect of transforming the integral and giving

$$A = 2r^2 \int_{-1}^{1} \sqrt{1 - w^2}\, dw.$$

Because we know that our expression for $A$ must reduce to $A = \pi r^2$, we know that we must have

$$2\int_{-1}^{1} \sqrt{1 - w^2}\, dw = \pi.$$

You can demonstrate this either geometrically or numerically or by using the substitution $w = \tan\theta$. (If your class is really sophisticated, point out that this could be a definition of $\pi$).

## Problems

1–27 — Be sure to assign a few of the problems that don't work using substitution (16, 26) or that don't follow from the most common substitution choices (e.g. 10, 22, 25).

28–32 — good for generating class discussion or models for matching questions on a test or quiz.

33 — hard for most students. Accept a numerical approximation if given.

34(c) — hard.

41–43 — application problems. 43 is hardest since numbers are missing.

**Suggested Problems:** 1, 3, 6, 7, 11, 12, 16, 20, 22, 24, 25, 26, 35, 38, 39, 41, 42.

**Problems Requiring Substantial Use of Algebra:** 33, 40.

## 7.3  INTEGRATION BY PARTS

**Class Time:** One class

## Key points

Integration by parts method for indefinite and definite integrals.

## Ideas for the class

Continue the theme of reversing rules of differentiation with the idea of reversing the product rule.

Start with an easy example, and explain the method and the $u, v$ notation. Do one of Examples 1 or 2, or vary them slightly by doing $\int xe^{-x}\, dx$ or $\int x \sin x\, dx$. Then do more complicated examples. You should do one example which requires integrating by parts twice, such as $\int x^2 e^x\, dx$, one which requires setting $v' = 1$, such as $\int \ln x\, dx$ or $\int \arctan x\, dx$, and one which "boomerangs," such as $\int e^x \sin x\, dx$ or $\int \cos^2 x\, dx$.

## Problems

1–27 — These problems are straightforward. Assign a variety of types (i.e., those that circle back to the original integral, those that require repeated integration by parts, and problems where the choices for $u$ and $v'$ may not be obvious at first).

28–36 — definite integrals using integration by parts.

43–46 — opportunities to develop some of the reduction formulas which will be used in the next section.

51 — students may need even more than the hint to get started on this. After that, the algebra will be hard for some students.

52 — conceptually easy, but the limits on part (b) may require discussion. Be open to a variety of methods on investigating the limits (i.e., graphical, numerical, etc.).

**Suggested Problems:** 1, 2, 3, 6, 7, 9, 10, 11, 12, 14, 15, 18, 20, 21, 22, 24, 25, 26, 27, 30, 32, 39, 43, 45, 53.

**Problems Requiring Substantial Use of Algebra:** 37–38, 51.

# 7.4  TABLES OF INTEGRALS

**Class Time:** One class, or more if you discuss completing the square and/or partial fractions

## Key points

Recognizing a given integral as a standard form in a table; Performing a substitution to convert a given integral into a standard form; Use of reduction formulas and partial fractions.

## Ideas for the class

We are replacing the standard collection of integration methods with the useful skill of using integral tables. Students find tables surprisingly hard—primarily because they have trouble identifying the form of an integral and so don't know where to look in the table. Discuss the general form of the table given in the text (here is a good place for a transparency!) and present a number of integral problems, all at once. For example, (assuming you include completing the square), you might put up

1. $\displaystyle\int \frac{1}{\sin x}\, dx.$

2. $\displaystyle\int \cos^3 4x\, dx.$

3. $\displaystyle\int \frac{1}{x^2 + 2x + 2}\, dx.$

4. $\displaystyle\int \frac{1}{x^2 + 2x - 3}\, dx.$

5. $\displaystyle\int \frac{x^3}{x^2 + 2x + 2}\, dx.$

6. $\displaystyle\int e^{5x} \sin(3x)\, dx.$

7. $\displaystyle\int (x^3 + 2x^2 - 5x + 7)\sin(3x)\, dx.$

8. $\displaystyle\int \frac{1}{\sqrt{x^2 + 2x + 2}}\, dx.$

9. $\displaystyle\int \frac{1}{\sqrt{3 - x^2 - 2x}}\, dx.$

10. $\displaystyle\int \sqrt{3 - x^2 - 2x}\, dx.$

The first step is to get the students to understand which formula in the table a given integrand resembles. Go through your list and ask students to suggest which entry in the table is the best fit. Compare examples that look similar but require different formulas; e.g (3) and (4), or (8) and (9). Show how to put integrals in a form necessary for the table, e.g., by completing the square, by factoring a quadratic, or by using long division. Select a few problems to work through completely. Do at least one definite integral as well.

The main point about reduction methods is to know that they are there. Derive one if you have time; if not, it is more important to give an example of using one. For example, do $\int t^3 e^{4t}\, dt$ using the reduction formula (make sure you work it out yourself first!). Make sure students understand that when they use reduction formulas, they will *not* need to do integration by parts—that was done in the derivation of the formula.

A discussion of partial fractions is optional but fits well at this point if you want to include it.

## Problems

Students sometimes mistakenly believe that using tables will be easy. In fact, there are many intricacies and techniques in this section, and you may want to return here for additional problems later. Be sure to give problems which require a variety of techniques in each assignment. To facilitate this, the problems are separated below by the techniques (or part of the table) used. If you do some in class, include some which should be worked *without* the table (like 11 or 28).

1, 8, 9, 16, 18, 30, 31, 32, 39, 40, 41 — all involve Section II of the table. 31, 32 and 40 are hardest, as they involve the general case.

2, 7, 10, 12, 13, 15, 17 — involve Section III of the table.

3, 4, 6, 19, 20, 21, 23, 29 — involve Section IV of the table.

5, 14, 22, 24, 25, 26, 27 — involve Section V of the table.

14, 24, 25, 33, 35, 36, 37, 38 — are partial fraction problems.

11, 28 — best worked without the tables.

14 — requires long division.

27 — requires completing the square.

**Suggested Problems:** Assign as appropriate for your class.

**Problems Requiring Substantial Use of Algebra:** 34–38.

## 7.5 APPROXIMATING DEFINITE INTEGRALS

**Class Time:** One class

## Key points

Comparison of the effectiveness of the Left, Right, Midpoint and Trapezoid rules.

## Ideas for the class

We now turn to numerical methods for calculating integrals. In this and the next section you should draw lots of graphs to explain the ideas. It also helps to have a programmable calculator or computer to show how the different methods converge for increasing values of $n$. If the students have calculators or are in a computer classroom, you might want to consider making this and the next class into a lab where the students do their own calculations and report the results and conclusions. If you don't have any technology, produce overheads with tables of numbers.

Describe geometrically what each method is computing and how to tell whether the approximation is an overestimate or an underestimate by looking at whether the function is increasing or decreasing, concave up or concave down.

A good strategy for teaching this section and the following one is to choose a small set of examples and follow them through using the various approximation methods. You should do this for one problem where the exact answer is known, and another for which it is not known. The text uses $\int_1^2 (1/x)\,dx = \ln 2$ and $\int_0^{2.5} \sin(t^2)\,dt$. Other examples you might use are $\int_1^4 \sqrt{x}\,dx = 14/3$ and

$\int_0^1 e^{-x^2}\,dx$. See Tables 7.5.1 and 7.5.2. If you make a transparency of Tables 7.5.1 and 7.5.2, cover up the Simpson's rule column until the rule is introduced (see Section 7.6). You should explain that you have found the value to a specified degree of accuracy (e.g. 3 decimal places)—by watching the decimal places stabilize in the numerical approximations.

**TABLE 7.5.1**   *Different methods for $\int_1^4 \sqrt{x}\,dx$.*

| $n$ | LEFT($n$) | RIGHT($n$) | TRAP($n$) | MID($n$) | SIMP($n$) |
|-----|-----------|------------|-----------|----------|-----------|
| 2   | 3.8717    | 5.3717     | 4.6217    | 4.6885   | 4.6662    |
| 10  | 4.5148    | 4.8148     | 4.6648    | 4.6676   | 4.6667    |
| 50  | 4.6366    | 4.6966     | 4.6666    | 4.6667   | 4.6667    |
| 250 | 4.6607    | 4.6727     | 4.6667    | 4.6667   | 4.6667    |

**TABLE 7.5.2**   *Different methods for $\int_0^1 e^{-x^2}\,dx$.*

| $n$ | LEFT($n$) | RIGHT($n$) | TRAP($n$) | MID($n$) | SIMP($n$) |
|-----|-----------|------------|-----------|----------|-----------|
| 2   | 0.8894    | 0.5733     | 0.7314    | 0.7546   | 0.7469    |
| 10  | 0.7778    | 0.7146     | 0.7462    | 0.7471   | 0.7468    |
| 50  | 0.7531    | 0.7405     | 0.7468    | 0.7468   | 0.7468    |
| 250 | 0.7481    | 0.7456     | 0.7468    | 0.7468   | 0.7468    |

The text does not discuss error bounds for the various rules using a formula for the error. Here, students learn that the true value of an integral is bracketed by the left and right rules if the integrand is monotonic, and by the midpoint and trapezoid rules if the function does not change concavity. Since most integrals can be broken into integrals in which the integrand is monotonic or doesn't change concavity, students can easily construct upper and lower estimates for their integrals, and hence bound the error in their approximations.

The reason for not including the formula for the error is that it is often sufficiently confusing to students that they forget the purpose of what they are doing—approximating a definite integral. Using the method described—where the true value is bracketed above and below—allows them to focus on the integral they are approximating while estimating the error.

You can generate discussion by drawing two curves, one gently rising the other rapidly rising and ask for which curve the left or right will give a better approximation for a given $n$. It is easy to see that the errors are smaller in the gently rising curve. Similarly, you can draw two curves which have small and large second derivatives, and examine the behavior of the midpoint and trapezoidal rules. This is done in more detail in the next section, but it can be done here to firm up students' understanding of the geometry.

## Problems

Most of the problems can (and should) be investigated by hand, but the graphical interpretations are very important. If students do not have access to a computer or programmable calculator, Problem 5 should not be assigned.

**Suggested Problems:** 1, 2, 6, 7, 13, 15, 17.

**Problems Requiring Substantial Use of Algebra:** 15.

## 7.6  APPROXIMATION ERRORS AND SIMPSON'S RULE

**Class Time:** One half to one class

## Key points

The idea of analyzing errors by observing their behavior as $n$ increases. Simpson's rule is the most accurate rule; it is defined as a weighted average of the midpoint rule and the trapezoid rule (rather than in terms of approximation by parabolas).

## Ideas for the class

Students will readily observe that doubling $n$ makes the error twice as small (or 4 or 16 times as small), but may have trouble understanding how this indicates that the error is proportional to $1/n$ (or $1/n^2$ or $1/n^4$), and how this in turn implies that increasing $n$ by a factor of 10 gives one (or 2 or 4) extra decimal places of accuracy. See Table 7.6.3.

Again, it is best to teach this class using technology; otherwise, you should use overheads. Be sure to emphasize that the rules presented are approximate, and won't hold exactly in every given case. For examples in this section you should continue with whatever examples you used in the previous section. A good conclusion to draw is that Simpson's rule gives reasonably accurate results in most cases for relatively small values of $n$.

**TABLE 7.6.3**   *Errors for the left and right rule Riemann sum approximation to $\int_1^4 \sqrt{x}\,dx = 14/3 = 4.6666\ldots$.*

| $n$ | Error | |
|---|---|---|
| | Lefthand rule | Righthand rule |
| 2 | 0.7950 | −0.7050 |
| 10 | 0.1519 | −0.1481 |
| 50 | 0.0301 | −0.0299 |

## Problems

2–8, 10 — require programs for numerical approximation techniques with a choice of number of subdivisions.

20, 21 — lead to the definition of Simpson's Rule as approximation by parabolas. Good, but difficult for some students.

**Suggested Problems:** 1, 9, 11, 13, 19.

# 7.7  IMPROPER INTEGRALS

**Class Time:** One class

## Key points

Graphical and numerical understanding of convergence and divergence. The behavior of $\int_1^\infty 1/x^p\,dx$ for different $p$.

## Ideas for the class

It is not a good idea to start out right away computing $\int_0^\infty f(x)\,dx$ by finding $\int_0^b f(x)\,dx$ as a function of $b$ and then letting $b$ tend to infinity. Many students will never get beyond the purely symbolic meaning of this. It is better to start with a purely numerical illustration of the convergence and nonconvergence of an integral. For example compute the integrals $\int_1^{10} 1/x^2\,dx$, $\int_1^{100} 1/x^2\,dx$, and $\int_1^{1000} 1/x^2\,dx$, either with a numerical integration program or by using the Fundamental Theorem. Concentrate initially on the actual numerical answers, and observe that they are getting closer and closer to 1. Then do $\int_1^\infty 1/\sqrt{x}\,dx$ the same way, and observe that the numbers are getting larger and larger.

Having made the point numerically, examine the two functions graphically. Before doing this, remind the students of the general shape of the two functions. They probably think of them as basically the same, which makes it mysterious that they should have different convergence behavior. However, if you graph them with a graphing program on a few different scales, you can see the difference quite dramatically. First graph them both on the same axes, with the scale going from 0 to 10 on each axis. It is quite clear from this that $1/\sqrt{x}$ is well above $1/x$. Then follow the tail out; graph them with $0 \le y \le 1$ and $10 \le x \le 100$, and then with $0 \le y \le 0.1$ and $100 \le x \le 1000$. On this last graph, $1/x^2$ is completely flat against the $x$-axis, whereas $1/\sqrt{x}$ is clearly visible. If you change the scale on the $y$-axis to $0 \le y \le 0.01$, then $1/x^2$ becomes just visible at the beginning, but now $1/\sqrt{x}$ is completely off the top of the viewing window, even when you get to $x = 1000$. If you play around with a few other scales, the conclusion is inescapable: $1/\sqrt{x}$ has a much fatter tail than $1/x^2$. The fact that the tail is getting infinitely thin is not enough to make its area finite, because you can take long pieces of it over which the thickness does not decrease very much, and so pile up a substantial area. The same thing does not work for $1/x^2$ because if you try to take a long piece of it, you find it thins out to nothing before you have gone very far.

You can really see all this on the graphs, by combining both numerical and graphical thinking. For example, graph $1/\sqrt{x}$ on the scales $0 \le y \le 0.1$ and $100 \le x \le 1000$. At $x = 100$, the tail is 0.1 thick; if you go out to $x = 1000$, it is still about $1/3$ as thick, so you have at least $1/3$ of the area of the viewing rectangle, which is about $0.1 \times 1000 = 100$. This trick gets better the further you go out; try graphing it on a scale $0 \le y \le 0.01$ and $10{,}000 \le x \le 100{,}000$ and you will see that you get at least one third the viewing rectangle again, which now has an area of approximately $100{,}000 \times 0.01 = 1{,}000$. If you try the same thing for $1/x^2$, it doesn't work at all. Try graphing $1/x^2$ on scales $0 \le y \le 0.01$ and $10 \le x \le 100$ (viewing rectangle has area approximately 1) and then on scales $0 \le y \le 0.0001$ and $100 \le x \le 1000$ (viewing rectangle has area approximately $1/10$).

Only after the students have grasped the numerical and graphical aspects of convergence should you give them the algebraic calculation:

$$\int_1^\infty \frac{1}{x^2}\,dx = \lim_{b \to \infty} \int_1^b \frac{1}{x^2}\,dx = \lim_{b \to \infty}\left(1 - \frac{1}{b}\right) = 1.$$

## Problems

Student performance may worsen at this point. In their rush to investigate the limiting behavior, students seem to forget the techniques of $w$-substitution and integration by parts. Remind them to tackle the problems one step at a time—integrate carefully and accurately first. Explore numerical and graphical methods of investigating limits. Students have difficulty recognizing the end behavior of functions and distinguishing between $\lim_{b \to \infty} f(b)$ and $\lim_{b \to a+} f(b)$.

The problems take more time than you expect, so go easy at first. Select problems involving a variety of integration techniques as well as a mixture of obvious and "hidden" improper intervals.

1–23 — can all be worked without the use of integration tables if you covered partial fractions. 12, 16, and 22 involve partial fractions or the use of the table.

25–31 — assign at least one of these. They are not as difficult as they look at first. Require explanations as appropriate.

32,33 — are hard because of the limits.

**Suggested Problems:** 2, 3, 7, 8, 9, 10, 12, 17, 24, 30.

**Problems Requiring Substantial Use of Algebra:** 32–33.

## 7.8   MORE ON IMPROPER INTEGRALS

**Class Time:** One class or skip

## Key points

Comparison test for improper integrals.

## Ideas for the class

Students find the use of comparison to determine convergence or divergence difficult. Illustrate this concept graphically; for example, take $\int_3^\infty 1/(x^2 \ln x)\, dx$. First compute the integral numerically with upper limit 10, 100, and 1000, as you did for $1/x^2$. Then graph the function against $1/x^2$. The graphs are quite comparable on all scales, and one is always a little below the other (more so the further out you go). Illustrate divergence with $1/\sqrt{x}$ and $\ln x/\sqrt{x}$. Before attempting to find a comparison function, make sure your students get a feel for how an integrand behaves as $x \to \infty$. If they know whether to expect convergence or divergence before making the comparison, they are much more likely to be able to choose a reasonable comparison function and to get the inequalities in the right direction. It is OK to treat this topic lightly.

## Problems

The problems you select will most obviously depend on the emphasis you wish to place on this section. There are a few exercises that are easily worked without comparison (e.g. 2, 7, and 10). These can be mixed with others in the section as a reminder that problems should be approached directly when possible. However, for these problems *and* the others in the section, be open to a variety of answers. Graders and lab assistants will need to be reminded that the approach to solving these problems is not unique.

2–16 — straightforward problems. 2, 7, and 10 can be integrated directly.

19, 20 — go well with Example 4 in the text. Good problems for classes emphasizing business, economics, or statistical applications.

24–25 – Of these, 25 is the most difficult. Problems 22 and 23 make a good pair but you may need to remind students to consider cases. The problems are long and involved but not terribly difficult.

**Suggested Problems:** 5, 7, 9, 12, 19.

**Problems Requiring Substantial Use of Algebra:** 22, 23.

## FOCUS ON PRACTICE: INTEGRATION

There are many problems on which students can practice their skills. These are good preparation for the gateway tests given later in this manual. Problems 1– 75 can be done without the integral tables as can many of the later problems.

# CHAPTER EIGHT

## Overview

This chapter has a parallel aim to Chapter 5: to show some ways the definite integral is used without resorting to templates. We start with a discussion of how to set up definite integrals that represent given physical quantities, and then give examples from geometry, physics, economics, and probability. The same comments apply as to Chapter 5: cover a few applications in depth, and encourage the students to make extended and repeated attacks on those problems.

We start in Section 8.1 with some standard applications to geometry: volumes and arc length. Since the student now can integrate numerically, we don't limit the arc length problems to the artificial ones that can only be done in elementary terms. Section 8.2 looks at adding slices of a region that varies in density rather than shape. In Section 8.3, we give some applications to physics: work, escape velocity, and fluid pressure. Section 8.4 gives some applications to economics. The Focus on Modeling section deals with the density distribution function and its relation to cumulative probability distributions, probability and the normal distribution, and defines the mean and median.

### Changes from the First Edition

Sections 8.5 and 8.6 have become the Focus on Modeling sections.

## 8.1  APPLICATIONS TO GEOMETRY

**Class Time:** One to two classes

## Key points

Volumes by slicing; arc length.

## Ideas for the class

Avoid the temptation to slip into teaching template methods such as "volumes by washers" and "volumes by shells." By all means give examples that use these techniques, but do each example by slicing, finding the volume of that slice, and summing.

It is a good idea to cover Example 1 in class (the volume of the Great Pyramid of Egypt) since it is revisited in the next section where the total work required to build it is computed. In addition, it is easy to think of the Great Pyramid as being laid down in layers of square cross sections.

Problem 18 is lovely (and hard); assign it with the expectation of going over it in class. As with all problems involving a table, if you are going to do this in class, it might be a good idea to hand out a copy of the table rather than writing it on the board. A simpler version of the same idea is problem 17. You might want to ask your students why it is natural to have circumference measures for the tree rather than radius measures.

Derive the general formula for the volume of a right circular cone, and discuss a few variations; a skewed cone, a pyramid (cone with square cross-sections). Without going through the derivation, you might want to mention the general formula; all of these figures have volume equal to 1/3 the area of their base times their height; this is the generalization to three dimensions of the formula for the area of a triangle.

If you cover arc length, you need not stick to examples that have been constructed so that the integral can be easily calculated using the Fundamental Theorem. You can pick any interesting curve, such as a piece of a parabola or a cubic, or an arch of the sine function, and use numerical methods to evaluate the arc length integral.

Although we don't cover surface area, you can assign it as a project. See the following project on viewing the earth from a spacecraft orbiting the earth and from the moon.

---

*Example 1*   On Christmas Day, 1968, the Apollo 8 crew orbited the moon. In April, 1983, two members of the space shuttle Challenger performed an activity outside the Challenger at an altitude of 280 km above the surface of the earth.

What percentage of the Earth's surface could the Apollo 8 team see? What percentage could the Challenger team see? How far above the surface of the earth would you have to be to see 10% of the earth's surface?

Here are some useful facts: the earth is approximately a sphere of radius 6,380 km, the moon is approximately 376,000 km from the center of the earth.

This requires the student to know the formula for the area of a segment of a sphere. Many will not be able to derive it correctly, but there is a lot to be learned from the effort. Most of them will make the standard mistake of trying to calculate the surface area using cylinders rather than frustums (sloped cylinders). It is good to let them make this mistake for two reasons; first, since it yields unreasonable answers, it provides a good test of how much they are using their common sense (only about 40% of the earth is visible from the moon; if they don't think that's unreasonable, ask them how much of the moon can be seen from the earth). Second, the correct way of calculating surface area is much better appreciated once the obvious approach has been seen to be wrong. A few students will probably look the formula up in a book; by all means give them full marks for this, as long as they can give the reference and explain why it works. The ability to find an answer by research will stand them in good stead and should not be discouraged. The point of this project is not to teach the students the method for calculating areas of solids of revolution, but to train them in solving real world problems where the method is not laid out before them.

## Problems

There are problems here for almost every level of ability. Again, mix up the types and avoid teaching set methods. Ask students to draw pictures and visualize the areas of the slices they are summing. For the most part, these problems are easier than those of the last section, so you might assign a few more.

1–13 — none are really tricky but students may have trouble visualizing some (like 12 or 13).

14, 17 — good problems. Not hard.

18 — as stated in the explanation for this section, lovely but hard. A good problem to assign for group work or homework and later class discussion.

19–26 — arc length. Several involve numerical techniques. 24 is hardest.

**Suggested Problems:** 3, 6, 10, 12, 15, 16 (plus some of 19–26 if you cover arc length).

**Problems Requiring Substantial Use of Algebra:** 21.

## 8.2  DENSITY AND CENTER OF MASS

**Class Time:** One or two classes

## Key points

How to divide up a region when the density varies; center of mass.

## Ideas for the class

The ideas embodied in this section are fundamental. You will need to come back again and again to the ideas that you set out in this class, so you should choose your examples and your explanations carefully.

The concept of density is important. You may want to start with an example of density along a line, such as Example 1 in the text. It is important that the students understand that the $\Delta x$ in a Riemann sum and the $dx$ in a definite integral are important elements that can have physical meaning, and not just pieces of notation that can be dispensed with. You can bring this out by being careful to specify units; if you have a piece of highway of length $\Delta x$ miles and the population density in the vicinity is $f(x)$ people per mile, then the population in the piece is $f(x)\Delta x$ people. You can vary this example by choosing a highway in your state, and by giving a specific function that approximates the density along this highway. A review of the section on the notation and units of the definite integral (Section 3.3) would be helpful here.

Don't try to cover all the examples in this section; it is better to cover one or two examples carefully. Here are some other examples you can use.

Squaresville is a city in the shape of a square 5 miles on a side, with a highway running along one side of it. The population density $d$ miles from the highway is $20 - 4d$ thousand people per square mile. What is the approximate population of Squaresville? You can work this one out in detail, then compare it with Ringsburg (Example 4 in the text). In particular, bring out the different ways of slicing (parallel to the highway in Squaresville, in concentric circles in Ringsburg). The key point to get across is that you want to slice the problem in such a way that the density is approximately constant along the slices.

A problem that forces students to think carefully about how to slice is the following. (You may also use this problem in Section 8.3, Applications to Physics.)

---

*Example 1*    A compressible liquid has density which varies with height. At the level of $h$ meters above the bottom, the density is $40(5 - h) \, \frac{\text{kg}}{\text{m}^3}$.

(a)    The liquid is put in the container in Figures 8.2.1 and 8.2.2. The cross sections of the container are isosceles triangles. It has straight sides, and looks like a triangular prism. How many kg will it hold when placed as shown in Figure 8.2.1, resting on the triangular side?

(b)    How many kg will it hold if it is placed (with some support, of course) as shown in Figure 8.2.2?

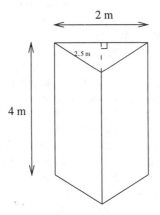

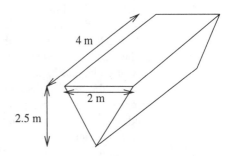

*Figure 8.2.1:* Resting on end                    *Figure 8.2.2:* Resting on side

A reasonably difficult example, suitable if you plan to spend more than one class on this section, is to use the function for the density of the earth's atmosphere given in Example 2 to calculate the entire mass of the earth's atmosphere. This requires slicing by spherical shells, which is probably best explained in a manner analogous with the Ringsburg example; the volume of a thin shell of thickness $\Delta r$ and radius $r$ is approximately its surface area times its thickness, $4\pi r^2 \Delta r$.

## Problems

Choose only a few problems, but advise students that the assignment will still take time. A selection where the appropriate "slices" vary (i.e. by distance, area, volume, etc.) will encourage students to work with units and concepts rather than memorize formulas.

1–6, 13, and 16 — reasonably straightforward and offer a variety of types to choose from.

7–11 — involve center of mass.

14, 15 — more difficult, partly because of the units but also because the slices are harder to determine. May want to discuss before assigning.

**Suggested Problems:** 2, 3, 7, 12, 16.

## 8.3  APPLICATIONS TO PHYSICS

**Class Time:** One to two classes

### Key points

Definition of work; Escape velocity; Getting total force from pressure.

### Ideas for the class

Use your judgement and interests to choose which applications you wish to cover from this section. The physicists' definition of work is often puzzling to students, so make it clear that work is done by the component of a force in the direction parallel to the motion. Explain in class, by holding a heavy object stationary and walking across the room that you are doing no work under this definition, since the force is perpendicular to the direction of motion. By all means do Example 3 in class.

The escape velocity examples are good if you have a class that has some background in physics—otherwise they may be mystifying. These problems show that improper integrals are often seen in physics. The examples on force and pressure are good for a wider audience—most people have experienced water pressure.

Here is an example that can generate some good discussion of the physical concepts of work and force. (Although this is a calculus course, not a physics course, it seems pointless to discuss applications to physics without getting some intuition for the concepts of physics.) Consider a large aquarium tank (say, in the New Orleans Aquarium). You are facing the front glass panel of this tank, which is 10 feet high and 20 feet long. The distance to the back of the tank is 5 feet. First find the force exerted on the front glass panel of this tank, then find the work required to pump all the water out of it. You will find that the work required is equal to force on the front panel times the distance to the back of the aquarium. This is true no matter what dimensions you choose. Is there another way of seeing this? Answer: you could pump all the water out of the tank by pushing the front glass panel to the back of the tank (assuming the seal with the side walls and floor did not leak). This brings out a number of physical concepts: first, that the work done is independent of the method used, and secondly that the force on the front panel does not depend on the distance to the back of the aquarium. This latter point is implicit in the way the force is calculated, but may not have been appreciated by the students. If they have an intuitive notion that the force *should* depend on the distance to the back of the aquarium, ask them to imagine that the glass is holding back an ocean; does it have to be twice as strong for an ocean twice as big?

### Problems

A variety of problems. Select carefully on the basis of your students' ability and interests, and the applications you choose to emphasize.

1 — area interpretation. Allow for variation in answers.

2–8 — work problems, all of which are quite reasonable.

9–11 — involve escape velocity. Discuss Examples 4 and 5 if you choose to assign these.

12–14 — straightforward force problems.

15–21 — more difficult. 17, 19, 20, and 21 involve the general case. For 18, you might remind students that work is based on vertical distance (not the slanted distance through the straw).

**Suggested Problems:** 1, 4, 7, 12, 13, 18.

# 8.4  APPLICATIONS TO ECONOMICS

**Class Time:** One or two classes

## Key points

Definitions of present and future value; Income streams; Consumer and producer surplus.

## Ideas for the class

Students of different ages react very differently to the material of present and future values. Adult students who have paid off mortgages or sent children to college understand the time value of money readily; for regular-age undergraduates or high school students the idea is much harder. If you cover this section be prepared to go slowly. Before you talk about any integrals at all, make sure you have clearly established the point that $100 now is not the same as $100 a year from now. Some students will understand this intuitively, others will have a great deal of trouble with it, particularly when you try to quantify the difference. Some of those who think there is a difference will think that the difference is due to inflation. (In fact, there would be a difference even with no inflation. The text does not consider inflation.) After explaining this point, do an example like Example 1, where you are given a choice between a lump sum payment now, or smaller payments in the future. How do you decide which is more favorable? Then do an example where you assume the income stream is continuous and evaluate an integral. Here are a couple of possibilities.

Suppose you are a writer working on a best seller. Publisher X offers you an advance of $50,000, and 5% royalties on sales, which, starting two years from now, are expected to increase exponentially for five years according to the function $S(t) = 1000000 \cdot e^{0.1t}$ dollars/year, and then abruptly die away. Publisher Y offers you no advance but 6% royalties, with the same expectations for sales. Which deal is better, assuming an interest of 10% for the next 7 years? (Answer: Both deals have the same present value.)

Here is another problem: the typical high school graduate will get a job starting at $20,000 a year, and the typical college graduate will get a job starting at $30,000 a year. Both can expect 5% annual pay raises. College tuition runs at about $10,000 a year. Does it pay to go to college? Assume an annual interest rate of 10%. This problem can be made more complicated and realistic, which would be suitable if you wanted to make it into a project. You can have different rates for the pay raises, have ceilings on the salaries, and take into account the shorter working life of the college graduate.

One point that persistently confuses students is the following; if you have a constant income stream of $1000 per year, at an interest rate of 10%, is the present value equal to $\int_0^\infty 1000e^{-0.1t}\, dt$, or is it $\int_0^\infty 1000te^{-0.1t}\, dt$? (Answer: the first.) Students have a tendency to want to multiply the rate money is coming in by the time before integrating. This is a sign that they are not thinking of the $dt$ in the correct way; it *is* the time by which you multiply the rate. This is a chance to repeat this point.

Problem 10, on the Siberian pipeline, is quite hard but a very good test of the students' modeling ability; the hard part is not evaluating the integral, but figuring what integral to evaluate. You may want to assign it as a project rather than a normal homework problem; if so, you can supplement it as follows.

Suppose that the Soviet Union followed the deal outlined in Problem 10, and delivers gas at the rate you have found until 1992. By this time, neither West Germany nor the Soviet Union exists; the newly unified Germany urgently needs cash, and is willing to accept a reduced return of 6% (compounded continuously); and the Commonwealth of Independent States wishes to discharge some of the contracts which its predecessor, the Soviet Union, negotiated. So it starts increasing the rate of gas delivery by 2 billion m$^3$ each year. When will the loan be paid off and at what rate will the Commonwealth be delivering gas in that year?

You can choose not to cover consumer/producer surplus, but it is a lovely application of integration. It probably takes about a half class to set up, since you have to explain supply and demand curves as well as the notion of equilibrium price.

## Problems

If you have economics majors, emphasize the way economists express ideas graphically. The beautiful economic applications are the graphical ones. However, all majors can relate on some level to money problems.

1–11 — economic applications. 10 is hard. (See "Ideas" for this section.) Of the others, pick problems that might be of interest to your students (e.g. Jaguars, repayment of a debt, wine, etc.)

12–14 — require the initial set-up of the text – consumer and producer surplus. Problem 14 (the graphical interpretation) may well be worth the set-up time, even for a class of non-economics majors.

**Suggested Problems:** 3, 7, 9, 11, 14.

**Problems Requiring Substantial Use of Algebra:** 6.

# FOCUS ON MODELING: DISTRIBUTION FUNCTIONS

**Class Time:** One class

## Key points

The notion of a continuous distribution as being a smoothed out histogram; general density functions; interpretation of cumulative distribution.

## Ideas for the class

Almost all the material in this section will be new to students. General density and distribution functions are introduced here, and it is useful to spend some time on these before introducing the definitions in the next Focus on Modeling section.

Introduce the histogram as a way of representing how some quantity is distributed through a population. (Examples are ages, incomes, grades, number of words on a page of printed page, the load that various beams of wood can bear without breaking.) Students often have trouble deciding what variables to put on the axes and also because they expect the frequency percentages to be represented by the height, not the area, of the bar. Smoothing out the histogram can also be difficult. As you may expect, students have a temptation to assign an interpretation to the value of the density function itself rather than to the area under the density function. In other words, many students believe that $p(20) = 0.18$ means that 18% of the population has $x = 20$.

Make sure that you emphasize the difference between a density and a cumulative distribution, giving several examples. We have found that frequently emphasizing the units on the vertical axis is the best way of driving home this difference.

You may find it helpful to have students construct their own histogram using data collected from the class (for example, the heights of the students). Make sure they plot both a density distribution and a cumulative distribution.

## Problems

1–5 — involve the interpretation of the density and cumulative distribution functions.

6–10 — are somewhat more difficult problems also concerned with interpretation.

11, 18 — involve formulas for the density distribution. 18 is hard.

**Suggested Problems:** 4, 5, 11, 15.

**Problems Requiring Substantial Use of Algebra:** 12.

# FOCUS ON MODELING: PROBABILITY AND MORE ON DISTRIBUTIONS

**Class Time:** One class

## Key points

Probability density; definitions of mean, median, and standard deviation; normal distribution.

## Ideas for the class

The material in this section draws heavily on the ideas of the previous section, so you should not continue without having first completed the preceding Focus on Modeling section.

The idea of this section is to teach probability as an application of the integral. It is important to remember that this is not a course on probability—resist the urge to include ideas about probability that are not needed for the applications of calculus (unless you have lots of time).

As in the previous section, students find the ideas unfamiliar and difficult, so it is important not to go too fast and to give plenty of basic examples. Students have some familiarity with "grading on a curve" so you can use this to motivate a discussion of the normal distribution.

When you talk about the normal distribution you should mention the connection between the standard deviation and the inflection point of the curve. This is a good opportunity to remind students of their earlier work on families of curves in Chapter 5. (The shape of the normal distribution curve and how it varied when the parameters changed was one of the examples in that section.)

A good class problem is to hand out a probability density function for the grades in a hypothetical class. Make the curve skewed in some way, and graph it on paper with grid squares so that areas can be estimated. Then ask various questions about the class: how many students are getting a B or better? How many are failing? What are the median and mean grades? (Note that the mean is harder to estimate from the graph.) Make sure you tie this exercise to the discussion of probability density functions.

## Problems

6–8 — involve the normal distribution.

8 — reflects the point of view of Section 5.2 by investigating the effect of the parameters $\mu$ and $\sigma$ on the graph of the normal distribution.

13 – involves data.

14–15 — involve formulas for the distribution functions. They are difficult.

**Suggested Problems:** 6, 8, 10, 13, 14.

**Problems Requiring Substantial Use of Algebra:** 9.

# CHAPTER NINE

## Overview

This chapter is a brief introduction to Taylor series and Fourier series via the idea of approximating functions by simpler functions; the Taylor series is a local approximation, the Fourier series a global one. The notion of a convergent series is permitted to evolve naturally out of the investigation of Taylor polynomials. The graphical and numerical points of view are kept at the forefront throughout. Geometric series and their applications are discussed.

Section 9.1 introduces Taylor polynomials as local approximations, obtained by matching higher derivatives at a point. It shows the approximations graphically and numerically, and brings out the fact that the approximation is better if you take a higher degree polynomial, and if you are closer to the point of expansion. The natural observation that each Taylor polynomial is obtained from the last by adding one more term leads naturally to the idea of a Taylor series. Intervals of convergence are examined in Section 9.2, first graphically and numerically and finally analytically through the ratio test and series of constants. Section 9.3 shows some methods of deriving new Taylor series from old (e.g. by substitution, multiplication, or integration), and Section 9.4 treats finite and infinite geometric series and their applications. Finally, Section 9.5 is an introduction to Fourier series.

The optional Focus on Theory sections examine convergence in more detail, give a sketch of a proof for the ratio test, and look at error bounds for Taylor approximations.

### Changes from the First Edition

The order of former Chapters 9 and 10 has been reversed. The introduction to Taylor series has been moved to 9.1; the ratio test for convergence of a series is introduced in Section 9.2; the material on error bounds has been moved to the Focus on Theory sections. The examples on present value involving geometric series and on using series to solve differential equations have been removed.

## 9.1 TAYLOR POLYNOMIALS AND SERIES

**Class Time:** One class

## Key points

Approximating functions by polynomials; making a local approximation around a point by matching values and derivatives at that point. Extension of Taylor polynomials to series; expansions for sine, cosine, and $e^x$.

## Ideas for the class

This class is greatly improved if you have graphing calculators or computer graphing programs in the classroom. Otherwise, you will want to prepare lots of overheads. It makes an enormous difference to be able to show the students the graphs of the Taylor approximations so that they can see the convergence as $n$ increases.

Start by reviewing the tangent line approximation, say for $e^x$ at $x = 0$. Compare the value $e^{0.1} = 1.1051709$, obtained on a calculator, with the value of the linear approximation $P_1(x) = 1+x$ ($P_1(0.1) = 1.1$). Draw the graph of $e^x$ and its linear approximation, and point out that the linear approximation has the same value and the same slope as $e^x$ at $x = 0$. Then, explain that you would expect a better approximation if you could make the approximating function bend like $e^x$. Then go through the derivation of the quadratic approximation and add the graph of the quadratic approximation to your picture. Show that

$$P_2(0.1) = 1 + 0.1 + \frac{(0.1)^2}{2} = 1 + 0.1 + 0.005 = 1.105.$$

Then add the graphs of $P_3$ and $P_4$ to your picture and calculate $P_3(0.1)$ and $P_4(0.1)$. Extend to the general case and give the general formula for a Taylor polynomial around $x = 0$. Show that each approximation is obtained by adding a term to the previously derived terms. Make sure that students understand the coefficients in the Taylor polynomials are *numbers* that must be obtained by *evaluating* derivatives at a specific point; they are likely to hand in homework answers where the coefficients are functions of $x$.

It is a natural extension at this point to extend the idea of summing terms to an infinite series. Introduce the notation and discuss (and develop, if you have time) the series expansion for sine or cosine. Leave a discussion of convergence for the next class. If possible, also do an example of an expansion around a point other than $x = 0$, for example $\sqrt{x}$ around $x = 1$. Each time you do an example, draw the graph of the function and its approximation, and perhaps calculate a value of the approximation and compare it with the function value.

**New:** Introduction to series expansions has been moved from the current Section 9.2 to this section.

## Problems

1–10 — are standard computations of Taylor polynomials about $a = 0$ (Maclaurin polynomials).

11–12 — good for checking understanding.

13–16 — are standard computations of Taylor polynomials for various values of $a \neq 0$.

17–20 — ask for graphical interpretation of the coefficients of second-degree Taylor polynomials. Good questions to assign.

21–24 — Taylor series about $a \neq 0$.

25–27 — involve the Taylor expansions of a finite polynomial.

30–32 — are applications of Taylor polynomials to help evaluate limits. Some algebra is needed. You may want to do one of these in class first.

29, 34 — starts students thinking about "easy" ways to find Taylor polynomials (i.e., by substitution).

**Suggested Problems:** 2, 3, 11, 14, 18, 20, 22, 30.

**Problems Requiring Substantial Use of Algebra:** 30–32.

## 9.2 CONVERGENCE OF SERIES

**Class Time:** One class

## Key points

Intervals of convergence graphically, numerically, and with the ratio test.

## Ideas for the class

This is another class where a graphing calculator or computer graphing program is enormously helpful, since the notion of an interval of convergence is easy to see graphically.

Draw the graphs of several approximations to $e^x$ to show that they seem to get closer and closer to the graph of $e^x$. Next, calculate $e^2$ using the Taylor series and compare the rather slow rate of convergence with the rapid rate for $e^{0.1}$. Point out that it does converge nonetheless.

Next do an example which has a finite interval of convergence. For example

$$\sqrt{x} = 1 + \frac{1}{2}(x-1) - \frac{1}{8}(x-1)^2 + \frac{1}{16}(x-1)^3 - \frac{5}{128}(x-1)^4 + \cdots$$

around $x = 1$ or one of the examples in the text. Show the contrast between what happens at a point inside the interval of convergence and outside, both graphically and numerically. Graphically, successive approximations bunch closer to the graph of the function inside the interval, and diverge outside. Numerically, try calculating $\sqrt{1/4}$ and $\sqrt{4}$ using the Taylor approximation for $\sqrt{x}$ around $x = 1$. Compare the convergence for $\sqrt{1/4}$ with the convergence for $\sqrt{0.9}$.

To teach the ratio test, you may need to spend some time explaining how to express the coefficients $C_n$ and $C_{n+1}$ in terms of $n$. Try not to make the class a series of formulas. Keep the focus on the graphical, as much as possible.

**New:** The ratio test for intervals of convergence is given, plus a brief discussion of checking convergence at the endpoints of the interval through series of constants.

## Problems

1–4 — deal with identifying power series.

5–8 — are standard computations of Taylor series with $a = 0$ (Maclaurin).

9–11 — are standard computations of Taylor series with $a \neq 0$.

12 — leads toward finding series by substitution.

16–20 — use the ratio test for convergence.

24–31 — deal with series of constants.

27–31 — use the series expansions for basic functions derived in Sections 9.1 and 9.2.

**Suggested Problems:** 2, 4, 6, 10, 14, 16, 20, 31.

## 9.3   FINDING AND USING TAYLOR SERIES

**Class Time:** One or two classes

## Key points

Shortcuts for finding Taylor series; applications of Taylor series.

## Ideas for the class

Make the point that the Taylor series is not much use as an approximation if you can't find the derivatives of $f$ at $x = a$ relatively easily, or come up with some other way of calculating the Taylor series. Then do some examples similar to those in the text. Here are some other examples: find the Taylor series for $e^{-x^2}$ by substitution; find the Taylor series for

$$\text{Si}(x) = \int_0^x \frac{\sin t}{t}\, dt$$

by dividing out $t$ from the Taylor series for $\sin t$ then integrating term by term. Check the accuracy of this by comparing its value at $x = 1$ with the value obtained numerically. Or, instead of $\text{Si}(x)$, do

$$\text{erf}(x) = \int_0^x e^{-t^2}\, dt.$$

Problems 20 and 22 are like Example 6; go over one of them in class if you plan to assign them. These examples are good examples of how scientists use Taylor series in practice.

Getting students comfortable with applications may take some time as the variables tend not to be $x$. However, this time is very well spent for students going into science and engineering.

## Problems

1–12 — uses known Taylor series and algebraic substitution to derive new series.

13–16 — similar to Example 5; 15 matches graphs with formulas. Nice problem.

17–18 — require some algebra.

20–30 — good applications of Taylor series, but assign sparingly. Some are long and involved.

30 — shows how to calculate $\pi$ from a series, with considerably faster convergence than the series used in the text. Machin's formula can even be used to calculate a few digits of $\pi$ by hand.

**Suggested Problems:** 2, 3, 11, 15, 16, 17, 28.

**Problems Requiring Substantial Use of Algebra:** 14.

# 9.4  GEOMETRIC SERIES

**Class Time:** One class

## Key points

A discussion of geometric series and their relationship to Taylor series; applications of geometric series.

## Ideas for the class

Many students will have been introduced to geometric series in high school. Use an example like that of repeated drug dosage given in this section to develop the general form for a geometric series. Talk about the idea of long-term effect. Either derive the formulas for the sums of both finite and infinite geometric series, or give this as a homework exercise. Point out that every geometric series is a Taylor series.

## Problems

1–10 — concern identifying the form of geometric series.

11–19 — are straightforward problems involving sums of geometric series.

20–22 — are more problems on repeated drug dosage and are quite interesting.

23, 24 — are bouncing ball problems. Students usually find these challenging.

23–27 — interesting financial problems.

**Suggested Problems:** 2, 4, 7, 12, 15, 17, 21, 23, 25.

## 9.5  FOURIER SERIES

**Class Time:** One class or skip

### Key points

Global approximations over an interval as opposed to local approximations near a point.

### Ideas for the class

This is intended to be a non-technical introduction to Fourier approximations. You don't necessarily need to give the justification for the formula for the coefficients. Use a graphing calculator or computer to graph the successive approximations to a function. Do a few examples showing how to calculate Fourier coefficients. The measles example is an example where Fourier polynomials are used not to approximate a function, but to analyze it. Another point to make is that the Fourier series for a periodic function is a way of breaking down a complex wave into simpler components. That this is possible is illustrated by the fact that when you listen to a recording of a symphony, you can hear all the different instruments individually; your ear (or brain) is performing a Fourier analysis on the sound it hears. Some of the graphs associated with different instruments are included in the text and the problems.

### Problems

1–4 — deal with identifying Fourier series.

5–10 — are straightforward computations of Fourier polynomials.

11 — a harder problem dealing with the square wave.

12, 13 — derive the Fourier polynomials for period $\neq 2\pi$.

14–22 — deal with harmonics and wave forms. These are interesting problems, particularly 15, which involves music.

17 — involves making a numerical approximation to a Fourier series of a function that is represented graphically.

18, 23–27 — justification of the Fourier coefficients.

**Suggested Problems:** 2, 4, 6, 8, 14, 15, 17.

**Problems Requiring Substantial Use of Algebra:** 5–6, 8–10.

# FOCUS ON THEORY

There are two parts to this section, one on the classical convergence tests for series of constants, motivated by applications to the convergence of power series, and one on the error in Taylor approximations. The parts are independent; in particular, students can profit from the section on the error in Taylor approximations without having run the gamut of convergence tests.

## FOCUS ON THEORY: CONVERGENCE THEOREMS

**Class Time:** One or two classes

### Key points

Convergence and divergence of series of constants; comparison of series; ratio test; interval of convergence.

### Ideas for the class

By the time they get to this section, students have worked with power series as a way of representing functions. One reason for studying the convergence of series of constants is because that's what you get when you substitute a number into a power series. Don't let this idea get lost in the shuffle.

The precise definition of convergence of a series of constants uses the terms of the sequence of partial sums, but don't linger on this. That definition is needed for proofs of the first few theorems, if you want to do them, but it is not what builds intuition for the phenomena of convergence and divergence. Intuition, and precision too, come from having model series and being able to compare a given series with a model series. Comparison lies behind all the convergence tests. The models are (mostly) geometric series and the series $\sum n^{-p}$. The fact that the latter diverge for $p \leq 1$ (a worked example in the book) and converge for $p > 1$ (Problem 9) is *not* intuitive. You will have accomplished a great deal if students understand these models and can use them for some simple comparisons. Do some examples, but don't get too exotic. Keep in mind that comparing terms, like comparing integrands for testing improper integrals (the right analogy to bring up), is not easy for students to do on their own.

The ratio test should be presented as mechanical process that works well and it is usually applied without much active thought. The mechanical aspect is fine—that's why the theorem was proved in the first place. You will have achieved even more if students genuinely understand that it's based on a comparison to a geometric series. You might point out that it's remarkable that the interval of convergence is symmetric about 0 (in this section we just look at power series about 0). For a series $\sum a_n x^n$, with radius of convergence 1, for example, why *couldn't* you have convergence, say for $-0.5 < x < 1.5$?

### Problems

**Suggested problems:** 3, 4, 5, 9, 10, 11.

## FOCUS ON THEORY: THE ERROR IN TAYLOR APPROXIMATIONS

**Class Time:** One class

### Key points

Approximation and error bounds; convergence of Taylor series.

## Ideas for the class

This section shows how to estimate the difference between a function and its Taylor polynomial approximations. Point out that it might appear to be disingenuous to talk about "estimating an error" when pushing a few buttons on a calculator gives the answer to higher accuracy than one would check by hand using the remainder formula. Still, this is a good case study and a first encounter with the the general need to be *able* to estimate how good an approximation is. Furthermore, understanding the remaider is necessary in proving the convergence of the series to the function it's approximating, and that's a very important mathematical idea. Convergence is a question that comes up in any approximation scheme.

To bound the error in the Taylor approximations, the arguments for the the degree one and degree two polynomials are carried out completely. These are straightforward and are nice to do in class. The general $n^{\text{th}}$ order result is then stated. Make sure that students understand what all the terms in the remainder formula mean, for instance that the bound on $|f^{(n+1)}|$ depends on the interval where you're making the approximation, and it has to hold in the entire interval.

Knowing the *order* of the error when using the first few terms in an expansion is important in many applications, and this is another reason to be familiar with the form of the remainder. There's a temptation here to introduce the 'big oh' notation when talking about Taylor polynomials versus Taylor series (just as there may have been a temptation to use 'little oh' when discussing differentiability and the tangent line approximation). This isn't done in the book, and it might be too much extra baggage for the students to carry right now. However, you probably should use phrases like "...this...(function) is equal to this ...(polynomial)... to $3^{\text{rd}}$ order ", and also make sure that students know what it means to "drop terms of higher order." They will hear these phrases all the time in science and engineering classes.

The model of using the remainder term to prove convergence is the series for $e^x$. You can show pictures of $e^x$ and its Taylor approximations (or do so for other functions), as you probably did in earlier sections, but emphasize that this time you'll get quantitative estimates on how good the approximations are depending on how far you are away from the base point and how many terms you take.

## Problems

**Suggested problems:** 3, 4, 10, 12, 13, 15.

**Problems Requiring Substantial Use of Algebra:** 16.

# CHAPTER TEN

## Overview

The chapter is an introduction to differential equations without many technicalities. It is intended to show the power of the methods we have developed with more realistic and complex applications than we have hitherto explored.

Differential equations are introduced in Section 10.1. In Section 10.2 we discuss the general first order differential equation from a graphical point of view using slope fields, and in Section 10.3 we do the same thing from a numerical point of view using Euler's method. Then we introduce the analytic method of separation of variables in Section 10.4. Section 10.5 covers exponential growth and decay, and Section 10.6 introduces the use of differential equations for modeling. Section 10.7 investigates the logistic model of population growth. Sections 10.8 and 10.9 look at oscillations and damped oscillations. Section 10.9 discusses the solution of a linear second-order differential equation with constant coefficients using the characteristic equation. Appendix D contains a discussion of complex numbers.

The Focus on Modeling sections cover systems of differential equations, including the $S$-$I$-$R$ model of the spread of disease and the predator-prey model. The phase plane and nullclines are applied to Darwin's Principle of Competitive Exclusion.

### Changes from the First Edition

The material on systems of differential equations, formerly in Sections 9.8 and 9.9, has been moved to the Focus on Modeling sections. The material on oscillations has been shortened; the former Section 9.11 has been omitted.

## 10.1   WHAT IS A DIFFERENTIAL EQUATION?

**Class Time:** A half to one class

## Key points

What a differential equation and its family of solutions look like; What it means for a particular function to be a solution; The significance of initial conditions and arbitrary constants in solutions.

## Ideas for the class

This class can be combined with the next one if you want to get straight into the visualization of differential equations using slope fields. One way to introduce differential equations is by analogy with algebraic equations. Differential equations have functions as solutions rather than numbers. Algebraic equations model simple problems where the solution is a number; differential equations model more complex problems where the solution is described by a function.

Start with a simple example that illustrates this modeling procedure, such as the following. A yam is placed inside a 200°C oven. The yam gets hotter at a rate proportional to the difference between its temperature and the oven's temperature. When the yam is at 120°C, it is getting hotter at a rate of 2° per minute. Write a differential equation that models the temperature, $T$, of the yam as a function of time, $t$. (Answer: $dT/dt = 0.025(200 - T)$. Make sure students understand why the equation has the form it does and how to find the constant 0.025.) Show by substitution that

$$T = 200 - Ce^{-0.025t}$$

is a solution to this differential equation for any constant $C$. Discuss the significance of the constant $C$ (it's the initial temperature difference between the yam and the oven). Solve for $C$ in the particular case when the initial temperature of the yam is $20°$. You do not need to explain how to get this solution now, but you should mention that part of this chapter will be devoted to methods of finding such solutions. Discuss from an intuitive point of view why you would expect an arbitrary constant in the solution (the differential equation describes many different situations, with different initial temperature differences) and how you calculate the specific value of the constant given a specific initial value.

Point out that antidifferentiation is a particular case of solving a differential equation, namely $dy/dx = f(x)$, and that there the arbitrary constant appears added to the solution, not multiplied.

Repeat that the solution to a differential equation is a *function*, and that unless specific conditions are given there are usually many solutions to a given differential equation. It is important to get across the idea—which many students find surprisingly difficult—that the way to tell if a given function is solution to a certain differential equation is by substitution. Make sure you include several examples where students must use this idea.

For example, verify that $y = 2x - 4$ is a solution to $dy/dx = x - (1/2)y$, and that $y = \sin 2t$ is a solution to $d^2y/dt^2 + 4y = 0$. At this stage you should also mention the concept of the order of a differential equation, and its relation to the number of arbitrary constants to expect in the solution. Solve a simple second-order differential equation such as $d^2y/dx^2 = x$ to show that you get two arbitrary constants in that case. Do not at this stage go too deeply into the question of determining these constants, for the next few sections the book concentrates on first-order differential equations.

## Problems

The problems are all quite straightforward, although some require a bit of algebra.

1 — concerned with representing a story by a graph.

**Suggested Problems:** 1, 3, 6, 9, 11.

**Problems Requiring Substantial Use of Algebra:** 6–7.

## 10.2  SLOPE FIELDS

**Class Time:** A half to one class

## Key points

Solving first-order differential equations graphically.

## Ideas for the class

It's best for this section (and others that follow) if you have available a graphing calculator or computer program that draws slope fields and can project them on a screen, such as the University of Arizona program SLOPES. Slope field programs for the graphing calculator are included in this manual. Graphing calculator slope fields can be used with an overhead projector, though they are generally not as good as those generated by computer. If no technology is available, you can photocopy some of the prepared slope fields in this manual, or make overhead transparencies of various slope fields and trace the solutions in pen. In any event, do at least one example by hand, just to make sure that the students see how a slope field is constructed. In particular, make sure that students remember what various slopes look like: a large positive slope, a small positive slope, a large negative slope, a slope of 1/2, 1 or 2. You can explain slope fields as a set of sign posts. There's one at each point, and wherever you are, it tells you in what direction to move. You move a little, and there's the next sign post, etc. Students are often uncomfortable with eyeballing slope fields at first. However, it is surprising how accurate you can be if you draw the solution curves carefully. Try drawing the solution to $dy/dx = 1/x$ from $x = 1$, $y = 0$ to $x = 2$, and see how close to $\ln 2 \approx 0.7$ you get (or get the students to do this on work sheets). If you are projecting slope fields onto a white board, get students to come up and draw solutions directly on the board, over the projected slope field, and then ask them to criticize each other's efforts. Make sure that they understand that the solutions they draw on the slope field are the same as the solutions given in the previous class. For example, if you gave the example $dy/dx = x - (1/2)y$ with solution $y = 2x - 4$ in the previous class, show in this class how the graph of $y = 2x - 4$ fits into the slope field of that differential equation.

One good problem that can be done either in the way described above or on worksheets that you hand out, is to give students the slope field of the yam equation from the previous class (or, if you gave them another example, give the slope field from that example). You can see a lot more about the general behavior of solutions from the slope field than from the specific solution. Illustrate how the general behavior of the solution depends on the initial conditions by getting the students to draw three solutions, one starting at the equilibrium solution ($T = 200$), one starting above it, and one starting below it. It is a good test of their understanding whether they will cross the equilibrium solution, or whether starting on it, they will stay on it. Ask them why a solution can never cross the equilibrium solution. (Once you are on the line $T = 200$ you can't leave it because the signposts don't let you.) Also, point out how to read the arbitrary constant in the previously derived analytic solution from the graph of the solution on the slope field (it is the difference between 200 and the point where the solution crosses the $y$-axis).

Another useful class example is to give a slope field and ask about the long-run behavior of the solution (i.e. what happens to $y$ as $x$ or $t \to \infty$.)

## Problems

For the homework problems you might want to hand out worksheets which are photocopies of the problems in the book. Students can hand these in instead of ripping out pages from their books. It is good to have students give reasons for the matching problems (like 3, 4 and 6). Some can get the correct answer for the *wrong* reasons. For example, on 4(a) some students give the correct graph (II) because "the antiderivative should look like a cubic." (Show students that $y' = y + y^3/3$ is *not* a solution.)

**Suggested Problems:** 1, 3, 4, 5, 8.

## 10.3  EULER'S METHOD

**Class Time:** One class

## Key points

Solving differential equations numerically.

## Ideas for the class

Having treated first-order differential equations graphically, we now treat them numerically. You can teach this class as a computer lab rather than a conventional lecture, but be sure that the students realize just exactly what it is they are computing—what the data they supply is and what the output is. Again, it is important that they realize that the solutions they produce numerically are the same as the ones encountered in the previous two classes. Make the connection with the graphical point of view by illustrating Euler's method on a slope field; show how to see graphically whether approximate values are greater than or smaller than the true value.

For example, give them $dy/dx = 1/x$, and ask them to compute the value at $x = 2$ of the solution that goes through the point $(1, 0)$, using two steps first, and then ten. This is of course the natural logarithm, so they can compare their answers with $\ln 2$. The first time they do Euler's method, they should do it by hand (i.e., using a calculator for the actual calculations, but not a program). However, don't give the impression that they will always do it by hand; in practice they will use a calculator or computer. The point of the problem is to understand the algorithm by going through it step by step. If you are using a slope field program that draws in solutions as well, you can introduce Euler's method by asking the students how they think the program draws the solution curves.

Another possibility is to take the yam equation, start at $T = 20°$ when $t = 0$, and follow its temperature for the first 5 minutes. These sorts of calculations are best set up as a table of values, with $t$, $T$, and $dT/dt$ in three columns (see Table 10.3.1).

**TABLE 10.3.1**   *The yam in the oven*

| $t$ | $T$ | $dT/dt = 0.025(200 - T)$ | Exact solution: $200 - 180e^{-.025t}$ |
|-----|-----|--------------------------|----------------------------------------|
| 0 | 20 | 4.50 | 20.00 |
| 1 | 24.5 | 4.39 | 24.44 |
| 2 | 28.89 | 4.28 | 28.78 |
| 3 | 33.17 | 4.17 | 33.01 |
| 4 | 37.34 | 4.07 | 37.13 |
| 5 | 41.41 | 3.96 | 41.15 |

This way they can see how to calculate each piece of data from the previous one. Compare this solution with the exact one obtained two classes ago, to show that the numerical solution is an approximation to that solution.

Mention that there are more efficient methods than Euler's method, and that in practice, differential equations are often solved numerically. Just as it's an exception to be able to find a simple antiderivative for a given function, it's an exception to be able to find a simple formula for the solution to a differential equation.

## Problems

1–3 — use Euler's method and relate the solutions to slope fields.

1, 4, 5 — compare the numerical approximation obtained by Euler's method to the exact value obtained by integration.

6, 7 — discuss error informally.

9 — an application of Euler's method to compound interest.

10 — more theoretical and relates Euler's method to Riemann sums..

**Suggested Problems:** 2, 5, 7, 9, 10.

## 10.4  SEPARATION OF VARIABLES

**Class Time:** One class

## Key points

Solving certain special first-order differential equations analytically.

## Ideas for the class

This is the only analytic technique students will be shown for solving first-order differential equations. Success with the method depends on being able to antidifferentiate both sides after the variables have been separated; this section provides a lot of practice with integration.

It is very important to maintain the graphical point of view while doing these problems; students often fail to make the connection between the analytic solutions and the ones pictured in the slope fields. Take the yam equation (or whatever other example you have been using) and solve it using separation of variables; then graph the solutions for various different values of the constant, and show that they look the same as the ones obtained from the slope field.

## Problems

The problems in this section provide an excellent review of integration. Make sure you assign some initial value problems as well as those with general solutions.

1–22 — are differential equations with initial conditions that are to be solved using separation of variables. All can be done without tables except 20.

23–28 — involve literal constants. Students sometimes have difficulty with these.

29–32 — use tables of integrals or a substitution.

33–35 — relates analytic solutions to solutions found from slope fields.

36–38 — lead students to more sophisticated substitution techniques.

**Suggested Problems:** 1, 3, 15, 19, 28, 29, 31, 34.

# 10.5  GROWTH AND DECAY

**Class Time:** One class

## Key points

Solutions of the exponential growth and decay equations; Applications to compound interest; radioactive decay, pollutions in the Great Lakes; Newton's Law of Cooling; Equilibrium solutions; stable and unstable equilibria.

## Ideas for the class

While this section covers some material that has been seen earlier, there is a shift in emphasis towards modeling which is a good preparation for the following section. Emphasize how to go from a verbal statement to a differential equation. Do a simple population or bank balance example. For instance, consider a population of rabbits that starts at 100 and grows at a continuous rate of 3% per year. How many rabbits are there after 10 years? Some students will know immediately that the answer is $100e^{0.03(10)}$, but they may not know how to translate the percentage growth rate into a statement about derivatives; that is the point of going over this problem in detail. Explain how the continuous growth rate of 3% per year translates into the equation

$$\frac{dP}{dt} = 0.03P,$$

where $P$ is the population after $t$ years. Something like the following will do: since the growth rate is 3% per year, the percentage growth during a time interval of $dt$ years is $0.03\,dt$, so the actual change in population is $0.03P\,dt$; therefore, $dP = 0.03P\,dt$. You need to be careful about the distinction between continuous and annual percentage growth rates. Students should have seen this distinction before in Chapter 1, but you might want to ask them to read the paragraphs in this section, where it is explained again. Emphasize that it is not necessary to know what $P$ is to write down the differential equation for it; in fact, that's the whole point. Then solve the differential equation by separation of variables ($P = P_0 e^{0.03t}$), and show how to go back and look at the problem to find the initial value ($P = 100$ when $t = 0$). Then use the initial value to find the arbitrary constant ($P_0 = 100$). Finally, use the solution to answer the question: $P(10) = 135$, so there are 135 rabbits after 10 years. Since we are interested in modeling the real world here, it is worthwhile discussing why it does not make sense to quote $P(10)$ to more decimal places ($100 e^{0.03} = 134.98588$). It is also worthwhile asking whether the answer makes sense. (Yes, the population grew in 10 years by 35%, which is close to, but more than, 10 times the annual percentage rate of 3%, as it should be.) In this and the next few sections you should continually remind the students to check their answers against common sense.

Also do a more complicated example, such as Example 3, where the differential equation itself contains an arbitrary constant (the constant of proportionality) whose numerical value is not given, but must be worked out. You can get an interesting class discussion by asking whether Newton's Law makes sense.

You may need to explain what it means to compound interest continuously. Some students, remembering that it has something to do with the exponential function, will want to say that if $B$ is a bank balance where interest is compounded continuously at a rate of 10% then $dB/dt = e^{0.1} B$ or some such error. Don't bring this up if they don't; just be prepared for it.

Explain how to read the equilibrium solution from the analytical form of the differential equation (look for a $y$-value that makes the right hand side zero), and point out that this is the same as looking for horizontal lines on the slope field where all the slopes are zero. Define stable and unstable equilibria and explain how to recognize them graphically.

## Problems

1, 2 — easy problems in which equations are provided.

3, 4 — analyze graphical representations of differential equations.

3, 8, 9 — are applications to compound interest.

10–12 — continue Example 2 on pollution in the Great Lakes. If you have not done this example in class, assign it for reading before assigning them.

13–18, 20 — applications to the natural sciences. 20 leads to lively discussion.

19, 20 — involve Newton's Law of Cooling.

21–22 — involve radioactive decay. 22 has an interesting history associated with it.

23 — a more difficult problem based on an incorrect conjecture made by Galileo about falling bodies.

**Suggested Problems:** 2, 3, 4, 11, 13, 19, 20, 22.

**Problems Requiring Substantial Use of Algebra:** 5, 7–9, 11–13, 19.

## 10.6  APPLICATIONS AND MODELING

**Class Time:** One to two classes

## Key points

Translating a verbal description into a differential equation.

## Ideas for the class

In this section we give more complicated examples of modeling with differential equations. It is better to do a couple of examples carefully than to do many perfunctorily. The examples in the text provide models for how the analysis could proceed. Some of your students will feel they should be able to write down the differential equation all at once, without breaking the problem up into pieces. A compartmental analysis problem (such as the problem about salt concentration in a reservoir) is a good example to counteract this tendency, because although it is too complex to solve in one step, it is susceptible to a such a logical analysis. To help students set up differential equations, urge them to write the equations in words first.

Show how to recognize an equilibrium solution from a differential equation of the form $dy/dt = f(y)$. (Set $dy/dt = 0$.) Show how to recognize if an equilibrium is stable or unstable from a graph of the solutions.

Here is an example you can use in class. A person is in an unventilated room, 3 m long, 2 m wide, and 2.5 m high. The person's rate of breathing depends linearly on the amount of carbon dioxide in the air. When the air has its usual amount of carbon dioxide, 0.04%, the person breathes at a rate of 0.015 m³ per minute, but when the carbon dioxide increases to 3.0%, the rate of breathing doubles. Expired air contains about 4.0 percentage points more carbon dioxide than the air breathed in. Write a differential equation for the concentration of carbon dioxide in the air at time $t$. Answer: Let $c\%$ be the concentration of carbon dioxide in the air in the room at time $t$. The rate of breathing $r$ depends linearly on $c$; we have $r = 0.015$ when $c = 0.04$, and $r = 0.03$ when $c = 3.0$, giving

$$r = 0.00507c + 0.0148.$$

Now the only way the quantity of carbon dioxide in the room can increase is from the *extra* carbon dioxide in expired air. Since expired air contains 4% more carbon dioxide than the air breathed in,

$$\text{Rate } additional \text{ carbon dioxide is being added} = 0.04 \left( \begin{array}{l} \text{Rate of} \\ \text{respiration} \\ \text{in m}^3\text{/min} \end{array} \right)$$
$$\text{to room (in m}^3\text{/min)}$$

If $Q$ m³ is the amount of carbon dioxide in the room at time $t$, then putting the previous two equations together gives

$$\frac{dQ}{dt} = 0.04r = 0.04(0.00507c + 0.0148).$$

In addition, the concentration, $c\% = c/100$, is given by

$$\frac{c}{100} = \frac{Q}{\text{volume of room}} = \frac{Q}{15 \text{ m}^3}$$

so

$$Q = \frac{15}{100}c = \frac{3}{20}c.$$

Thus, rewriting our differential equation in terms of $c$, we get

$$\frac{3}{20}\frac{dc}{dt} = 0.04(0.00507c + 0.0148)$$

so

$$\frac{dc}{dt} = 0.001352c + 0.00395.$$

This equation can be solved using separation of variables or a slope field.

Problem 2, which has to do with weight gain and loss, can generate lively class discussion. Notice that the equilibrium solution for this problem has a physical meaning (the person's equilibrium weight), whereas the equilibrium solution for the carbon dioxide problem is negative and has no physical meaning.

In working any examples, make sure that you pause to ask whether the numbers given make sense. For example, in the respiration problem above, ask whether a breathing rate of 0.015 m$^3$/min makes sense. Get the students to give rough estimates of the amount of air they expel with each breath and the number of breaths per minute. In the body weight problem, ask the students how many calories there are in a typical bowl of cereal, and convert the given caloric intake in part (c) into bowls of cereal to see if it makes sense.

## Problems

In general, students have a more difficult time in this section than in the previous section. Students should be encouraged to produce a table of values for a given scenario in order to help them develop a general equation. In Problem 1, begin by asking students "How many leaves are on the forest floor after 1 year? after 2 years? after 10 years?" Similarly in Problem 14, let students try some specific prices for an actual market price and some equilibrium price. Stress the fact that solutions should make sense.

1–2 — are easy once the model has been set up.

6, 7, 14 — are all from economics. These problems are particularly useful in classes with students from many different majors.

11–13, 15–16 — are of general interest drawn from medicine and psychology. 12, 15 and 16 are hard for students.

11–13, 15–17 — are problems in compartmental analysis. 17 is hard for students.

18–21 — are taken from cosmology. Good for physics or astronomy majors.

**Suggested Problems:** 1, 2, 5, 12, 13, 17.

**Problems Requiring Substantial Use of Algebra:** 2, 6, 8–9, 11, 13.

## 10.7  MODELS OF POPULATION GROWTH

**Class Time:** One to one and a half classes

### Key points

Exponential and logistic models of population growth; Analyzing the logistic equation using slope fields.

### Ideas for the class

It is sufficient to cover the logistic model qualitatively—you needn't derive the analytic solution unless you want to. If you do, you will need to explain partial fractions or use the table of integrals.

Explain how to recognize the general form of the logistic differential equation, as distinct from the exponential growth or Newton's law type. The logistic equation is very good for teaching students to read differential equations (without solving them); one can easily see the equilibrium solutions are $P = 0$ and $P = L$, and this in turn gives an interpretation of the constant $L$. One can also see that when $P$ is small relative to $L$, the equation is approximately the same as the exponential growth equation, with relative growth rate $k$. This means that when the population is small, it grows exponentially, with growth rate $k$. It is well worth pointing out that the inflection point in the logistic curve occurs when the population reaches half the carrying capacity. You can see this from the graph of $dP/dt$ against $P$, as in the book, or you can simply observe it from the solution curves on the slope field. It also makes sense that the growth rate should be at its maximum when you are half way to the maximum population.

As a variation on Problem 9 you can try to fit a logistic curve to US population data (given in that problem) in the following way. First, determine the initial exponential growth rate, $k$, either numerically by taking successive ratios of the initial data, or graphically on a computer by finding experimentally an exponential function which fits the data initially. (The University of Arizona program TWIDDLE would be useful for this.) Then plot all the data and estimate where the inflection point is (there is a lot of room for disagreement here). This enables one to estimate the carrying capacity $L$. As a follow-up you can assign Problem 10 to see if it works any better. No matter how you do it, you can't get a really excellent fit with the logistic curve; this can lead to a discussion of models vs. real world data, how good a fit one should expect, and what constitutes a good fit.

Problem 6 is a good one for generating discussion. Ask the class to justify (or dispute) the two models proposed for the spread of information.

## Problems

1, 2, 5 — are straightforward. 1 is exponential; 2 and 5 are logistic.

6 — an excellent problem for in-class discussion.

8 — gives students some trouble, especially part (c).

9, 10 — are excellent problems for in-class discussion and deal with alternative models for long-term US population statistics.

11 — gives an alternative method of solving the logistic equation analytically.

12–14 — investigate the various possible numerical estimates for the derivative used in fitting a logistic model to the US population data.

15, 16 — continue the applications to the US population.

17–19 — investigate the solutions to a new differential equation and introduce the concept of a threshold population.

**Suggested Problems:** 1, 6, 9, 16, 18, 19.

**Problems Requiring Substantial Use of Algebra:** 7, 11.

## 10.8  SECOND-ORDER DIFFERENTIAL EQUATIONS: OSCILLATIONS

**Class Time:** One or two classes

## Key points

Deriving the differential equations from the laws of motion; two parameter families of solutions need two initial conditions or boundary conditions; physical interpretation of coefficients and initial conditions.

## Ideas for the class

Concentrate on interpretation and understanding in this section, rather than algebraic manipulation. Make sure, however, that you do a few examples showing how to find the constants using the initial conditions. Start with an example (perhaps a sideways spring so you don't have to mention gravity), guess the solutions, then substitute and check.

Show graphically that the two ways of parameterizing the solutions of the undamped spring equation ($C_1 \cos t + C_2 \sin t$ and $A \sin(t + \phi)$) yield the same set of solutions (the University of Arizona program FORTUNE or a graphing calculator is useful for this). You can make a good class problem using computers out of this; write down both forms of the solution, and ask if this means there are four arbitrary constants in the solutions. Then get the students to investigate both families on the computer. Do not, however, emphasize the mechanics of going from one form to the other.

In doing examples of initial value problems, continually ask what the solution means in practical terms, and whether it makes sense. For example, if the initial position is zero and the initial velocity is nonzero, it makes sense to get a sine curve, whereas if it's the other way around it makes sense to get a cosine curve. Also discuss the physical significance of the spring constant, $k$; a large constant means a stiff spring and a small constant means a weak spring. Relate this to the fact that the period is $2\pi\sqrt{m/k}$; a stiff spring oscillates rapidly (small period) and a weak spring oscillates slowly (large period). Also discuss the effect of the mass on the frequency from the point of view of both the differential equation and common sense.

Problems 10 and 11 are very much in the right spirit, and may be used for class discussion.

Remember that the students do not usually know any linear algebra, so don't talk about linear combinations of solutions.

## Problems

1–3 — straightforward.

5–7 — are also straightforward and deal with motion of a mass on a spring.

9 — involves graphically identifying the solution to a second-order differential equation.

7, 10–11 — concern interpretation of a solution.

13–17 — give practice in going back and forth between $C_1 \cos t + C_2 \sin t$ and $A \sin(wt + \phi)$.

20–22 — apply oscillations to electric circuits.

**Suggested Problems:** 1, 9, 10, 11.

**Problems Requiring Substantial Use of Algebra:** 3, 8.

## 10.9 LINEAR SECOND-ORDER DIFFERENTIAL EQUATIONS

**Class Time:** One class

## Key points

Solutions using complex numbers; The characteristic equation; under- and overdamped cases; Superposition.

## Ideas for the class

Explain the qualitative difference between the underdamped and overdamped cases, both algebraically and from the point of view of common sense (Ask students to compare in their minds a spring oscillating in air and one trying to oscillate in molasses.) Do not spend much time on the critically damped case, where the characteristic equation has repeated roots. However, it is worth mentioning that the critically damped solution does have practical value, since it represents the case where the object returns to its equilibrium as fast as possible without overshooting. This is useful in electronic circuits. For example, the circuit governing a car's speedometer should be critically damped so that the needle will react to changes in speed quickly but without overshooting the mark. (You used to be able to see examples of both over- and underdamped speedometers in old cars.)

Work plenty of examples, introducing complex numbers as necessary. It may be a good idea to have students read the appendix on complex numbers before you give this class.

## Problems

1–18 — are straightforward. Initial-value and boundary-value problems are included.

20 — asks students to match graphs of solutions to second-order differential equations.

23–27 — involve interpretations of damped oscillations.

28–30 — identifying the different kinds of damping.

31 — involves the long-term behavior of a solution.

33–36 — involve applications to electric circuits.

37 — a surprising and fairly hard problem.

38 — concerns rewriting a system of differential equations as a second-order equation.

**Suggested Problems:** 1, 3, 4, 7, 9, 13, 15, 18, 19, 28, 31, 38.

**Problems Requiring Substantial Use of Algebra:** Most of the problems in this section.

# FOCUS ON MODELING: SYSTEMS OF DIFFERENTIAL EQUATIONS

**Class Time:** One class

## Key points

Systems of differential equations; phase planes; trajectories; equilibrium points.

## Ideas for the class

Introduce the idea of a *system* of differential equations, in which there are two dependent variables (often two populations) and one independent variable (usually time). Start by explaining that you might well expect the solution of such equations to be represented by two graphs of population vs. time, and that we will eventually draw such graphs. However, a more useful picture of the solution is provided by a *trajectory* (curve) in the *phase plane*. Such trajectories show very clearly the qualitative, global behavior of the solution: Is there an equilibrium solution? (This is represented by a dot in the phase plane, and is much harder to see on two separate graphs of population against time.) What is the long-run behavior of the system? Does one population die out while the other prospers? Do both die out? Do both prosper? Although time is not shown explicitly in the phase plane, the trajectory shows the evolution of the system over time more clearly than the two graphs of population vs. time.

To teach this section, you could base your classes on the examples in the text—perhaps changing flu to measles or robins and worms to lynxes and hares. Explain the phase plane carefully, and keep emphasizing what points on the trajectory mean in practical terms. Make sure you point out that the trajectory is *not* the graph of population against time (time is not shown on either axis), but a graph of one population against the other. Explain that time is shown by the direction of the arrow on the trajectory. Also be sure to explain how to see in what direction each trajectory is traversed, both from the signs in the differential equation, and from common sense. (For example, the population of infecteds first increases, when there are many susceptibles available to get sick, and then decreases. Alternatively, it makes sense that the maximum in the predator population should be closely followed by the minimum in the prey population, but not the other way around).

It is also a good idea to assign or to discuss the models for competing and symbiotic populations. The pictures of slope fields are a great help here. See, for example, Problems 21–23. Put some equations like the ones in these problems on the board and ask the students what sort of situations they represent; predator-prey, symbiosis, competition. Problem 12 is also good for discussion.

If you want to say more, an excellent reference for additional material is M. Braun's book *Differential Equations and Their Applications*, published by Springer. In Chapter 4, Braun has a discussion of the history of Volterra's investigation of the populations of predator fish and prey fish in the Mediterranean. There he proves that the average values of each population over a period are their equilibrium values. This allows one to take into account the effects of fishing, for example. This was part of Volterra's original problem, according to Braun.

## Problems

1 — straightforward.

2–5 — make sure students can interpret trajectories.

6–12 — are standard robin/worm predator-prey problems and generate lively classroom discussion.

15, 16, 17 — are military applications based on the Lanchester model.

21–23 — ask for qualitative interpretations of differential equations and their slope fields.

**Suggested Problems:** 1, 2–5, 7, 14.

# FOCUS ON MODELING: ANALYZING THE PHASE PLANE

**Class Time:** One class.

## Key points

Understanding how to analyze the phase plane using the concept of nullclines.

## Ideas for the class

The purpose of this section is to show students how to get an idea of the qualitative behavior of the solution without using slope fields. A good way to teach the class is to use a system of equations that you have used previously (probably flu or robins and worms), and to redo this system by first finding the nullclines and equilibrium points, and then finding the approximate direction of the trajectory in that region. Be on the watch for students who conclude that there is an equilibrium point at the intersection of any two nullclines. (It's only where a nullcline representing $dx/dt$ and a nullcline representing $dy/dt$ meet.)

## Problems

All the problems in this section will take the students a long time because so many separate computations have to be made. Consequently, assign relatively few.

1, 2 — involve redoing the examples of the previous section using nullclines.

3–8 — are reasonably straightforward.

9 — a biological example involving data.

11 — models the US-Soviet arms race, and predicts something close to the actual expenditures.

**Suggested Problems:** 1, 2, 3, 11.

# CHAPTER ELEVEN

## Overview

We introduce functions of many variables from several points of view, using surface graphs, contour diagrams, and tables. This chapter is as crucial for this course as Chapter 1 is for the single variable course. This chapter gives students the skills to read graphs and contour diagrams and think graphically, to read tables and think numerically, and to apply these skills, along with their algebraic skills, to modeling the real world. We pay particular attention to the idea of a cross-section of a function, obtained by varying one variable independently of the others. It is important that the student thoroughly understand this notion both graphically and numerically before being exposed to the ideas of partial derivatives and gradients. We study linear functions in detail from all points of view, in preparation for the notion of local linearity.

## 11.1 FUNCTIONS OF TWO VARIABLES

**Class Time:** One class

**Suggested transparencies:** Figure 11.1 (p. 564 of text, p. 173 of manual), Table 11.1 (p. 565 of text, p. 174 of manual), bar graph for Table 11.1 (p. 565 of text, p. 175 of manual), table for solution to Problem 4 (p. 569 of text, p. 176).

## Key points

Representing functions of two variables graphically (as in a weather map), numerically (as in a table of values), and by formulas. Understanding that for a function $z = f(x, y)$, $x$ and $y$ can vary *independently*. Interpreting functions by varying one variable at a time.

## Ideas for the class

Start by discussing the concept of a function. For example:

- The chirping rate $C$ of crickets depends on the time of day $t$ and the temperature $T$, so $C = g(t, T)$.

- The temperature $T$ seems to vary with latitude $a$ and longitude $o$, so $T = h(a, o)$.

- Make connections to single variable calculus. Recall how the height $s$ of a ball tossed directly upwards is a function of time $t$, so $s = f(t)$. Then explain that the height is in fact a function of other variables such as the initial velocity $v_o$, so we could say that $s = f(t, v_o)$. As we add variables, things get more complicated and that is why in earlier courses we gave constant values for all but one variable.

- Ask for examples from the students.

   In each case, consider holding one variable constant and varying the other. What sort of single-variable function do you get? Is it increasing, decreasing, or neither?

   Present some examples of functions represented in different ways.

- A graphical example, such as the weather map in Figure 11.1 (p. 173 of manual), or a topographical map.

- A table of values, such as the beef data in Table 11.1 (p. 174 of manual), or the table of monthly payments as a function of interest rate and term of the loan, that you can find in the daily newspaper.

- An example given by a formula, such as the volume of a sphere or cylinder, or the same monthly payment example, or the function representing a wave.

Ask the same questions as before: How does the function behave when you hold one variable fixed and vary the other?

Work through Problem 4 on page 569, which asks you to find the amount $M$ spent on beef as a function of income $I$ and price $p$. Get the students to supply several different values of $M$ to partially complete the table for $M = g(I, p)$. Briefly discuss how they determined the values in general and then show the transparency with the solution (p. 176 of manual). (The students should have a better conceptual feel for the data, having derived a few values prior to seeing the table.) Again ask: What do you notice? They should see that this time, as $I$ increases, the function increases as before; however now, as $p$ increases, the function also increases. Ask: Why the change? How could this have been predicted?

The wave example is more demanding but worthwhile; it is good preparation for the problem of interpreting partial derivatives and for partial differential equations.

As a classroom activity to get students involved, consider the following. Put up the transparency of Table 11.1. Pass out unifix cubes or small blocks to groups. Task: Represent the data in Table 11.1 (Students tend to be more creative if they are not restricted to a task with specific instructions.) If they are stumped, consider one row or one column of data and show an approximate two dimensional representation on the overhead projector using cubes. Then let them loose to work in groups. They will have to use approximations because of non-integer data. You can promote discussion by viewing their formations and asking why some structures look different than others when they are built from the same data. This should lead to the importance of ordering independent variables, labeling axes, and scaling factors. Show transparency on page 175 of this manual to compare to their models. Discuss the fact that only the top surface of the cube structure gives values of $C$. Ask: What if we had data for $I = 5, 10, 15, 20, 25, 30, ..., 100$ and $p = 3.0, 3.1, 3.2, 3.3, ...4.5$. How would that change the cube model? How would that change the associated surface? This leads to the transparency of more refined beef consumption data (p. 177 of manual). Connect this idea to the single variable calculus concept of chopping finer and finer rectangles to reach a smoother *curve*. Only now, we are chopping finer and finer rectangular solids to reach a smoother *surface*. Other discussion question: What is the advantage of reaching a smooth surface?

Another fun ice breaker class activity is to get volunteers to sit in a row of chairs in the front of the class and act out the stadium wave, as described on page 566 of the text.

**Suggested Problems:** 4, 7, 12, 18.

## 11.2  A TOUR OF THREE-DIMENSIONAL SPACE

**Class Time:** One half to one class

## Key points

Thinking in three dimensions and using coordinates. The dimension of a space as the number of coordinates needed to determine position.

## Ideas for the class

Some students have an instinctive understanding of three-dimensional coordinates and will find parts of this class unnecessary; others have a lot of trouble. It is good to spend a little extra time now on the latter group. One way to explain three-dimensional coordinates is to stand in a corner of the room and imagine that the $x$ and $y$ axes are the lines where the walls meet the floor and the $z$-axis is where the two walls meet. You can ask students to give approximate coordinates of points, or give coordinates and ask where the points are (e.g., in the next room, outside the window, on the floor below).

To help students develop a sense of dimension, have them graph $x = 2$ in the real line, in the plane, and in 3-space. Here are some questions to ask:

- How many free variables are there left after we fix $x = 2$ in each case?
- Why does the graph of $x = 2$ in the plane look like a line (one free variable)? Why does the graph of $x = 2$ in 3-space look like a plane (two free variables)?
- How can we further reduce the plane $x = 2$ in 3-space to obtain a line in 3-space? (Answer: we could fix $y$ or $z$ to be constant.)

Sketch graphs of $z = 5$, $y = 7$, $z = -4$, etc. Plot some points to show 3-D perspective. Give the distance formula between two points (with derivation if time allows) and derive the equation of a sphere.

**Suggested Problems:** 3, 8, 9, 10, 14, 15, 16.

## 11.3  GRAPHS OF FUNCTIONS OF TWO VARIABLES

**Class Time:** One and one half to two classes

**Suggested transparencies:** Graphs of $f(x, y) = 4 - x$ (p. 178 of manual), $z = x^2 + y^2$ (p. 179 of manual), the unit sphere $x^2 + y^2 + z^2 = 1$ (p. 180 of manual), the surface $z = x^2$ (p. 181 of manual), the cylinder $x^2 + y^2 = 1$ (p. 182 of manual), the cylinder $x^2 + z^2 = 1$ (p. 183 of manual), and $z^2 = x^2 + y^2 + 1$ (p. 184 of manual).

## Key points

The graph of a function of two variables. Reading a table of values to visualize the graph. Reading a formula (by fixing one variable at a time, or by seeing where the formula is positive, zero, or negative) to visualize the graph. Reading a graph to give verbal descriptions of the function (particularly by taking cross-sections and describing how the function behaves when you fix one variable).

## Ideas for the class

Explain that, just as a function $y = f(x)$ tells us how high above (or below) the $x$-axis the graph lies for each value of $x$, a function $z = f(x, y)$ tells us how high above (or below) the $xy$-plane the graph lies for each $(x, y)$. If you have explained three dimensional coordinates as suggested in the last section, you can visualize the graph of a function by walking around the room, imagining the graph above your head, and measuring its height at various points.

Bring in an overhead of a graph from a science magazine and ask students what it is telling them. Ask the same questions as suggested for Section 11.1; is the function increasing or decreasing as a function of each variable? Does the answer make sense?

The following exercises will help students with some of the basic properties of graphs of functions, with the differences between the graph of a function and an arbitrary surface in 3-space, and with level sets (in preparation for the next section.)

- Give a function $z = f(x, y)$ which describes the following surfaces:
  - the plane parallel to the $xy$-plane and four units above it
  - the plane parallel to the $xy$-plane and four units below it
  - the $xy$-plane itself.

  How do we describe a general horizontal plane?

- Show the transparency of the graph of $f(x, y) = 4 - x$ (p. 178 of manual). Consider the following:
  - For what values of $(x, y)$ is the graph above, below, or on the $xy$-plane? How can we determine these three regions by looking at the $z$-values of the points on the surface?

- Observe that the line $x = 4$ in the $xy$-plane is the intersection of the graph of $z = 4 - x$ with the graph of $z = 0$.
- Also observe that since the surface is the graph of a *function* $z = f(x, y)$, there is a unique point on the graph for each $(x, y)$ in the $xy$-plane.

• Show the transparency of the graph of $f(x, y) = x^2 + y^2$ (p. 179 of manual). Ask the following questions:

- Why is this graph never below the $xy$-plane?
- What is the intersection of this surface with the $yz$-plane? the $xz$-plane? (Answers: standard parabolas; see this by putting $x = 0$, $y = 0$, respectively, into the equation $z = x^2 + y^2$. We are looking at the intersections of this surface with the surfaces $x = 0$ and $y = 0$.)
- Why does the graph open up and not down? (Consider its intersections with the planes $z = 1, z = 4, z = 9, \ldots$.)
- Observe again, since this surface is the graph of a *function* $z = f(x, y)$, each $(x, y)$ corresponds to a unique point in the surface.

• Show the graph of the sphere, $x^2 + y^2 + z^2 = 1$ (p. 180 of manual). Ask the following questions:

- Is this the graph of a function $f(x, y) = z$? Why or why not?
- How can we describe the top hemisphere only? Is this the graph of a function? Why does this graph open down (in contrast to the previous example)?
- Where does the sphere intersect the $xy$-plane?

Additional examples to study in this section, if time permits, include the following:
• the surface $y = x^2$ (p. 181 of manual)
• the cylinder $x^2 + y^2 = 1$ in 3-space (p. 182 of manual)
• the cylinder $x^2 + z^2 = 1$ (p. 183 of manual)
• $z^2 = x^2 + y^2 + 1$ (p. 184 of manual). Why are there two branches?

**Suggested Problems:** 3, 5, 6, 8, 9.

## 11.4  CONTOUR DIAGRAMS

**Class Time:** Two classes

**Suggested transparencies:** Figures for Problem 10 (p. 591 of text, p. 185 of manual), Problem 24 (p. 594 of text, p. 186 of manual), various surfaces, their horizontal cross sections, and their level curves.

## Key points

Contour diagrams as an alternative to graphs for representing functions graphically. Obtaining sections from a contour diagram. Relation between the graph of a function and its contour diagram.

## Ideas for the class

Although students should understand the relation between contour diagrams and graphs in terms of level curves, it is important not to make the concept of contour diagrams dependent on the concept of graphs. Many students who have trouble visualizing graphs have no trouble reading contour diagrams. Contour diagrams are the preferred method of presenting information in the scientific literature, often without any reference to the graph. For example, contour diagrams are the most natural graphical method of presenting heat in a room as a function of time and distance from the heater, or monthly payment as a function of loan amount and interest rate; it doesn't make much sense in these cases to visualize the surface.

Thus, it is a good idea to present at least one example which simply involves reading the contour diagram directly. Find an example from scientific magazine, or use the overhead masters (pp. 185,187 of manual) to discuss Problem 10 on page 590, or Problem 1 on page 610. Ask the same questions as in Sections 11.1 and 11.3; fix one variable and follow the sections across the diagram. Graph the sections from the contour diagram and see if they make sense.

It is important that students understand the effect of the spacing of the contours. For example, present the two contour diagrams in Figure 11.4.1 and Figure 11.4.2. Ask which of these might be the contour diagram of a plane. What might the other surface look like?

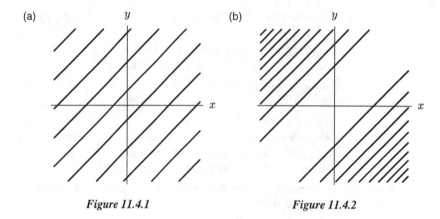

Figure 11.4.1                           Figure 11.4.2

Here are some exercises to help develop the relation between contour diagrams and graphs.
*   Draw the graphs and contour diagrams for $z = x^2 + y^2$ and $z = 1 - x - y$. Choose a point on each level set and determine a path from that point
    (a)  on which the altitude of the surface (value of the function) remains constant
    (b)  on which the altitude changes most quickly.
*   Consider the contour diagram for $z = y - \sin(x)$. If you walk along the line $x = \pi/2$, are you on a ridge or a valley? If you walk along the line $x = 3\pi/2$, are you on a ridge or a valley?

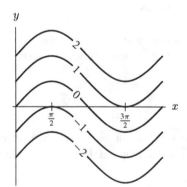

*Figure 11.4.3:* Level curves for
$z = y - \sin(x)$

*   Compare and contrast the surfaces whose level curves (with lowest level in the center, increasing toward the ouside) are in Figures 11.4.4, 11.4.5, 11.4.6:

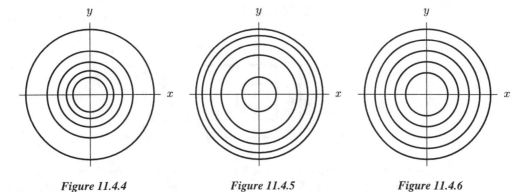

*Figure 11.4.4*          *Figure 11.4.5*          *Figure 11.4.6*

**Suggested Problems:** 1, 3, 4, 10, 11, 12, 16, 17, 20, 25, 26.

## 11.5  LINEAR FUNCTIONS

**Class Time:** One to two classes

**Suggested transparencies:** Table 11.10 (p. 597 of text, p. 188 of manual), Figure 11.70 (p. 599 of text, p. 189 of manual), and Figure 11.71 (p. 599 of text, p. 190 of manual)

### Key points

A linear function of two variables can be characterized by the property that its value increases by equal amounts over equal intervals in a given direction. Visually, this means the contour diagram consists of equally spaced parallel lines. Thus the rule of three continues as linear functions are represented graphically (as planes and level sets), numerically (tables of data), and symbolically.

### Ideas for the class

It is not immediately apparent to many students that the slope at a particular point on a (nonhorizontal) plane is *not* the same in all directions. Understanding this concept is crucial in the development of this course. Appeal to the skiers in the crowd. Perhaps try a piece of flat cardboard leaning against a wall. Draw a person $A$ on the upper portion of the cardboard and draw paths from $A$ to different points $B$ on the bottom edge of the cardboard. Measure rise over run. Have the class determine the steepest path by noting that the rise from $A$ to and $B$ is constant, so in order to maximize the slope, they must minimize the run. Be sure to connect these ideas to contour diagrams as well.

The following problem helps students think visually about movement on a plane. Suppose that a plane has a $z$-intercept of 7, has a slope of $-3$ in the $x$ direction and a slope of 2 in the $y$ direction. If you walk on the plane until you are at $(x, y) = (3, 5)$, what is your $z$-value? Explain your solution. Students may have varying approaches to this problem. After discussing these, try a problem like Example 1 on page 596 in the text to help students derive the general equation $z = c + mx + ny$ for the plane with $z$ intercept $c$, slope in the $x$ direction $m$, and slope in the $y$ direction $n$. (This form is analogous to the slope intercept form $y = b + mx$ in 2-space.)

To connect the equation of a plane to the table representation, consider the example $z = 7 - 3x + 2y$ from above, in table form. See Table 11.5.1. Ask: What observations can you make?

**TABLE 11.5.1**   $z = 7 - 3x + 2y$

|   |   | \(x\) | | | |
|---|---|---|---|---|---|
|   |   | 0 | 1 | 2 | 3 |
|   | 0 | 7 | 4 | 1 | -2 |
| \(y\) | 1 | 9 | 6 | 3 | 0 |
|   | 2 | 11 | 8 | 5 | 2 |
|   | 3 | 13 | 10 | 7 | 4 |

To assess whether the class has gleaned the necessary information from this last example, try the following example: Table 11.5.2 gives some values of a linear function. Fill in the empty blanks and determine a formula for the function.

**TABLE 11.5.2**   *Values for a linear function*

|   |   | \(x\) | | | |
|---|---|---|---|---|---|
|   |   | 10 | 15 | 20 | 25 |
|   | 4 |  | 186 |  | 246 |
| \(y\) | 6 | 132 |  |  |  |
|   | 8 |  |  |  |  |

Use transparencies of Table 11.10 (p. 597 of text, p. 188 of manual) and Figure 11.73 (p. 600 of text, p. 189) to connect tabular data to its contour diagram. Use a transparency of Figure 11.74 (p.600of text, p. 190) for an example of a contour diagram of a linear function from which students should determine an equation.

**Suggested Problems:** 5, 6, 8, 11, 12, 14, 19.

## 11.6  FUNCTIONS OF MORE THAN TWO VARIABLES

**Class Time:** One half to one class

**Suggested Resources:** Thomas Banchoff's book *Beyond the Third Dimension*, Scientific American Library, Freeman, 1990 has wonderful visuals and patterns leading to a comprehension of hyperspace. In addition he has produced computer generated films available in video including *The Hypercube* and *Fronts and Centers, Hyperspheres* that are well worth viewing. Another entertaining book is *Flatland* by Edwin A. Abbott.

## Key points

Making the connection between functions of two variables with the associated level curves and functions of three variables with corresponding level surfaces. Understanding the two different ways in which surfaces can arise: as graphs of two-variable functions and as level surfaces of three-variable functions.

## Ideas for the class

Consider the temperature $T(x, y, z)$ at a point in space. Most students have seen pictures where colors denote different temperatures. (Some may be familiar with the CAT scan which uses X-rays to produce images of slices of the body where the shades and textures indicate different densities so that bone, tissue, and other various parts can be identified.) If temperature $T(x, y, z) = x^2 + y^2 + z^2$, only one location has a temperature of $0°$, namely the point $(0, 0, 0)$. However, an infinite number of points have a temperature of $1°$, namely all points on the sphere $x^2 + y^2 + z^2 = 1$. If we were to process each set of points with common temperatures by giving them the same color, we would have a concentric sphere rainbow, each sphere being a level surface of $T(x, y, z)$.

To understand level surfaces, start with a function of one variable, say $y = x^2$. To determine its level sets choose $y = 0, 1, 2, 3, 4$ and mark the corresponding points on the $x$-line; the contour diagram of a function of one variable is a set of points. Notice the level points get closer together as $y$ increases, implying that the slope is increasing. Imagine lifting the points off the $x$-axis to the corresponding height and reconstructing the parabola in 2-space.

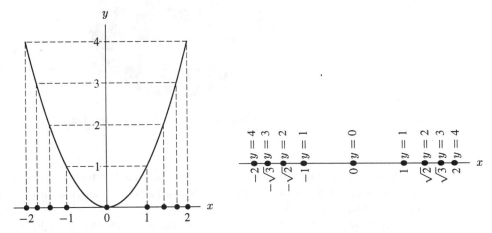

**Figure 11.6.7:** The function: $y = x^2$          **Figure 11.6.8:** The level set: $y = x^2$

Next consider the function of two variables $z = x^2 + y^2$. To determine level sets in the same manner, let $z = 0, 1, 2, 3, 4$ and draw the corresponding curves in the $xy$-plane. This time the contour diagram is a set of curves. Notice again that the level curves get closer together as $z$ increases, implying that the surface gets steeper as we move directly away from $(0, 0)$.

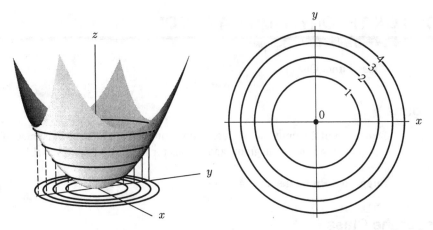

**Figure 11.6.9:** The function: $z = x^2 + y^2$    **Figure 11.6.10:** The level set: $z = x^2 + y^2$

Finally, consider the function of three variables, $w = x^2 + y^2 + z^2$. (Mention that it is not easy to visualize a four-dimensional graph.) Again, to determine the level sets, let $w = 0, 1, 2, 3,$

4 and graph the corresponding surfaces in $xyz$-space. The contour diagram of a function of three variables is a set of surfaces. Notice the level surfaces get closer together as $w$ increases. What does this imply?

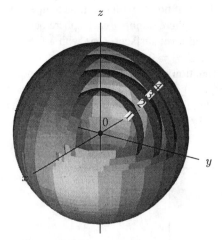

*Figure 11.6.11:* The level set (only first octant shown): $w = x^2 + y^2 + z^2$

This analogy may help students understand that linear functions of three variables have equally spaced parallel planes for their level surfaces, since a linear function of two variables has a contour diagram of equally spaced parallel lines.

A classroom activity which can bring oohs and ahs from your class, dip a wire frame cube into soap bubble solution. (Remove any froth from the surface before dripping.) Then pull it out and, with surface intact from the first dip, dip it again about 3/4 of the way. The double dipped cube will have a bubble suspended in the center and is a great 3-D model of a tesseract. (The tesseract is a view of a hypercube analogous to looking at a square head on where, in perspective, it looks like a square within a square. Here the hypercube looks like a cube within a cube.)

**Suggested Problems:** 3, 6, 7.

# FOCUS ON THEORY: LIMITS AND CONTINUITY

**Class Time:** One class

## Key Points

Definition of the limit and of a continuous function. Predicting existence of limits and continuity at a point using contour diagrams and graphs for functions of two variables.

**Suggested Problems:** 2, 3, 4, 9, 12.

## Ideas for the Class

One of the main ideas here is that the behavior of functions near a "bad point" can be profitably analyzed with the help of contour diagrams and graphs. The intuitive concept of continuity at a point is easier for students to grasp than the concept of a limit, so this is first introduced informally.

# CHAPTER TWELVE

## Overview

We define vectors as geometric objects having direction and magnitude, with displacement vectors as the model, and then show how to resolve vectors into components. We define the dot and cross product of two vectors purely in terms of their direction and magnitude, and then give the formulas in terms of components. We continue this approach to vectors throughout the book; the geometric definition first, and the formula in terms of components immediately afterward.

## 12.1  DISPLACEMENT VECTORS

**Class Time:** One half to one class

### Key points

Displacement vectors as a model for general vector quantities, which are defined as quantities having both magnitude and a direction, as opposed to scalar quantities, which are defined by a single number. Resolution of vectors into components along the coordinate directions.

### Ideas for the class

Introduce vectors without coordinates initially; we want the students to think of vectors as geometric objects, not as lists of numbers. Also, notice that in this course the *components* of a vector are always vectors, not scalars.

To gain an intuitive sense of vector addition, discuss rearranging furniture in a room that contains a large piano. The piano starts in the southwest corner of the room. After trying it out on the east wall, north wall, west wall, the owner is finally satisfied that if fits best in the southeast corner. (See Figure 12.1.1.) Each move is represented by a vector; the sum of all these vectors is the vector from the place of origin to the place of termination of movement, that is vector $\overrightarrow{PP'}$. If the owner finally gives up in disgust and returns the piano to its original location, then no matter how many moves took place in between, the sum is the zero vector $\vec{0}$ since the starting and finishing points are the same.

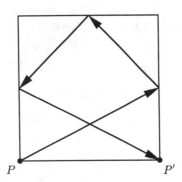

*Figure 12.1.1*

In defining components, start with graphical examples where the vector does not come already equipped with components. For example, resolve the following vectors into components and find a unit vector pointing in the same direction.

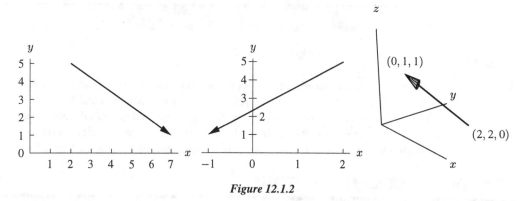

*Figure 12.1.2*

It is important that the student realize that there is no basepoint attached to the definition of a vector. To make this clear, find the displacement vector from $P$ to $Q$ in each of the following cases:

(a)   $P = (8, 5)$,   $Q = (1, -2)$

(b)   $P = (6, 3)$,   $Q = (-1, -4)$

(c)   $P = (7, -3)$,   $Q = (0, -10)$

Note that the displacement vectors are all the same, even though we may draw them with different starting points.

**Suggested Problems:** 1, 2, 11, 25, 28, 30, 31.

## 12.2  VECTORS IN GENERAL

**Class Time:** Half to one class

## Key points

General vector quantities. Addition and scalar multiplication modeled on that for displacement vectors.

## Ideas for the class

After giving several examples of vector and scalar quantities, see if the class can come up with more examples of both, such as temperature, magnetic field, mass, velocity, gravity, volume, etc.

Imagine a lifeguard swinging a whistle on a string in a circle with constant speed. Ask the students to draw some velocity vectors on the circle. How would the velocity vectors change if the constant speed of the whistle were lower? higher? Pick a point $A$ on the circle. If the lifeguard lets go of the string when the whistle is at point $A$, what will its velocity be?

Another exapmle is a car racing around an elliptical track. If the car goes as fast as it can and also stays on the track, draw a few velocity vectors. Where on the track is it likely the car attains maximum speed, minimum speed, maximum acceleration, minimum acceleration?

You can also continue the piano example of the previous section. Reggie and Cory are moving the piano with two ropes. If Reggie and Cory both pull with equal force and the angle between the two ropes is less than 180°, then the resultant path of the piano will be along the angle bisector of the two ropes. (What would happen if the angle were equal to 180°?) If Reggie pulls with greater force than Cory, the piano will travel more toward Reggie than Cory. This makes sense since the person that pulls the hardest expects more motion in his direction.

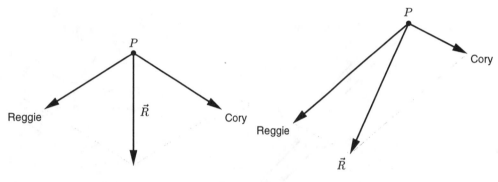

*Figure 12.2.3*

If $\vec{a}$ = airplane velocity (relative to the air), $\vec{w}$ = wind velocity, and $\vec{r}$ = resultant airplane velocity, draw in the missing vector with correct magnitude and direction.

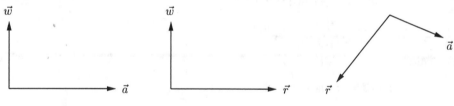

*Figure 12.2.4:* determine $\vec{r}$     *Figure 12.2.5:* determine $\vec{a}$     *Figure 12.2.6:* determine $\vec{w}$

If a river boat is attempting to travel at 20 mph in the direction S 65° E (meaning 65° to the east of south) and the river current is 4 mph due east, at what speed and angle should the captain point the boat? (If students have trouble, suggest drawing a diagram and representing the vectors with components.)

In the Figure 12.2.7, forces $\vec{u}$ and $\vec{v}$ each have magnitude 10 pounds. Determine the magnitude and direction of the force needed to counterbalance the combined action of $\vec{u}$ and $\vec{v}$.

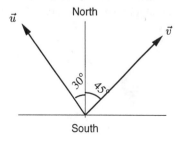

*Figure 12.2.7*

A pilot flying in a wind blowing 80 mph due south discovers that she is heading due east when she points her plane in the direction N 60° E. Determine the airspeed of the plane.

What heading and airspeed are required for a plane to fly 837 mph due north if a wind of 31.5 mph is blowing in the direction S 11.5° E?

The following problem will help link Chapters 11, 12, and 13. The contour diagram for some function $z = f(x, y)$ is given in Figure 12.2.8, together with a point, $P$. In each case, draw a vector, in the (instantaneous) direction you would travel from point $P$, to walk on the

1. steepest uphill path

2. steepest downhill path

3. path on which your altitude remains constant

Observe the relationship between the three vectors above in each case.

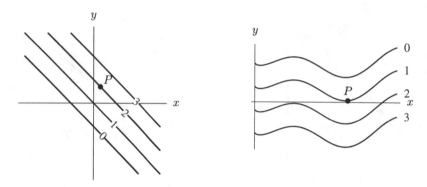

*Figure 12.2.8*

**Suggested Problems:** 8, 9, 13, 15.

## 12.3  THE DOT PRODUCT

**Class Time:** One to two classes

## Key points

The dot product defined geometrically and algebraically (in terms of components). Its properties. Its applications: determining work and the equation of a plane.

## Ideas for the class

Discuss the concept of work to motivate the idea of the dot product. Consider a wagon with a handle that a child pulls along a horizontal sidewalk.

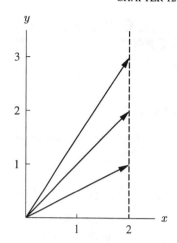

Figure 12.3.9                    Figure 12.3.10

If the child pulls the wagon with two pounds of force and moves the wagon one foot, the amount of work done will depend on the angle of the handle with respect to the ground. Suppose the force vector is $\vec{F} = 2\vec{i}$ pounds and the distance vector is $\vec{D} = 1\vec{i}$ feet. Then the work is $\vec{F} \cdot \vec{D} = 2$ ft-lbs. Notice that if $\vec{F} = \sqrt{2}\vec{i} + \sqrt{2}\vec{j}$ lbs, the magnitude of $\vec{F}$ is still 2; however, now the work has been reduced to $\sqrt{2}$ ft-lbs. When $\vec{F} = \vec{i} + \sqrt{3}\vec{j}$ lbs, the work is reduced further to 1 ft-lb. This can be continued through to $\vec{F} = 2\vec{j}$. Providing that $\vec{D}$ is held at a constant $1\vec{i}$ ft and the magnitude of the force vector remains 2, less work is done as the angle between $\vec{F}$ and $\vec{D}$ increases. This is because less and less of the force is in the direction that the wagon is being moved. (See Figure 12.3.9.)

Alternatively, keep $\vec{D} = 1\vec{i}$ feet and let $\vec{F} = 2\vec{i}, 2\vec{i} + \vec{j}, 2\vec{i} + 2\vec{j}, 2\vec{i} + 3\vec{j}, \ldots$ lbs. This time the work remains a constant 2 ft-lbs as the angle between $\vec{F}$ and $\vec{D}$ increases, but the magnitude of the force increases as the angle grows. Draw pictures of various $\vec{F}$ vectors and the $\vec{i}$ components (projections of $\vec{F}$ in the $\vec{D}$ direction), as in Figure 12.3.10.

In discussing components in arbitrary directions, you might want to point out that the dot product is the product of the magnitude of the component of $\vec{a}$ in the direction of $\vec{b}$ with the magnitude of $\vec{b}$. This can give a useful intuitive picture of the dot product. Point out that by the symmetry of the dot product in $\vec{a}$ and $\vec{b}$, there are two such ways to visualize $\vec{a} \cdot \vec{b}$.

Before deriving the equation of a plane using the dot product, try the following activity. Choose a plane, say $2x + 3y + z = 5$ (or have the class make up an equation). Write the vector $2\vec{i} + 3\vec{j} + \vec{k}$ on the board and explain that you are simply writing the components from the coefficients of the $x$, $y$, and $z$ terms from this particular form of the equation of the plane. Next ask them to determine any two points on the plane, to take the displacement vector between them (in either order), and finally to take the dot product of $2\vec{i} + 3\vec{j} + \vec{k}$ with the displacement vector. Compare their answers. Of course they should get zero. Some will choose other points and try to beat you at this game, but most will be motivated to see if they can generalize the result and why it works.

Other examples to try in class:

- Determine the angle between vectors $\vec{i} + \vec{j} + 2\vec{k}$ and $-\vec{i} + 2\vec{j} + 5\vec{k}$.

- A wagon is pulled horizontally by exerting a force of 10 pounds on the handle at an angle of 60° with the horizontal. How much work is done in moving the wagon 50 feet?

- Determine the magnitude of the component of $\vec{P} = 2\vec{i} + 2\vec{j}$ in the direction of the vector $\vec{Q} = \vec{i} + 2\vec{j}$.

- Determine the equation of the plane passing through the point $2\vec{i} + 6\vec{j} + 3\vec{k}$ and perpendicular to $\vec{n} = 3\vec{i} - 2\vec{j} + \vec{k}$.

- Determine the smaller of the two angles between the following planes: $3x - y - 2z = 2$ and $-6x + 2y + 4z = -4$.

**Suggested Problems:** 3, 9, 11, 17, 21, 22, 28.

## 12.4 THE CROSS PRODUCT

**Class Time:** One to two classes

## Key points

The geometric definition of the cross product (direction as a normal and magnitude as an area). Its formula in Cartesian coordinates ($3 \times 3$ dereminant). Its properties.

## Ideas for the class

A good exercise to test the right hand rule as well as the geometric understanding of the cross product is to choose any two of the vectors $\vec{i}$, $\vec{j}$, or $\vec{k}$ and ask for the cross product. Note that since any pair determines a square of side one, the magnitude of the cross product is one.

Compare and contrast the cross product with the dot product. (Both operations need two vectors, however one operation produces a scalar and the other a vector.)

Some examples to try in class:

- What area is determined by the vectors $\vec{a} = 4\vec{i} + -2\vec{j} + \vec{k}$ and $\vec{b} = -2\vec{i} + 3\vec{j} + -2\vec{k}$?
- Determine an equation for the plane through the points $(-1, -2, -3), (4, -2, 1)$, and $(5, 1, 6)$.
- Determine an equation for the plane which contains the points $(1, 2, -1)$ and $(-2, 1, -3)$, and is perpendicular to the plane $x + 3y - 2z = 3$.

**Suggested Problems:** 6, 7, 8, 12.

# CHAPTER THIRTEEN

## Overview

We introduce the basic notions of partial derivative, directional derivative, gradient, and differential. In keeping with the spirit of the single variable book, we put all the different notions of derivative in the framework of local linearity. We also use local linearity as the basis for the multivariable chain rule. We discuss higher order partial derivatives, their interpretation in partial differential equations, and their application to quadratic Taylor approximations. The chapter concludes with a section on differentiability.

## 13.1  THE PARTIAL DERIVATIVE

**Class Time:** One class

**Suggested transparencies:** Figure 13.6 (p. 657 of text, p. 191 of manual), and figure for Problem 31 (p. 706 of text, p. 192 of manual)

## Key points

Definition of partial derivatives. Estimating partial derivatives graphically from surfaces and contour diagrams, and numerically from tables of data. Understanding the meaning of the partial derivative in terms of units.

## Ideas for the class

It is a good idea to start with an example where the two independent variables have some non-spatial meaning, and are in different units, to illustrate the essential independence of the partial derivatives. The vibrating string in the text is one example. Here are some others.

Find in the local newspaper a table showing monthly payment as a function of the term of the loan and the interest rate, and compute the rate of change at a point with respect to each variable. Is it positive or negative? (The monthly payment increases with the interest rate and decreases with the term of the loan.) What is the practical meaning of the answer? Does the answer make sense?

Do the same thing with the contour diagram showing monthly payment on a loan as a function of interest rate and loan amount (p. 706 of text, p. 192 of manual). Notice that for a fixed interest rate, the spacing between contours is constant. Why? How can this be expressed using partial derivatives? Does constant spacing hold for a fixed loan amount?

Alternatively, use the contour diagram showing heat in a room as a function of time and distance from the heater (p. 657 of text, p. 191 of manual). Show that heat increases with time but decreases with distance. Or, find a contour diagram in a scientific magazine and analyze it.

To explain the relation between partial derivatives and slopes on the graph, sketch $z = f(x, y) = 16 - x^2 - y^2$. Consider the point $f(1, 3) = 6$. Draw a slice parallel to the $x$-axis through $(1, 3, 6)$ as shown in Figure 13.1.1.

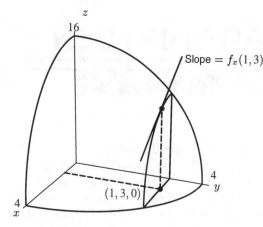

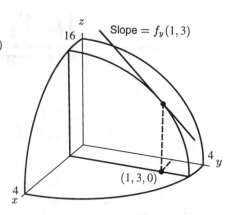

*Figure 13.1.1:* Graph of $z = 16 - x^2 - y^2$, showing line with slope $f_x(1, 3)$.

*Figure 13.1.2:* Graph of $z = 16 - x^2 - y^2$, showing line with slope $f_y(1, 3)$.

Estimate the slope of the tangent line drawn; it is $f_x(1, 3)$. It appears to be negative. Note that $y$ is fixed at 3 on this slice and we are considering $\Delta z / \Delta x$. Draw the secant line from $(1, 3, 6)$ to $(2, 3, 3)$ and calculate $\Delta z / \Delta x = -3$. To get a better estimate, use a difference quotient $[f(1.0001, 3) - f(1, 3)]/0.0001 \approx -2.0001$. It appears that $f_x(1, 3) \approx -2$.

Now draw a slice parallel to the $y$-axis through $(1, 3, 6)$ as shown in Figure 13.1.2, and consider $\Delta z / \Delta y$ to estimate $f_y(1, 3)$. First compare the slopes of the tangent lines in the $x$ and $y$ directions visually. Do they appear to have the same slopes? Then estimate

$$f_y(1, 3) \approx [f(1, 3.0001) - f(1, 3)]/0.0001 \approx -6.0001,$$
$$\text{so} \quad f_y(1, 3) \approx -6.$$

Place points on several transparencies of surfaces and associated contour diagrams. Ask for the sign of the different partial derivatives. Also ask for the sign of the slope in various directions other than the positive coordinate axes.

Have students draw a contour diagram for which:

(a) $f_x(a, b) < 0$ and $f_y(a, b) < 0$.

(b) $f_x(a, b) > 0$ and $f_y(a, b) = 0$.

(c) $f_x(a, b) = 0$ and $f_y(a, b) > 0$ and so on.

Assign Problems 4 and 5 on page 658 from the text for the students to try in class.

**Suggested Problems:** 3, 6, 8, 10, 11, 12, 13.

## 13.2 COMPUTING PARTIAL DERIVATIVES ALGEBRAICALLY

**Class Time:** One class

## Key points

Computing partial derivatives algebraically. Partial derivatives of functions of more than two variables.

## Ideas for the class

Look again at $f(x, y) = 16 - x^2 - y^2$. The number $f_x(1, 3)$ is the slope of the tangent line to $f$ at $(1, 3)$ in the positive $x$ direction while $y$ is fixed at 3. Thus $f_x(1, 3)$ is the derivative with respect to $x$ of the one-variable function $f(x, 3) = 16 - x^2 - 9$, evaluated at $x = 1$. Hence $f_x(x, 3) = \frac{d}{dx}(16 - x^2 - 9) = -2x$, and $f_x(1, 3) = -2(1) = -2$. Likewise you get $f_y(1, 3)$ by differentiating $f(1, y) = 16 - 1 - y^2$ with respect to $y$. Here, $f_y(1, y) = -2y$, $f_y(1, 3) = -2(3) = -6$. In general, $f_x(x, y) = -2x$ (holding $y$ constant) and $f_y(x, y) = -2y$ (holding $x$ constant).

Do several computational examples.

**Suggested Problems:** 2, 8, 9, 15, 21, 29, 36.

## 13.3  LOCAL LINEARITY AND THE DIFFERENTIAL

**Class Time:** One and a half to two classes

**Suggested Transparency** Figure 13.19 (p. 667 of text, p. 193 of manual)

### Key points

Using local linearity to connect the tangent line approximation for functions of one variable to the analogous tangent plane approximation for functions of two variables. The concept of the differential of a function.

### Ideas for the class

If the technology is available, zoom in several times on a smooth function of one variable to open the discussion of local linearity. Review the equations of lines from a visual perspective. That is, $y = b + f'(0)x$ is the line with the initial height $b$, changing by the amount $f'(0)$ per unit change in $x$. Given $y$-intercept 3 and slope 2, the line is $y = 3 + 2x$. But what if instead of the intercept, we are given the point $(5, 13)$? Then

$$y = \underbrace{13}_{\substack{\text{starting} \\ \text{height}}} + \underbrace{2}_{\substack{\text{rate at which} \\ \text{ht. is changed} \\ \text{per change in } x}} + \underbrace{(x - 5)}_{\substack{\text{change in } x \\ \text{from } x = 5}}.$$

This may be written

$$y = f(5) + f'(5) \cdot (x - 5).$$

[Note that $y = 13 + 2(x - 5)$ is equivalent to $y = 3 + 2x$.] So for a given function $y = f(x)$, an estimate for $f(x)$ for $x$ near $a$ is the tangent line approximation:

$$f(x) \approx f(a) + f'(a)(x - a).$$

Recall the equation of a plane $z = c + mx + ny$. In terms of movement, start at a height of $c$ at the origin and move with slope $m$ in the positive $x$ direction and slope $n$ in the positive $y$ direction. But in Section 13.1 we learned that $m = f_x(0, 0)$ and $n = f_y(0, 0)$, so the equation of a plane becomes $z = f(x, y) = c + f_x(0, 0)x + f_y(0, 0)y$. Thus, the tangent plane approximation to a function $z = f(x, y)$ for $(x, y)$ near $(a, b)$ is:

$$f(x, y) \approx \underbrace{f(a, b)}_{\substack{\text{starting} \\ \text{height}}} + \underbrace{f_x(a, b)}_{\substack{\text{height change} \\ \text{per change in } x}} \cdot \underbrace{(x - a)}_{\substack{\text{change in } x \\ \text{from } x = a}} + \underbrace{f_y(a, b)}_{\substack{\text{height change} \\ \text{per change in } y}} \cdot \underbrace{(y - b)}_{\substack{\text{change in } y \\ \text{from } y = b}}$$

For example, $z = 5 + 2x - 3y$ has $z$-intercept 5, $m = f_x(0, 0) = 2$, $n = f_y(0, 0) = -3$. If the starting point were given to be $(1, 3, -2)$, and $m$ and $n$ remained the same, then $z = -2 + 2(x - 1) - 3(y - 3)$ which is equivalent to $z = 5 + 2x - 3y$.

Other examples:

1. (a)  Determine the equation of the tangent plane to the surface $z = y - x^2$ at $(4, 3)$.

    (b)   Use the tangent plane to estimate $2.996 - 4.013^2$. (How close is your estimate?)

2.    Determine the equation of the tangent plane to each surface at the given point:
    (a)   $f(x, y) = x/y$ at $(3, -2)$
    (b)   $f(x, y) = x^2 \ln y$ at $(-1, e)$
    (c)   $f(x, y) = e^{xy}$ at $(\ln 2, 5)$

    The difference (differential) between two values is conceptually and visually clearer than the ratio between two values (the derivative). Start with a linear approximation for a function of one variable, $y = f(x)$. In that case $dy = f'(x)dx$ is the change in the value of $y$ along the tangent line for a move of $\Delta x = dx$. The actual difference in the value of the function, for a move of $\Delta x$, is $\Delta y$. Due to local linearity, as we zoom in, $\Delta y \approx dy = f'(x)dx$.

    Point out the convenience of the notation for the derivative, $f'(x) = \dfrac{dy}{dx}$. Here, $\dfrac{dy}{dx}$ is a number which tells us the slope of the tangent line to the graph of $y = f(x)$ at the point $(x, f(x))$. This means that if we change $x$ by $dx$ and move along the tangent line, then $y$ changes by $f'(x)\,dx$. If we denote this change in $y$ by $dy$, then we can write $dy = f'(x)\,dx$.

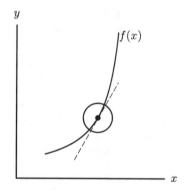

*Figure 13.3.3*

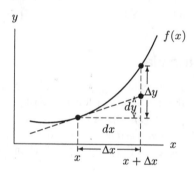

*Figure 13.3.4*

    For a smooth function of two variables, $z = f(x, y)$, to change the value, $z$, of the function, we now have *two* variables to vary, $x$ and $y$. The actual difference in the value of the function for moves $\Delta x$ and $\Delta y$ is $\Delta z$. We use the linear approximation:

$$z \approx f(a, b) + f_x(a, b)(x - a) + f_y(a, b)(y - b) \quad \text{or}$$
$$z - f(a, b) \approx f_x(a, b)(x - a) + f_y(a, b)(y - b)$$
$$\Delta z \approx f_x(a, b)\Delta x + f_y(a, b)\Delta y.$$

Both Figure 13.3.5 and the transparency for Figure 13.19 (p. 667 of text, p. 193 of this manual) illustrate two variable local linearity.

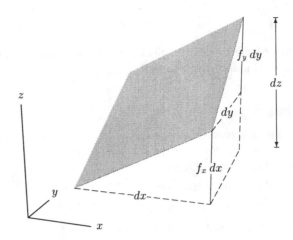

*Figure 13.3.5*

Remind the students that the graph of a function of two variables is a surface and that the linear *surface* which best approximates it at a point $(x, y, f(x, y))$ is the tangent *plane*. In the case of a function $y = f(x)$ of one variable, to move along the tangent *line*, we only vary one independent variable, $x$. Now we must vary both $x$ and $y$ to move in the tangent plane to approximate the change in $z$.

John Verosky from the Mathematics Department at Western Washington University suggests building differential models from blocks of wood. Start with a $4 \times 4$ and saw at an angle as shown. A long enough post could make a classroom set. The slanted surface represents the linear approximation (plane) to $z = f(x, y)$. The changes in variables can be marked on the wood.

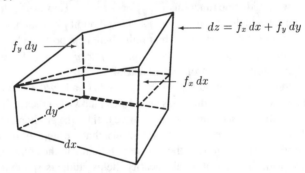

*Figure 13.3.6*

**Suggested Problems:** 1, 4, 10, 11, 21, 22.

## 13.4   GRADIENTS AND DIRECTIONAL DERIVATIVES IN THE PLANE

**Class Time:** One class

**Suggested transparencies:** The contour diagrams of Figure 13.26 (p. 674 of text, pp. 194–196 of manual), and a sampling of the surfaces and contour diagrams for

(a)  $z = x^2 - y^2$ (pp. 197–198),

(b)  $z = x^2 + y^2$ (pp. 199–200),

(c)  $z = 6y - 4y^3 - x^2 + 1$ (pp. 201–202),

(d)  $z = 3(\sin y) - x^3 + 1$ (pp. 203–204),

(e)  $z = (\cos y)e^{-x}$ (pp. 205–206),

(f)  $z = (\cos x)(\cos y)e^{-(x^2+y^2)}$ (pp. 207–208),

(g)  $z = -10x^3y^2$ (pp. 209–210),

(h)  $z = y^2(\sin 2x)$ (pp. 211–212),

(i)  $z = -2(\sin x)(\sin y)$ (pp. 213–214),

(j)  $z = \cos(x^2+y^2)/(1+x^2+y^2)$ (pp. 215–216),

(k)  $z = x^3 - 3xy^2$ (pp. 217–218),

(l)  $z = x^2 + 3(\sin y)$ (pp. 219–220).

## Key points

Definition of directional derivatives using difference quotient. Definition of gradient vectors in the plane. Local linearity gives the formula $f_{\vec{u}} = f_x u_1 + f_y u_2 = \text{grad } f \cdot \vec{u}$.

## Ideas for the class

Draw the level curves for the plane $z = 2 + .5x - y$ for $z = 0, 1, 2, 3, 4$. Mark the point $P = (2, 1)$ on the contour diagram. From the graph approximate:

(a) the slope in the $\vec{i}$ direction

(b) the slope in the $\vec{j}$ direction

(c) the slope in the direction $(1, 2)$

(d) the slope in the direction $(2, 1)$

(e) the slope in the direction $(1, -2)$

Note: relate the answers to (a) and (b) to the equation of the plane.

   Use the transparencies from Figure 13.26 (p. 674 of the text, pp. 194 – 196 of manual), which show contour diagrams for three functions. Mark in vectors pointing in various directions and ask whether the directional derivative at the indicated point is positive, negative, or zero.

   The following exercises will help students become familiar with the gradient vectors. Draw some level curves for $f(x, y) = x^2 + y^2$, and put in some gradient vectors on different contour lines. Does the length of the gradient increase, decrease, or remain constant as the radius of the level curves (circles) increases? Why? How are the lengths of the gradient vectors at points on the same level curve related? (They are the same.) Is this the case for a level curve of any surface? Have the class think of an example where this is not true.

   Now consider the function $g(x, y) = -x^2 - y^2$. How are the length and direction of grad $f$ related to the length and direction of grad $g$ at a fixed point $p$? What happens at $f(x, y) = g(x, y) = (0, 0)$? From looking at the surfaces, why might there be a problem here?

   Do the same analysis for the graph of $f(x, y) = -\sqrt{1 - x^2 - y^2}$ or the surfaces on some of the other transparencies from Section 13.4.

   Before deriving grad $f(a, b) = f_x \vec{i} + f_y \vec{j}$, allow the class to discuss, review, and rediscover some past work. The gradient has been foreshadowed in the text since Chapter 11. To incorporate the hints from the past sections into an intuitive feel for the gradient, review Problem 20 on page 601 of the text. If $f(x, y) = c + mx + ny$, it was shown that the slope of the contour lines is $-m/n = -f_x/f_y$. This implies that the slope of the line perpendicular to the contour lines must be $f_y/f_x$. This concept, coupled with the idea of local linearity, helps students see that the direction in which a function changes fastest from a point is perpendicular to the level curve at that point, and that this direction is the gradient vector $f_x \vec{i} + f_y \vec{j}$. See Figure 13.4.7.

   Although the formula $f_{\vec{u}} = \text{grad } f \cdot \vec{u}$ has already been derived using local linearity, it is a good idea to understand it from a geometric point of view also. First, note that the slope of the surface in the direction:

-   perpendicular to the gradient is zero.

-   of the gradient is the maximum.

-   opposite the gradient is negative.

Tie this in with the dot product of a fixed vector with a rotating vector. Now, consider Figure 13.4.8. Compare the signs of dot products with the rate of change in the direction of each vector.

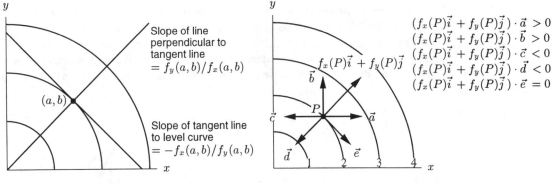

Figure 13.4.7                    Figure 13.4.8

A problem to test students' understanding of gradient is the following: An ant is on a metal plate whose temperature at $(x,y)$ is $3x^2y - y^3$ degrees Celsius. When it is at the point $(5,1)$ it is anxious to move in the direction in which the temperature drops most rapidly. Give the unit vector in that direction.

**Suggested Problems:** 1, 2, 5, 6, 9.

## 13.5  GRADIENTS AND DIRECTIONAL DERIVATIVES IN SPACE

**Class Time:** One to one and a half classes

### Key points

Visualizing the gradient and directional derivatives of $z = f(x,y)$ using the function's graph. Geometric and algebraic definitions of the gradient and directional derivatives for functions of three variables.

### Ideas for the class

Consider the function $f(x,y)$ whose graph is the portion of the unit sphere in the first octant. Draw several direction vectors at the point $P$. (See Figure 13.5.9.) Use the surface to determine whether the directional derivative is positive, negative, or zero at $P$. Ask for the direction in which the function increases the fastest and also the directions in which the function shows no change.

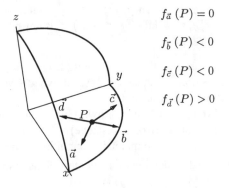

$$f_{\vec{a}}(P) = 0$$

$$f_{\vec{b}}(P) < 0$$

$$f_{\vec{c}}(P) < 0$$

$$f_{\vec{d}}(P) > 0$$

Figure 13.5.9

There is often confusion when a two component vector is used for direction on a 3-D surface. An idea to clear up this confusion is to consider walking on a surface (a mountain) while using a compass. The compass gives 2-D directions even though you are walking on a 3-D surface.

The following figures aid in understanding directional derivatives of functions of two variables. They show that the directional derivative is the slope of the surface at a point in a particular direction.

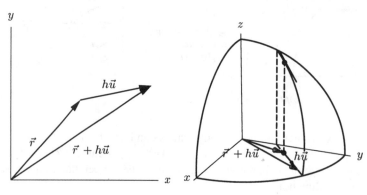

Figure 13.5.10          Figure 13.5.11

When presenting the limit of the difference quotient definition of the directional derivative, it is helpful to present it in 3-space as well as in 2-space since students must continually make this connection.

Determining the normal vector to a level surface can yield the equation of the tangent plane to the surface. A good question is to determine the equation of the tangent plane to $f(x, y) = 6 - x^2 - y^2$ at $(1, 1, 4)$.

Method one: $f_x(1, 1) = -2$, $f_y(1, 1) = -2$, so the equation of the plane is $z = 4 - 2(x - 1) - 2(y - 1)$.

Method two: Consider a function of three variables $w(x, y, z) = z + x^2 + y^2 - 6$ where $z = 6 - x^2 - y^2$ is a level surface when $w = 0$. Then $\text{grad}\, w(x, y, z) = (2x, 2y, 1)$ and is normal to the level surface at $(x, y, z)$. Specifically $\text{grad}\, w(1, 1, 4) = (2, 2, 1)$. So the tangent plane is of the form $2x + 2y + z = D$ and given the point $(1, 1, 4)$ we get $D = 8$. The equation $2x + 2y + z = 8$ is equivalent to the result obtained using method one.

Although method two looks more complicated, it is often useful. Some sample problems follow.

1. Determine the directional derivative of $f$ at $P$ in the given direction. Let $O =$ origin.
    (a) $f(x, y) = \sin(xy^2)$, $P = (\pi/4, 2)$, $\vec{u} = \vec{i}$.
    (b) $f(x, y) = \sin(xy^2)$, $P = (\pi/4, 2)$, southeast.
    (c) $f(x, y) = \sqrt{x^2 + y^2}$, $P$ is any point but the origin, in a direction perpendicular to the gradient of $f(P)$.
    (d) $f(x, y) = \arctan(y/x)$, $P$ is any point not on the $y$-axis, in the direction of $\overrightarrow{OP}$.
    (e) $f(x, y, z) = \ln(x^2 + y^2 + z^2)$, $P$ is any point $(x, y, z)$ except the origin, in the direction of $\overrightarrow{OP}$.

2. (a) You are standing at the point $(1, 1, 3)$ on a hill $z = 5y - x^2 - y^2$. If you climb in the direction of the steepest ascent, what is your rate of ascent with respect to horizontal distance as you start?
    (b) If you decide to go northwest, will you be ascending or descending? At what rate (with respect to horizontal distance)?
    (c) If you decide to maintain your altitude, in what directions can you go?

3. Determine the equation of the tangent plane to the surface at $(x, y)$:
    (a) $f(x, y) = xe^y$, $(x, y) = (1, 0)$
    (b) $xy^2z^3 = 12$, $(x, y) = (3, 2)$

4.   Determine all points on $x^2 + y^2 + z^2 = 1$ where the tangent plane is parallel to the plane $2x + y - 3z = 2$.

**Suggested Problems:** 1, 3, 7, 8, 9, 14.

## 13.6   THE CHAIN RULE

**Class Time:** One to two classes

### Key points

Understanding the chain rule in terms of related rates of change. Using tree diagrams to keep track of rates of change.

### Ideas for the class

Many students do not understand the concept behind the chain rule; rather they are following an algorithm. The chain rule is based upon multiplying related rates of change and can be understood with some simple examples. Why multiply the rates? An intuitive question for the class: If Sally runs twice as fast as Patty and Patty runs five times as fast as Joey, how much faster does Sally run than Joey? Students will automatically *multiply* 2 by 5 and conclude that Sally runs 10 times as fast as Joey without a thought of the chain rule. This opens the door to analyze why. After several other simple examples they can formalize that if $S$=Sally's position, $P$=Patty's position, and $J$=Joey's position, then $(dS/dP)(dP/dJ) = (dS/dJ)$. In a multivariable setting, we first multiply related rates. Then, from our ideas on local linearity, we must *add* the contributions from the unrelated variables. A tree diagram can be built to keep track of these rates.

Sample Problems:
1.   Determine $dz/dt$ or $dw/dt$:
     (a)   $z = x/y, x = \sin t, y = \cos t$
     (b)   $z = \ln(xy), x = e^t, y = e^{-t}$
     (c)   $w = e^{xyz}, x = t, y = t^2, z = t^3$
     (d)   $w = \sqrt{x^2 + y^2 + z^2}, x = \cos t, y = \sin t, z = \sin t$

2.   Suppose the temperature at each point of the plane is given by $T = \sqrt{x^2 + y^2}$ and a bug's position at time $t$ is $x = t^2, y = t^3$. Determine the rate of change of temperature experienced by the bug as it passes through the point $(4, 8)$.

3.   If $w = u^2 e^v, u = x/y, v = y \ln x$, determine $\frac{\partial w}{\partial x}$ and $\frac{\partial w}{\partial y}$ at $(x, y) = (1, 2)$.

4.   If $z = (x - y)/(x + y)$ where $x = uvw, y = u^2 + v^2 + w^2$, determine $\frac{\partial z}{\partial u}, \frac{\partial z}{\partial v}, \frac{\partial z}{\partial w}$ where $u = 2, v = -1, w = 1$.

5.   If $z = y/x, x = e^u \cos v, y = e^u \sin v$, determine $\frac{\partial z}{\partial u}$ and $\frac{\partial z}{\partial v}$.

**Suggested Problems:** 1, 2, 7, 8, 17, 18.

## 13.7   SECOND-ORDER PARTIAL DERIVATIVES

**Class Time:** One class

### Key points

Definition and practical interpretations of second-order partial derivatives.

## Ideas for the class

As with the section on partial derivatives, it is a good idea to start with an example where the two independent variables are in different units, such as the vibrating string example in the text. This is also good preparation for the next section on partial differential equations.

Figures 13.7.12 and 13.7.13 help in visualizing the second order partial derivatives $f_{xx}(a, b)$ and $f_{xy}(a, b)$ on a graph of the function $f(x, y)$. First, $f_{xx}(a, b)$ gives the concavity in the $x$-direction; $f_{xx}(a, b) < 0$ in this case since the curve is concave down. Second, $f_{xy}(a, b)$ gives the rate of change of $f_x(a, b)$ as you move in the positive $y$-direction. Move the tangent line along the curve shown in the postive $y$ direction. Again, $f_{xy}(a, b) < 0$ in this case since the slope of the successive tangent lines is decreasing.

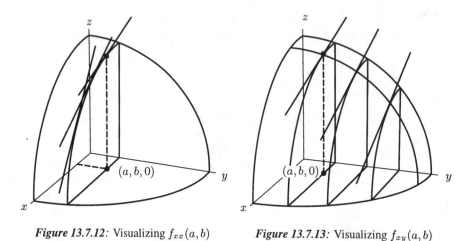

*Figure 13.7.12:* Visualizing $f_{xx}(a, b)$     *Figure 13.7.13:* Visualizing $f_{xy}(a, b)$

Figures 13.7.14 and 13.7.15 can be used to visualize $f_{yy}(a, b)$ and $f_{yx}(a, b)$, respectively.

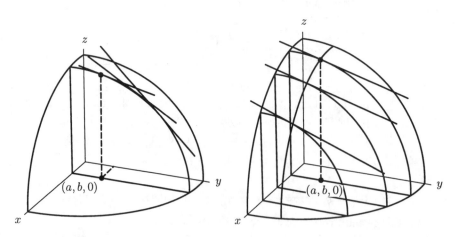

*Figure 13.7.14:* Visualizing $f_{yy}(a, b)$     *Figure 13.7.15:* Visualizing $f_{yx}(a, b)$

Next use contour diagrams of functions of two variables to determine the signs of $f_x$, $f_y$, $f_{xx}$, $f_{yy}$ at a point. Use some examples from the exercises in the text or create others. See if the students can draw contour diagrams that match the signs of a given set of first and second partial derivatives. For example, sketch the contours of a function $z = f(x, y)$ for which all of the following hold at a point $P$: $f_x(P) < 0$, $f_y(P) > 0$, $f_{xx}(P) < 0$, $f_{yy}(P) < 0$, $f_{xy}(P) > 0$, $f_{yx}(P) > 0$. A possible solution is shown in Figure 13.7.16.

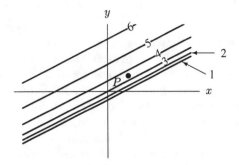

*Figure 13.7.16*

A good drill problem is to determine all second partial derivatives for the following functions:

(a)   $f(x, y) = e^{xy}$

(b)   $f(x, y) = x^2 + x \ln y$

(c)   $f(x, y, z) = 3x^2y + 2xz - yz + 2y^2xz$ (there are 9)

**Suggested Problems:** 4, 5, 9, 10, 14, 17, 19.

## 13.8  TAYLOR APPROXIMATIONS

**Class Time:** One class or skip

### Key points

Using second-order partial derivatives to determine a quadratic approximation to a surface near a given point. Using second- and third-order partial derivatives to compute error bounds for the linear and quadratic approximations.

### Ideas for the class

This section is used in Chapter 14 for deriving the second derivative test used to classify maxima, minima, and saddle points for functions of two variables.

Start with a review of Taylor polynomials for functions of one variable. Use a numerical example to illustrate the superiority of the quadratic approximation. Then point out that for functions of two variables there are more quadratic terms and more second order derivatives, and they match up. Do a two-variable example numerically as well.

Derive the quadratic Taylor expansion of $e^{-x-y}$ in two ways: using the two-variable approximation, and substituting $t = -x - y$ into the one-variable approximation for $e^t$.

**Suggested Problems:** 1, 2, 5, 7, 10.

## FOCUS ON THEORY: DIFFERENTIABILITY

**Class Time:** One class (optional)

### Key points

Review the concept of differentiability for functions of one variable from the viewpoint of local linear approximation with small relative error. Generalize this to differentiability for functions of two variables in terms of local linear approximation with small relative error. Connect this to partial derivatives and continuity.

## Ideas for the class

A main point is that "local linearity" and "local linear approximation" are not meaningful unless we can quantify how good the approximation is. Examples for the one-variable case are the functions $y = x^2$ and $y = |x|$. Both functions are "approximated" near the origin, in some sense, by the $x$-axis, but we would not consider this to be a "good" approximation to $y = |x|$ near the origin. The goal of this section is to make the concept of a "good local linear approximation" precise and to explain its implications. After discussing some examples such as these, lead the students to the new definition of differentiability for one-variable functions in terms of small relative error.

Once the idea of differentiability in terms of local linear approximation with small relative error is in place, the technical definition of differentiability for functions of two (or more) variables is easier to motivate. Many of the examples and exercises come alive when their contour diagrams and graphs are plotted: it often becomes clear then why a certain function cannot be differentiable and the graphical data can suggest proofs when a certain function is not differentiable. Bear in mind that some of these functions can pose difficulties for even sophisticated computer graphing programs.

**Suggested Problems:** 2, 5, 7, 10.

# CHAPTER FOURTEEN

## Overview

We apply the ideas of the previous chapter to optimization problems, both constrained and unconstrained. We derive the second derivative test for local extrema by first considering the case of quadratic polynomials, and then appealing to the quadratic Taylor approximation. We discuss the existence of global extrema for continuous functions on closed and bounded regions. In the section on constrained optimization, we discuss Lagrange multipliers and equality and inequality constraints. The Focus on Modeling section considers the Lagrangian and its interpretation.

## 14.1  LOCAL EXTREMA

**Class Time:** Two classes

**Suggested transparencies:** Various surfaces on pages 221–230 of the manual.

## Key points

Local extrema; the second derivative test.

## Ideas for the class

Review local extrema for functions of one variable before introducing the multivariable case. Then use transparencies of various surfaces and their contour diagrams to view extrema for a function of two variables. It is important that students recognize critical points both on the surface and on the contour diagram. Have them mark critical points on contour diagrams and ask them to make conjectures about the gradient vectors in the vicinity of critical points. Finally, determine all local extrema and saddle points for several surfaces by solving the appropriate equations. Students often have difficulty solving the systems of equations.

The second derivative can be illuminated geometrically with the series of transparencies on pages 221–230 of this manual. In the discriminant $D = f_{xx}f_{yy} - f_{xy}^2$, the first term, $f_{xx}f_{yy}$, determines whether the concavities of the function in the $x$ and $y$ directions have the same sign. We look at functions where $f_{xy} = 0$ and see what effect the sign of $f_{xx}f_{yy}$ has on the nature of a critical point. In the transparences on pages 221 and 222, we see the graphs of $x^2 + y^2$ and $-x^2 - y^2$. In the first case, $f_{xx}$ and $f_{yy}$ are both positive, so $f_{xx}f_{yy} > 0$. In the second, $f_{xx}$ and $f_{yy}$ are both negative, so $f_{xx}f_{yy} > 0$ In both these cases, $f_{xy} = 0$, and $f_{xx}$ and $f_{yy}$ are of the same sign, so the discriminant is positive. Notice that we have a maximum or a minimum. In the transparency on page 223, $f_{xx}$ and $f_{yy}$ are of opposite signs and the discriminant is negative; we have a saddle point.

Geometrically, if a surface is concave up in one direction and concave down in another, there is no possibility of a local maximum or a local minimum, and we expect a saddle point. Hence, if $f_{xx}$ and $f_{yy}$ are of opposite signs, there is no possibility of a maximum or minimum. Also, since $f_{xy}^2 \geq 0$, if $f_{xx}$ and $f_{yy}$ are of opposite signs, there is no possibility that the discriminant is positive. If $f_{xx}$ and $f_{yy}$ are of the same sign, we know that the curve's concavity is appropriate in the $x$ and $y$ directions for a local maximum or local minimum. However, this does not mean necessarily that the concavity in all directions has the same sign.

The second term of the discriminant, $f_{xy}^2$, represents the magnitude of the rate of change from $f_x(x, y)$ to $f_x(x, y + \Delta y)$. We can describe this geometrically as the twist in the function.

The transparencies on pages 224 and 225 show functions where $f_{xy}$ is either positive or negative. It can be seen from these pictures that, regardless of the sign of $f_{xy}$, the magnitude of $f_{xy}$ and correspondingly of $f_{xy}^2$ is indicative of a tendency to form a saddle point.

So far, we have that if $f_{xx}$ and $f_{yy}$ are of opposite signs, the discriminant is negative and we have a saddle. If $f_{xx}f_{yy} = 0$ and $f_{xy} \neq 0$, then the discriminant is negative and once again we have a saddle.

If $f_{xx}$ and $f_{yy}$ are of the same sign, then the concavity in the $x$ and $y$ directions indicates a local maximum or minimum. The only question is whether the twist in the surface is significant enough to cause a change in concavity in some direction. The interplay between these two terms is shown in the surfaces of $f(x, y) = x^2 + y^2 - kxy$ on pages 226–230. As $k$ increases, the magnitude of $f_{xy}$ increases, and the discriminant goes from positive to zero to negative.

Hence, when the discriminant is positive, we have a local maximum or local minimum. When the discriminant is zero, the slope of the surface at the critical point is flat in some direction, and when the discriminant is negative, the critical point is a saddle.

Sample problems:

1. Determine all critical points of $f(x, y) = e^x + 3y + x + e^y$.

2. Determine all maxima and minima of $f(x, y) = xy + 2x - \ln(x^2 y)$ in the first quadrant or show why there are none.

3. When it rains on the surface $z = 1/x + 1/y + xy$, at what point will a puddle form?

**Suggested Problems:** 2, 3, 4, 5, 6, 7, 8, 11, 12.

## 14.2   GLOBAL EXTREMA: UNCONSTRAINED OPTIMIZATION

**Class Time:** One class

**Suggested transparencies:** The graph of $z = e^{-y^2}(2x^3 - 3x^2 + 1) + e^{-y}(2x^3 - 3x^2)$ (p. 231 of manual)

## Key points

Global extrema. Applications of optimization: maximizing profit, least squares approximation, gradient search. Criteria for existence of global extrema.

## Ideas for the class

Explain the difference between local and global extrema. Use some of the examples done in the previous section and ask whether the local maxima and minima are global maxima and minima. Investigate behavior as $x \to \infty$ and $y \to \infty$.

A strong class may be intrigued by the following challenge problem from *Calculus*, by Philip Gillett, D.C. Heath and Co., 1988, p. 785, suggested by Professor David A. Smith. (Problem 22 of the text is similar.)

Given $f(x, y) = e^{-y^2}(2x^3 - 3x^2 + 1) + e^{-y}(2x^3 - 3x^2)$, (See page 231 of the manual.)

(a)  show that $(0, 0)$ is the only critical point and $f(0, 0) = 1$ is a local maximum,

(b)  by analogy with single variable calculus, we might be tempted to conclude that $f(0, 0)$ is a global maximum. (Surely a smooth surface with only one peak and no other point where the terrain bottoms out to a local minimum cannot rise higher than the peak!) Confirm, however, that $f(2, 0) > f(0, 0)$, thus showing that there is a point of the surface higher than the peak.

If you have time to do applications, students may be interested in the derivation of the least squares line. Most calculators now accept data and give the least squares line, as well as the other best fit curves, at the push of a button.

The gradient search is a practical method for solving real optimization problems. Instead of doing a numerical example, you may prefer to illustrate the method graphically using a transparency of a complex surface and drawing in the steps of the search as you go along.

**Suggested Problems:** 9, 18, 14.

## 14.3  CONSTRAINED OPTIMIZATION: LAGRANGE MULTIPLIERS

**Class Time:** Two to three classes

**Suggested transparencies:** Select a sampling from the various surfaces and contour diagrams provided, eg. contour diagram of $z = y^2 - x^2$ on page 198 of manual.

## Key points

Constrained optimization and the method of Lagrange multipliers.

## Ideas for the class

To introduce the concept of constraints for functions of two variables, build a playdough solid on a horizontal domain. The top is the surface of interest. Use dental floss to slice constraints through the playdough in a direction perpendicular to the base. An easy figure to start with is a paraboloid.

Next draw constraints on transparencies of level curves and ask for the approximate positions of the global maximum and minimum. Draw the students' attention to the fact that optimal points subject to a constraint occur where the constraint is tangent to a level curve. After several visual examples, it is reasonable to conjecture that, at the optimal point, the gradient of the function to be optimized must be parallel to the gradient of the constraint function.

Sample Problems:

1.  Using the contour diagram for $z = y^2 - x^2$ (p. 198 of manual) draw in the constraint triangle (including the interior) with vertices $(0, 0)$, $(1, 2)$, $(2, -2)$. Determine the global maximum and global minimum.

2.  Determine the top of the mountain defined by $z = 2x^2 + xy - y^2$ on the domain $D = \{(x, y) : -3 \le x \le 3, -3 \le y \le 3\}$.

3.  Find the point on $4x + 3y + z = 2$ that is closest to $(1, -1, 1)$.

4.  A triangular plate has vertices $(0, 4)$, $(0, -2)$, and $(3, -2)$. The temperature at each point of the plate is given by $T = x^2 + xy + 2y^2 - 3x + 2y$. Determine the hottest and coldest points of the plate.

**Suggested Problems:** 2, 4, 7, 13, 19, 21, 22.

## FOCUS ON MODELING: THE LAGRANGIAN AND ITS INTERPRETATION

**Class Time:** One class or omit

**Suggested Resource:** *Microeconomics with Calculus*, by Brian R. Bingerard and Elizabeth Hoffman (Harper Collins: 1988). This book gives many geometric explanations.

## Key points

The economic interpretations of the Lagrangian function and the Lagrange multiplier

## Ideas for the Class

This section is of particular importance to students taking microeconomics. There, they are likely to see constrained optimization approached using the Lagrangian function rather than the first order conditions (grad $f = \lambda$ grad $g$) of Section 14.3. To teach this section, you can reflect on some of the examples covered earlier, but from the point of view of the Lagrangian function. Pay particular attention to the interpretation of $\lambda$.

**Suggested Problems:** 1, 3.

# CHAPTER FIFTEEN

## Overview

We motivate the multivariable definite integral graphically by considering the problem of estimating total population from a contour diagram for population density, using finer and finer grids. We continue with numerical examples using tables, and then give two methods of calculating multiple integrals: analytically, by means of iterated integrals, and numerically, by the Monte Carlo method. We discuss both double and triple integrals in Cartesian, polar, spherical, and cylindrical coordinates. We also discuss applications to multivariate probability.

The definite integral of a one-variable function is often introduced using area. Similarly, the double integral of a two-variable function could be introduced as a volume. We, however, introduce double integrals using density. The reason for this choice is that the idea of a density function can more easily be generalized to higher dimensions.

## 15.1  THE DEFINITE INTEGRAL OF A FUNCTION OF TWO VARIABLES

**Class Time:** One to one and a half classes

**Suggested transparencies:** Weather map (p. 564 of text, p. 173 of manual), topographic map (p. 584 of text, p. 232 of manual), grids (pp. 233–235 of manual), Figure 15.1 (p. 754 of text, p. 236 of manual), figure from Problem 4 (p. 760 of text, p. 237 of manual), and figure from Problem 5 (p. 760 of text, p. 238 of manual).

### Key points

Expanding the idea of a Riemann sum to two dimensions, interpreting the limit of these Riemann sums.

### Ideas for the class

There are two natural ways to introduce the Riemann sum definition of the two-variable definite integral. You can start with an example of a population density contour diagram, such as the fox population example (p. 754 of text, p. 236 of manual), or you can start with a table of values, for example the widths of a boat hull in Problem 9 (p. 761).

Using the weather map (or topographic map) and the various size grids, estimate the average temperature (or height) by various techniques: making over- and under-estimates, sampling consistently from one of the corners, averaging the four corner samples, sampling at the center of a grid rectangle.

Display a local topographic map of a mountain, lake, or bay, and use Riemann sums to estimate its volume.

**Suggested Problems:** 2, 4, 5, 10.

## 15.2  ITERATED INTEGRALS

**Class Time:** Two classes

**Suggested transparencies:** Contour diagram on page 239 of manual, graphs on page 240 of manual, figure from Problem 6 (p. 769 of text, p. 241 of manual), figure from Problem 7 (p. 769 of text, p. 242 of manual), and figure from Problem 8 (p. 769 of text, p. 243 of manual).

## Key points

Reducing double integrals to nested one-variable integrals. Integrating over non-rectangular regions.

## Ideas for the class

Depending on the approach you used for the previous section, you can motivate iterated integrals by dividing a contour diagram into horizontal and vertical strips, or by summing a two-variable table by rows or columns. The numerical approach makes it clear that reversing the order of integration is no more than reversing the order of summation.

The students may be rusty on finding antiderivatives. The table of antiderivatives in the end-papers, along with some common trigonometric identities, and the formulas for substitution and integration by parts will help them review the mechanics of one variable integral calculus if this is needed.

Before you discuss why the order of integration does not matter, you may want to try the following activity. Divide students into pairs and pick a double integral (or a different one for each pair.) Have one student calculate the iterated integral by integrating with respect to $x$ first; have the other student integrate with respect to $y$ first. Having both students get the same answer should convince them that the order of integration does not matter, and provide a lead-in to why this should be so.

Many examples of setting up iterated integrals over non-rectangular regions will be required before the students will be comfortable. A good first question: Is it going to be $dy\,dx$, $dx\,dy$, or does it not really matter?

**Suggested Problems:** 4, 6, 7, 8, 11, 12, 14, 15, 16, 23, 24, 26.

## 15.3 TRIPLE INTEGRALS

**Class Time:** One class

## Key points

Evaluating definite integrals over three-dimensional regions using Cartesian coordinates.

## Ideas for the class

After introducing the basic ideas, calculate the volume of a solid in two different ways, using a double integral and a triple integral. Make sure the students understand why there is a function to be integrated in the double integral, but only the constant function 1 in the triple integral.

Do an example of finding the total mass by integrating density. Don't neglect the steps of setting up the integral by multiplying density by a small volume $dV$; it is important for applications that students continue to think of integrals in terms of subdivisions and not purely algebraically.

Give some examples where the limits in the integrals don't make sense, for example because they contain variables that have already been integrated.

The examples of setting up iterated integrals in three dimensions can take a lot of time, and it is easy to get carried away with these exercises. Such exercises may not be worth it if they take time away from the calculus that is presented in later chapters. One possibility is to do a few representative examples of triple integrals from the problem set and assign a few more as homework. Then misunderstandings can be worked out with comments on the homework or during office hours.

**Suggested Problems:** 1, 3, 5, 6, 7, 8, 9, 10, 11, 14.

## 15.4  DOUBLE INTEGRALS IN POLAR COORDINATES

**Class Time:** One class

**Suggested transparencies:** Figures 15.26 (p. 775 of text, p. 244 of manual) and 15.27 (p. 775 of text, p. 245 of manual).

### Key points

Evaluating definite integrals in two dimensions using polar coordinates.

### Ideas for the class

Put a polar grid over a contour diagram and discuss how you would estimate the definite integral from it; this leads to a discussion of the area of the curved grid rectangles and the area element $dA = r\,dr\,d\theta$.

Put up various regions on the blackboard, both rectangular and polar, and ask what the appropriate coordinate system is and how to set up an integral over the region in that coordinate system.

For class discussion, you could have the students figure out how to express a rectangular region $0 \le x \le a, 0 \le y \le b$ in polar coordinates.

**Suggested Problems:** 1, 2, 3, 4, 9, 10, 14, 16, 21.

## 15.5  INTEGRALS IN CYLINDRICAL AND SPHERICAL COORDINATES

**Class Time:** One to two classes

**Suggested transparencies:**
(a)  Figure 15.31 (p. 779 of text, p. 246 of manual),
(b)  Figure 15.32 (p. 779 of text, p. 247),
(c)  Figure 15.33 (p. 779 of text, p. 248 of manual),
(d)  Figure 15.34 (p. 779 of text, p. 249 of manual),
(e)  Figure 15.36 (p. 780 of text, p. 250 of manual),
(f)  Figure 15.38 (p. 781 of text, p. 251 of text),
(g)  Figure 15.39 (p. 782 of text, p. 252 of manual),
(h)  Figure 15.40 (p. 782 of text, p. 253 of manual),
(i)  Figure 15.41 (p. 782 of text, p. 254), and
(j)  Figure 15.42 (p. 782 of text, p. 255 of manual).

### Key points

Evaluating definite integrals in three dimensions using cylindrical and spherical coordinates.

### Ideas for the class

Use the transparencies showing the surfaces where the coordinates are constant to visualize the way each coordinate system divides space up into regions. Use the transparencies showing the volume elements in cylindrical and spherical coordinates to derive their formulas.

After deriving the volume elements for each coordinate system, present various familiar shapes such as portions of spheres, cones and rectangles, and ask the students to set up integrals over these regions. Students often have no trouble picking out the correct system, but do have trouble choosing the limits, especially when they are given a segment of a sphere or cylinder.

**Suggested Problems:** 1, 4, 5, 7, 8, 9, 10, 11, 16.

## 15.6   APPLICATIONS OF INTEGRATION TO PROBABILITY

**Class Time:** One to two classes

### Key points

Extending the concept of a probability density function to two variables, and using the density function to compute probabilities.

### Ideas for the class

For some students, this will be their first exposure to probability and density functions. Thus, care will be needed in introducing the concepts. Throughout the discussion, in using histograms and adding volumes, or in using density functions and integrating to find a volume, emphasize that the probability that random quantities take values in a certain region is equal to the volume above that region. In particular, the value of a density function at a point, $p(x_0, y_0)$, is *not* the probability that the value is $(x_0, y_0)$.

When we study two random quantities at a time, we have the possibility of studying the interaction between the two quantities. Independence means that the probability that $x$ takes on a value in an interval $[a, b]$ is the same no matter what the condition is put on values for $y$. This leads to the property that the joint probability density function $p(x, y)$ factors into a product of $p_1(x)$ and $p_2(y)$.

**Suggested Problems:** 1, 3, 4.

## FOCUS ON THEORY: CHANGE OF VARIABLES IN A MULTIPLE INTEGRAL

**Class Time:** One class (optional)

**Suggested transparencies:** Figures 15.54–15.55 (p. 794 of text, pp. 256–259 of manual.)

### Key points

Performing changes of coordinates analytically by means of the Jacobian.

### Ideas for the class

We want to develop a general procedure for changes of variables which will lead to the same results obtained earlier with geometry for the special cases of polar, cylindrical, and spherical coordinates. The idea is to relate an area of a region in the $st$-plane to the area of the corresponding region in the $xy$-plane. Transparencies are provided for explaining this.

Use the Jacobian to verify our previous changes of variables for polar, cylindrical, and spherical coordinates. Make sure the students don't forget that they have to take the absolute value of the Jacobian in the integral.

**Suggested Problems:** 1, 3, 5, 7.

# CHAPTER SIXTEEN

## Overview

We start with the problem of representing curves parametrically and then consider the problem of representing motion in space. This leads to the study of velocity and acceleration of moving particles. In keeping with our approach to vectors, we define velocity and acceleration geometrically, then give the formulas in terms of components.

## 16.1  PARAMETERIZED CURVES

**Class Time:** One class

## Key points

Describing the motion of an object with parametric equations. Parametric representations for curves in the plane and in space.

## Ideas for the class

Throughout the chapter, it is useful to do computer demonstrations in class and experiment with solutions to problems proposed by students.

Start with a simple example, such as the circle. (Many students have seen the parameterization of the circle before.) Starting with $(\cos t, \sin t)$, ask what happens when you make the following changes. (Perhaps have the students experiment for themselves on their graphing calculators and ask them to explain the results.)

1. Replace $t$ with $-t$.
2. Replace $\sin t$ with $-\sin t$. (Why does this give the same result as change 1?)
3. Replace $t$ with $t^3$. (Looking at this on a calculator in connected mode for $0 \le t \le 10$ shows a mess because of the increasing speed of parameterization. Explaining this mess is instructive, since, in theory, the graph should be a circle.)
4. Add 1 to the $x$-coordinate.
5. Replace $\cos t$ with $\sin t$. (The circle becomes a line segment.)
6. Replace $\cos t$ with $t \cos t$, and $\sin t$ with $t \sin t$. (the circle becomes a spiral.)

Each time, ask for predictions beforehand. You can continue onto more complicated examples, such as Lissajous figures.

A classical example is the cycloid. You can draw this on the blackboard by taping a piece of chalk to a coffee can and rolling the can along a ruler.

Continuing with the circle example, here are some graphing calculator exercises designed for class demonstration with an overhead projector. Graph the basic circle $x(t) = \cos(t)$, $y(t) = \sin(t)$, $0 < t < 2\pi$. Then ask the following questions and have the class try to answer, testing their responses on the calculator. Try to determine why any incorrect answers didn't work.

1. How do we trace out only the top half of the circle? the bottom half?
2. How do we start the path at the top of the circle?
3. Shrink the circle to a smaller radius.
4. Translate the circle up, down, or to the right or left.

5.   Trace it out clockwise.

6.   Trace it out clockwise starting at $(1, 0)$.

There are many possible answers which are quite different and which illustrate different ideas about parametric curves. Explore several solutions in class. For example, two possible answers to the first question are:

(a)   $x(t) = \cos(t/2)$,   $y = \sin(t/2)$,   $0 < t < 2\pi$.

(b)   $x(t) = \cos(t)$,   $y = \sin(t)$,   $0 < t < \pi$.

These solutions differ only by a change of variables, but students need to learn to recognize this and see that they both solve the problem. For the last question, two solutions are:

(a)   $x(t) = \sin(t)$,   $y(t) = \cos(t)$,   $\pi/2 < t < 5\pi/2$

(b)   $x(t) = \cos(t)$,   $y(t) = -\sin(t)$,   $0 < t < 2\pi$

You can try a similar series of exercises parameterizing a line. Given a parameterization of a line: How do you parameterize a segment of the line? How do you parameterize a line in the opposite direction? How do you parameterize a line at four times the speed?

If $(-x(t), y(t))$ describes the same curve as $(x(t), y(t))$, what property does the curve have?

One example of a curve in the plane not connected to motion in space is provided by the constrained optimization problems in Chapter 14. Optimize $f(x, y)$ subject to the constraint $g(x, y) = c$. You can choose an old example for this. However, this time, leave the constraint value $c$ unspecified. Solving gives an optimal solution, $(x(c), y(c))$, for each constraint value $c$. Taken together they describe a curve of optimal solutions in the plane.

**Suggested Problems:** 1, 2, 8, 11, 14, 16, 17, 20, 21, 25, 28, 33.

# 16.2  MOTION, VELOCIY, AND ACCELERATION

**Class Time:** One or two classes

## Key points

Parametric representation for curves using position vectors. Position, velocity, and acceleration vectors of a particle moving in the plane or space.

## Ideas for the class

Remind students of position vectors and rewrite some of the examples from the previous section using $\vec{r}(t)$ instead of $(x(t), y(t))$. Discuss the ideas of velocity and acceleration and derive the formulas in Cartesian coordinates. Calculate the velocity and acceleration vectors for uniform circular motion. Start with a specific example, e.g. $(3\cos 2t, 3\sin 2t)$, and then put in a variable radius and period: $(a\cos \omega t, a\sin \omega t)$. Ask what the effect of changing $\omega$ and $a$ should be; draw circles of larger and smaller radius, and imagine traversing them with different periods. Then calculate the answers using the formula to test the students' predictions.

To explain the direction of the acceleration vector for uniform circular motion, recall that Newton's law says that mass times acceleration is the tug that we feel when the velocity changes. This can be illustrated by swinging around a ball attached to a string — the tug can only be in the direction of the string.

To introduce arc length, find a local topographic map having both city streets and hiking trails. First ask for the distance between two landmarks both situated on the same straight street. Now ask for the distance between two points on a hiking trail. The students will soon realize that a polygonal path is all that is available and that taking a more dense set of points along the trail is likely to give a better estimate. They may also note that the estimates are always too short, and a perceptive student may realize that the map really represents a curve in three dimensions and that gains and loses in elevation really ought to be taken into account. The answer is going to be a sum of terms of the form $\sqrt{(\Delta x^2 + \Delta y^2 + \Delta z^2)}$.

Point out that arclength integrals often cannot be computed in elementary terms (the ellipse, for example gives rise to eponymous elliptic integrals). The cycloid is an exception. Here the integrand can be simplified using one of the double angle formulas for cosine.

**Suggested Problems:** 5, 6, 7, 8, 9, 15, 17, 22.

# CHAPTER SEVENTEEN

## Overview

In this brief chapter we introduce vector-valued functions of two or three variables, or vector fields. This chapter lays the foundation for the geometric approach in the next three chapters to line integrals, flux integrals, divergence, and curl. We start with physical examples, such as velocity vector fields and force fields, and include many sketches of vector fields to help build geometric intuition. We also discuss flow lines of vector fields and their relation to systems of differential equations.

## 17.1  VECTOR FIELDS

**Class Time:** One class

**Suggested transparencies:** Gulf stream vector field in Figure 17.1 (p. 822 of text, p. 260 of manual) and Figures 17.2–17.7 (pp. 823–825 of text, pp. 261–266 of manual).

## Key points

The concept of a vector field. Relating the sketch of a vector field to its formula. Velocity fields, force fields, and gradient fields.

## Ideas for the class

Show many pictures of vector fields. Ask students to describe each field, interpreting it as a velocity vector field. Ask students to come up with possible formulas for the vector fields (covering up the formula on the transparency).

Show the overhead of the Gulf stream velocity vector field. Work through one of Problems 6–9 on page 834.

Other questions for class discussion:

- What do vector fields of the form $g(x)\vec{i}$ look like? What is the formula for the vector field that we obtain by taking all of the vectors in this vector field and rotating them 90 degrees counterclockwise?

- Show a picture of the vector field $y\vec{i}$ and ask students to explain purely graphically why this vector field cannot be the gradient of some function.

- Give the students pictures of gradient vector fields and ask them to draw the contour maps. Also show pictures of vector fields that are not gradient vector fields. Find a method, e.g. trying to draw the contours, for checking that these vector fields are not gradients.

For a class demonstration of a vector field, bring in a magnet and some iron shavings and exhibit the magnetic field.

**Suggested Problems:** 1–17.

## 17.2  THE FLOW OF A VECTOR FIELD

**Class Time:** One or two classes

**Suggested transparancies:** Figure 17.17 (p. 828 of text, p. 267 of manual), Figure 17.18 (p. 829 of text, p. 268 of manual), Figure 17.20 (p. 830 of text, p. 269 of manual), Figure 17.21 (p. 831 of text, p. 270 of manual ).

## Key points

Flow lines of a vector field and their relation to first order differential equations.

## Ideas for the class

Introduce flow lines of a vector field by picking a point and asking the students to draw a curve through the given point so that along the curve the velocity vector for the curve coincides with the vector field. This can be explained in terms of fluid flow. In addition, these examples will be helpful in the discussion on flux integrals in Chapter 19. Now, at least visually, the students are solving a first order ordinary differential equation.

Making the connection between the geometric idea of a flow line and the system of differential equations

$$\vec{r}\,'(t) = \vec{F}\left(\vec{r}\,(t)\right)$$

needs some time – most students do not find the symbolic formulation easy to understand.

You may want to reassure students that you do not expect them to be able to solve these differential equations. However, you probably do want them to be able to check that a certain set of parametric equations represents the flow of a given vector field. Give an example of this type in class and see whether the class knows what to do. (Don't assume that they understand that they should substitute and check, as this is often not the case.)

**Suggested Problems:** 3–7.

# CHAPTER EIGHTEEN

## Overview

We present the concept of integrating a vector field along a path with a coordinate-free definition. We spend some time building intuition using sketches of vector fields with paths superimposed, before introducing the method of calculating line integrals using parameterizations. We then discuss path-independent fields, gradient fields, and the Fundamental Theorem of Calculus for Line Integrals. We conclude with sections on path-dependent vector fields and Green's Theorem.

## 18.1 THE IDEA OF A LINE INTEGRAL

**Class Time:** One class

**Suggested transparencies:** Various vector fields (pp. 271–275 of manual).

### Key points

The line integral as a sum of dot products of the vector field with path elements. Interpretation as work and circulation.

### Ideas for the class

The student's fundamental idea of the line integral should be geometric: adding up dot products of the vector field at a point on the curve with a small tangent vector $d\vec{r}$ in the direction of the curve.

Draw paths on transparencies of various different vector fields, and ask whether the line integral is positive, negative, or zero (given an orientation of the curve).

Compute some simple line integrals using the definition to convert the Riemann sum into a one-variable integral. For example, compute the line integrals of $\vec{F}(x, y) = x\vec{i} + y\vec{j}$ and $\vec{G}(x, y) = y\vec{i} + x\vec{j}$ along the $x$ and $y$ axes from the origin to $(1, 0)$ and $(0, 1)$. Then draw the vector fields and explain geometrically why you got zero in two of the cases. Another example is to compute the line integrals of $\vec{F}$ and $\vec{G}$ along the line segment from $(1, 0)$ to $(0, 1)$ and along the unit circle from $(1, 0)$ to $(0, 1)$.

**Suggested Problems:** 1, 2, 3, 5, 6, 7, 8, 17, 28.

## 18.2 COMPUTING LINE INTEGRALS OVER PARAMETERIZED CURVES

**Class Time:** One class

### Key Points

Computing the line integral using a parametrization of the oriented curve.

## Ideas for the class

You may want to review parameterizations of curves, particularly emphasizing the direction in which a given parameterization travels along a curve, and the beginning and ending points.

Compute $\int_C \vec{F} \cdot d\vec{r}$ for $\vec{F} = y\vec{i} + 2\vec{j}$ over one quarter of a unit circle from $P = (1,0)$ and $Q = (0,1)$, over the line from $P$ to $Q$, and over the L-shaped path from $P$ to $(0,0)$ to $Q$. This vector field is not conservative so the answers will be different. This example helps review parametrizations of some basic curves. Ask students to predict the sign of the answer before doing the computation, to keep them thinking geometrically.

Introduce the notation $\int P\,dx + Q\,dy + R\,dz$.

**Suggested Problems:** 1, 3, 5, 10, 11, 12, 14, 15.

## 18.3  GRADIENT FIELDS AND PATH-INDEPENDENT FIELDS

**Class Time:** One to two classes

## Key Points

Gradient field of a scalar function. The Fundamental Theorem of Calculus for Line Integrals. Definition and properties of path-independent, or conservative, vector fields. Explanation of why gradient fields are path-independent and the converse.

## Ideas for the class

Draw the graph of $z = f(x,y) = 25 - (x^2 + y^2)$, its contour diagram, a curve between two points on the contour diagram, and the gradient drawn at various points on the curve. This will aid in showing how the line integral of the gradient along the curve gives the total change in the scalar function – this is the Fundamental Theorem of Calculus for Line Integrals.

Stress that if you have the potential function $f$ for a vector field $\vec{F} = \text{grad} f$, then

1. the line integral $\int_C \vec{F} \cdot d\vec{r}$ can be computed simply by subtracting values of $f$ at the endpoints of the curve (make sure they see how to substitute coordinates of the endpoints as arguments to the function),

2. the integral only depends on the endpoints, and

3. will be zero for any closed curve.

Thus, having the potential function allows one to avoid the method of the previous section. Students will enjoy this observation!

For students interested in physics, there are problems in the exercises that demonstrate how conservative vector fields "conserve" the sum of kinetic and potential energy. Spend some time on the summary at the end of this section. It is important for students to understand that if one property of a vector field (say, being gradient) is true (or false), then all the other properties are true (or false) for this vector field.

**Suggested Problems:** 3, 4, 5, 11, 13, 14, 15, 20.

## 18.4  PATH-DEPENDENT VECTOR FIELDS AND GREEN'S THEOREM

**Class Time:** One class

## Key Points

Path independence is the same as circulation free. Path-independence implies zero curl. Green's Theorem. Zero curl and all loops contractible imply path-independence.

## Ideas for the class

Review the idea that having a potential function for a vector field allows easy line integral computations by the Fundamental Theorem. It is worthwhile to do examples similar to those in the text; show both graphically and algebraically that a given vector field is path-dependent. Strongly emphasize that path-independent vector fields always have zero curl, but $\vec{F}$ having zero curl implies that $\vec{F}$ is path-independent only if the domain of $\vec{F}$ is simply-connected (has no holes). Students want the (false!) statement that if the mixed partials are equal, then the vector field is path-independent, to be true. Example 4 on page 863 in the text provides a nice counterexample, and it is good to go over this. If a vector field is path-dependent, one must compute the line integral using parameterization or Green's Theorem. Emphasize that the Green's Theorem double integral computation may be better. Another good example is to show by Green's theorem how the line integral of $\vec{F} = x\vec{j}$ around a simple closed curve gives the area enclosed by the curve. Verify this for an ellipse.

**Suggested Problems:** 1, 3, 4, 5, 8, 9, 11, 12.

# FOCUS ON THEORY: PROOF OF GREEN'S THEOREM

**Class Time:** One class (optional)

## Key Points

A more precise justification of Green's Theorem in three steps: for rectangles, for regions parametrized by rectangles using the change of variables formula for double integrals, and for arbitrary regions.

## Ideas for the class

As the section title suggests, this material is suitable primarily for students who are comfortable with more theoretical arguments and who have already seen the change of variables formula in Section 15.6. However, if they are familar with the change of variables formula, it is worthwhile to try to convey the basic idea by first guiding them through the calculation for a rectangle. Then ask them how they might use this to verify Green's Theorem for curvilinear rectangles and finally for a general region. Example 1 on page 874 or a disk with two circular holes can serve as a useful introduction to the method before discussing the general case.

The method described in this section has the advantage that it adapts in a fairly convincing way to the proofs of Stokes' Theorem and the Divergence Theorem in Chapter 20.

**Suggested Problems:** 2, 3, 5, 6.

# CHAPTER NINETEEN

## Overview

We introduce the flux integral of a vector field through a parameterized surface in the same way as we introduced line integrals. First we give a coordinate-free definition, then we discuss examples where the flux integral (or at least its sign) can be calculated geometrically. Then we show how to calculate flux integrals over surface graphs, spheres, and cylinders.

## 19.1  THE IDEA OF A FLUX INTEGRAL

**Class Time:** One to two classes

### Key Points

Orientations for surfaces, and general properties of a flux integral. Interpretation of this integral as giving a flow rate (in volume/time) of some fluid through a surface. Flux through a closed surface.

### Ideas for the class

It is very important for the rest for the rest of the chapter to understand the idea of the infinitesimal area vector $d\vec{A}$. One suggestion to illustrate this is to bring in a balloon with area patches drawn on it. Take a pen (not too sharp) and show its length pointing away from the patch with length equal to the area of the patch.

As in Chapter 18, do examples where the question is to decide whether the flux integral is positive, negative, of zero. Emphasize that the integral, like the line integral, adds up all the dot products of $\vec{F} \cdot d\vec{A}$. A good example for class is to compute the flux of $\vec{F} = 3\vec{k}$ across first the disc of radius 2 centered at the origin in the $xy$-plane oriented upward and then downward, and then for the same disc in the $xz$-plane.

It is very instructive to go through the derivation of the tube of volume swept out from the fluid moving through the surface.

**Suggested Problems:** 1, 2, 4, 5, 10, 14, 15.

## 19.2  FLUX INTEGRALS FOR GRAPHS, CYLINDERS, AND SPHERES

**Class Time:** One to two classes

### Key points

To compute the flux integral of a vector field through graphs of functions of two variables, through cylinders, and through spheres.

### Ideas for the class

Emphasize that this section develops a computational technique for flux integrals in the most common and useful special cases of geometric and physical interest.

Highlight that the section develops a formula for the vector area at various points on the graph of $f(x, y)$. With the balloon mentioned above, tape one corner of a playing card on an area patch drawn on the balloon. This will show how to approximate the area patch by the tangent plane (the card). Point out that students need to know which orientation of the surface is being used in order to choose the appropriate expression for $d\vec{A}$. The main idea of the section is to reduce the computation of the flux integral to a double integral. It is important for the students to see several examples worked out in full to get a feel for use of the formula and subsequent computation.

A good example problem is to compute $\int_S \vec{F} \cdot d\vec{A}$ for $\vec{F} = x\vec{i} + y\vec{j}$ when $S$ is the graph of $z = f(x, y) = a - (x^2 + y^2)$ over the unit disk in the $xy$ plane for various values of $a$.

**Suggested Problems:** 7, 8, 9, 10.

# CHAPTER TWENTY

## Overview

We introduce divergence and curl in a coordinate-free way: the divergence in terms of flux density, and curl in terms of circulation density. We then give the formulas in Cartesian coordinates. In the single variable calculus we derived the Fundamental Theorem of Calculus by pointing out that the integral of the rate of change is the total change. In much the same way, we derive the divergence theorem by showing that the integral of flux density over a volume is the total flux out of the volume. Similarly, we derive Stokes' theorem by showing that the integral of circulation density over a surface is the total circulation around its boundary.

## 20.1  THE DIVERGENCE OF A VECTOR FIELD

**Class Time:** One class

**Suggested transparencies:** Various vector fields (pp. 271–275 of manual).

### Key points

Definition of divergence as flux density. Using this to get an intuitive understanding of the divergence. Formula for the divergence in Cartesian coordinates.

### Ideas for the class

Use some of the transparencies of vector fields and put regions around points of the field. Be sure to emphasize the outward orientation of the surrounding volumes and the sign of the flux of the vector fields. Define divergence and give units. It is important for the students to see that positive divergence means more fluid exiting the surface than entering. A picture of a lit candle with a sphere around it is good for an intuitive idea of a source. Bathtub drains are good to illustrate sinks.

**Suggested Problems:** 2, 3, 5, 6, 9, 10, 17, 22, 25, 28.

## 20.2  THE DIVERGENCE THEOREM

**Class Time:** One half to one class

### Key points

The divergence theorem as an analogue of the Fundamental Theorem of Calculus: the integral of flux density gives total flux.

### Ideas for the class

Emphasize the units on both sides of the theorem, especially showing how the volume unit cancels in the triple integral. A good example is to compute the flux of $\vec{F} = \vec{r}$ over a cone $z = f(x, y) =$

$\sqrt{x^2 + y^2}$ above the unit disc in the $xy$-plane, including the top face. The flux integral is difficult; the volume integral is easy.

Another good example is Problem 12 on page 908 about the flux of the gravitational field through a sphere of radius $a$.

**Suggested Problems:** 1, 2, 6.

# 20.3  THE CURL OF A VECTOR FIELD

**Class Time:** One to Two Classes

## Key Points

Definition of the curl vector in terms of circulation density. Intuitive understanding of the direction and magnitude of the curl vector. Formula for curl in Cartesian coordinates.

## Ideas for the class

Spend a good deal of time carefully setting up all the various orientations, curves, and planes to compute the circulation density. It is worthwhile to emphasize that the curl vector, like the gradient of a scalar function at a point, points out the direction of maximum circulation density. State the coordinate definition of curl.

Use the idea of a curl meter to get a physical feel for the curl. Note that a paddle-wheel is appropriate, but a pinwheel is not a good model, since it spins in a constant velocity vector field (which has zero curl everywhere).

It is important in the graphic problems for students to relate the ideas from Chapter 18 on whether the line integral is positive, negative, or zero. Carefully go over an example similar to Example 2 on page 911 in the text.

Problem 15 is not to be missed as it relates the Fundamental Theorem for Line Integrals to the curl test for a gradient vector field.

**Suggested Problems:** 1, 6, 11, 15, 16.

# 20.4  STOKES' THEOREM

**Class Time:** One to one and a half classes

## Key points

Stokes' theorem as an analog of the Fundamental Theorem of Calculus: the integral of circulation density equals total circulation.

## Ideas for the class

Be careful in defining the relation between the orientation of a surface and the orientation of its boundary. Examples like a cylinder with a two circle boundary are hard for the students. The best way to think of the orientation of a surface is to imagine small circulations around positive normal vectors (circulation in the direction determined by the right hand rule). These circulations in turn determine the orientation of the boundary.

As for Stoke's Theorem, stress how the circulation density embodied in the curl vector gives units of circulation on both sides of the theorem. One of the main physics ideas can be related back to the Ampere's law (Problem 28 on page 844 in Chapter 18). For a loop of wire bent around the main wire, as the curl vector of the magnetic field (represented in that problem by the electric current down the wire) moves through the surface (which is the area enclosed by a loop around the main wire), it induces an electric current to flow around the loop. (See *Div, Grad, Curl, and all that* by H.M. Schey, also pg. 102-3 of *The Cartoon Guide to Physics* by L. Gonick.)

**Suggested Problems:** 3, 11, 14, 15.

# FOCUS ON THEORY: THE THREE FUNDAMENTAL THEOREMS

**Class Time:** One class

## Key points

A unified view of the Fundamental Theorem for Line Integrals, Stokes' Theorem, and the Divergence Theorem. Applications to geometry and physics.

## Ideas for the class

Explain that curl $\vec{F} = 0$ implies that $\vec{F}$ is a gradient vector field. Explain that div $F = 0$ implies that $\vec{F}$ is a curl vector field. Two fundamental examples are the electric vector field due to a point charge at the origin, and the magnetic vector field due to a current through an infinite straight wire.

**Suggested Problems:** 1, 4, 5, 7, 12.

# PART III

# SAMPLE SYLLABI

## Syllabus for Calculus I (Chapters 1--5)

### (Based on a 14-week semester with three 1-hour class meetings per week.)

| Monday | Wednesday | Friday |
|---|---|---|
| 1.1 | 1.2 | 1.3 |
| 1.4 | 1.5/1.6 | 1.7 |
| 1.8 | 1.9 | 1.10 |
| 1.11 & Review | Exam 1 (100 pts) | 2.1 |
| 2.2 | 2.3 | 2.4 |
| 2.5 | Review | Exam 2 (100 pts) |
| 3.1 | 3.2 | 3.3 |
| 3.4 & Review | First half of Exam 3 (50 pts) | 4.1 |
| 4.2 | 4.3 | 4.4 |
| 4.5 | Review | Second half of Exam 3 (50 pts) |
| 4.6 | 4.7 | 4.8 |
| 5.1 | 5.2 | 5.3 |
| 5.4 | 5.5 | 5.6 |
| Review | Exam 4 (100 pts) | Review for Final Exam |

## Syllabus for Calculus II (Chapters 6--10)

### (Based on a 14-week semester with three 1-hour class meetings per week.)

| Monday | Wednesday | Friday |
|---|---|---|
| Short Review of Calc I | 6.1 | 6.2 |
| 6.3 | 6.4 | Review |
| First half of Exam 1 (50 pts) | 7.1 | 7.2 |
| 7.3 | Review | Second Half of Exam 1 (50 pts) |
| 7.4 | 7.4 (cont'd) | 7.5 |
| 7.6 | 7.7 | 7.8 |
| Review | First half of Exam 2 | 8.1 |
| 8.2 | 8.3 | 8.3 (cont'd) |
| 8.4 | Review | Second half of Exam 2 (50 pts) |
| 9.1 | 9.2 | 9.3 |
| 9.4 | 9.5 | Review |
| First half of Exam 3 (50 pts) | 10.1 | 10.2 |
| 10.3 | 10.4 | 10.5 |
| Review | Second Half of Exam 3 (50 pts) | Review for Final Exam |

## Syllabus for Calculus I (Chapters 1--7.1) with Integration Delayed

### (Based on a 42-day schedule.)

| Day 1, 4, 7, etc. | Day 2, 5, 8, etc. | Day 3, 6, 9, etc. |
| --- | --- | --- |
| 1.1,1.2 | 1.3 | 1.4 |
| 1.5,1.6 | 1.7,1.8 | 1.8,1.9 |
| 1.10 | 1.10,1.11 | Review |
| Test #1 | 2.1 | 2.2 |
| 2.3 | 2.4,2.5 | Diff. & Linear Approx. |
| 4.1,4.2 | 4.3 | 4.4 |
| 4.5 | 4.6 | 4.7,4.8 |
| Review | Test #2 | 5.1 |
| 5.2 | 5.3 | 5.5,5.6 |
| 3.1 | 3.2 | 3.3 |
| 3.4 | Review | Test #3 |
| 6.1 | 6.2 | 6.3 |
| 6.4 | Motion | 7.1 |
| 7.2 | Review | Test #4 |

## Syllabus for Calculus II (Chapters 7.2--10)

### (Based on a 39-day schedule.)

| Day 1, 4, 7, etc. | Day 2, 5, 8, etc. | Day 3, 6, 9, etc. |
| --- | --- | --- |
| 7.1 | 7.1,7.2 | 7.3 |
| 7.4 | 7.4,7.5 | 7.5,7.6 |
| 7.7 | 7.8 | 8.1 |
| 8.2 | 8.2,8.3 | 8.3 |
| Dist. Functions | Review | Test #1 |
| 9.1 | 9.1,9.2 | 9.2,9.3 |
| 9.3,9.4 | 9.4 | 9.5 |
| Error terms | Review | Test #2 |
| 10.1 | 10.2 | 10.3 |
| 10.4 | 10.4,10.5 | 10.5 |
| 10.6 | 10.6,10.7 | 10.7 |
| 10.8 | 10.9 | Systems of DE |
| Review | Test #3 | Review |

## Syllabus for Calculus III (Chapters 11--20)

This is a packed syllabus. It might be better to either stop at the end of Chapter 18 with Green's Theorem, or omit Sections 17.2 and 19.2 for an express route through to Stokes' Theorem.

### (Based on a 14-week semester with four 1-hour class meetings per week)

| Monday | Tuesday | Wednesday | Thursday |
|---|---|---|---|
| 11.1 | 11.2, 11.3 | 11.4 | 11.5 |
| 11.6 | 12.1,12.2 | 12.3 | 12.4 |
| 13.1, 13.2 | 13.3 | 13.3 | Review |
| First Exam | 13.4 | 13.5 | 13.6 |
| 13.7 | 13.8 | 14.1 | 14.2 |
| 14.3 | 14.3 | Review | Second Exam |
| 15.1 | 15.2 | 15.3 | 15.4 |
| 15.5 | 16.1 | 16.2 | 16.2 |
| Review | Third Exam | 17.1 | 17.2 |
| 18.1 | 18.1, 18.2 | 18.2 | 18.3 |
| 18.3, 18.4 | 18.4 | Review | Fourth Exam |
| 19.1 | 19.1, 19.2 | 19.2 | 20.1 |
| 20.1 | 20.2 | 20.2 | 20.3 |
| 20.3 | 20.4 | 20.4 | Review |

# Syllabus for Calculus I-II-III, Chapters 1-20 (Based on five 9-week Quarters)

### Quarter I

| Monday | Wednesday | Friday |
|--------|-----------|--------|
| 1.1 | 1.2 | 1.3 |
| 1.4 | 1.5 – 1.6 | 1.7 |
| 1.8 | 1.9 | 1.10 |
| 1.11 | Review | Exam 1 |
| 2.1 | 2.2 | 2.3 |
| 2.4 | 2.5 | 3.1 |
| 3.2 | 3.3 | 3.4 |
| Review | Exam 2 | 4.1 |
| 4.2 | 4.3 | 4.4 |

### Quarter II

| Monday | Wednesday | Friday |
|--------|-----------|--------|
| Brief Review | 4.5 | 4.6 |
| 4.7 | 4.8 | 5.1 |
| 5.2 | 5.3 | Review |
| Exam 1 | 5.4 | 5.5 |
| 5.6 | 6.1 | 6.2 |
| 6.3 | 6.4 | Review |
| Exam 2 | 7.1 | 7.2 |
| 7.3 | 7.4 | 7.5 |
| 7.6 | 7.7 | 7.8 |

### Quarter III

| Monday | Wednesday | Friday |
|--------|-----------|--------|
| Brief Review | 8.1 | 8.1 – 8.2 |
| 8.2 | 8.3 or 8.4 | 8.3 or 8.4 |
| 9.1 | 9.1 – 9.2 | 9.2 |
| Review | Exam 1 | 9.3 |
| 9.3 | 9.4 | 9.5 |
| 10.1 – 10.2 | 10.3 | 10.4 |
| Review | Exam 2 | 10.5 |
| 10.6 | 10.6 | 10.7 |
| 10.8 | App B | 10.9 |

### Quarter IV

| Monday | Wednesday | Friday |
|--------|-----------|--------|
| 11.1 – 11.2 | 11.3 | 11.4 |
| 11.5 | 11.6 | 12.1 – 12.2 |
| 12.3 | 12.4 | Review |
| Exam 1 | 13.1 – 13.2 | 13.3 |
| 13.4 | 13.5 | 13.6 |
| 13.7 – 13.8 | 14.1 | 14.2 |
| 14.3 | 14.3 | Review |
| Exam 2 | 15.1 | 15.2 |
| 15.3 | 15.4 | 15.5 |

### Quarter V

| Monday | Wednesday | Friday |
|--------|-----------|--------|
| Brief Review | 15.6 | 16.1 |
| 16.2 | 16.2 | 17.1 |
| 17.2 | Review | Exam 1 |
| 18.1 | 18.2 | 18.3 |
| 18.3 | 18.4 | 18.4 |
| Review | Exam 2 | 19.1 |
| 19.1 – 19.2 | 20.1 | 20.1 |
| 20.2 | 20.2 | 20.3 |
| 20.3 | 20.4 | 20.4 |

# PART IV

## MASTERS FOR OVERHEAD TRANSPARENCIES

**Transparency Master for Section 1.4**

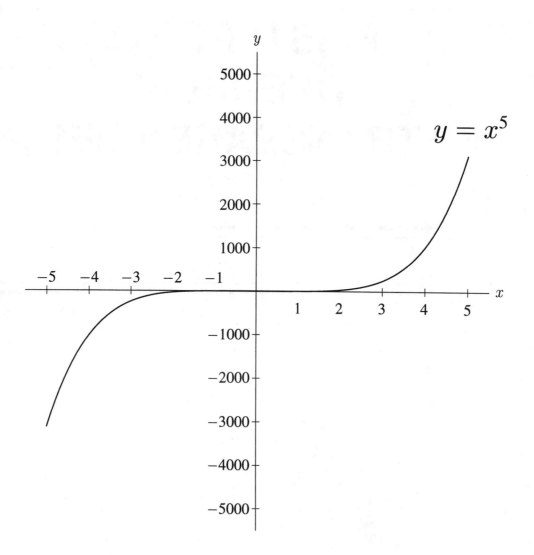

**Transparency Master for Section 1.4**

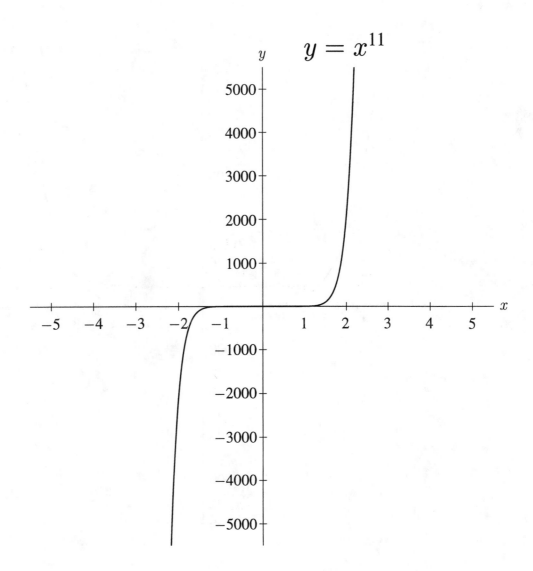

$y = x^{11}$

**Transparency Master for Section 1.4**

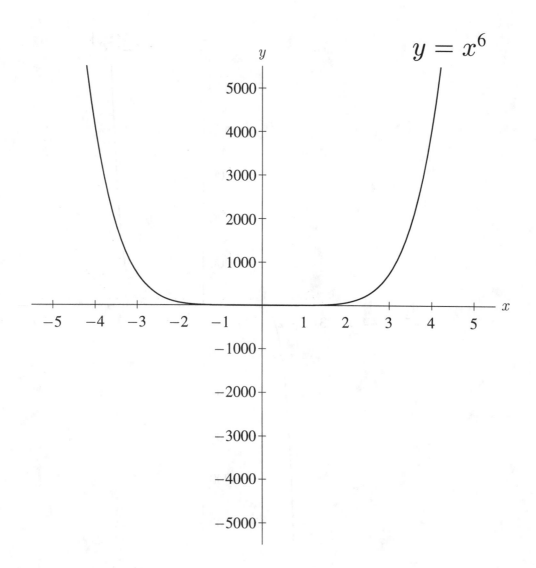

$$y = x^6$$

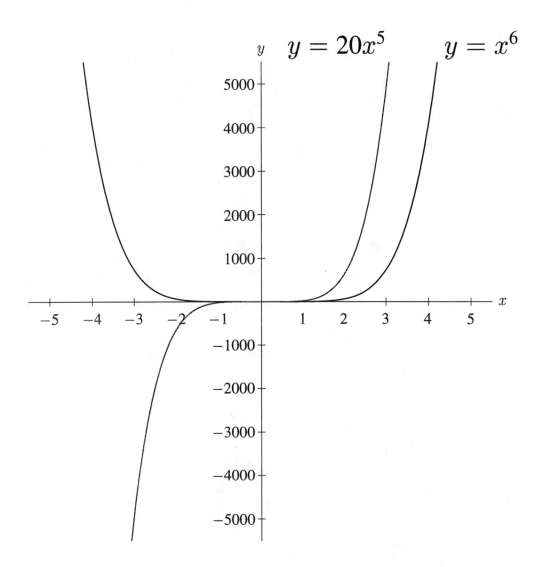

152

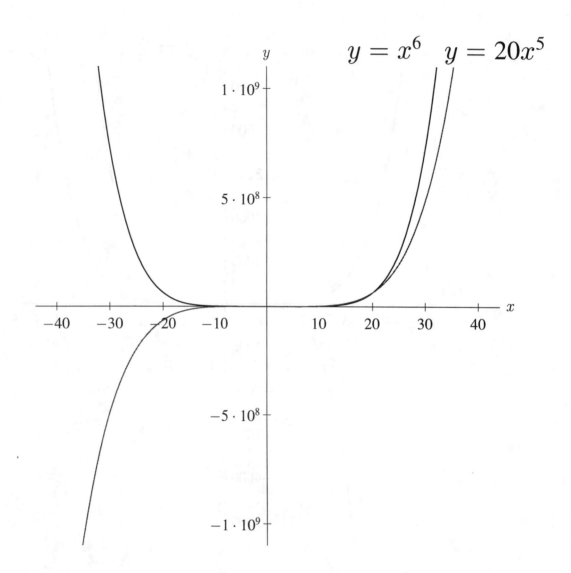

$$y = x^6 \quad y = 20x^5$$

**Transparency Master for Section 1.7**

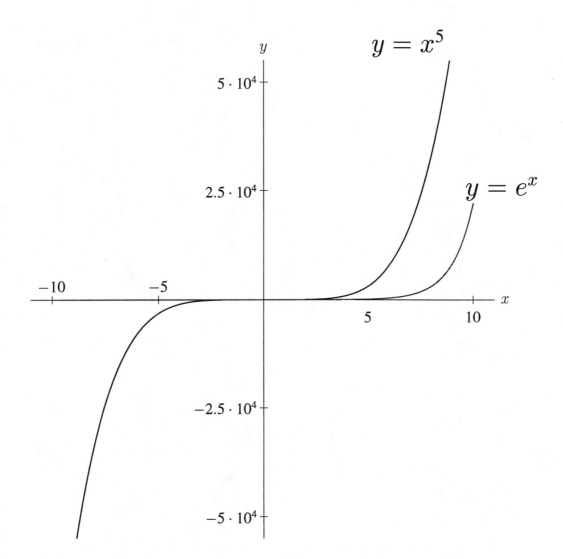

**Transparency Master for Section 1.7**

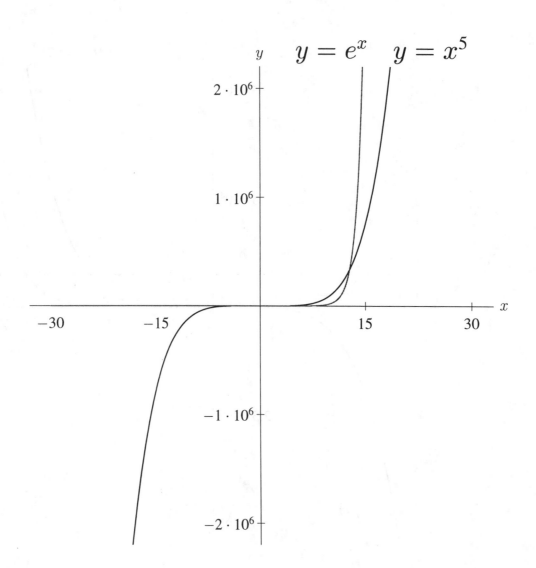

**Transparency Master for Section 1.9**

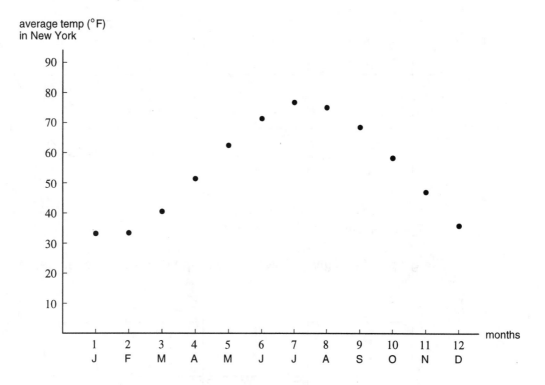

**TABLE 0.0.1**

*Average
Temperature (°F)
in New York by
Month*

| Jan | 33.2 |
|------|------|
| Feb | 33.4 |
| Mar | 40.5 |
| April | 51.4 |
| May | 62.4 |
| Jun | 71.4 |
| July | 76.8 |
| Aug | 75.1 |
| Sept | 68.5 |
| Oct | 58.3 |
| Nov | 47.0 |
| Dec | 35.9 |

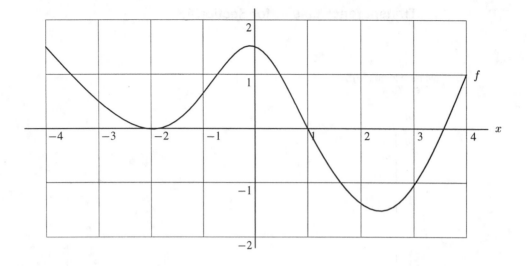

**Transparency Master for Section 2.3**

**The graph of $f$ is given. Sketch the graph of $f'$ on the axes below.**

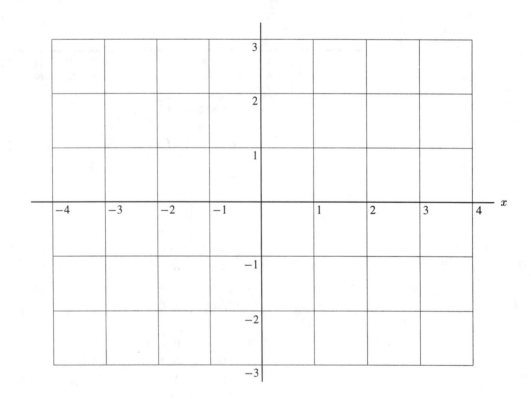

**Transparency Master for Section 5.2**

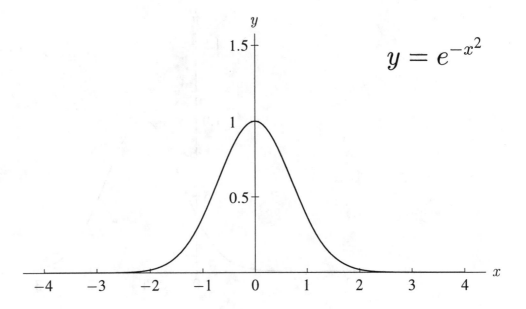

$$y = e^{-x^2}$$

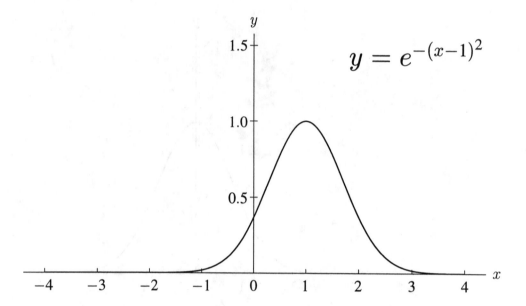

**Transparency Master for Section 5.2**

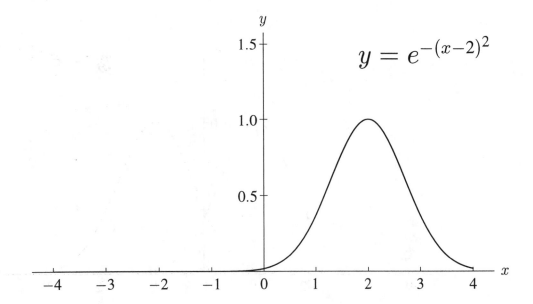

$$y = e^{-(x-2)^2}$$

**Transparency Master for Section 5.2**

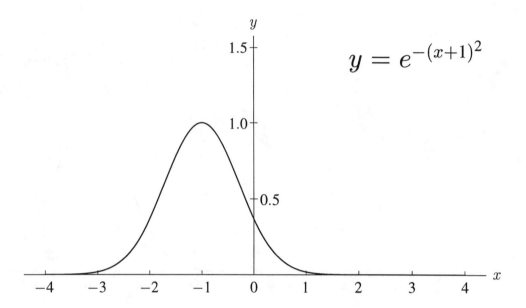

$$y = e^{-(x+1)^2}$$

**Transparency Master for Section 5.2**

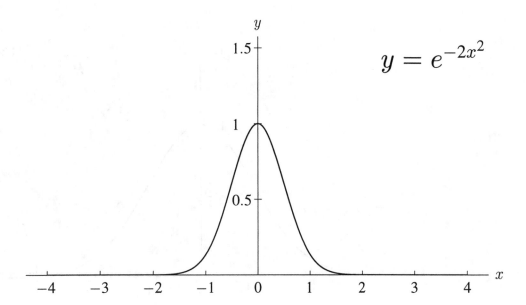

$$y = e^{-2x^2}$$

**Transparency Master for Section 5.2**

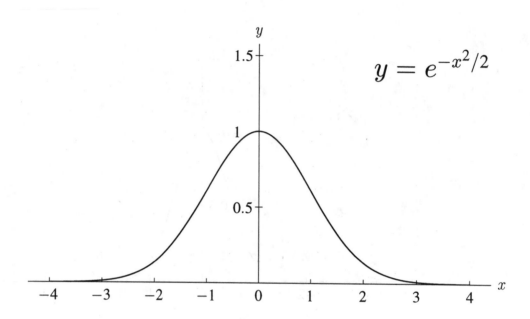

$$y = e^{-x^2/2}$$

**Transparency Master for Section 5.2**

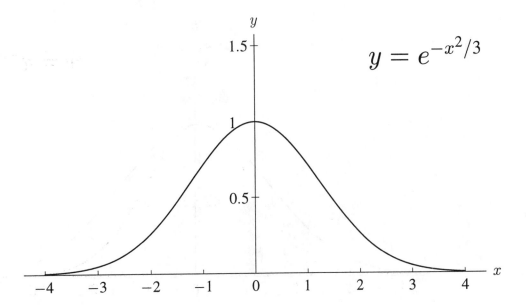

**Transparency Master for Section 5.2**

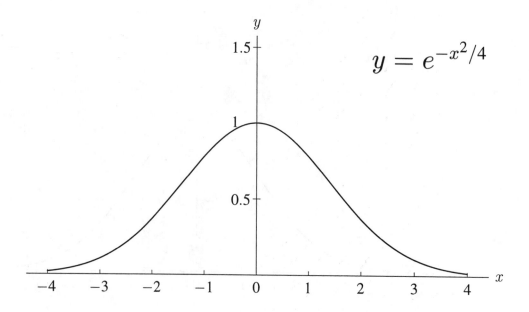

**Transparency Master for Section 10.2**

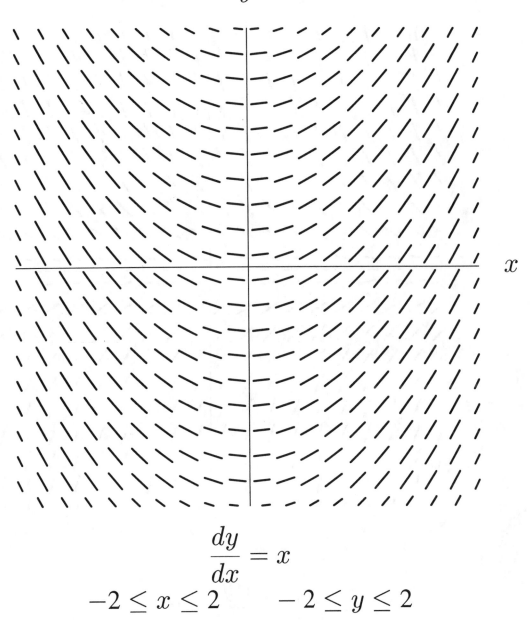

$$\frac{dy}{dx} = x$$

$$-2 \le x \le 2 \qquad -2 \le y \le 2$$

$y$

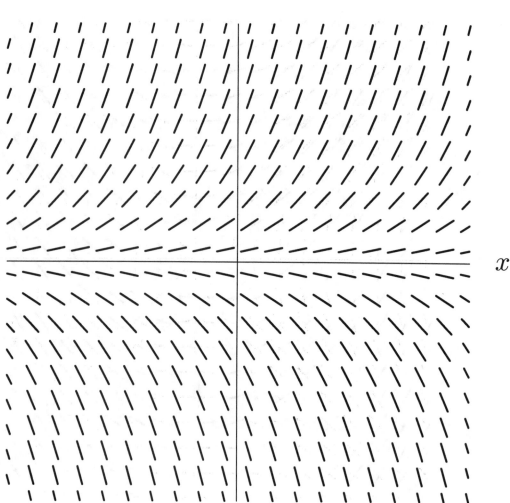

$x$

$$\frac{dy}{dx} = y$$

$$-4 \le x \le 4, \qquad -4 \le y \le 4$$

**Transparency Master for Section 10.2 or Section 10.3**

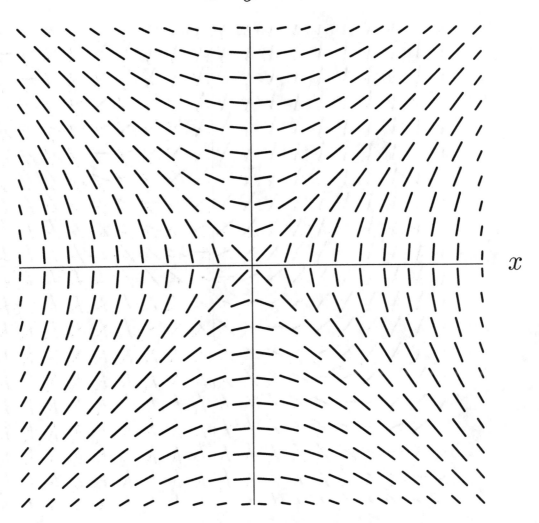

$$\frac{dy}{dx} = \frac{x}{y}$$

$$-4 \le x \le 4, \qquad -4 \le y \le 4$$

168

$y$

$x$

$$\frac{dy}{dx} = x - y$$

$$-4 \le x \le 4, \qquad -4 \le y \le 4$$

$$\frac{dy}{dx} = x^2 - y^2$$

$$-4 \le x \le 4, \qquad -4 \le y \le 4$$

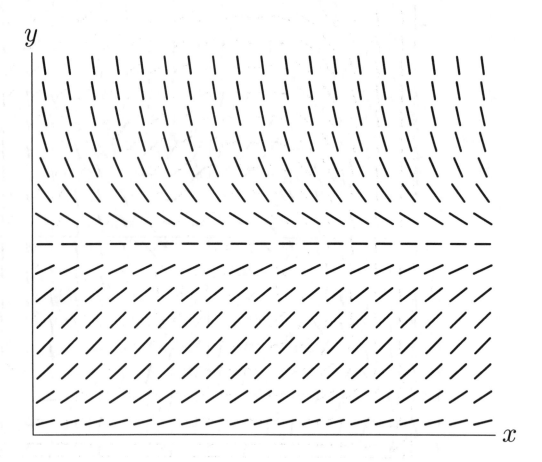

$$\frac{dy}{dx} = 2y - y^2$$

$$0 \le x \le 4, \qquad 0 \le y \le 4$$

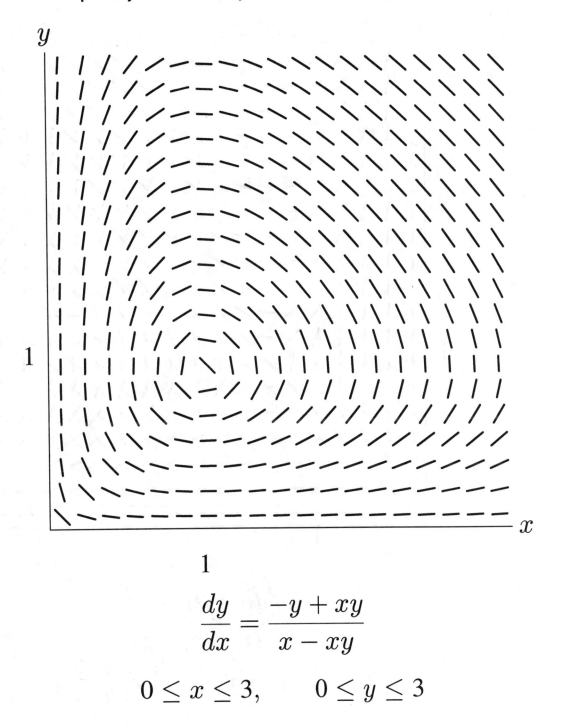

$$\frac{dy}{dx} = \frac{-y + xy}{x - xy}$$

$$0 \le x \le 3, \qquad 0 \le y \le 3$$

**Transparency Master for Chapter 10, Focus on Modeling**

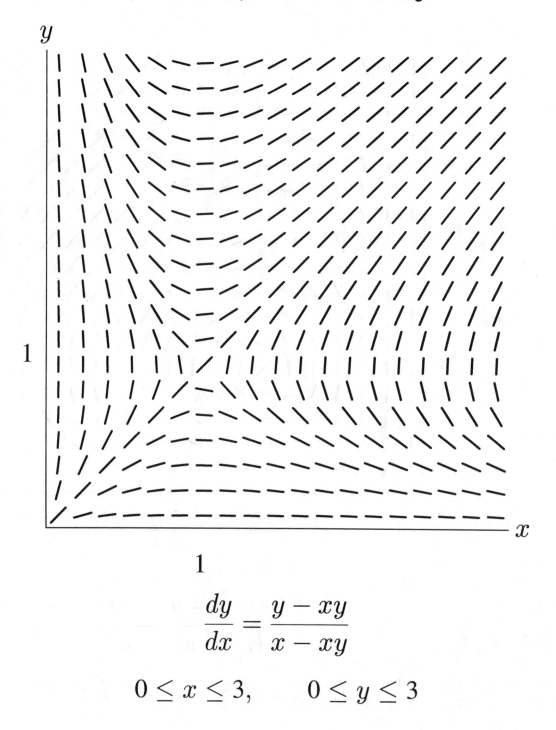

$$\frac{dy}{dx} = \frac{y - xy}{x - xy}$$

$$0 \leq x \leq 3, \qquad 0 \leq y \leq 3$$

**Transparency Master for Figure 11.1 on page 564 of text**

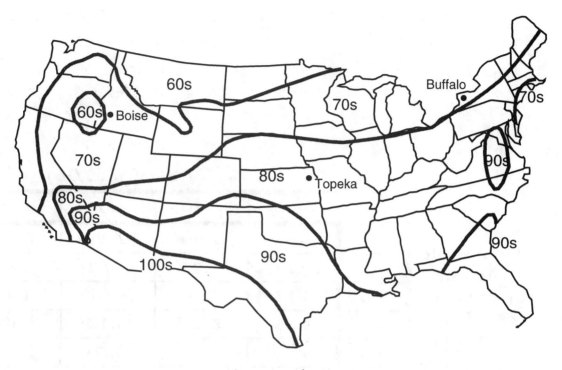

A weather map

Price of beef, $p$ ($/lb)

|  | | 3.00 | 3.50 | 4.00 | 4.50 |
|---|---|---|---|---|---|
| Household income per year, $I$ ($1000) | 20 | 2.65 | 2.59 | 2.51 | 2.43 |
| | 40 | 4.14 | 4.05 | 3.94 | 3.88 |
| | 60 | 5.11 | 5.00 | 4.97 | 4.84 |
| | 80 | 5.35 | 5.29 | 5.19 | 5.07 |
| | 100 | 5.79 | 5.77 | 5.60 | 5.53 |

Quantity of beef bought
(pounds/household/week)

**Transparency Master for bar graph of Table 11.1 in the text**

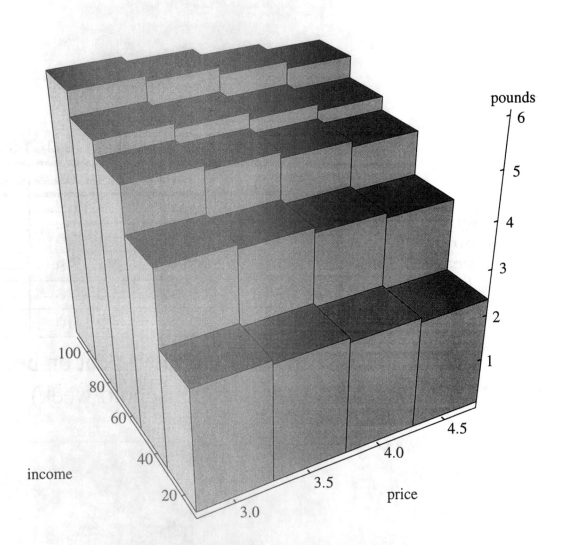

A three-dimensional bar graph

Price of beef, $p$ ($/lb)

|  | | 3.00 | 3.50 | 4.00 | 4.50 |
|---|---|---|---|---|---|
| Household income per year, $I$ ($1000) | 20 | 7.95 | 9.07 | 10.04 | 10.94 |
| | 40 | 12.42 | 14.18 | 15.76 | 17.46 |
| | 60 | 15.33 | 17.50 | 19.88 | 21.78 |
| | 80 | 16.05 | 18.52 | 20.76 | 22.82 |
| | 100 | 17.37 | 20.20 | 22.40 | 24.89 |

Amount of money spent on beef
(dollars/household/week)

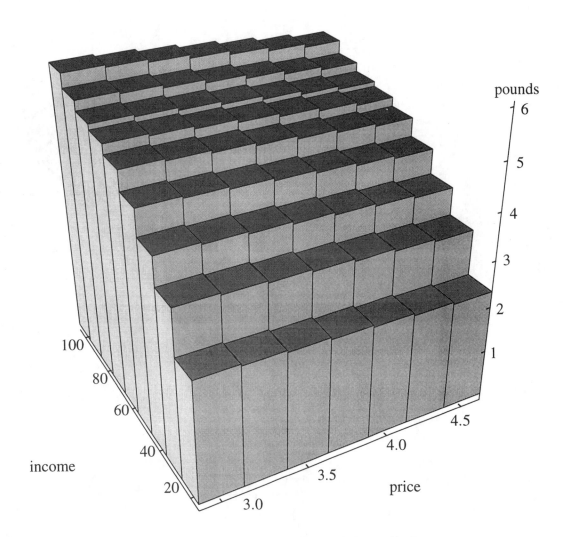

More and more refined beef data

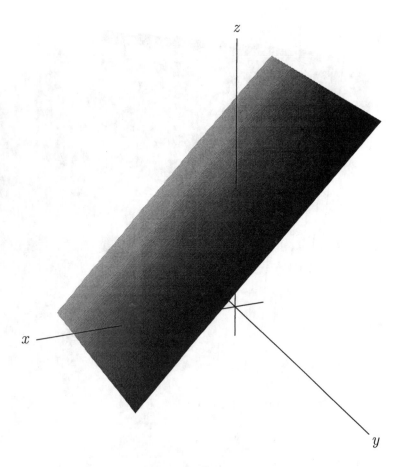

The plane $z = 4 - x$

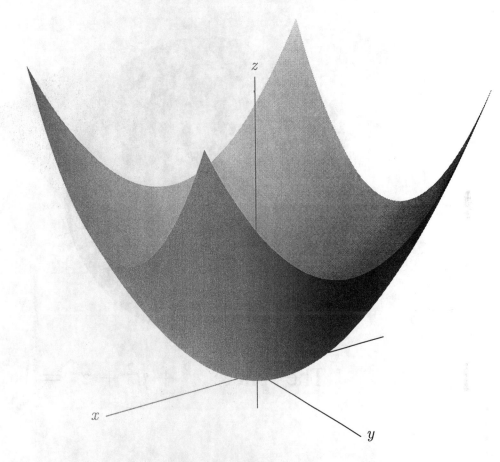

Graph of $z = x^2 + y^2$

The sphere $x^2 + y^2 + z^2 = 1$

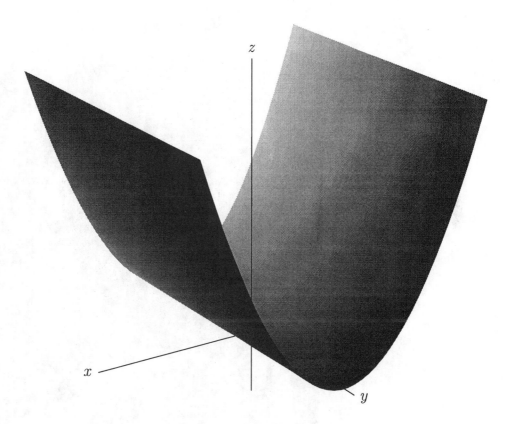

Graph of $z = x^2$

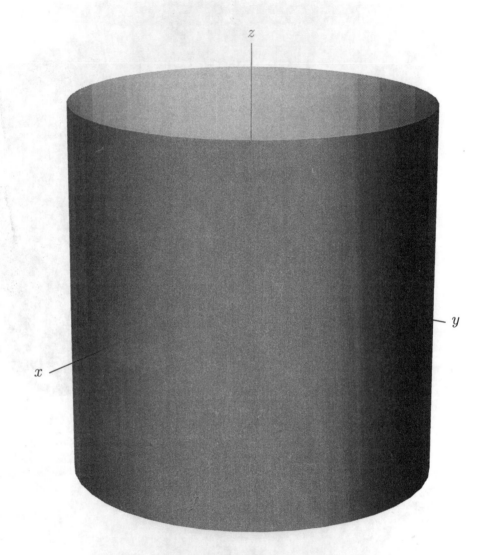

The cylinder $x^2 + y^2 = 1$

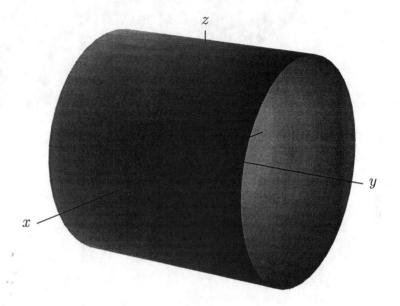

The cylinder $x^2 + z^2 = 1$

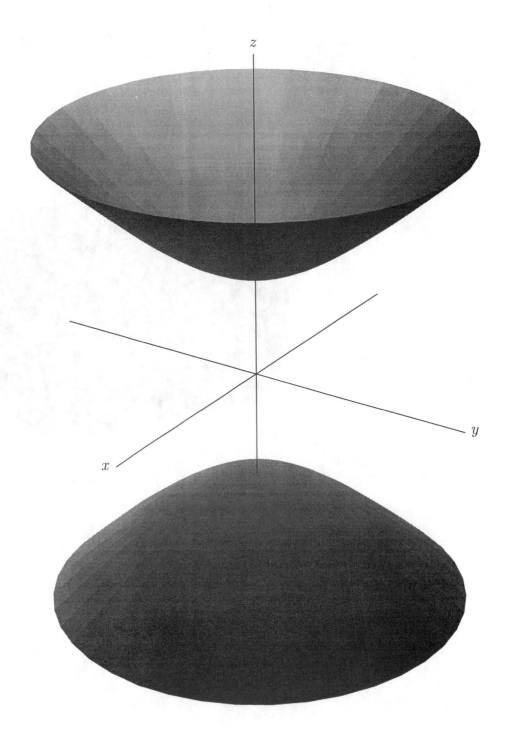

The surface $z^2 = x^2 + y^2 + 1$

**Transparency Master for contour graph for Problem 10 on page 591 of the text**

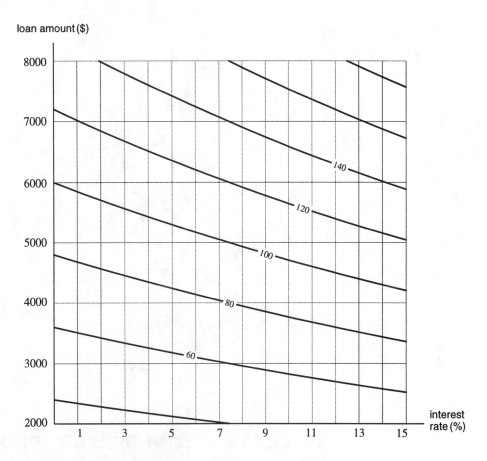

Monthly payment on a car loan

**Transparency Master for contour graph for Problem 24 on page 594 of the text**

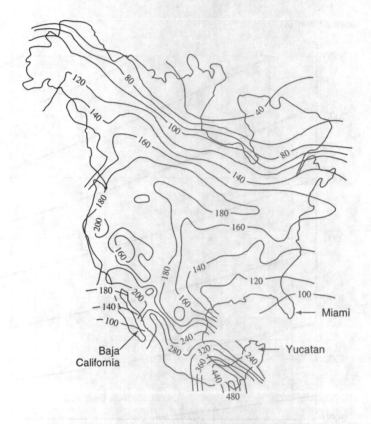

Species density of breeding birds

**Transparency Master for contour graph on page 610 of the text**

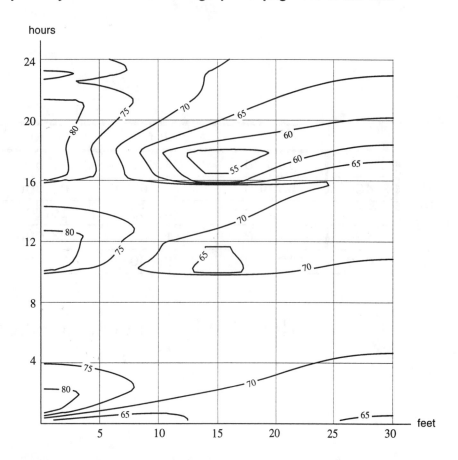

Temperature along a wall of a heated room

**Transparency Master for Table 11.10 on page 597 of the text**

Full-price tickets ($f$)

| | | 100 | 200 | 300 | 400 |
|---|---|---|---|---|---|
| | 200 | 39,700 | 63,600 | 87,500 | 111,400 |
| | 400 | 55,500 | 79,400 | 103,300 | 127,200 |
| Discount tickets ($d$) | 600 | 71,300 | 95,200 | 119,100 | 143,000 |
| | 800 | 87,100 | 111,000 | 134,900 | 158,800 |
| | 1000 | 102,900 | 126,800 | 150,700 | 174,600 |

## Revenue from ticket sales (dollars)

**Transparency Master for contour graph for Figure 11.70 on page 599 of the text**

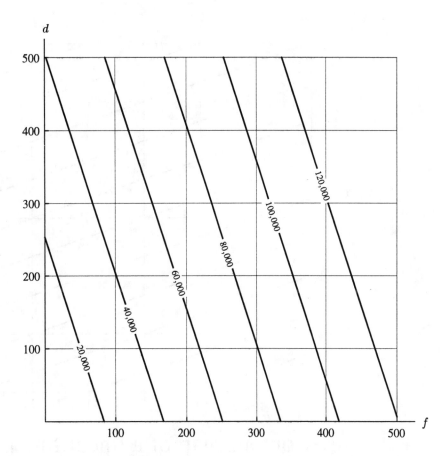

Revenue as a function of fares sold

**Transparency Master for contour graph for Example 4 on page 599**

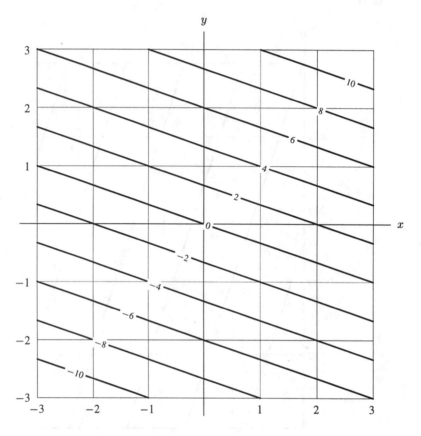

Contour map of a linear function

**Transparency Master Figure 13.6 on page 657 of the text**

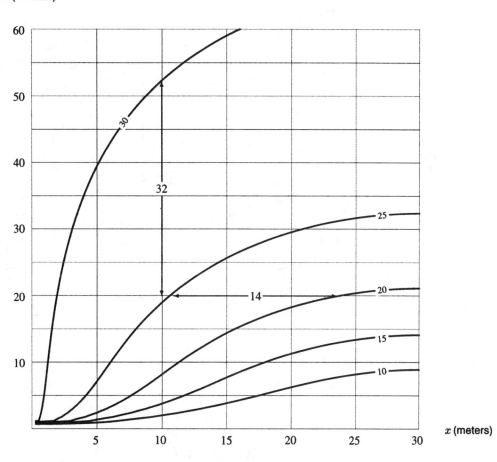

A contour diagram

**Transparency Master for graph for Problem 10 on page 591 of the text**

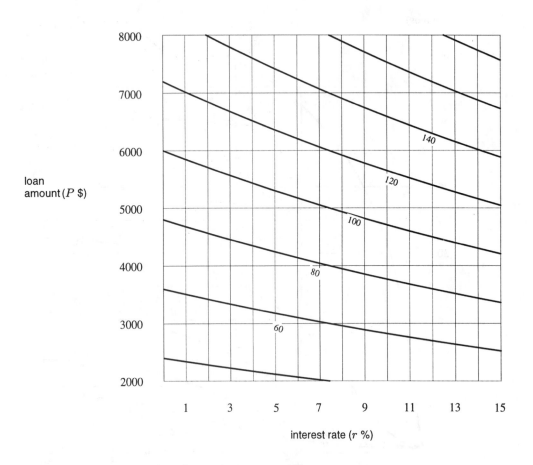

A contour diagram

**Transparency Master Figure 13.19 on page 667 of the text**

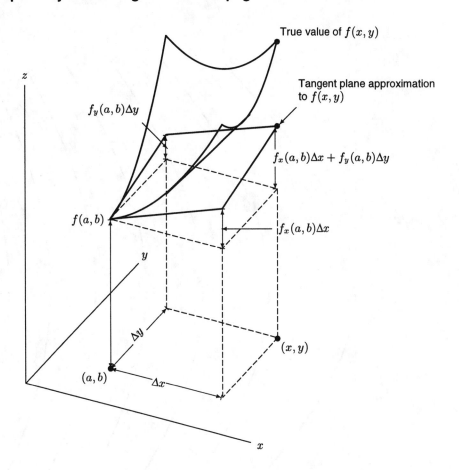

Local Linearization

**Transparency Master for Figure 13.26 on page 674 of the text**

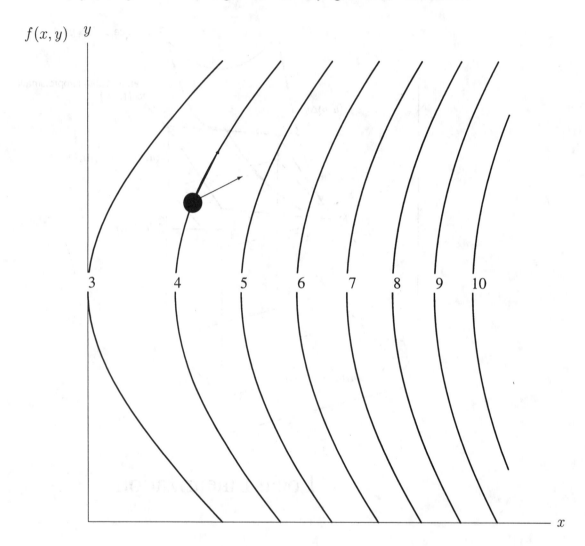

A contour diagram

**Transparency Master for Figure 13.26 on page 674 of the text**

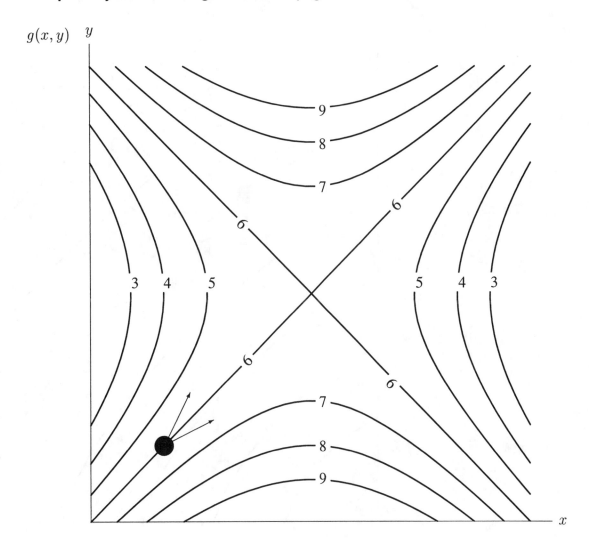

A contour diagram

**Transparency Master for Figure 13.26 on page 674 of the text**

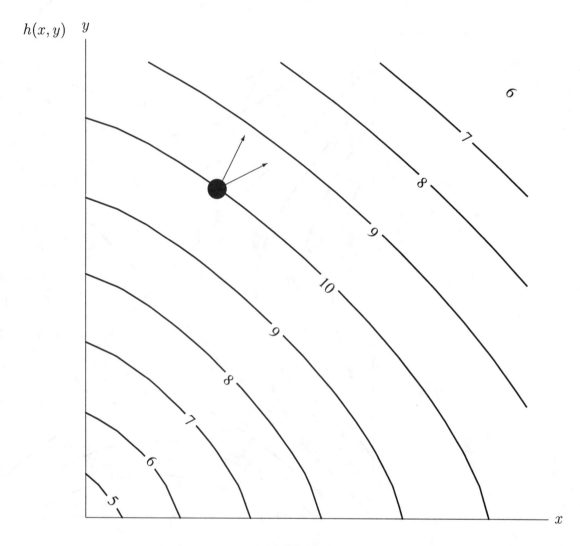

A contour diagram

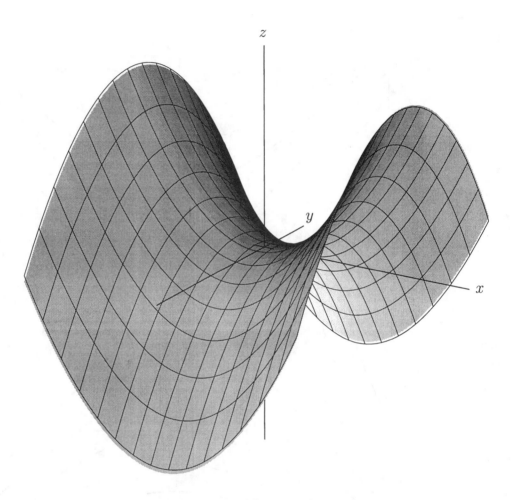

$$z = x^2 - y^2$$

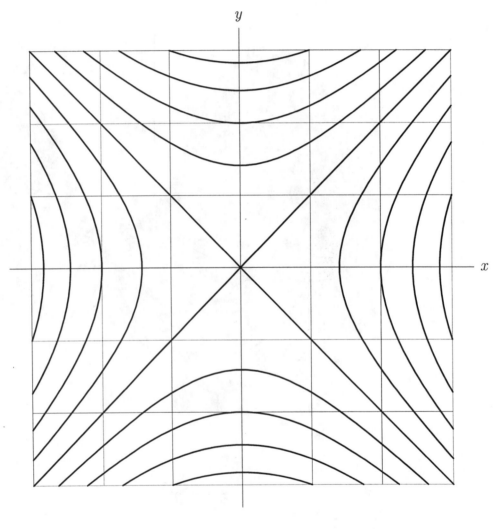

$$z = x^2 - y^2$$

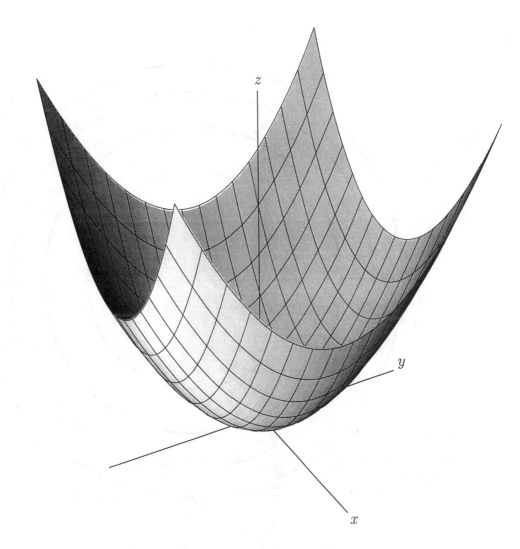

$$z = x^2 + y^2$$

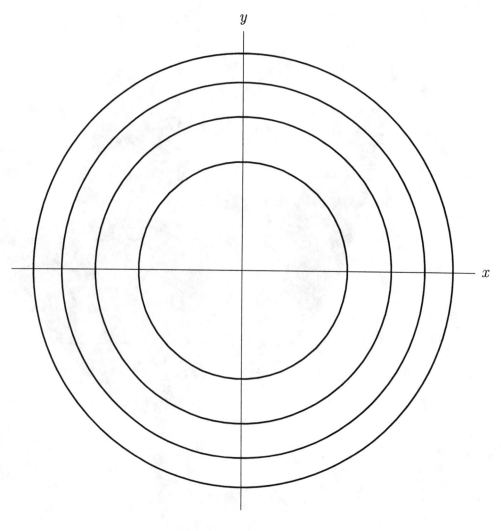

$$z = x^2 + y^2$$

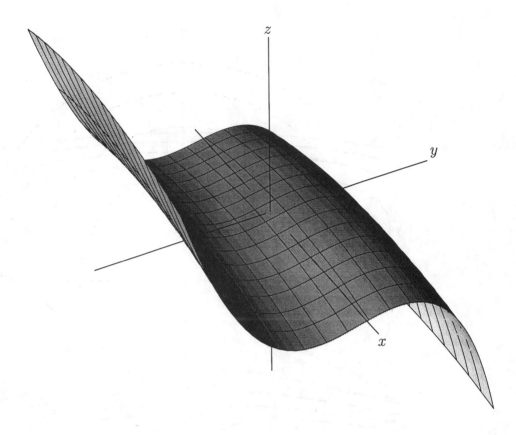

$$z = 6y - 4y^3 - x^2 + 1$$

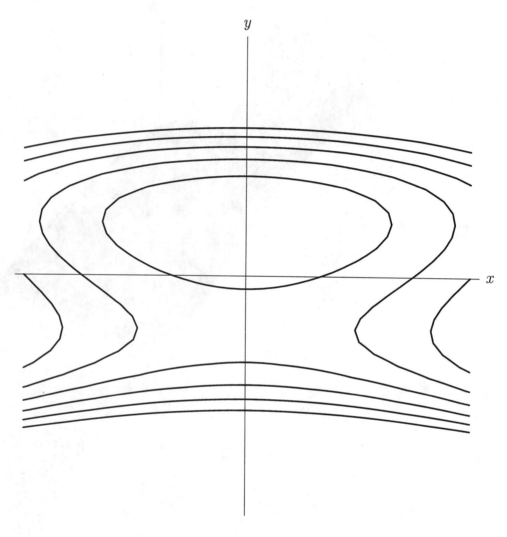

$$z = 6y - 4y^3 - x^2 + 1$$

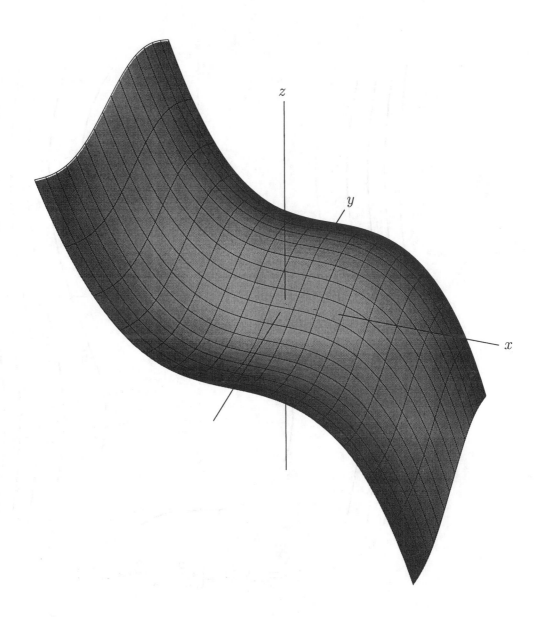

$$z = 3\sin y - x^3 + 1$$

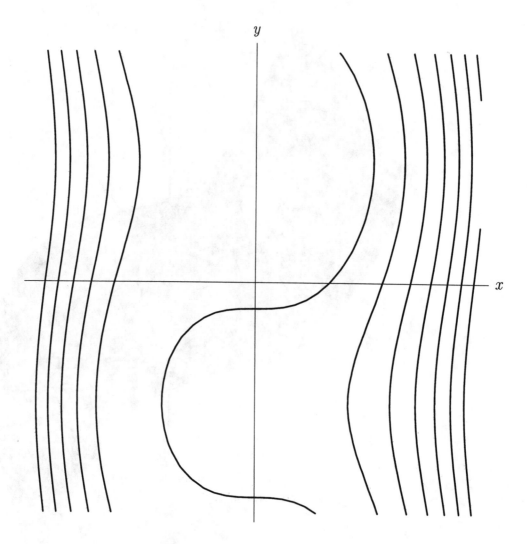

$$z = 3\sin y - x^3 + 1$$

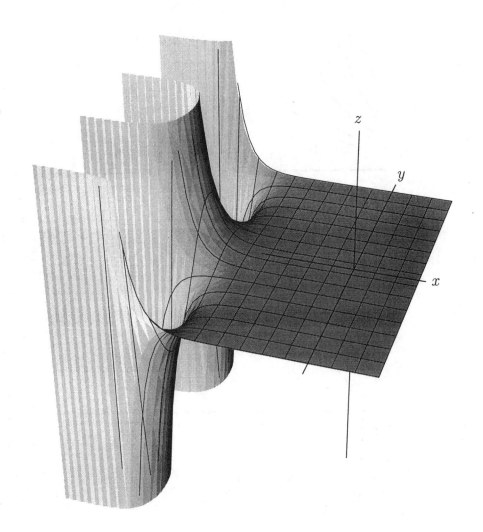

$$z = (\cos y)e^{-x}$$

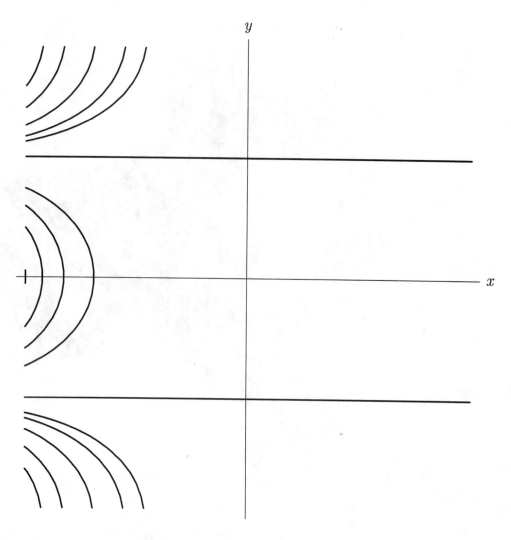

$$z = (\cos y)e^{-x}$$

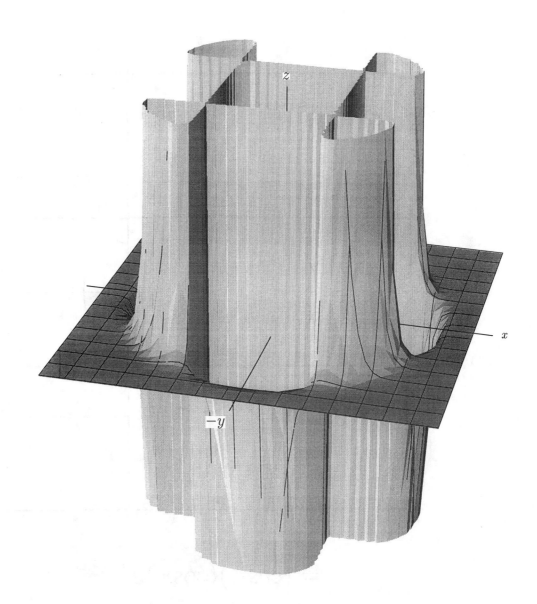

$$z = (\cos x)(\cos y)e^{-(x^2+y^2)}$$

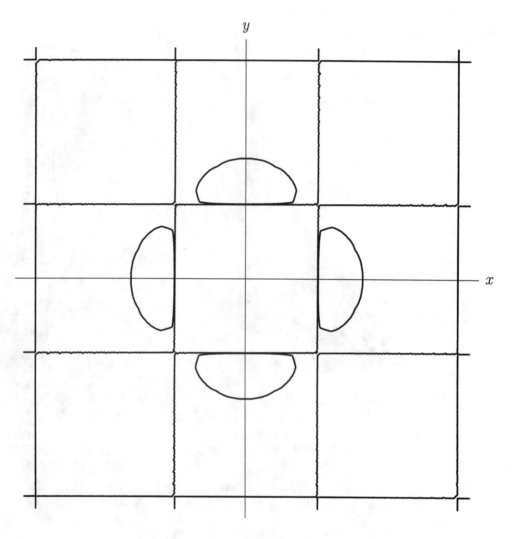

$$z = (\cos x)(\cos y)e^{-(x^2+y^2)}$$

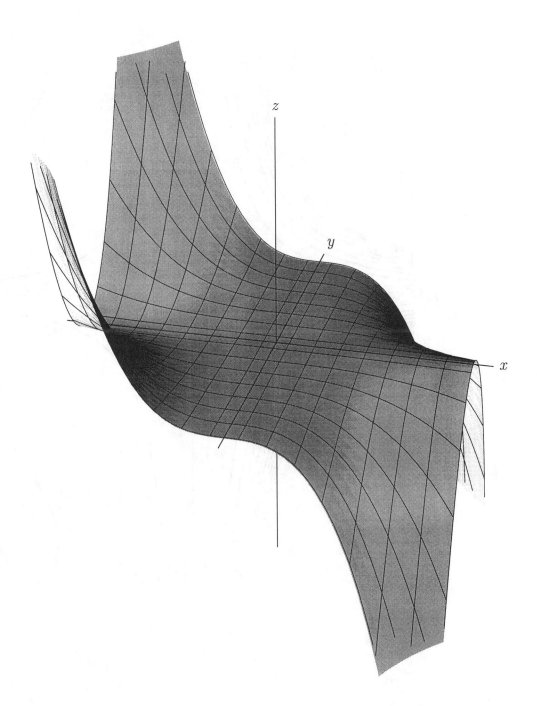

$$z = -10x^3y^2$$

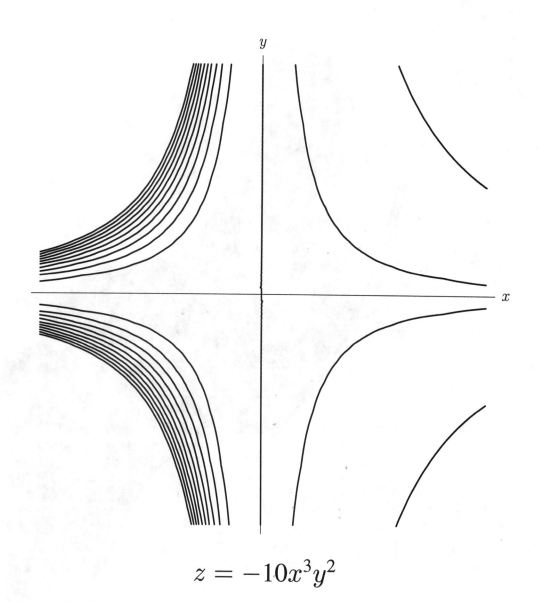

$$z = -10x^3y^2$$

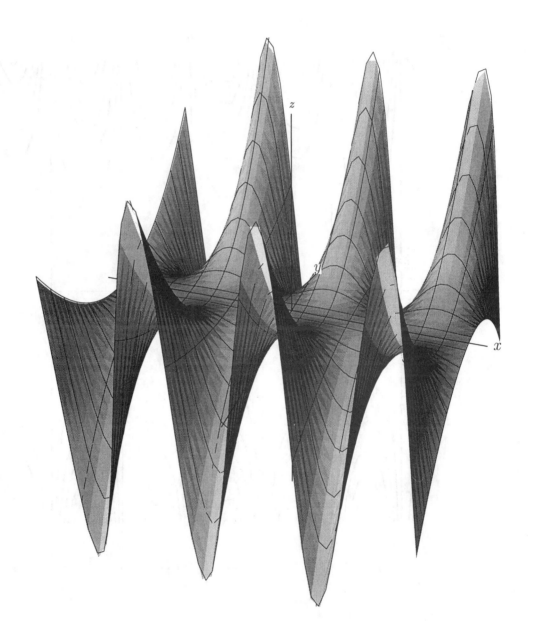

$$z = y^2 \sin 2x$$

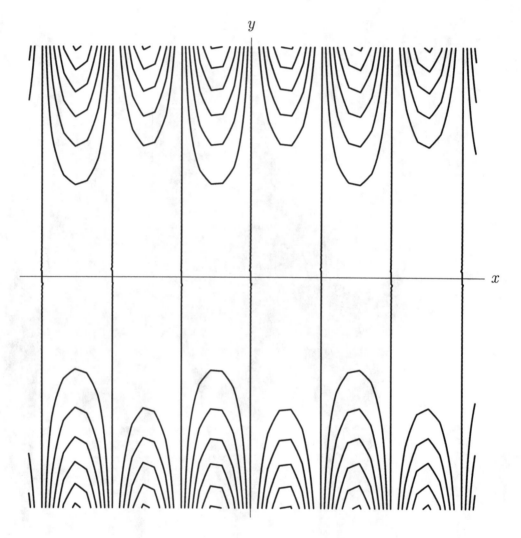

$$z = y^2 \sin 2x$$

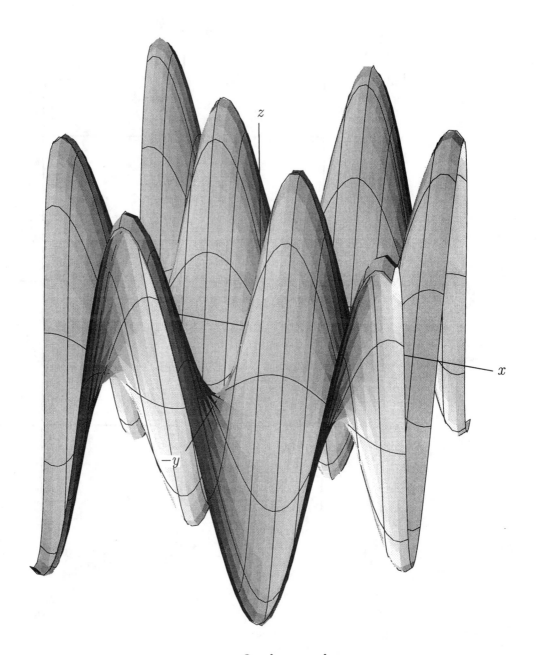

$$z = -2 \sin x \sin y$$

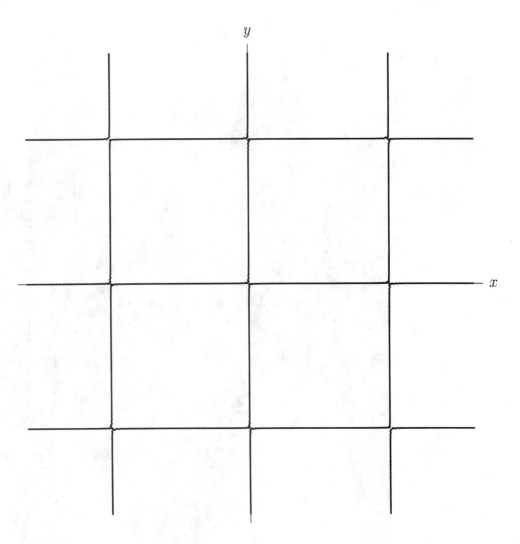

$$z = -2\sin x \sin y$$

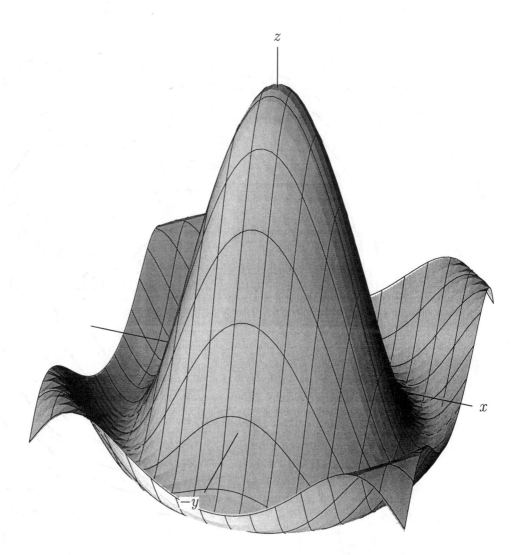

$$z = \cos{(x^2 + y^2)}/(1 + x^2 + y^2)$$

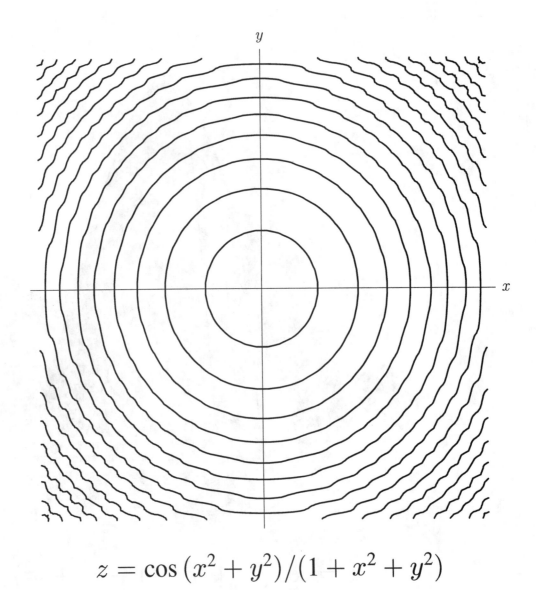

$$z = \cos(x^2 + y^2)/(1 + x^2 + y^2)$$

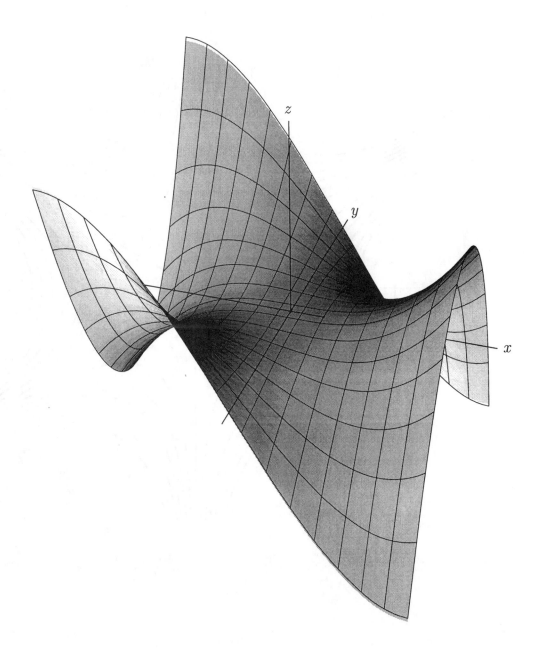

$$z = x^3 - 3xy^2$$

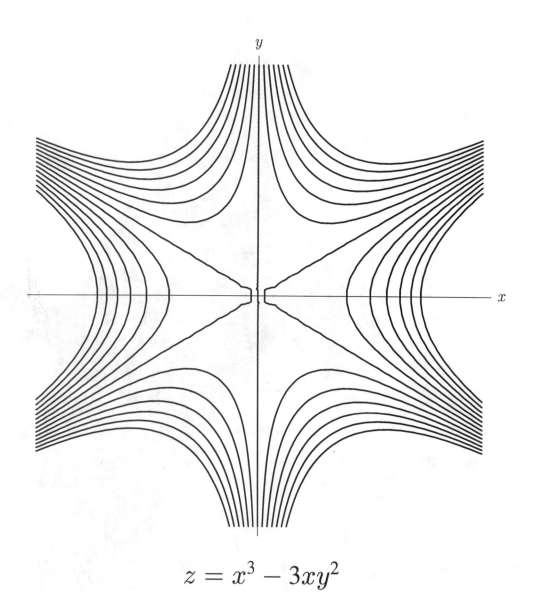

$$z = x^3 - 3xy^2$$

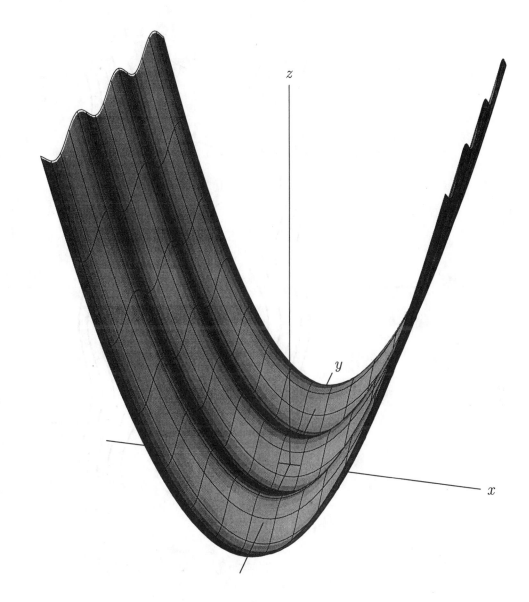

$$z = x^2 + 3\sin y$$

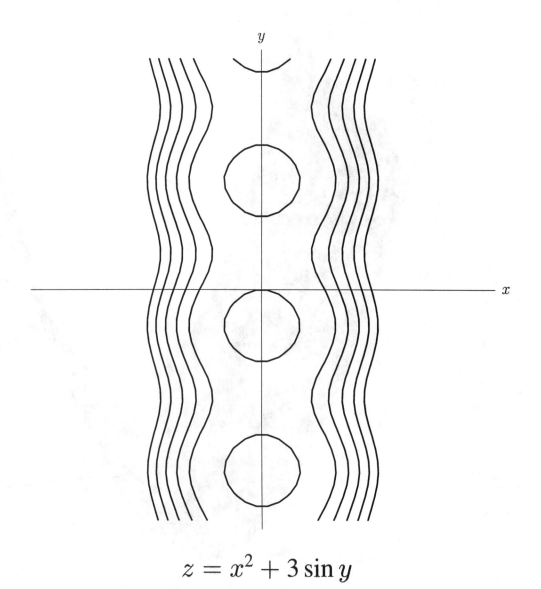

$$z = x^2 + 3 \sin y$$

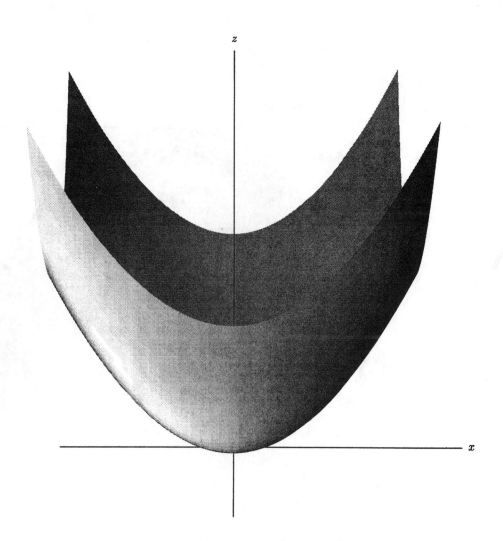

$$f(x, y) = x^2 + y^2$$
$$f_{xx}f_{yy} > 0$$
$$f_{xy} = 0$$

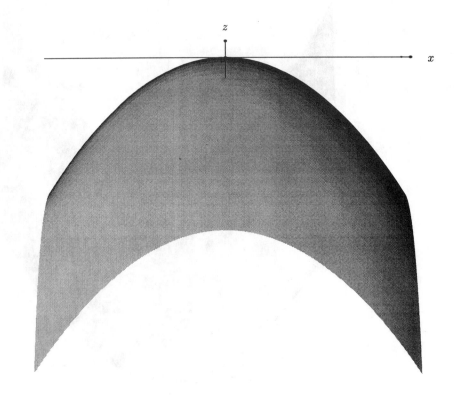

$$f(x, y) = -x^2 - y^2$$
$$f_{xx}f_{yy} > 0$$
$$f_{xy} = 0$$

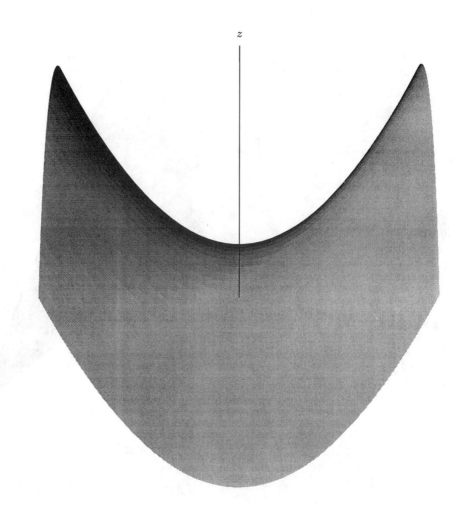

$$f(x,y) = x^2 - y^2$$
$$f_{xx}f_{yy} < 0, f_{xy} = 0$$

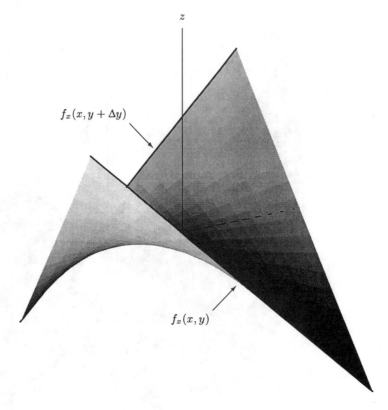

$$f(x, y) = xy$$
$$f_{xy} > 0$$

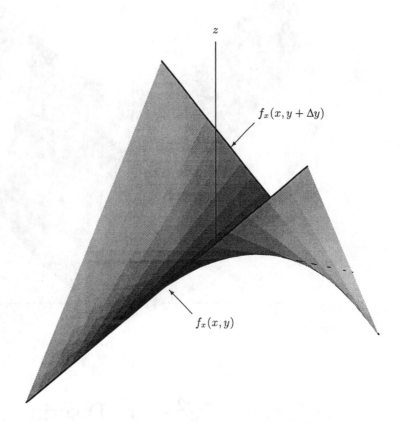

$$f(x, y) = -xy$$
$$f_{xy} < 0$$

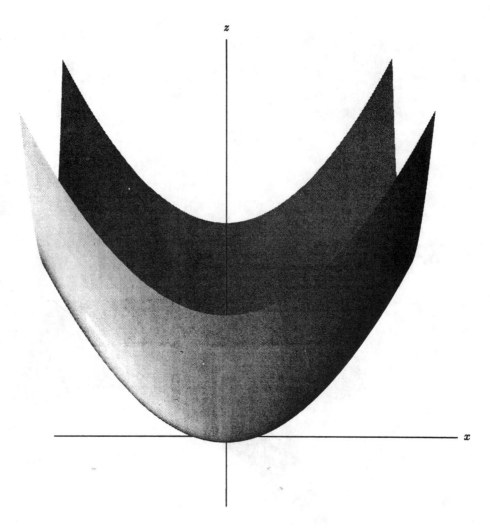

$$f(x, y) = x^2 + y^2, \text{Discriminant} = 4$$

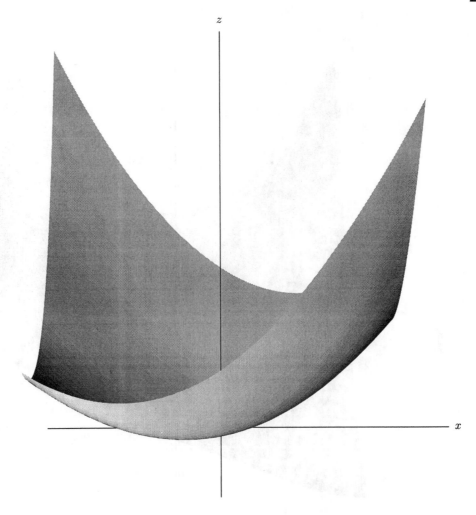

$$f(x, y) = x^2 + y^2 - xy, \text{Discriminant} = 3$$

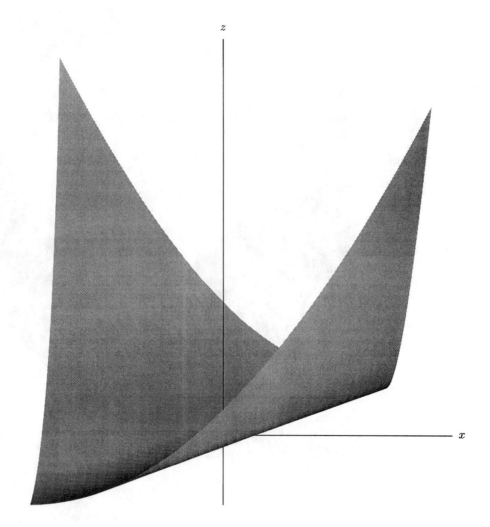

$$f(x, y) = x^2 + y^2 - 2xy, \text{Discriminant} = 0$$

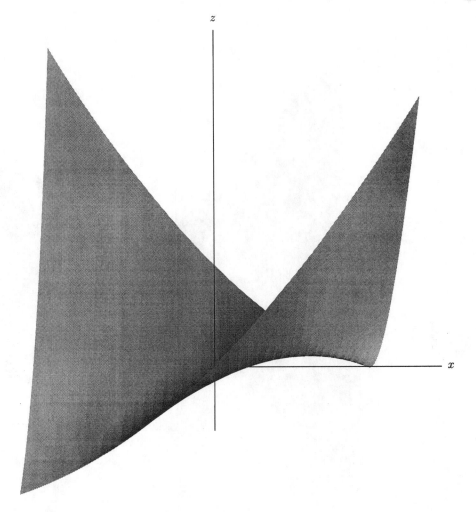

$$f(x, y) = x^2 + y^2 - 3xy, \text{Discriminant} = -5$$

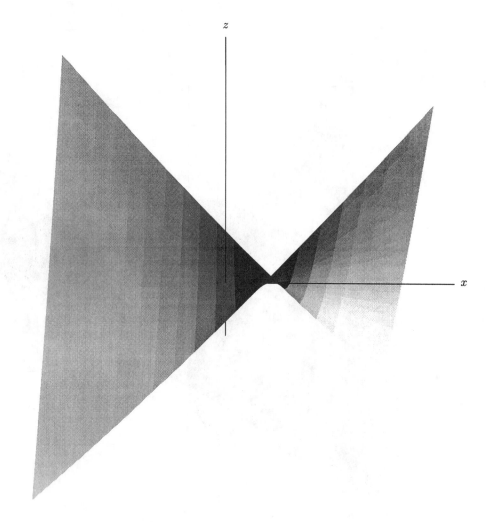

$$f(x, y) = x^2 + y^2 - 15xy, \text{Discriminant}$$
$$= -221$$

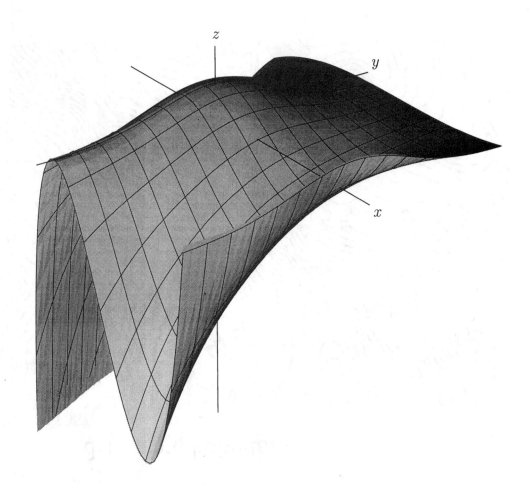

$$z = e^{(-y^2)}(2x^3 - 3x^2 + 1) + e^{(-y)}(2x^3 - 3x^2)$$

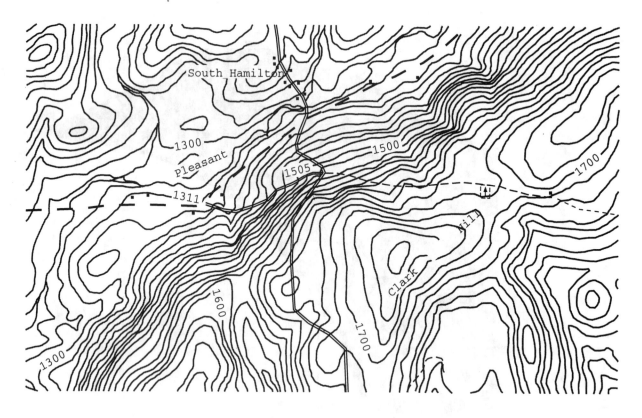

A topographical map

**Grid for estimating definite integrals from contour diagrams**

# Grid for estimating definite integrals from contour diagrams

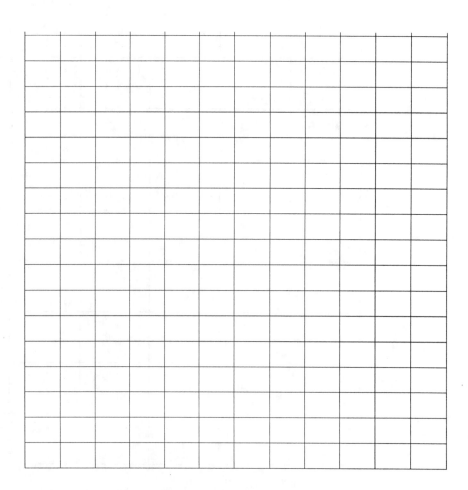

**Grid for estimating definite integrals from contour diagrams**

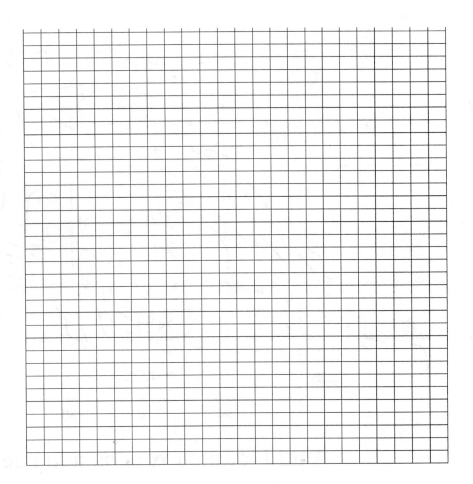

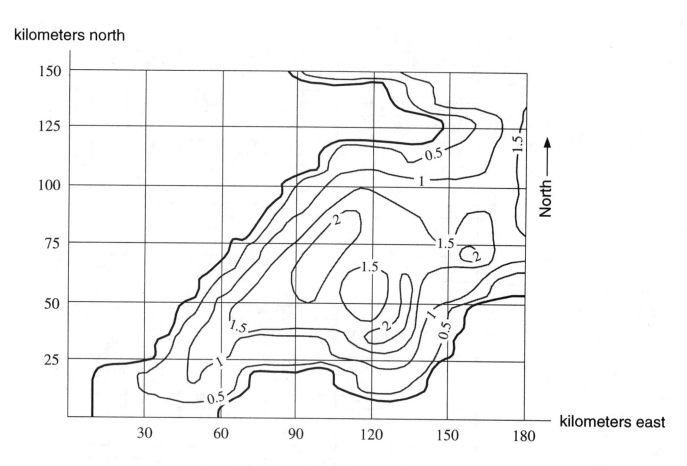

A grid for the fox population density

**Transparency Master for Problem 4 on page 760 in the text**

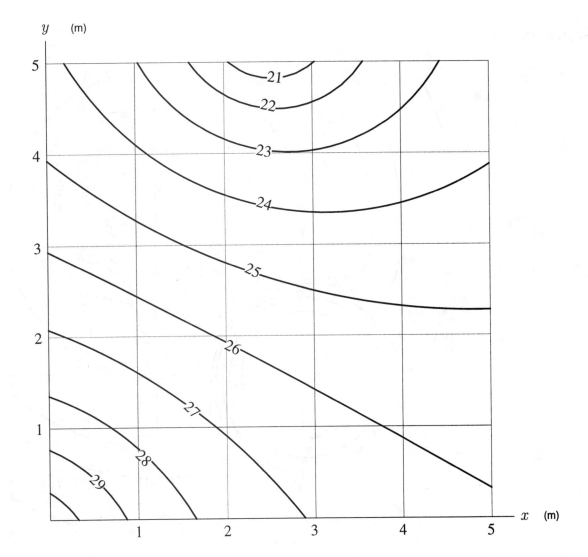

**Transparency Master for Problem 5 on page 760 in the text**

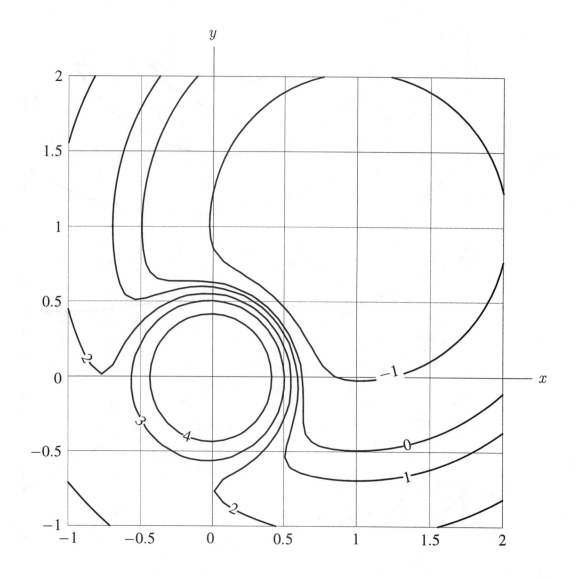

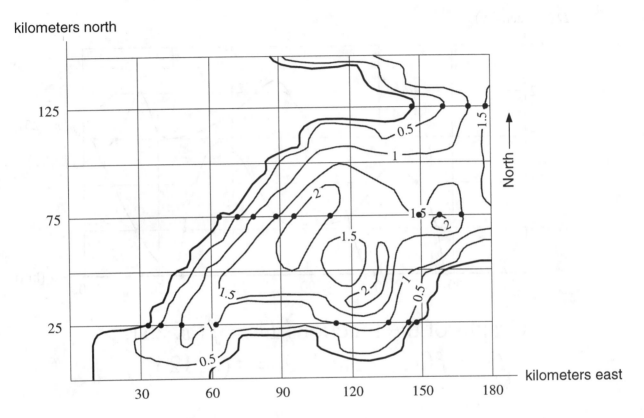

Fox population density with kilometers north
fixed at 25, 75, and 100 kilometers

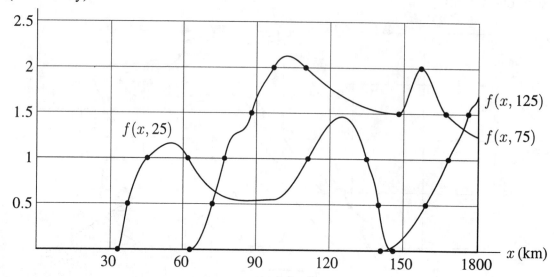

Graphs of the functions $D = f(x, 25)$,
$D = f(x, 75)$, and $D = f(x, 125)$

**Transparency Master for Problem 6 on page 769 in the text**

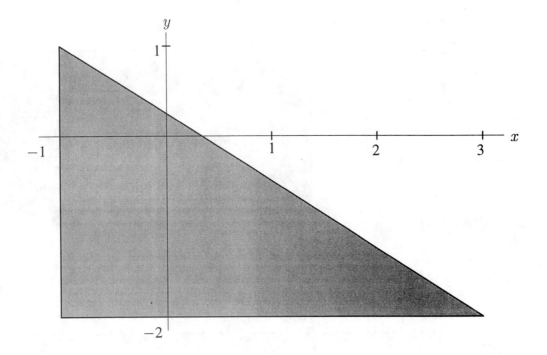

242

**Transparency Master for Problem 7 on page 769 in the text**

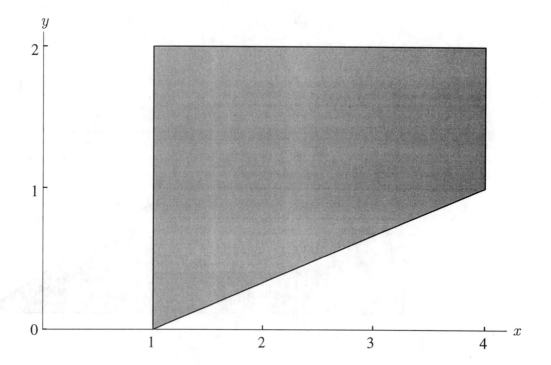

**Transparency Master for Problem 8 on page 769 in the text**

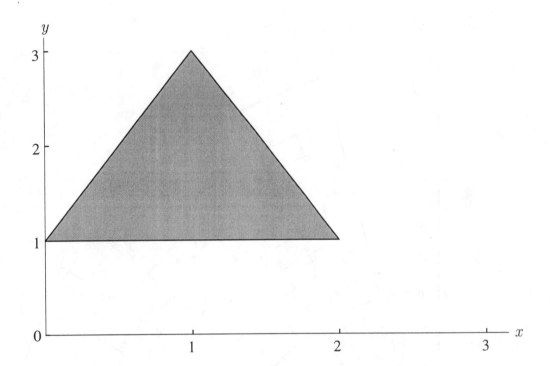

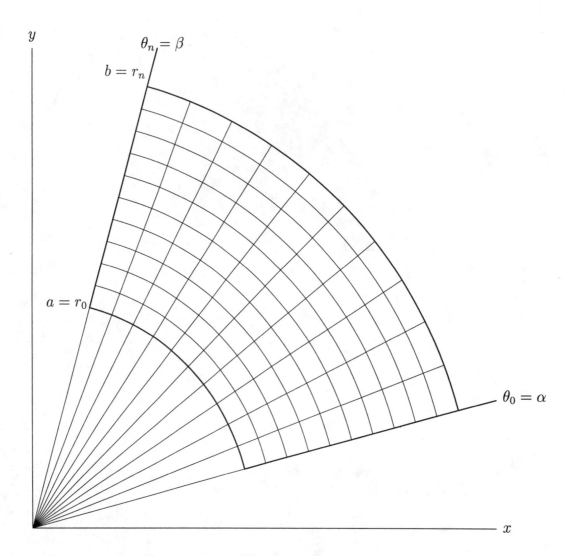

How to divide up a region using polar coordinates

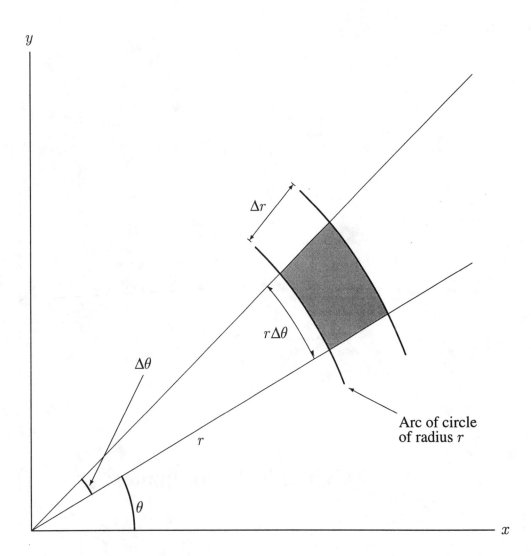

Area $\Delta A$ in polar coordinates

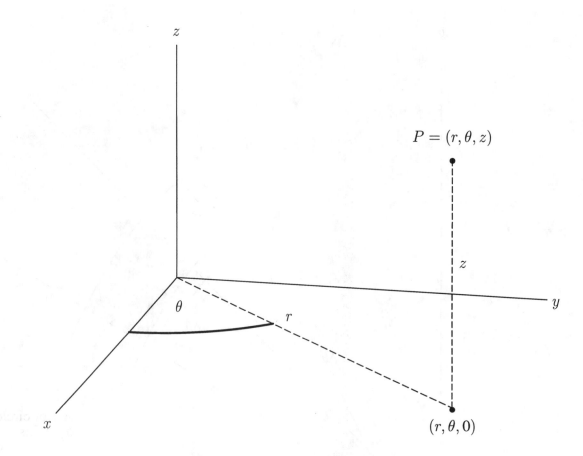

Cylindrical coordinates: $(r, \theta, z)$

**Transparency Master for Figure 15.32 on page 779 in the text**

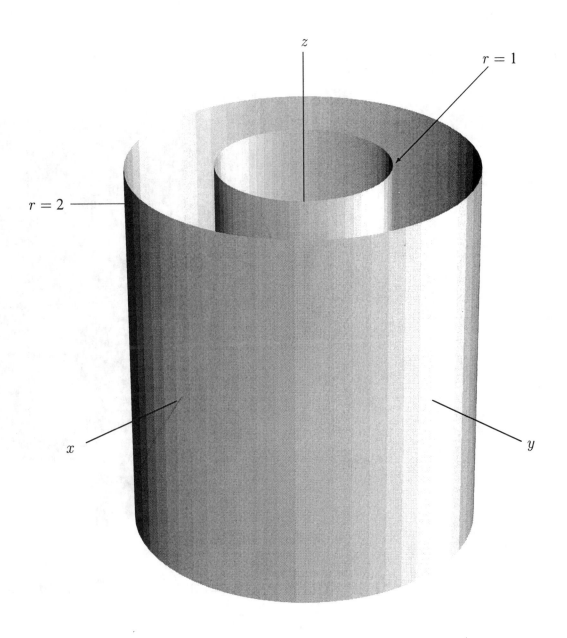

The surfaces $r = 1$ and $r = 2$

**Transparency Master for Figure 15.33 on page 779 in the text**

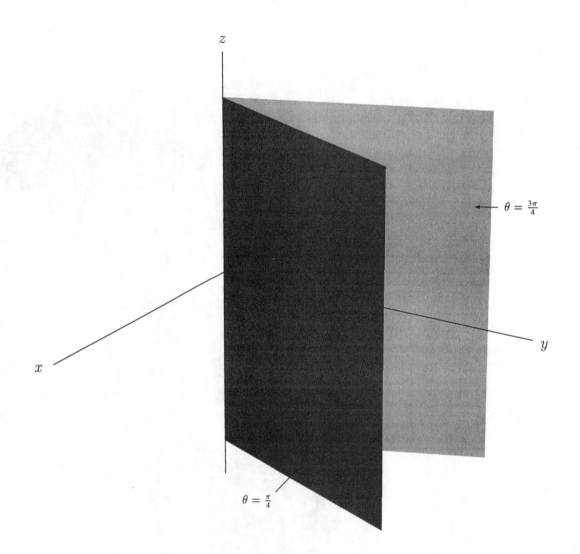

The surfaces $\theta = \pi/4$ and $\theta = 3\pi/4$

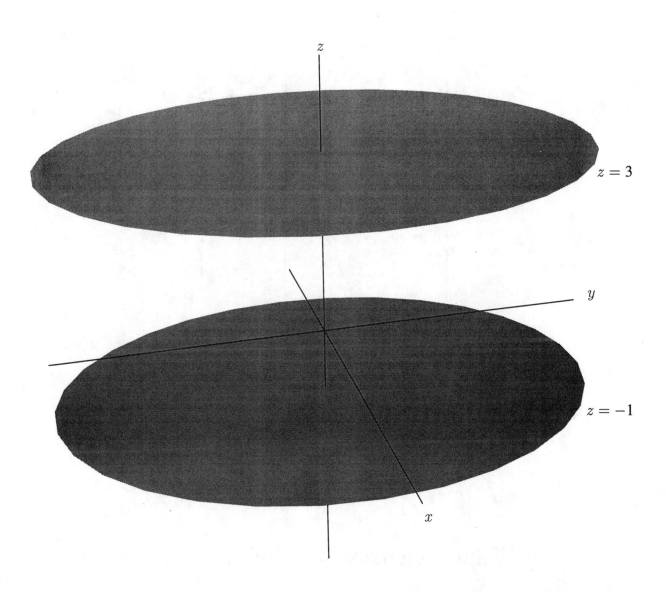

The surfaces $z = -1$ and $z = 3$

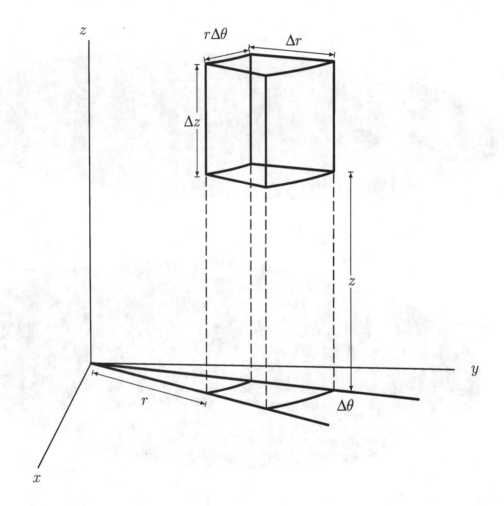

Volume element in cylindrical coordinates

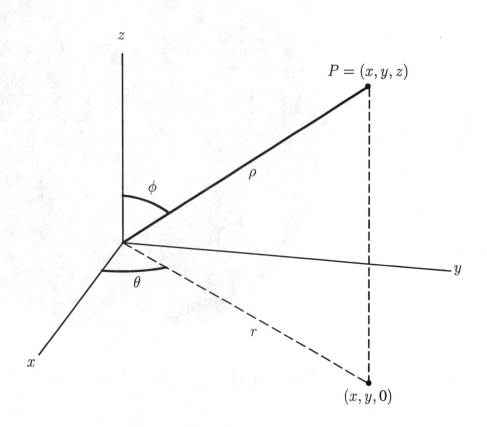

Spherical coordinates

**Transparency Master for Figure 15.39 on page 782 in the text**

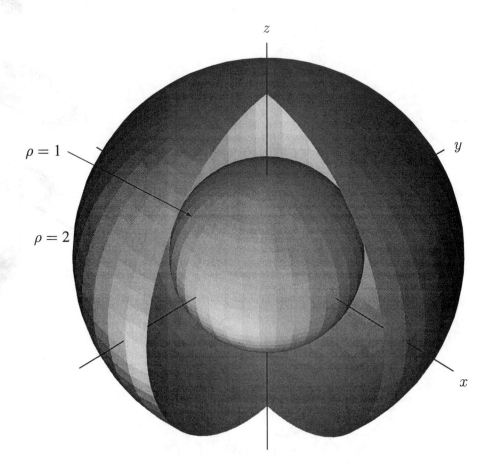

The surfaces $\rho = 1$ and $\rho = 2$

**Transparency Master for Figure 15.40 on page 782 in the text**

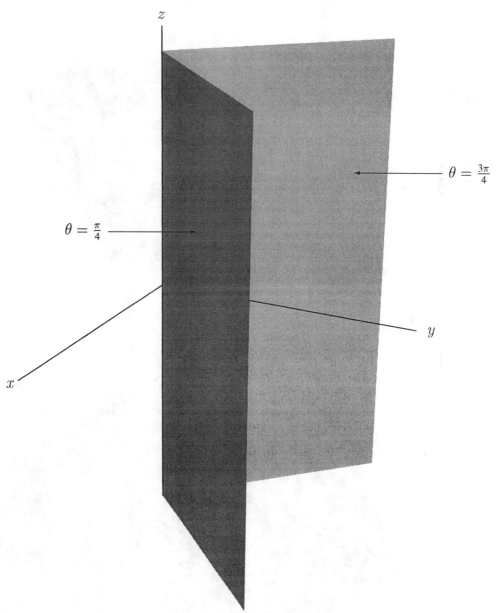

The surfaces $\theta = \pi/4$ and $\theta = 3\pi/4$

**Transparency Master for Figure 15.41 on page 782 in the text**

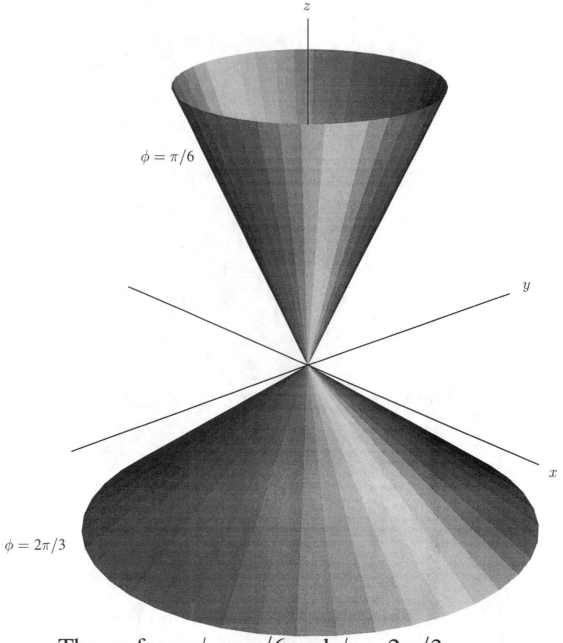

The surfaces $\phi = \pi/6$ and $\phi = 2\pi/3$

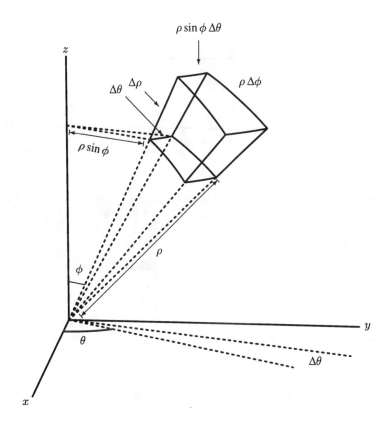

The volume element in spherical coordinates

**Transparency Masters for Figure 15.54 on page 794 in the text**

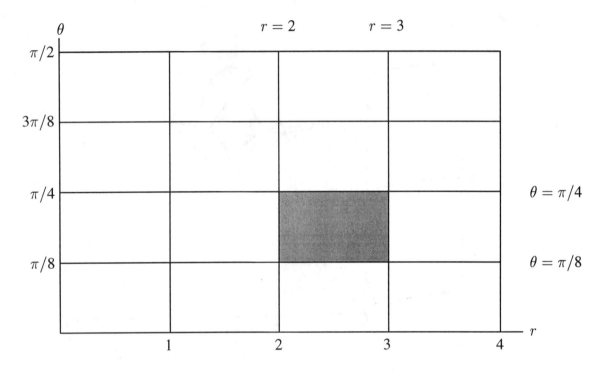

The $r, \theta$ plane with a grid

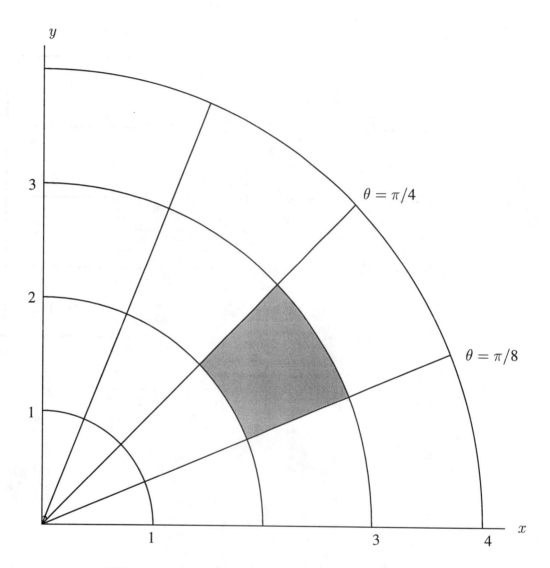

The $x, y$-plane with an $r, \theta$ grid

**Transparency Masters for Figure 15.55 on page 795 in the text**

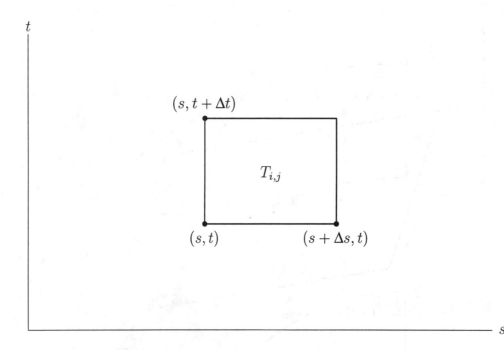

**Transparency Masters for Figure 15.55 on page 795 in the text**

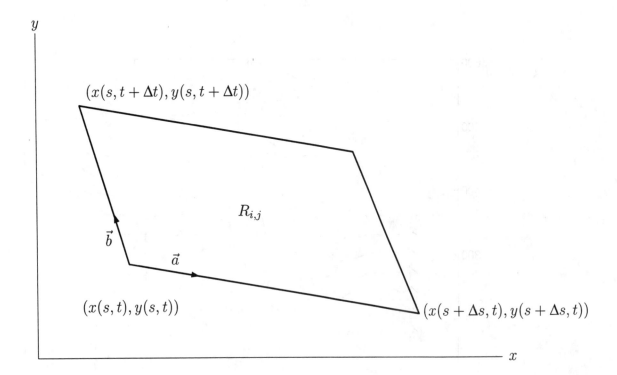

**Transparency Master for Figure 17.1 on page 822 in the text**

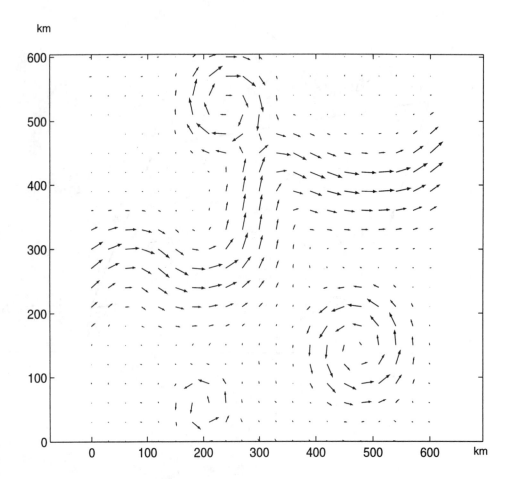

The velocity vector field of the Gulf stream

The gravitational field of the earth

**Transparency Master for Figure 17.3 on page 824 in the text**

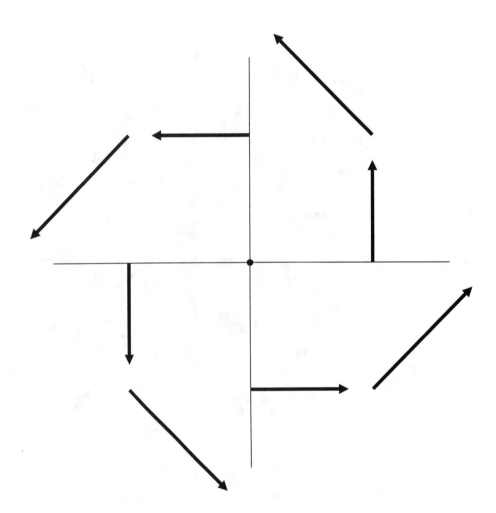

A few values of $\vec{F}(x, y) = -y\vec{i} + x\vec{j}$

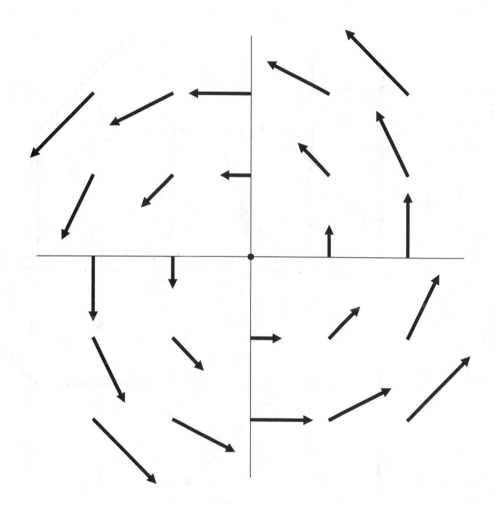

The vector field $\vec{F}(x, y) = -y\vec{i} + x\vec{j}$, vectors scaled smaller to fit in diagram

**Transparency Master for Figure 17.5 on page 824 in the text**

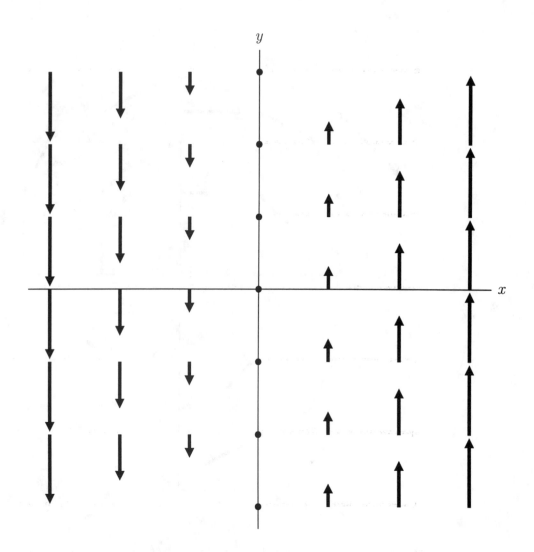

The vector field $\vec{F}(x, y) = x\vec{j}$

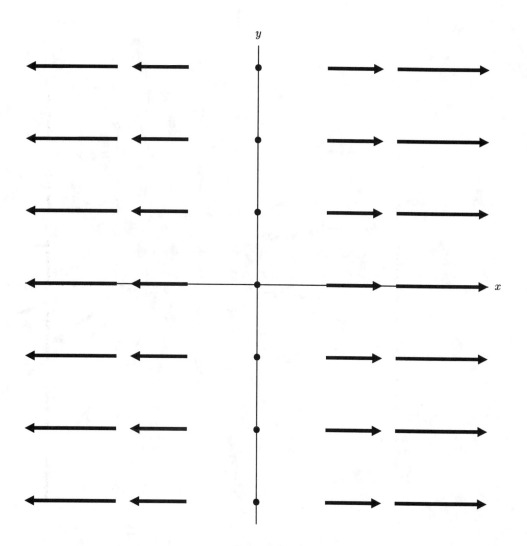

The vector field $\vec{F}(x, y) = x\vec{i}$

**Transparency Master for Figure 17.7 on page 825 in the text**

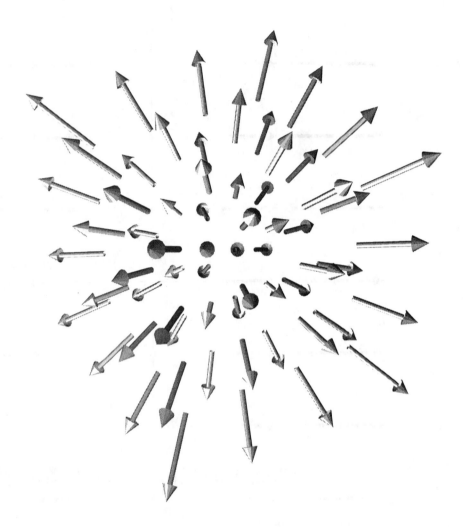

The vector field $\vec{F}(\vec{r}) = \vec{r}$

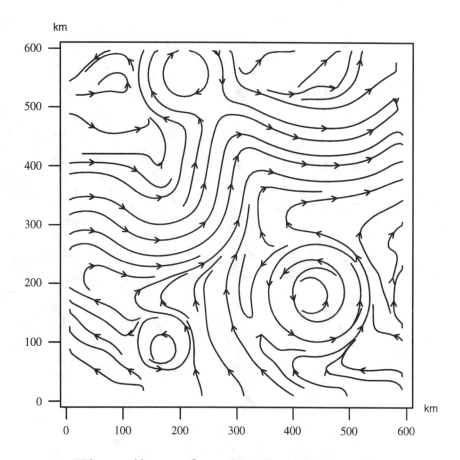

Flow lines for the Gulf stream

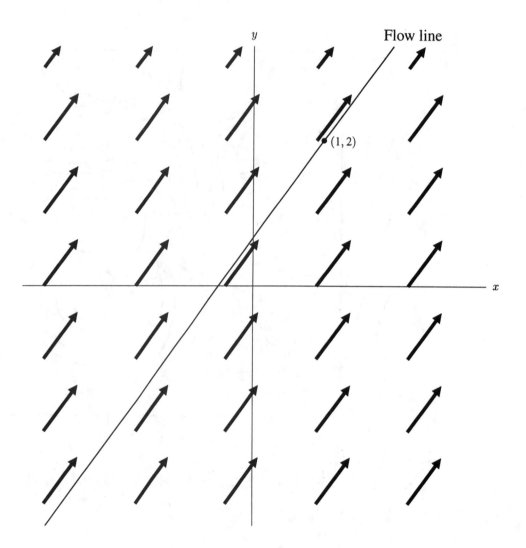

Vector field $\vec{F} = 3\vec{i} + 4\vec{j}$ with a flow line
through $(1, 2)$

**Transparency Master for Figure 17.20 on page 830 in the text**

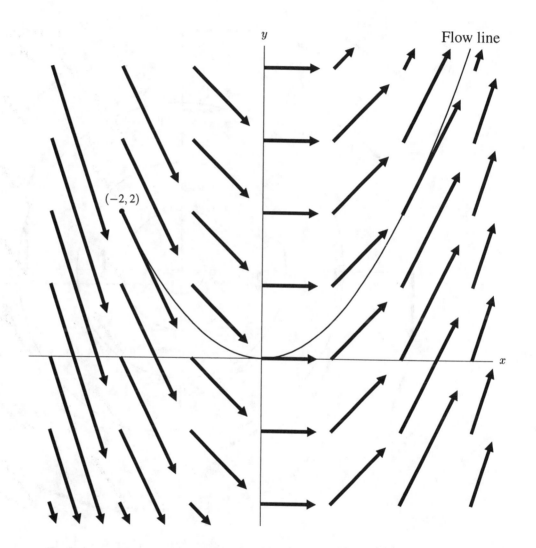

$(-2, 2)$

Flow line

A flow line of the vector field $\vec{v} = \vec{i} + x\vec{j}$

**Transparency Master for Figure 17.21 on page 831 in the text**

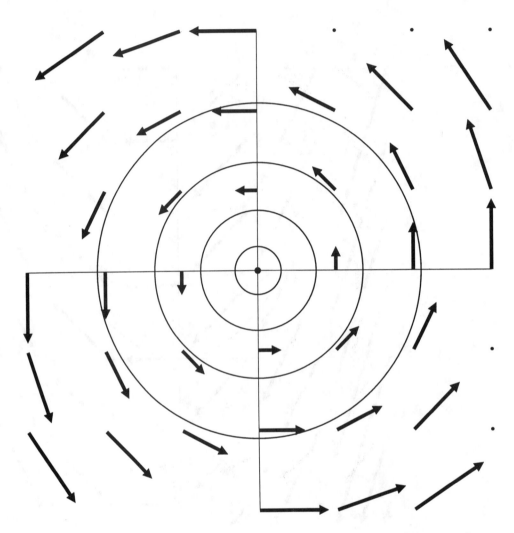

The flow of a vector field $\vec{v} = -y\vec{i} + x\vec{j}$

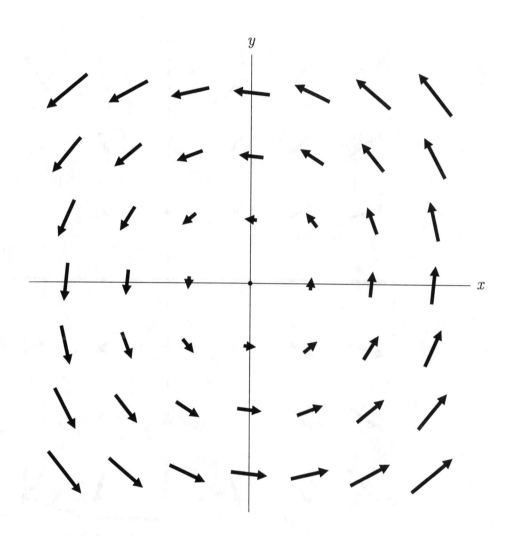

$$\vec{F}(x, y) = -y\vec{i} + x\vec{j}$$

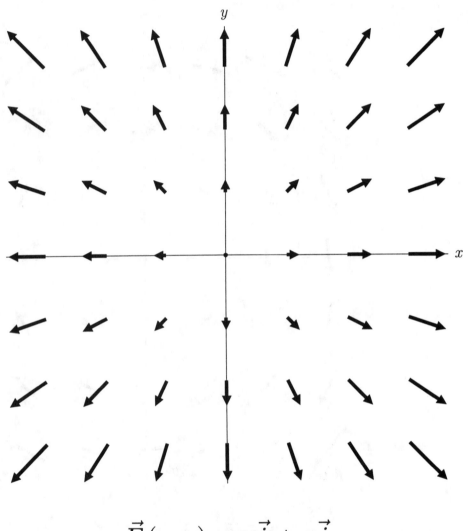

$$\vec{F}(x, y) = x\vec{i} + y\vec{j}$$

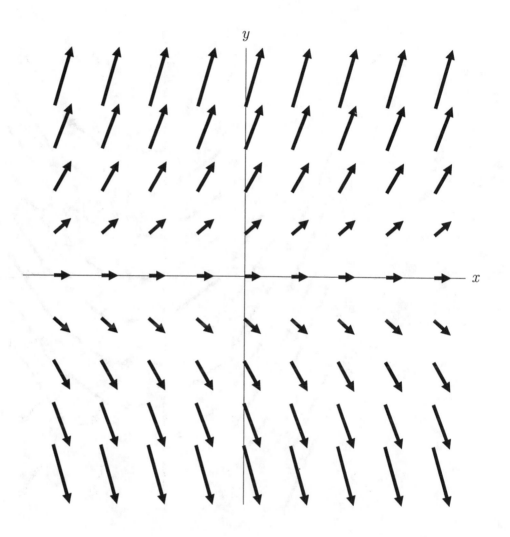

$$\vec{F}(x,y) = \vec{i} + y\vec{j}$$

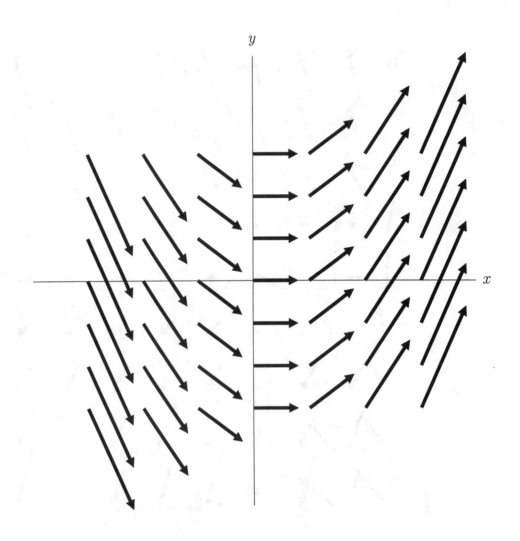

$$\vec{F}(x, y) = \vec{i} + x\vec{j}$$

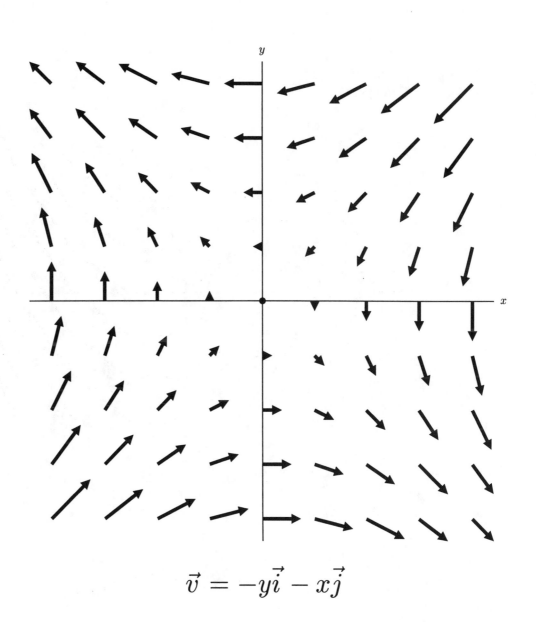

$$\vec{v} = -y\vec{i} - x\vec{j}$$

# PART V

# CALCULATOR PROGRAMS

# CALCULATOR PROGRAMS

for the

# TI - 81

### Program to Calculate Riemann Sums to Evaluate a Definite Integral (TI-81)

Select 'PRGM' to get the program menu, move to 'EDIT' to enter a program. When you select a program number, you must first give it a name (for example, 'RSUMS') to the right of the program number.

| Prgm: RSUMS | *Where to Find The Commands* |
|---|---|
| :Disp "LOWER LIMIT" | Disp and Input are accessed via PRGM, I/O, pressed while editing a program. |
| :Input $A$ | The " " are on the $+$ key when you have pressed the ALPHA key. |
| :Disp "UPPER LIMIT" | |
| :Input $B$ | |
| :Disp "DIVNS" | |
| :Input $N$ | |
| :$A \to X$ | $\to$ is on the STO key. |
| :$0 \to S$ | 0 is Zero, not oh. |
| :$1 \to I$ | |
| :$(B - A)/N \to H$ | |
| :Lbl P | Lbl is accessed via PRGM, CTL. |
| :$S + H * Y_1 \to S$ | $Y_1$ is accessed via Y-VARS, i.e., 2nd VARS. (Do not use $Y$ followed by 1, which means $Y$ multiplied by 1.) |
| :$X + H \to X$ | |
| :$IS > (I, N)$ | $IS >$ ( and Goto are accessed via PRGM, CTL. |
| :Goto P | |
| :Disp "LEFT SUM" | |
| :Disp $S$ | |
| :$S + Y_1 * H \to S$ | |
| :$A \to X$ | |
| :$S - Y_1 * H \to S$ | |
| :Disp "RIGHT SUM" | |
| :Disp $S$ | |

Things to watch for:

1. Difference between $-$, which means subtract, and (-), which means negative. For example, $-2 - 3$ must be entered as (-)$2 - 3$.

2. Disp and Input are not typed in letter-by-letter, but are obtained by highlighting them under PRGM, I/O and hitting ENTER.

To run this program:

1. The integrand (the function you want to integrate) $f(x)$ must be entered into $Y_1$, with $X$ as the independent variable.

2. Make sure the lower limit of the integral you're approximating is less than the upper limit.

3. Test on $\int_1^3 x^3 \, dx = 20$ with 100 subintervals. You should get left- and right-hand sums of 19.7408 and 20.2608, respectively.

## Numerical Integration Program (TI-81)

This program calculates left- and right-hand Riemann sums, and the trapezoidal, midpoint and Simpson approximations. Since there's not room on the calculator to label each approximation separately, we use a compressed method of displaying the results. For instance, the label LEFT/RIGHT indicates that the next two numbers are the left- and right-hand Riemann sums, respectively.

**Notes:**

1. To enter a program, hit PRGM and select EDIT and a program number. To finish a line, hit ENTER; to finish editing a program, hit 2nd QUIT.

2. The function to be integrated must be entered as $Y_1$ (accessed by the "$Y =$" button). When $Y_1$ occurs in a program, it is evaluated at the current value of $X$.

3. The lower limit of integration must be less than the upper limit.

4. $IS > ($ means that the PRGM button must be pushed and then $IS > ($ selected, not that $I, S, >$ and $($ are to be entered separately. 'Disp' and 'Input' are to be found under PRGM, I/O, pushed while entering a program.

5. To run a program, select PRGM, EXEC. To stop a program while it is running, hit ON.

6. Test the program by evaluating $\int_1^3 x^3 \, dx = 20$, using 100 subdivisions. You should get left- and right-hand sums of 19.7408 and 20.2608, respectively. For the trapezoid approximation, you should get 20.0008. For the mid point approximation, you should get 19.9996. For Simpson's rule, you should get exactly 20.

| Prgm: INTEGRAL | *Where to Find The Commands* |
|---|---|
| :Disp "LOWER LIMIT" | Disp and Input are accessed via PRGM, I/O |
| :Input $A$ | Enter lower limit of integration. |
| :Disp "UPPER LIMIT" | |
| :Input $B$ | Enter upper limit of integration. |
| :Disp "DIVNS" | |
| :Input $N$ | Enter number subdivisions. |
| :$(B - A)/N \rightarrow H$ | Stores size of one subdivision in $H$ (Note that $\rightarrow$ means hit STO button). |
| :$A \rightarrow X$ | Start $X$ off at beginning of interval. |
| :$0 \rightarrow L$ | Initialize $L$, which keeps track of left sums, to zero. |
| :$0 \rightarrow M$ | Initialize $M$, which keeps track of midpoint sums, to zero. |
| :$1 \rightarrow I$ | Initialize $I$, the counter for the loop. |
| :Lbl P | Label for top of loop. Lbl is accessed via PRGM, CTL. |
| :$L + H * Y_1 \rightarrow L$ | Increment $L$ by $Y_1 H$, the area of one more rectangle. ($Y_1$ is accessed via $Y$-VARS, or 2nd VARS.) |
| :$X + .5H \rightarrow X$ | Move $X$ to middle of interval. |
| :$M + H * Y_1 \rightarrow M$ | Evaluate $Y_1$ at the middle of interval and increment $M$ by rectangle of this height. |
| :$X + .5H \rightarrow X$ | Move $X$ to start of next interval. |
| :$IS > (I, N)$ | $IS > ($ is accessed via PRGM, CTL. This is the most difficult step in the program: adds 1 to $I$ and does the the next step if $I \leq N$ (i.e., if haven't gone through loop enought times); otherwise, skips next step. Thus, if $I \leq N$, goes back to Lbl P and loops through again. If $I > N$, loop is finished and goes on to print out results. Continue here if $I > N$, in which case the value of $X$ is now $B$. |
| :Goto P | Goto is accessed via PRGM, CTL. Jumps back to Lbl P if $J \leq N$. |
| :Disp "LEFT/RIGHT" | |
| :Disp $L$ | $L$ now equals the left sum, so display it. |
| :$L + H * Y_1 \rightarrow R$ | Add on area of right-most rectangle, store in $R$. |
| :$A \rightarrow X$ | Reset $X$ to $A$. |
| :$R - H * Y_1 \rightarrow R$ | Subtract off area of left-most rectangle. |
| :Disp $R$ | $R$ now equals right sum, so display it. |
| :$(L + R)/2 \rightarrow T$ | Trap approximation is average of $L$ and $R$. |
| :Disp "TRAP/MID/SIMP" | |
| :Disp $T$ | Display trap approximation. |
| :Disp $M$ | Display midpoint approximation. |
| :$(2M + T)/3 \rightarrow S$ | Simpson is weighted average of $M$ and $T$. |
| :Disp $S$ | Display Simpson's approximation. |

## Slope Field Program (TI-81)

This program draws the slope field for the differential equation $\dfrac{dy}{dx} = f(x, y)$.

| | *Where To Find The Commands* |
|---|---|
| Prgm:SLOPES | |
| :ClrDraw | 2nd Draw |
| :All-Off | 2nd Y-VARS, OFF |
| :7$(X_{max} - X_{min})/83 \to H$ | VARS, RNG; $\to$ is on STO key. |
| :7$(Y_{max} - Y_{min})/55 \to K$ | |
| :1$/(0.4H)^2 \to A$ | |
| :1$/(0.4K)^2 \to B$ | |
| :$X_{min} + 0.5H \to X$ | |
| :$Y_{min} + 0.5K \to Z$ | |
| :1 $\to I$ | |
| :Lbl P | Prgm |
| :1 $\to J$ | |
| :$Z \to Y$ | |
| :Lbl Q | |
| :$Y_1 \to T$ | |
| :1$/\sqrt{(A + B * T^2)} \to C$ | |
| :$T * C \to S$ | |
| :$X \to U$ | |
| :$Y \to V$ | |
| :Line$(U - C, V - S, U + C, V + S)$ | 2nd Draw |
| :$V + K \to Y$ | |
| :$IS > (J, 8)$ | |
| :Goto Q | Prgm |
| :$U + H \to X$ | |
| :$IS > (I, 12)$ | Prgm |
| :Goto P | Prgm |

To run this program:

1. Enter $\dfrac{dy}{dx} = f(x, y)$ as $Y_1 = f(X, Y)$.

2. Choose an appropriate RANGE.

3. Run the program.

4. To get rid of previously drawn slope field, press "ClrDraw" (from the DRAW menu) or change the RANGE.

### Euler's Method (TI-81)

This program for the TI-81 calculates and graphs an approximate solution for the differential equation $y' = f(x, y)$ using Euler's method.

The function $f$ is entered as $Y_1 = f(X, Y)$. When called, the program asks for the coordinates of the starting point and the step size. The graph is then drawn. The program does not clear the screen to start with, so solutions with different starting points or step sizes can be graphed consecutively on the same axes, or solution curves can be superimposed on a slope field. When the program is finished, the final $Y$-value remains in cell $Y$.

| Prgm:EULER | *Where to Find The Commands* |
|---|---|
| :All-Off | All-Off is a single symbol from the 2nd VARS OFF menu. |
| :Disp "INITIAL X" | Disp and Input are single symbols from the PRGM I/O menu. |
| :Input $X$ | |
| :Disp "INITIAL Y" | |
| :Input $Y$ | |
| :Disp "STEP SIZE" | |
| :Input H | |
| :Lbl P | Lbl and Goto are single symbols from the PRGM CTL menu. |
| :$X + H \to U$ | |
| :$Y + H * Y_1 \to V$ | $Y_1$ is a single symbol from the 2nd VARS menu. |
| :Line$(X, Y, U, V)$ | Line( is a single symbol from the DRAW (i.e., 2nd PRGM) menu. |
| :$U \to X$ | |
| :$V \to Y$ | |
| :Goto P | |

To run this program:
1. Enter $y' = f(x, y)$ as $Y_1 = f(X, Y)$.
2. Choose an appropriate RANGE.
3. Run the program; if you have seen enough of the trajectory, press ON and 2. Then press ENTER to continue with other initial values, or another step size.
4. To get rid of previously drawn graphs, press ClrDraw (from the DRAW menu) or change the RANGE.
5. If you get an edgy, disconnected, or otherwise weird graph, try a smaller step size.

## Program for Trajectories (TI-81)

The program below graphs the *trajectory* in the $xy$ phase plane of the system

$$\frac{dx}{dt} = f(x, y), \quad x(0) = x_0,$$

$$\frac{dy}{dt} = g(x, y), \quad y(0) = y_0.$$

The functions $f(x, y)$ and $g(x, y)$ are entered into $Y_2$ and $Y_3$. If you want to plot a trajectory on top of a slope field, enter $\dfrac{dy}{dx}$ as $Y_1 = \dfrac{g(x, y)}{f(x, y)}$ and run the slope field program first.

Notice that you are graphing the relation between $x$ and $y$ in the phase plane; $t$ does not appear. To graph $x$ and $y$ against $t$, use the Time Series program on the next page.

Prgm: TRAJECT
:All-Off
:Disp "INITIAL X"
:Input $X$
:Disp "INITIAL Y"
:Input $Y$
:Disp "STEP SIZE"
:Input $H$
:Lbl P
:$X + H * Y_2 \to U$
:$Y + H * Y_3 \to V$
:Line($X, Y, U, V$)
:$U \to X$
:$V \to Y$
:Goto P

| Command | Menu | Selection |
|---------|--------|-----------|
| All-Off | Y-VARS | OFF,1 |
| Disp | PRGM | I/O,1 |
| Input | PRGM | I/O, 2 |
| Lbl | PRGM | CTL,1 |
| Line( | DRAW | 2 |
| Goto | PRGM | CTL, 2 |
| $Y_2, Y_3$ | Y-VARS | $Y$, 2, 3 |

To run this program:
1. Enter the differential equation as $Y_2 = f(X, Y)$ and $Y_3 = g(X, Y)$.

2. Choose an appropriate RANGE.

3. Run the program; if you have seen enough of the trajectory, press ON and 2. Then press ENTER to continue with other initial values, or another step size.

4. To get rid of previously drawn trajectories, press ClrDraw (from the DRAW menu) or change the RANGE.

5. If you get an edgy, disconnected, or otherwise weird trajectory, choose a smaller step size $H$. If the program runs too slowly, choose a larger step size $H$. Try starting with $H = 0.05$.

## Program for Time Series (TI-81)

This program graphs the *solutions* $x(t)$ and $y(t)$ of the system

$$\frac{dx}{dt} = f(x,y), \quad x(0) = x_0,$$

$$\frac{dy}{dt} = g(x,y), \quad y(0) = y_0.$$

Notice that here we are graphing both $x$ and $y$ as functions of $t$. Compare the Trajectory program on the previous page, which graphs the relation between $x$ and $y$, and in which $t$ does not appear.

| Prgm: TIMESER | Command | Menu | Selection |
|---|---|---|---|
| :ClrDraw | | | |
| :All-Off | All-Off | Y-VARS | OFF,1 |
| :Disp "INITIAL X" | Disp | PRGM | I/O,1 |
| :Input $X$ | Input | PRGM | I/O, 2 |
| :Disp "INITIAL Y" | Lbl | PRGM | CTL,1 |
| :Input $Y$ | Line | DRAW | 2 |
| :Disp "STEP SIZE" | | | |
| :Input $H$ | Goto | PRGM | CTL, 2 |
| :$0 \to T$ | $Y_2, Y_3$ | Y-VARS | $Y$, 2, 3 |
| :Lbl P | If | PRGM | CTL, 3 |
| :$X + H * Y_2 \to U$ | $X_{\min}$ | VARS | RNG, 1 |
| :$Y + H * Y_3 \to V$ | $X_{\max}$ | VARS | RNG, 2 |
| :$T + H \to W$ | | | |
| :Line($T, X, W, U$) | > | TEST | 3 |
| :Line($T, Y, W, V$) | | | |
| :$U \to X$ | | | |
| :$V \to Y$ | | | |
| :$W \to T$ | | | |
| :Goto P | | | |

To run this program:

1. Enter the differential equation as $Y_2 = f(X, Y)$ and $Y_3 = g(X, Y)$.

2. Choose an appropriate RANGE (note that $X_{\min}$ and $X_{\max}$ refer to the horizontal axis of the window, which is time in our case; $Y_{\min}$ and $Y_{\max}$ refer to the vertical axis: $x$ and $y$ in our case).

3. Run the program. To continue with other initial values, press CLEAR and ENTER. To quit, press CLEAR twice.

# CALCULATOR PROGRAMS

for the

# TI - 82

## Introduction to the TI-82

The following are programs for the TI-82 calculator to do numerical integration, graph slope fields, demonstrate solutions to differential equations using Euler's method, and plot trajectories and solutions to systems of differential equations.

**Notes on Using the TI-82:** The commands on the TI-82 are basically the same as on the TI-81, though they may be in different menus. Select 'PRGM' to get the program menu, move to 'NEW' to enter a new program. You must first give it a name (for example, 'RSUMS') when prompted; to finish entering/editing a program, hit 2nd QUIT. To delete a program, press 2nd MEM and select [2:Delete]. The quantity AB represents the product of A and B. Writing $Y_3 = Y_1 Y_2$ defines $Y_3$ as the product $Y_1$ and $Y_2$. Writing $Y_3 = Y_1(Y_2)$ defines $Y_3$ as the composition of $Y_1$ and $Y_2$.

## Program to Calculate Riemann Sums to Evaluate a Definite Integral (TI-82)

Select 'PRGM' to get the program menu, move to 'NEW' to enter a new program. You must first give it a name (for example, 'RSUMS') when prompted; to finish entering/editing a program, hit 2nd QUIT.

| | |
|---|---|
| Name= RSUMS | *Where to Find The Commands* |
| :Disp "LOWER LIMIT" | Disp and Input are accessed via PRGM, I/O, pressed while in the middle of a program. |
| :Input $A$ | The " " are on the + key when you have pressed the ALPHA key. |
| :Disp "UPPER LIMIT" | |
| :Input $B$ | |
| :Disp "DIVNS" | |
| :Input $N$ | |
| :$A \rightarrow X$ | $\rightarrow$ is on the STO key. |
| :$0 \rightarrow S$ | 0 is Zero, not oh. |
| :$1 \rightarrow I$ | |
| :$(B - A)/N \rightarrow H$ | |
| :Lbl P | Lbl is accessed via PRGM, CTL. |
| :$S + H * Y_1 \rightarrow S$ | $Y_1$ is accessed via Y-VARS, i.e., 2nd VARS. (Do not use $Y$ followed by 1, which means $Y$ multiplied by 1.) |
| :$X + H \rightarrow X$ | |
| :$IS > (I, N)$ | $IS > ($ and Goto are accessed via PRGM, CTL. |
| :Goto P | |
| :Disp "LEFT SUM" | |
| :Disp $S$ | |
| :$S + Y_1 * H \rightarrow S$ | |
| :$A \rightarrow X$ | |
| :$S - Y_1 * H \rightarrow S$ | |
| :Disp "RIGHT SUM" | |
| :Disp $S$ | |

Things to watch for:
1. Difference between $-$, which means subtract, and (-), which means negative. For example, $-2 - 3$ must be entered as (-)2 - 3.
2. Disp and Input are not typed in letter-by-letter, but are obtained by highlighting them under PRGM, I/O and hitting ENTER.

To run this program:
1. The integrand (the function you want to integrate) $f(x)$ must be entered into $Y_1$, with $X$ as the independent variable.
2. Make sure the lower limit of the integral you're approximating is less than the upper limit.
3. Test on $\int_1^3 x^3 \, dx = 20$ with 100 subintervals. You should get left- and right-hand sums of 19.7408 and 20.2608, respectively.

## Numerical Integration Program (TI-82)

This program calculates left- and right-hand Riemann sums, and the trapezoidal, midpoint and Simpson approximations. Since there's not room on the calculator to label each approximation separately, we use a compressed method of displaying the results. For instance, the label LEFT/RIGHT indicates that the next two numbers are the left- and right-hand Riemann sums, respectively.

**Notes:**

1. Select 'PRGM' to get the program menu, move to 'NEW' to enter a new program. You must first give it a name (for example, 'INTEGRAL') when prompted; to finish entering/editing a program, hit 2nd QUIT.

2. The function to be integrated must be entered as $Y_1$ (accessed by the "$Y =$" button). When $Y_1$ occurs in a program, it is evaluated at the current value of $X$.

3. The lower limit of integration must be less than the upper limit.

4. $IS > ($ means that the PRGM button must be pushed and then $IS > ($ selected, not that $I, S, >$ and $($ are to be entered separately. 'Disp' and 'Input' are to be found under PRGM, I/O, pushed while entering a program.

5. To run a program, select PRGM, EXEC. To stop a program while it is running, hit ON.

6. Test the program by evaluating $\int_1^3 x^3 \, dx = 20$, using 100 subdivisions. You should get left- and right-hand sums of 19.7408 and 20.2608, respectively. For the trapezoid approximation, you should get 20.0008. For the mid point approximation, you should get 19.9996. For Simpson's rule, you should get exactly 20.

| Name= INTEGRAL | *Where to Find The Commands* |
|---|---|
| :Disp "LOWER LIMIT" | Disp and Input are accessed via PRGM, I/O |
| :Input $A$ | Enter lower limit of integration. |
| :Disp "UPPER LIMIT" | |
| :Input $B$ | Enter upper limit of integration. |
| :Disp "DIVNS" | |
| :Input $N$ | Enter number subdivisions. |
| :$(B - A)/N \rightarrow H$ | Stores size of one subdivision in $H$ (Note that $\rightarrow$ means hit STO button). |
| :$A \rightarrow X$ | Start $X$ off at beginning of interval. |
| :$0 \rightarrow L$ | Initialize $L$, which keeps track of left sums, to zero. |
| :$0 \rightarrow M$ | Initialize $M$, which keeps track of midpoint sums, to zero. |
| :$1 \rightarrow I$ | Initialize $I$, the counter for the loop. |
| :Lbl P | Label for top of loop. Lbl is accessed via PRGM, CTL. |
| :$L + H * Y_1 \rightarrow L$ | Increment $L$ by $Y_1 H$, the area of one more rectangle. ($Y_1$ is accessed via $Y$-VARS, or 2nd VARS.) |
| :$X + .5H \rightarrow X$ | Move $X$ to middle of interval. |
| :$M + H * Y_1 \rightarrow M$ | Evaluate $Y_1$ at the middle of interval and increment $M$ by rectangle of this height. |
| :$X + .5H \rightarrow X$ | Move $X$ to start of next interval. |
| :$IS > (I, N)$ | $IS > ($ is accessed via PRGM, CTL. This is the most difficult step in the program: adds 1 to $I$ and does the the next step if $I \leq N$ (i.e., if haven't gone through loop enought times); otherwise, skips next step. Thus, if $I \leq N$, goes back to Lbl P and loops through again. If $I > N$, loop is finished and goes on to print out results. Continue here if $I > N$, in which case the value of $X$ is now $B$. |
| :Goto P | Goto is accessed via PRGM, CTL. Jumps back to Lbl P if $J \leq N$. |
| :Disp "LEFT/RIGHT" | |
| :Disp $L$ | $L$ now equals the left sum, so display it. |
| :$L + H * Y_1 \rightarrow R$ | Add on area of right-most rectangle, store in $R$. |
| :$A \rightarrow X$ | Reset $X$ to $A$. |
| :$R - H * Y_1 \rightarrow R$ | Subtract off area of left-most rectangle. |
| :Disp $R$ | $R$ now equals right sum, so display it. |
| :$(L + R)/2 \rightarrow T$ | Trap approximation is average of $L$ and $R$. |
| :Disp "TRAP/MID/SIMP" | |
| :Disp $T$ | Display trap approximation. |
| :Disp $M$ | Display midpoint approximation. |
| :$(2M + T)/3 \rightarrow S$ | Simpson is weighted average of $M$ and $T$. |
| :Disp $S$ | Display Simpson's approximation. |

## Slope Field Program (TI-82)

This program draws the slope field for the differential equation $\dfrac{dy}{dx} = f(x, y)$.

|  |  |
|---|---|
| Name=SLOPES | *Where To Find The Commands* |
| :ClrDraw | 2nd Draw |
| :FnOff | 2nd Y-VARS, On/Off, |
| :7$(X_{\max} - X_{\min})/83 \to H$ | VARS, Window; $\to$ is on STO key. |
| :7$(Y_{\max} - Y_{\min})/55 \to K$ |  |
| :1$/(0.4H)^2 \to A$ |  |
| :1$/(0.4K)^2 \to B$ |  |
| :$X_{\min} + 0.5H \to X$ |  |
| :$Y_{\min} + 0.5K \to Z$ |  |
| :1 $\to I$ |  |
| :Lbl P | Prgm |
| :1 $\to J$ |  |
| :$Z \to Y$ |  |
| :Lbl Q |  |
| :$Y_1 \to T$ |  |
| :1$/\sqrt{(A + B * T^2)} \to C$ |  |
| :$T * C \to S$ |  |
| :$X \to U$ |  |
| :$Y \to V$ |  |
| :Line$(U - C, V - S, U + C, V + S)$ | 2nd Draw |
| :$V + K \to Y$ |  |
| :$IS > (J, 8)$ |  |
| :Goto Q | Prgm |
| :$U + H \to X$ |  |
| :$IS > (I, 12)$ | Prgm |
| :Goto P | Prgm |

To run this program:

1.  Enter $\dfrac{dy}{dx} = f(x, y)$ as $Y_1 = f(X, Y)$.
2.  Choose an appropriate WINDOW.
3.  Run the program.
4.  To get rid of previously drawn slope field, press "ClrDraw" (from the DRAW menu) or change the WINDOW.

## Euler's Method (TI-82)

This program for the TI-82 calculates and graphs an approximate solution for the differential equation $y' = f(x, y)$ using Euler's method.

The function $f$ is entered as $Y_1 = f(X, Y)$. When called, the program asks for the coordinates of the starting point and the step size. The graph is then drawn. The program does not clear the screen to start with, so solutions with different starting points or step sizes can be graphed consecutively on the same axes, or solution curves can be superimposed on a slope field. When the program is finished, the final $Y$-value remains in cell $Y$.

| Name=EULER | *Where to Find The Commands* |
|---|---|
| :FnOff | FnOff is a single symbol from the 2nd VARS On/Off menu. |
| :Disp "INITIAL X" | Disp and Input are single symbols from the PRGM I/O menu. |
| :Input $X$ | |
| :Disp "INITIAL Y" | |
| :Input $Y$ | |
| :Disp "STEP SIZE" | |
| :Input H | |
| :Lbl P | Lbl and Goto are single symbols from the PRGM CTL menu. |
| :$X + H \to U$ | |
| :$Y + H * Y_1 \to V$ | $Y_1$ is a single symbol from the 2nd VARS menu. |
| :Line$(X, Y, U, V)$ | Line( is a single symbol from the DRAW (i.e., 2nd PRGM) menu. |
| :$U \to X$ | |
| :$V \to Y$ | |
| :Goto P | |

To run this program:

1. Enter $y' = f(x, y)$ as $Y_1 = f(X, Y)$.

2. Choose an appropriate WINDOW.

3. Run the program; if you have seen enough of the trajectory, press ON and 2. Then press ENTER to continue with other initial values, or another step size.

4. To get rid of previously drawn graphs, press ClrDraw (from the DRAW menu) or change the WINDOW.

5. If you get an edgy, disconnected, or otherwise weird graph, try a smaller step size.

## Program for Trajectories (TI-82)

The program below graphs the *trajectory* in the $xy$ phase plane of the system

$$\frac{dx}{dt} = f(x, y), \quad x(0) = x_0,$$

$$\frac{dy}{dt} = g(x, y), \quad y(0) = y_0.$$

The functions $f(x, y)$ and $g(x, y)$ are entered into $Y_2$ and $Y_3$. If you want to plot a trajectory on top of a slope field, enter $\frac{dy}{dx}$ as $Y_1 = \frac{g(x, y)}{f(x, y)}$ and run the slope field program first.

Notice that you are graphing the relation between $x$ and $y$ in the phase plane; $t$ does not appear. To graph $x$ and $y$ against $t$, use the Time Series program on the next page.

Name= TRAJECT
:FnOff
:Disp "INITIAL X"
:Input $X$
:Disp "INITIAL Y"
:Input $Y$
:Disp "STEP SIZE"
:Input $H$
:Lbl P
:$X + H * Y_2 \to U$
:$Y + H * Y_3 \to V$
:Line$(X, Y, U, V)$
:$U \to X$
:$V \to Y$
:Goto P

| Command | Menu | Selection |
| --- | --- | --- |
| FnOff | Y-VARS | On/Off, 2 |
| Disp | PRGM | I/O, 3 |
| Input | PRGM | I/O, 1 |
| Lbl | PRGM | CTL, 9 |
| Line( | DRAW | 2 |
| Goto | PRGM | CTL, 0 |
| $Y_2, Y_3$ | Y-VARS | Y, 2, 3 |

To run this program:

1. Enter the differential equation as $Y_2 = f(X, Y)$ and $Y_3 = g(X, Y)$.

2. Choose an appropriate WINDOW.

3. Run the program; if you have seen enough of the trajectory, press ON and 2. Then press ENTER to continue with other initial values, or another step size.

4. To get rid of previously drawn trajectories, press ClrDraw (from the DRAW menu) or change the WINDOW.

5. If you get an edgy, disconnected, or otherwise weird trajectory, choose a smaller step size $H$. If the program runs too slowly, choose a larger step size $H$. Try starting with $H = 0.05$.

## Program for Time Series (TI-82)

This program graphs the *solutions* $x(t)$ and $y(t)$ of the system

$$\frac{dx}{dt} = f(x,y), \quad x(0) = x_0,$$

$$\frac{dy}{dt} = g(x,y), \quad y(0) = y_0.$$

Notice that here we are graphing both $x$ and $y$ as functions of $t$. Compare the Trajectory program on the previous page, which graphs the relation between $x$ and $y$, and in which $t$ does not appear.

| | Command | Menu | Selection |
|---|---|---|---|
| Name= TIMESER | | | |
| :ClrDraw | FnOff | Y-VARS | On/Off, 2 |
| :FnOff | Disp | PRGM | I/O, 3 |
| :Disp "INITIAL X" | | | |
| :Input $X$ | Input | PRGM | I/O, 1 |
| :Disp "INITIAL Y" | Lbl | PRGM | CTL, 9 |
| :Input $Y$ | Line( | DRAW | 2 |
| :Disp "STEP SIZE" | | | |
| :Input $H$ | Goto | PRGM | CTL, 0 |
| :$0 \rightarrow T$ | $Y_2, Y_3$ | Y-VARS | Y, 2, 3 |
| :Lbl P | If | PRGM | CTL, 1 |
| :$X + H * Y_2 \rightarrow U$ | $X_{min}$ | VARS | Window, 1 |
| :$Y + H * Y_3 \rightarrow V$ | | | |
| :$T + H \rightarrow W$ | $X_{max}$ | VARS | Window, 2 |
| :Line($T, X, W, U$) | > | TEST | 3 |
| :Line($T, Y, W, V$) | | | |
| :$U \rightarrow X$ | | | |
| :$V \rightarrow Y$ | | | |
| :$W \rightarrow T$ | | | |
| :Goto P | | | |

To run this program:

1. Enter the differential equation as $Y_2 = f(X,Y)$ and $Y_3 = g(X,Y)$.

2. Choose an appropriate WINDOW (note that $X_{min}$ and $X_{max}$ refer to the horizontal axis of the window, which is time in our case; $Y_{min}$ and $Y_{max}$ refer to the vertical axis: $x$ and $y$ in our case).

3. Run the program. To continue with other initial values, press CLEAR and ENTER. To quit, press CLEAR twice.

# CALCULATOR PROGRAMS

for the

# TI - 85

## Introduction to the TI-85

The following are programs for the TI-85 calculator to do numerical integration, graph slope fields, demonstrate solutions to differential equations using Euler's method, and plot trajectories and solutions to systems of differential equations.

**Notes on Using the TI-85:** When you want to multiply two quantities, say $A$ and $B$, on the TI-85 you must use "*". On a TI-81, $AB$ means $A * B$, whereas on a TI-85 $AB$ is a single variable. If you can't find a command, try 2nd, CATALOG, which gives a list of all the commands. Press a letter to go quickly to the commands beginning with that letter. Press ENTER to select. Letters can be both upper and lower case. Upper case letters are obtained by hitting ALPHA; lower case by hitting 2nd ALPHA. To enter a function (for example, $y1 =$) under the GRAPH menu, lower case variables should be used.

## Program to Calculate Riemann Sums to Evaluate a Definite Integral (TI-85)

Select 'PRGM' to get the program menu, then select 'EDIT' to enter a program. When you enter a program, you must first give it a name (for example, 'RSUMS'). To finish editing, hit EXIT.

| | |
|---|---|
| Name=RSUMS | *Where to Find The Commands* |
| :Disp "LOWER LIMIT" | Disp, " ", and Input are accessed via I/O, pressed while in the middle of a program. |
| :Input $A$ | |
| :Disp "UPPER LIMIT" | |
| :Input $B$ | |
| :Disp "DIVNS" | |
| :Input $N$ | |
| :$A \to x$ | $\to$ is on the STO key; use x-VAR key for $x$. |
| :$0 \to S$ | 0 is Zero, not "oh". |
| :$1 \to I$ | |
| :$(B - A)/N \to H$ | |
| :Lbl P | Lbl is accessed via CTL or CATALOG. |
| :$S + y1 * H \to S$ | $y1$ is typed in by entering 2nd ALPHA $Y$ and then 1. |
| :$x + H \to x$ | |
| :$IS > (I, N)$ | $IS >$ ( and Goto are accessed via CTL or CATALOG.) |
| :Goto P | |
| :Disp "LEFT SUM" | |
| :Disp $S$ | |
| :$S + y1 * H \to S$ | |
| :$A \to x$ | |
| :$S - y1 * H \to S$ | |
| :Disp "RIGHT SUM" | |
| :Disp $S$ | |

Things to watch for:

1.  Difference between $-$, which means subtract, and (-), which means negative. For example, $-2 - 3$ must be entered as (-)2 $- 3$.

2.  Disp and Input can also be typed in letter-by-letter.

To run this program:

1.  The integrand (the function you want to integrate) $f(x)$ must be entered into $y_1$, under the GRAPH menu, with $x$ as the independent variable.

2.  Make sure the lower limit of the integral you're approximating is less than the upper limit.

3.  Test on $\int_1^3 x^3 \, dx = 20$ with 100 subintervals. You should get left- and right-hand sums of 19.7408 and 20.2608, respectively.

## Numerical Integration Program (TI-85)

This program calculates left and right Riemann sums, and the trapezoidal and midpoint approximations. Since there's no room on the calculator for a separate labeling of each approximation, we use a compressed method of displaying the results. For instance, the label LEFT/RIGHT indicates that the next two numbers are the left- and right-hand Riemann sums, respectively.

**Notes:**

1. Select 'PRGM' to get the program menu, then select 'EDIT' to enter a program. When you enter a program, you must first give it a name (for example, 'INTEG'). To finish editing, hit EXIT.

2. The function to be integrated must be entered as $y1$ (accessed by GRAPH, followed by $y(x) =$). When $y1$ occurs in a program, it is evaluated at the current value of $x$.

3. The lower limit of integration must be less than the upper limit.

4. $IS > ($ is selected from under CTL, while enter entering the program. "Disp" and "Input" are selected from under I/O.

5. Use MORE to see items on a menu which are currently off the screen.

6. To run a program, select PRGM, NAMES. To stop a program while it is running, hit ON.

7. Test the program by evaluating $\int_1^3 x^3\,dx = 20$, using 100 subdivisions. You should get left- and right-hand sums of 19.7408 and 20.2608, respectively. For the trapezoid approximation, you should get 20.0008. For the mid point approximation, you should get 19.9996. For Simpson's rule, you should get exactly 20.

| | *Where to Find The Commands* |
|---|---|
| Name=INTEG | |
| :Disp "LOWER LIMIT" | Disp, Input, and " " are accessed via PRGM, I/O. |
| :Input $A$ | Enter lower limit of integration. |
| :Disp "UPPER LIMIT" | |
| :Input $B$ | Enter upper limit of integration. |
| :Disp "DIVNS" | |
| :Input $N$ | Enter number subdivisions. |
| :$(B - A)/N \rightarrow H$ | Stores size of one subdivision in $H$. (Note that $\rightarrow$ means hit STO button). |
| :$A \rightarrow x$ | Start $x$ off at beginning of interval. |
| :$0 \rightarrow L$ | Initialize $L$, which keeps track of left sums, to zero. |
| :$0 \rightarrow M$ | Initialize $M$, which keeps track of right sums, to zero. |
| :$1 \rightarrow I$ | Initialize $I$, the counter for the loop. |
| :Lbl P | Label for top of loop. Lbl is accessed via CTL |
| :$L + H * y1 \rightarrow L$ | Increment $L$ by $H * y1$, the area of one more rectangle. ($y1$ is typed in as $y$ and then 1.) |
| :$x + 0.5H \rightarrow x$ | Move $x$ to middle of interval. |
| :$M + H * y1 \rightarrow M$ | Evaluate $y1$ at the middle of interval and increment $M$ by a rectangle of this height. |
| :$x + 0.5H \rightarrow x$ | Move $x$ to start of next interval. |
| :$IS > (I, N)$ | Access $IS > ($ from under CTL. This is the most difficult step in the program: adds 1 to $I$ and does the next step if $I \leq N$ (i.e., if haven't gone through loop enought times); otherwise, skips next step. Thus, if $I \leq N$, goes back to Lbl 1 and loops through again. If $I > N$, loop is finished and goes on to print out results. |
| :Goto P | Goto is accessed via CTL. Jumps back to Lbl P if $I \leq N$. |
| :Disp "LEFT/RIGHT" | |
| :Disp $L$ | $L$ now equals the left sum, so display it. |
| :$L + H * y1 \rightarrow R$ | Add on area of right-most rectangle, store in $R$. |
| :$A \rightarrow x$ | Reset $x$ to $A$. |
| :$R - H * y1 \rightarrow R$ | Subtract off area of left-most rectangle. |
| :Disp $R$ | $R$ now equals right sum, so display it. |
| :$(L + R)/2 \rightarrow T$ | Trap approximation is average of $L$ and $R$. |
| :Disp "TRAP/MID/SIMP" | |
| :Disp $T$ | Display trap approximation. |
| :Disp $M$ | Display midpoint approximation. |
| :$(2 * M + T)/3 \rightarrow S$ | Simpson is weighted average of $M$ and $T$. |
| :Disp $S$ | Display Simpson's approximation. |

### Slope Field Program (TI-85)

This program graphs the slope field for differential equation $\dfrac{dy}{dx} = f(x, y)$.

| | *Where To Find The Commands* |
|---|---|
| Name=SLOPE | |
| :ClDrw | GRAPH, DRAW |
| :FnOff | GRAPH, VARS |
| :7($X_{\max} - X_{\min}$)/83 $\rightarrow$ H | GRAPH, RANGE; $\rightarrow$ is on STO key. |
| :7($Y_{\max} - Y_{\min}$)/55 $\rightarrow$ K | |
| :1/(0.4H)$^2$ $\rightarrow$ A | |
| :1/(0.4K)$^2$ $\rightarrow$ B | |
| :$X_{\min} + 0.5H \rightarrow x$ | |
| :$Y_{\min} + 0.5K \rightarrow Z$ | |
| :1 $\rightarrow$ I | |
| :Lbl P | CTL |
| :1 $\rightarrow$ J | |
| :$Z \rightarrow y$ | |
| :Lbl Q | |
| :$y1 \rightarrow T$ | $y1$ is entered by 2nd, ALPHA, $Y$, then 1 |
| :1/$\sqrt{(A + B * T^2)} \rightarrow C$ | |
| :$T * C \rightarrow S$ | |
| :$x \rightarrow U$ | |
| :$y \rightarrow V$ | |
| :Line($U - C, V - S, U + C, V + S$) | GRAPH, DRAW |
| :$V + K \rightarrow y$ | |
| :$IS > (J, 8)$ | |
| :Goto Q | CTL |
| :$U + H \rightarrow x$ | |
| :$IS > (I, 12)$ | CTL |
| :Goto P | CTL |

To run this program:

1. Enter $\dfrac{dy}{dx} = f(x, y)$ as $y1 = f(x, y)$. Select $y1$ under the GRAPH menu. Note the variables $x$ and $y$ must be in lower case, entered by pressing 2nd, ALPHA, then $X$, or $Y$.

2. Choose an appropriate RANGE.

3. Run the program.

4. To get rid of previously drawn slope field, press ClDrw (from the DRAW menu) or change the RANGE.

### Euler's Method (TI-85)

This program for the TI-85 calculates and graphs an approximate solution for the differential equation $y' = f(x, y)$ using Euler's method.

The function $f$ is entered as $y1 = f(x, y)$. When called, the program asks for the coordinates of the starting point and the step size. The graph is then drawn. The program does not clear the screen to start with, so solutions with different starting points or step sizes can be graphed consecutively on the same axes, or solution curves can be superimposed on a slope field. When the program is finished, the final $y$-value remains in cell $y$.

| Name=EULER | *Where to Find The Commands* |
|---|---|
| :FnOff | FnOff is accessible from the GRAPH, VARS menu. |
| :Disp "INITIAL X" | Disp and Input are accessible from the I/O menu. |
| :Input $x$ | |
| :Disp "INITIAL Y" | |
| :Input $y$ | |
| :Disp "STEP SIZE" | |
| :Input $H$ | |
| :Lbl P | Lbl and Goto are accessible from the CTL menu. |
| :$x + H \to U$ | |
| :$y + H * y1 \to V$ | |
| :Line$(x, y, U, V)$ | Line( is accessible from the GRAPH DRAW menu. |
| :$U \to x$ | |
| :$V \to y$ | |
| :Goto P | |

To run the program:

1. Enter $y' = f(x, y)$ as $y1 = f(x, y)$.

2. Choose an appropriate RANGE.

3. Run the program; if you have seen enough of the trajectory, press ON and QUIT. Then press ENTER to continue with other initial values, or another step size.

4. To get rid of previously drawn graphs, press ClDrw (accessed via DRAW from the GRAPH menu) or change the RANGE.

5. If you get an edgy, disconnected, or otherwise weird graph, try a smaller step size.

## Program for Trajectories (TI-85)

The program below graphs the *trajectory* in the $xy$ phase plane of the system

$$\frac{dx}{dt} = f(x, y), \quad x(0) = x_0,$$

$$\frac{dy}{dt} = g(x, y), \quad y(0) = y_0.$$

The functions $f(x, y)$ and $g(x, y)$ are entered into $y2$ and $y3$. If you want to plot a trajectory on top of a slope field, enter $\frac{dy}{dx}$ as $y1 = \frac{g(x, y)}{f(x, y)}$ and run the slope field program first.

Notice that you are graphing the relation between $x$ and $y$ in the phase plane; $t$ does not appear. To graph $x$ and $y$ against $t$, use the Time Series program on the next page.

<table>
<tr><td>Name=TRAJ</td><td></td><td></td><td></td></tr>
<tr><td>:FnOff</td><td>Command</td><td>Menu</td><td>Mode</td></tr>
<tr><td>:Disp "INITIAL X"</td><td>FnOff</td><td>GRAPH</td><td>VARS</td></tr>
<tr><td>:Input $x$</td><td>Disp</td><td>PRGM</td><td>I/O</td></tr>
<tr><td>:Disp "INITIAL Y"</td><td>Input</td><td>PRGM</td><td>I/O</td></tr>
<tr><td>:Input $y$</td><td>Lbl</td><td>PRGM</td><td>CTL</td></tr>
<tr><td>:Disp "STEP SIZE"</td><td>Line</td><td>GRAPH</td><td>DRAW</td></tr>
<tr><td>:Input $H$</td><td>Goto</td><td>PRGM</td><td>CTL</td></tr>
<tr><td>:Lbl P</td><td></td><td></td><td></td></tr>
<tr><td>:$x + H * y2 \to U$</td><td></td><td></td><td></td></tr>
<tr><td>:$y + H * y3 \to V$</td><td></td><td></td><td></td></tr>
<tr><td>:Line$(x, y, U, V)$</td><td></td><td></td><td></td></tr>
<tr><td>:$U \to x$</td><td></td><td></td><td></td></tr>
<tr><td>:$V \to y$</td><td></td><td></td><td></td></tr>
<tr><td>:Goto P</td><td></td><td></td><td></td></tr>
</table>

To run this program:

1. Enter the differential equation as $y2 = f(x, y)$ and $y3 = g(x, y)$.

2. Choose an appropriate RANGE from the GRAPH menu.

3. Run the program; if you have seen enough of the trajectory, press ON and QUIT. Then press ENTER to continue with other initial values, or another step size.

4. To get rid of previously drawn trajectories, press ClDrw (accessed via DRAW from the GRAPH menu) or change the RANGE.

5. If you get an edgy, disconnected, or otherwise weird trajectory, choose a smaller step size $H$. If the program runs too slowly, choose a larger step size $H$. Try starting with $H = 0.05$.

## Program for Time Series (TI-85)

This program graphs the *solutions* $x(t)$ and $y(t)$ of the system

$$\frac{dx}{dt} = f(x, y), \quad x(0) = x_0,$$

$$\frac{dy}{dt} = g(x, y), \quad y(0) = y_0.$$

Notice that here we are graphing both $x$ and $y$ as functions of $t$. Compare the Trajectory program on the previous page, which graphs the relation between $x$ and $y$, and in which $t$ does not appear.

Name=TIMES
:ClDrw
:FnOff
:Disp "INITIAL X"
:Input $x$
:Disp "INITIAL Y"
:Input $y$
:Disp "STEP SIZE"
:Input $H$
:$0 \to T$
:Lbl P
:$x + H * y2 \to U$
:$y + H * y3 \to V$
:$T + H \to W$
:Line$(T, x, W, U)$
:Line$(T, y, W, V)$
:$U \to x$
:$V \to y$
:$W \to T$
:Goto P

| Command | Menu | Mode |
|---------|------|------|
| FnOff | GRAPH | VARS |
| Disp | PRGM | I/O |
| Input | PRGM | I/O |
| Lbl | PRGM | CTL |
| Line | GRAPH | DRAW |
| Goto | PRGM | CTL |
| If | PRGM | CTL |
| $X_{min}$ | GRAPH | RANGE |
| $X_{max}$ | GRAPH | RANGE |
| > | TEST (=2nd 2) | |
| Goto | PRGM | CTL |

To run this program:

1.  Enter the differential equation as $y2 = f(x, y)$ and $y3 = g(x, y)$.

2.  Choose an appropriate RANGE.

3.  Run the program. To stop the program, press ON, then QUIT.

# CALCULATOR PROGRAMS

for the

# TI - 92

To enter a program, press $\boxed{\text{APPS}}$ and choose the program editor. To run a program, type the name, such as euler(), in the home screen.

## Slope Field Program (TI-92)

This program plots the slope field of the differential equation $\frac{dy}{dx} = f(x, y)$. The function $f(x, y)$ and the window are input by the user during the running of the program.

```
:slope()
:Prgrm
:setMode("Graph", "FUNCTION")
:PlotsOff
:FnOff
:ClrDraw
:ClrGraph
:ClrIO
:Request "Enter f(x,y) =", ff
:Input "Enter xmin =", xmin
:Input "Enter xmax =", xmax
:Input "Enter ymin =", ymin
:Input "Enter ymax =", ymax
:Local h, k, a, b, c, x, y, z, i, j, t, u, v
:7 * (xmax−xmin)/83 → h
:7 * (ymax−ymin)/55 → k
:1/(.4 * h)² → a
:1/(.4 * k)² → b
:Define f(x,y) =Func
:expr(ff)
:EndFunc
:xmin+.5 * h → x
:ymin+.5 * k → z
:1 → i
:For i, 1, 12, 1
:1 → j
:z → y
:For j, 1, 8, 1
:f(x,y) → t
:1/(√(a + b * t²)) → c
:t * c → s
:x → u
:y → v
:Line u − c, v − s, u + c, v + s
:v + k → y
:EndFor
:u + h → x
:EndFor
:EndPrgm
```

### Euler's Method (TI-92)

This program plots solutions to the differential equation

$$\frac{dy}{dx} = f(x, y).$$

The function $f(x, y)$ is input by the user during the running of the program.

```
:euler()
:Prgm
:setMode("Graph", "FUNCTION")
:PlotsOff
:FnOff
:ClrDraw
:ClrGraph
:ClrIO
:Local x, y, h, u, v, p
:Request "Enter f(x,y) =", ff
:Input "Initial x =", x
:Input "Initial y =", y
:Input "Stepsize =", h
:Text "Press ON to stop"
:Define f(x,y) = Func
:expr(ff)
:EndFunc
:Lbl p
:x + h → u
:y + h * f(x,y) → v
:Line x, y, u, v
:u → x
:v → y
:Goto p
:EndPrgm
```

To see the solution curves superimposed on the slope field, comment out the lines :ClrDraw and :ClrGraph by putting @ in front of them. (@ is found under the Control menu or by typing $\boxed{\text{2nd}}$ $x$.) Run slope() followed by euler().

### Program for Trajectories (TI-92)

This program plots trajectories of the differential equations

$$\frac{dx}{dt} = f(x, y)$$
$$\frac{dy}{dt} = g(x, y)$$

The functions $f(x, y)$ and $g(x, y)$ are input during the running of the program.

```
:traj()
:Prgm
:setMode("Graph", "FUNCTION")
:PlotsOff
:ClrDraw
:ClrGraph
:ClrIO
:FnOff
:Local x, y, h, u, v
:Request "Enter f(x, y) =", fden
:Request "Enter g(x, y) =", fnum
:Input "Inital x =", x
:Input "Inital y =", y
:Input "Step size=", h
:Text "Press ON to stop"
:Define f(x, y) = Func
:expr(fden)
:EndFunc
:Define g(x, y) = Func
:expr(fnum)
:EndFunc
:Lbl p
:x + h * f(x, y) → u
:y + h * g(x, y) → v
:Line x, y, u, v
:u → x
:v → y
:Goto p
:EndPrgm
```

To see the trajectories superimposed on the slope field, comment out the lines :ClrDraw and :ClrGraph from the traj() program by putting @ in front of them. (@ is found under the Control menu or by typing 2nd x.) Run slope() followed by traj().

## Program for Time Series (TI-92)

This program plots solutions $x(t)$, $y(t)$ to the system of differential equations

$$\frac{dx}{dt} = f(x, y)$$

$$\frac{dy}{dt} = g(x, y)$$

The functions $f(x, y)$ and $g(x, y)$ are input during the running of the program; the window must be set beforehand.

```
:times()
:Prgm
:setMode("Graph", "FUNCTION")
:PlotsOff
:ClrDraw
:ClrGRaph
:ClrIO
:FnOff
:Local x, y, t, h, u, v, w
:Request "Enter f(x, y) =", fden
:Request "Enter g(x, y) =", fnum
:Input "Inital x =", x
:Input "Inital y =", y
:Input "Step size=", h
:Text "Press ON to stop"
:Define f(x, y) = Func
:expr(fden)
:EndFunc
:Define g(x, y) = Func
:expr(fnum)
:EndFunc
:0 → t
:Lbl p
:x + h * f(x, y) → u
:y + h * g(x, y) → v
:t + h → w
:Line t, x, w, u
:Line t, y, w, v
:u → x
:v → y
:w → t
:Goto p
:EndPrgm
```

# CALCULATOR PROGRAMS

for the

# CASIO fx-7700GB

## Introduction to the CASIO fx-7700GB

The following are programs for the CASIO fx-7700GB calculator to do numerical integration, graph slope fields, demonstrate solutions to differential equations using Euler's method, and plot trajectories and solutions to systems of differential equations.

### Notes on Using the CASIO fx-7700GB:

- All the Casio integration programs call on the function you put in $f_1$. To store a function in $f_1$, first select the Function Memory Menu by pressing SHIFT then [F]MEM. Clear the screen by pressing AC if needed. Type out the function, then press STO (F1 key) followed by 1. Press LIST (F4 key) to see the list of stored functions.

- You can put either a colon (:) or a carriage return (EXE) after each instruction (to separate them), except after display sign ◢, which provides its own carriage return.

### Riemann Sums Program (CASIO)

To enter the program, press 'MODE' then '2' to select 'WRT' mode. Move the cursor to an empty program number, then press 'EXE'. You'll see a blank screen with the blinking cursor at the upper left corner. Now you can proceed to the beginning of the program. When finished, press 'MODE' then '1' to get back to 'RUN' mode.

| Program | Where to Find The Commands |
|---|---|
| "RSUMS" | |
| "L-LIM" ?$\to$ A | '?' is accessed by SHIFT, PRGM |
| "R-LIM" ?$\to$ B | |
| "DIVNS" ?$\to$ N | |
| A $\to$ X | |
| 0 $\to$ S | |
| $f_1 \to$ Y | '$f_1$' is accessed by SHIFT, $\boxed{F}$MEM, $f_n$, 1 |
| (B$-$A)div N $\to$ H | |
| Lbl 1 | 'Lbl' is in JMP menu |
| X + H $\to$ X | |
| $f_1$ + S $\to$ S | |
| Dsz N | 'Dsz' is in JMP menu |
| Goto 1 | 'Goto is also in JMP menu |
| "L-SUM=" | |
| (S $-$ $f_1$ + Y)H ◢ | |
| "R-SUM=" | |
| HS | |

To run this program:

1. The integrand (the function you want to integrate) $f(x)$ must be entered into $f_1$, with $X$ as the independent variable.

2. Make sure the lower limit of the integral you're approximating is less than the upper limit.

3. Test on $\int_1^3 x^3 \, dx = 20$ with 100 subintervals. You should get left- and right-hand sums of 19.7408 and 20.2608, respectively.

## Numerical Integration Program (CASIO)

This is a **Casio fx series** calculator program for various numerical integrals. It will display the Left and Right Riemann Sums and the Trapezoid Rule, Midpoint Rule, and Simpson's Rule approximations all at once. The way this program evaluates integrals is by keeping a running total of function values on $n$ subintervals, and then multiplying by the width of the rectangles to obtain the area at the very end. At the end of the program, hitting EXE will let you reevaluate the integral with a different number of subdivisions, and hitting AC will let you out of the program.

| Program | Comments |
|---|---|
| "INTEGRAL" | |
| "L-LIM"?→A | Integrate from X=a |
| "U-LIM"?→B | to X=b |
| "DIVNS"?→N | over N subdivisions. |
| (B−A)div (2N)→H | calculates half the width of a subdivision. |
| 0→L | initialize L, which will keep track of the left sums. |
| 0→M | initialize M, the midpoint sum. |
| A→X | place X at A, the beginning of the interval. |
| Lbl 1 | top of loop: |
| $f_1$+L→L | evaluate the function at the left edge of the interval add the result to the left-hand sum running total. |
| X+H→X | move X to the middle of the interval. |
| $f_1$+M→M | evaluate the function at the middle of the interval add the result to the midpoint running total. |
| X+H→X | move X to the beginning of the next interval. |
| Dsz N | decrease N by 1; if N=0, skip the next step and go on. |
| Goto 1 | bottom of loop. |
| "LEFT,RIGHT,TRAP" | |
| 2HL→L | multiply the sum of the left-hand function values by width 2H. |
| L◢ | display the left-hand sum. |
| L+2H$f_1$→T | evaluate the function at X=b: the rightmost function value add the area of the rightmost rectangle with the left-hand sum. |
| A→X | put X back at A. |
| T−2H$f_1$→T | evaluate the function at the left-most edge of the interval take the area of the leftmost rectangle out of T. |
| T◢ | display what is now the right-hand sum. |
| (L+T)div 2→T | average the left- and right-hand sums. |
| T◢ | display the trapezoid approximation. |
| MID,SIMP" | |
| 2HM→M | multiply the midpoint values sum by the interval width. |
| M◢ | display the midpoint approximation. |
| (2M+T)div 3→M | calculate Simpson's Rule by weighted averaging. |
| M | display Simpson's Rule approximation. |

### CASIO Slope Field Program

Notice that the ranges of $x$ and $y$ are set in the program itself $-4.7 \leq X \leq 4.7$ and $-3.1 \leq Y \leq 3.1$. The program will work, however, with whatever range you give it; change the first two lines of this program by putting different values other than 4.7 and 3.1 in D and E respectively.

| Program | Comments |
|---|---|
| "SLOPE" | |
| 4.7→D | half the width of the screen area. |
| 3.1→E | half the height of the screen area. |
| Range −D,D,1,−E,E,1 | sets the range as just defined. |
| 14Ddiv 83→H | calculates the widths for 12 scaled horizontal divisions. |
| 14Ediv 55→K | calculates the heights for 8 scaled vertical divisions. |
| 1div $(0.4H)^2$ →A | factor needed to calculate segment components. |
| 1div $(0.4K)^2$ →B | factor needed to calculate segment components. |
| −D+.5H→X | left edge margin. |
| −E+.5K→Z | bottom margin. |
| 12→I | do this twelve times. |
| Lbl 1 | top of the outer loop (moves across rows). |
| Z→Y | start down by the bottom of the screen. |
| 8→J | do this eight times. |
| Lbl 2 | top of inner loop (moves up columns). |
| $f_1$→ T | slope of segment. |
| 1div $\sqrt{(A+BT^2)}$→C | cosine, or x-component of segment. |
| TC→S | sine, or y-component (don't need slope now). |
| X→U:Y→V | free up memories X and Y for Plot to use. |
| Plot U−C,V−S | mark the end of slope segment from center at X,Y. |
| Plot U+C,V+S | backtrack and mark other end. |
| Line | connect-the-dots. |
| U→X | put U back to X. |
| V+K→Y | move Y up $\frac{1}{8}$ the way. |
| Dsz J | have I done this twelve times? |
| Goto 2 | if not, go to the top of the inner loop. |
| U+H→X | if so, move right $\frac{1}{12}$ the way across. |
| Dsz I | have I done this twelve times? |
| Goto 1 | if not, go to the top of the outer loop start all over. |
| Lbl 3 | if so, the program goes into a dead loop in order to hold |
| Goto 3 | the display. |

## Euler's Method Program (CASIO)

This is a **Casio fx series** calculator program that will demonstrate graphical solutions to differential equation $\frac{dy}{dx} = f(x, y)$ using Euler's Method.

The function $f$ is entered as $f_1 = f(X, Y)$. When called, the program asks for the coordinates of the starting point and the step size. The graph is then drawn. The program does not clear the screen to start with, so solutions with different starting points or step sizes can be graphed consecutively on the same axes. If you want the solution curves superimposed on the slope field, make sure the range parameters are the same as those in the slope field program. When the program is finished, the final $Y$-value remains in cell $Y$.

| Program | Comments |
|---|---|
| "EULER" | |
| "INITIAL X"?→X | initial X value |
| "INITIAL Y"?→Y | initial Y value |
| "STEP SIZE"?→H | length of a horizontal step. |
| Lbl 1 | top of loop. |
| X+H→U | move horizontally 1 step. |
| Y+Hf₁→V | figure out how much to move vertically. |
| Plot X,Y | plot the old point. |
| Plot U,V | plot the new point. |
| Line | connect-the-dots. |
| U→X | |
| V→Y | |
| Goto 1 | keep going. |

## Trajectory Program (CASIO)

The program below graphs the *trajectory* in the $xy$ phase plane of the system

$$\frac{dx}{dt} = f(x,y), \quad x(0) = x_0,$$

$$\frac{dy}{dt} = g(x,y), \quad y(0) = y_0.$$

The functions $f(x,y)$ and $g(x,y)$ are entered into $f_2$ and $f_3$. If you want to plot a trajectory on top of a slope field, enter $\frac{dy}{dx}$ as $f_1 = \frac{g(x,y)}{f(x,y)}$ and run the Slope Field program first.

Notice that you are graphing the relation between $x$ and $y$ in the phase plane; $t$ does not appear. To graph $x$ and $y$ against $t$, use the Time Series program on the next page.

| | |
|---|---|
| "TRAJECT" | |
| "INITIAL X"?→X | press SHIFT then PRGM to access ? |
| "INITIAL Y"?→Y | |
| "STEP SIZE"?→H | |
| Lbl 1 | Lbl is accessed in JMP menu, selected by pressing SHIFT then PRGM. |
| X+ Hf$_2$→U | f$_2$ is entered by SHIFT, F MEM, fn (F3 key), then 2. |
| Y+ Hf$_3$→V | |
| Plot X, Y | |
| Plot U, V | |
| Line | |
| U→X | |
| V→Y | |
| Goto 1 | Goto is in JMP menu. |

To run this program:

1.  Enter the differential equation as $f_2 = f(X,Y)$ and $f_3 = g(X,Y)$.

2.  Choose an appropriate RANGE.

3.  Run the program; if you have seen enough of the trajectory, press AC. Then press EXE to continue with other initial values, or another step size.

4.  To get rid of previously drawn trajectories, press SHIFT then Cls (F5 key).

5.  If you get an edgy or disconnected trajectory, choose a smaller step size $H$. If the program runs too slowly, choose a larger step size $H$. Try starting with $H = 0.05$.

## Time Series Program (CASIO)

This program graphs the *solutions* $x(t)$ and $y(t)$ of the system

$$\frac{dx}{dt} = f(x,y), \quad x(0) = x_0,$$

$$\frac{dy}{dt} = g(x,y), \quad y(0) = y_0.$$

Notice that here we are graphing both $x$ and $y$ as functions of $t$. Compare the Trajectory program on the previous page, which graphs the relation between $x$ and $y$, and in which $t$ does not appear.

```
"TIMESER"
"INITIAL X"?→X
"INITIAL Y"?→Y
"STEP SIZE"?→H
Cls
0→T
Lbl 1
X+Hf₂→U
Y+Hf₃→V
T+H→W
X→P
Y→Q
Plot T, P
Plot W, U
Line
Plot T, Q
Plot W, V
Line
U→X
V→Y
W→T
Goto 1
Lbl 3
Goto 3
```

To run this program:
1. Enter the differential equation as $f_2 = f(X,Y)$ and $f_3 = g(X,Y)$.
2. Choose an appropriate RANGE (note that $X_{min}$ and $X_{max}$ refer to the horizontal axis of the window, which is time in our case; $Y_{min}$ and $Y_{max}$ refer to the vertical axis: $x$ and $y$ in our case).
3. Run the program. To continue with other initial values, press AC and EXE. To quit, press AC twice.

# CALCULATOR PROGRAMS

for the

# SHARP EL-9200 and EL-9300

## Introduction to the Sharp EL-9200 and EL-9300

The following programs are for the Sharp EL-9200 and Sharp EL-9300 calculators. Enclosed you will find programs to do numerical integration, graph slope fields, demonstrate solutions to differential equations using Euler's method, and plot trajectories and solutions to systems of differential equations.

**Notes:**

1. All the following programs are in REAL mode.

2. To access the commands, first press 2ndF COMMAND, then select them via the appropriate menus.

3. After editing a line in a program, make sure to press ENTER or the button with downward pointing triangle before you quit; otherwise the changes will not be saved.

4. Since the user-defined functions ($Y_1$ ... etc.) are not shared by different programs, the formula for a function has to be given when it is used in a program. Thus, each programs has a subroutine that starts with the line "Label eqn" and ends with "Return", where the desired function should be entered.

5. Variables are case sensitive. Single uppercase letters (A to Z) are global variables, i.e., the values stored in memories designated by single letter A to Z can be shared by different programs. Lowercase letters and lowercase words are local variables, i.e., the values of local variables are specific to the program in which they're used. You can use a string of up to 12 lowercase letters to designate a local variable. Note also that you can not mix uppercase and lowercase letters to form a variable.

## Riemann Sums Program (SHARP)

Select NEW in the program menu. Then select REAL in the MODE menu. When prompted for a title, use "riemann." The "..." in the following program is where the integrand–the function to be integrated–should be entered.

| Program | Where the Commands are |
|---|---|
| Goto start | Goto is in BRANCH menu |
| Label eqn | Label is in BRANCH menu |
| f=... | replace "..." by the integrand $f(x)$ |
| Return | Return is in BRANCH menu |
| Label start | |
| Print "l-limit | Print and " are in PROG menu |
| Input a | Input is in PROG menu |
| Print "u-limit | |
| Input b | |
| Print "divns | |
| Input n | |
| x=a | = is also in INEQ menu |
| s=0 | reset memory s to zero |
| i=1 | |
| h=(b−a)/n | |
| Label 1 | |
| Gosub eqn | Gosub is in BRANCH menu |
| s=s+f*h | |
| x=x+h | |
| i=i+1 | |
| If i <= n Goto 1 | If and Goto are in BRANCH menu; <= is in INEQ menu |
| Print "left sum | |
| Print s | |
| Gosub eqn | |
| s=s+f*h | |
| x=a | |
| Gosub eqn | |
| s=s−f*h | |
| Print "right sum | |
| Print s | |
| End | End is in PROG menu |

To run this program:

1. The integrand (the function you want to integrate) $f(x)$ must be entered into where "..." is, with x as the independent variable.

2. Make sure the lower limit of the integral you're approximating is less than the upper limit.

3. Test on $\int_1^3 x^3\, dx = 20$ with 100 subintervals. You should get left- and right-hand sums of 19.7408 and 20.2608, respectively.

## Numerical Integration Program (SHARP)

This program calculates left- and right-hand Riemann sums, and the trapezoidal, midpoint and Simpson approximations. Since there's not room on the calculator to label each approximation separately, we use a compressed method of displaying the results. For instance, the label "left/right" indicates that the next two numbers are the left- and right-hand Riemann sums, respectively.

To enter the program select NEW in the program menu. Then select REAL in the MODE menu. When prompted for a title, use "integral."

| Program | Where the Commands are |
|---|---|
| *Program* | *Where the Commands are* |
| Goto start | Goto is in BRANCH menu |
| Label eqn | Label is in BRANCH menu |
| f=... | replace "..." by the integrand $f(x)$ |
| Return | Return is in BRANCH menu |
| Label start | |
| Print "l-limit | Print and " are in PROG menu |
| Input a | Input is in PROG menu |
| Print "u-limit | |
| Input b | |
| Print "divns | |
| Input n | |
| x=a | = is also in INEQ menu |
| s=0 | reset memory s to zero |
| m=0 | reset memory m to zero |
| i=1 | |
| h=(b−a)/n | |
| Label 1 | |
| Gosub eqn | Gosub is in BRANCH menu |
| s=s+f*h | |
| x=x+ .5h | |
| Gosub eqn | |
| m=m+f*h | |
| x=x+ .5h | |
| i=i+1 | |
| If i <= n Goto 1 | If and Goto are in BRANCH menu; <= is in INEQ menu |
| Print "left/right | |
| Print s | |
| Gosub eqn | |
| r=s+f*h | |
| x=a | |
| Gosub eqn | |
| r=r−f*h | |
| Print r | |
| Wait | Wait is in PROG menu |
| Print "trap/mid/simp | |
| t=.5(s+r) | |
| Print t | |
| Print m | |
| s=(2m+t)/3 | |
| Print s | |
| End | End is in PROG menu |

To run this program:

1. The integrand (the function you want to integrate) $f(x)$ must be entered into where "..." is, with x as the independent variable.

2. Make sure the lower limit of the integral you're approximating is less than the upper limit.

3. Test on $\int_1^3 x^3 \, dx = 20$ with 100 subintervals. You should get left- and right-hand sums of 19.7408 and 20.2608, respectively.

## Slope Field Program (SHARP)

This program draws the slope field for the differential equation $\dfrac{dy}{dx} = f(x, y)$. You should enter $f(x, y)$ in the third line, where "..." is.

To enter the program select NEW in the program menu. Then select REAL in the MODE menu. When prompted for a title, use "slope".

| *Program* | *Where the Commands are* |
|---|---|
| Goto start | Goto is in BRANCH menu |
| Label eqn | Label is in BRANCH menu |
| f=... | replace "..." by the function $f(x, y)$ |
| Return | Return is in BRANCH menu |
| Label rng | |
| xmin=$-4.7$ | minimum x value |
| xmax=4.7 | maximum x value |
| ymin=$-3.1$ | minimum y value |
| ymax=3.1 | maximum y value |
| h=7(xmax$-$xmin)/83 | |
| k=7(ymax$-$ymin)/55 | |
| Range xmin,xmax,1,ymin,ymax,1 | Range is in GRAPH menu |
| Return | |
| Label start | |
| Gosub rng | Gosub is in BRANCH menu |
| a=1/(0.4h)$^2$ | |
| b=1/(0.4k)$^2$ | |
| x=xmin+0.5h | |
| z=ymin+0.5k | |
| i=1 | |
| Label 1 | |
| j=1 | |
| y=z | |
| Label 2 | |
| Gosub eqn | |
| t=f | |
| c=1/$\sqrt{(a+b*t^2)}$ | |
| s=t*c | |
| u=x | |
| v=y | |
| Line u$-$c, v$-$s, u+c, v+s | Line is in GRAPH menu |
| y=v+k | |
| j=j+1 | |
| If j <= 8 Goto 2 | If and Goto are in BRANCH menu; <= is in INEQ menu |
| x=u+h | |
| i=i+1 | |
| If i <= 12 Goto 1 | |
| End | |

**Note:** You can also use different range parameters other than xmin= $-4.7$, xmax= 4.7, ymin= $-3.1$, ymax= 3.1.

## Euler's Method Program (SHARP)

This program calculates and graphs an approximate solution for the differential equation $y' = f(x, y)$ using Euler's method.

The function $f(x, y)$ is entered in the third line. When called, the program asks for the co-ordinates of the starting point and the step size. The graph is then drawn. The program does not clear the screen to start with, so solutions with different starting points or step sizes can be graphed consecutively on the same axes. If you want the solution curves superimposed on the slope field, make sure the range parameters are the same as those in the slope field program.

To enter the program select NEW in the program menu. Then select REAL in the MODE menu. When prompted for a title, use "euler".

| *Program* | *Where the Commands are* |
|---|---|
| Goto start | Goto is in BRANCH menu |
| Label eqn | Label is in BRANCH menu |
| f=... | replace "..." by the function $f(x, y)$ |
| Return | Return is in BRANCH menu |
| Label start | |
| Print "initial x | Print and " are in PROG menu |
| Input x | Input is in PROG menu |
| Print "initial y | |
| Input y | |
| Print "step size | |
| Input h | |
| Label 1 | |
| u=x+h | |
| Gosub eqn | Gosub is in BRANCH menu |
| v=y+f*h | |
| Line x, y, u, v | Line is in GRAPH menu |
| x=u | |
| y=v | |
| Goto 1 | |
| End | End is in PROG menu |

## Trajectory Program (SHARP)

The program below graphs the *trajectory* in the $xy$ phase plane of the system

$$\frac{dx}{dt} = f(x, y), \quad x(0) = x_0,$$

$$\frac{dy}{dt} = g(x, y), \quad y(0) = y_0.$$

The functions $f(x, y)$ and $g(x, y)$ are entered in the third and fourth line, respectively. If you want to plot a trajectory on top of a slope field, enter $\dfrac{dy}{dx}$ as $\dfrac{g(x, y)}{f(x, y)}$ into the slope field program and run the slope field program first.

Notice that you are graphing the relation between $x$ and $y$ in the phase plane; $t$ does not appear. To graph $x$ and $y$ against $t$, use the Time Series program on the next page.

To enter the program select NEW in the program menu. Then select REAL in the MODE menu. When prompted for a title, use "traject".

| *Program* | *Where the Commands are* |
|---|---|
| Goto start | Goto is in BRANCH menu |
| Label eqn | Label is in BRANCH menu |
| f=... | replace "..." by the function $f(x, y)$ |
| g=... | replace "..." by the function $g(x, y)$ |
| Return | Return is in BRANCH menu |
| Label start | |
| Print "initial x | Print and " are in PROG menu |
| Input x | Input is in PROG menu |
| Print "initial y | |
| Input y | |
| Print "step size | |
| Input h | |
| Label 1 | |
| Gosub eqn | Gosub is in BRANCH menu |
| u=x+h*f | |
| v=y+h*g | |
| Line x, y, u, v | Line is in GRAPH menu |
| x=u | |
| y=v | |
| Goto 1 | |
| End | End is in PROG menu |

## Time Series Program (SHARP)

This program graphs the *solutions* $x(t)$ and $y(t)$ of the system

$$\frac{dx}{dt} = f(x,y), \quad x(0) = x_0,$$

$$\frac{dy}{dt} = g(x,y), \quad y(0) = y_0.$$

You should enter $f(x,y)$ and $g(x,y)$ in the third and fourth line, respectively.

Notice that here we are graphing both $x$ and $y$ as functions of $t$. Compare the trajectory program on the previous page, which graphs the relation between $x$ and $y$, and in which $t$ does not appear.

To enter the program select NEW in the program menu. Then select REAL in the MODE menu. When prompted for a title, use "timeser".

| Program | Where the Commands are |
|---|---|
| *Program* | *Where the Commands are* |
| Goto start | Goto is in BRANCH menu |
| Label eqn | Label is in BRANCH menu |
| f=... | replace "..." by the function $f(x,y)$ |
| g=... | replace "..." by the function $g(x,y)$ |
| Return | Return is in BRANCH menu |
| Label start | |
| Print "initial x | Print and " in PROG menu |
| Input x | Input is in PROG menu |
| Print "initial y | |
| Input y | |
| Print "step size | |
| Input h | |
| ClrG | ClrG is in SCRN menu |
| t=0 | |
| Label 1 | |
| Gosub eqn | Gosub is in BRANCH menu |
| u=t+h | |
| p=x+h*f | |
| q=y+h*g | |
| Line t, x, u, p | Line is in GRAPH menu |
| Line t, y, u, q | |
| x=p | |
| y=q | |
| t=u | |
| Goto 1 | |
| End | End is in PROG menu |

# CALCULATOR PROGRAMS

for the

# HP-48S and HP-48G

## Riemann Sums for the HP-48S/G

The following is a directory for experimenting with different Riemann sums. To use a directory press VAR to get the user's menu and then press the name of directory on menu keys, in this case RSUM. To leave the directory when you are finished, press (left shift) UP. To create a directory, type the name, say 'RSUM' followed by CRDIR on the MEMORY menu.

### RSUM Directory

These short programs can be entered by hand or transferred via infrared from another HP-48. Programs are given in the order you will find most convenient to use on the menu. The name of each program is given before the program. As you enter each program, store it under the given name. Thus for first program, type << ANS − >> followed by ENTER and then type 'ERR' and press STO.

ERR << ANS − >>
LFT << A SUM >>
RGT << A H + SUM >>
MID << A H 2 / + SUM >>
TRP << LFT B F A F − H * 2 / + >>
SMP << MID 2 * TRP + 3 / >>
NSTO << 'N' STO B A − N / 'H' STO >>
ABSTO << 'B' STO 'A' STO >>
FSTO << 'F(X)' SWAP = DEFINE >>
SUM << → X 'H*Σ(I=0, N−1,F(X+I*H))' >>

The other variables used by these programs will also be on your menu: A, B, F, N, H, ANS. To make sure your menu is in the most convenient order, just use FSTO, ABSTO, and NSTO once, which will creat variables A, B, F, N, and H. Also do 0 'ANS' STO to create a variable called ANS. Then press (left shift) {} and press menu buttons to get this:
{ERR LFT RGT MID TRP SMP NSTO ABSTO FSTO ANS}
Press ENTER. Then type in ORDER followed by ENTER (or find ORDER on the MEMORY menu and press the menu button).

### How to Use Directory RSUM

Here is an example. If you want to experiment with $\int_0^1 \frac{1}{1+x^2}\,dx$ with $N = 10$ subdivisions do this:
Enter '$1/(1 + X^2)$' and press FSTO.
Enter 0. Enter 1. Press ABSTO.
Enter 10 and press NSTO.
Now press LFT, RGT, MID, TRP, SMP to get the left, right, midpoint, trapezoid, and Simpson approximations for the given integral. If you know the actual value of the integral, store that value in ANS. Then when you press ERR the value of ANS will be subtracted from whatever is at level one of the stack. Thus, if you press MID followed by ERR, the error for the midpoint approximation will appear on the stack. This is especially useful if you are trying to study how the errors of the different methods are related to each other and to N.

## Directory S.FLD for slope fields on HP-48S

Type 'S.FLD' then CRDIR to create directory S.FLD Here are the programs:
FSTO << 'F(X,Y)' SWAP = DEFINE >>
DRW << RCLF −19 SF −2 SF ERASE { # 0d # 0d } PVIEW DRAX PPAR 2 GET
        PPAR 1 GET − 9 * OBJ→ 64 / SWAP 131 / SWAP DUP2 →V2 0.5 *
        PPAR 1 GET + OBJ→ PPAR 2 GET OBJ→ → H K XLO YLO XHI YHI

```
    << XLO XHI FOR X YLO YHI FOR Y X Y →V2 X Y ATAN DUP COS 0.4
    * H * SWAP SIN 0.4 * K * →V2 DUP2 − 3 ROLLD + LINE K STEP H
    STEP >>
 STOF  GRAPH >>
```

## How to Use S.FLD

Enter the right side of $\frac{dy}{dx} = f(x, y)$ as an expression in $X$ and $Y$ and then press FSTO. Then press DRW. Change the viewing window as usual on the PLOTR submenu of PLOT. The 9 in the second line of the program DRW controls how often slope lines are plotted. Replace 9 by 10 and fewer lines are plotted; replace 9 by 8 and more lines are plotted.

## Slopefields on the HP-48G

The HP-48G has built-in slopefields. Simply press PLOT, move the black box to highlight the TYPE of plot and press CHOOS on the menu. Then scroll through the displayed window until you have SLOPEFIELD in the black box. Then press ENTER. Move the black box to EQ and type the desired expression for right side of $\frac{dy}{dx} = f(x, y)$ and then press ENTER. Press ERASE and DRAW to get the slopefield. On the PLOT SLOPEFIELD window, if you press OPTS menu key, you can change the XRNG and YRNG for the viewing window. To draw more slope lines increase XSTEP and/or YSTEP on the PLOT window; XSTEP of 20 and YSTEP of 10 are pretty good but you might want to try more or less.

## Differential Equations Directories for the HP-48S/G

The following are two directories for differential equations, FIRST and SYS. The directory FIRST is for getting solutions to a first order differential equation $\frac{dy}{dx} = f(x, y)$, using either Euler's method or Improved Euler's method. SYS is for plotting solutions to the system of equations

$$\frac{dx}{dt} = f(x, y), \quad \frac{dy}{dt} = g(x, y).$$

The plot can be as the user chooses: $y$ versus $x$, $x$ versus $t$, or $y$ versus $t$.

### The Directory FIRST

```
EUL << << DUP2 F DX * + SWAP DX + SWAP >> 'STP' STO >>
I.EUL << << DUP2 DUP2 F DX 0.5 * * + SWAP DX 0.5 * + SWAP F DX * +
    SWAP DX + SWAP >> 'STP' STO >>
FSTO << 'F(X,Y)' SWAP = DEFINE >>
DRW << { # 0d # 0d } PVIEW DRAX PPAR 2 GET RE X0 Y0 DO DUP2 R→C
    3 ROLLD STP DUP2 R→C 4 ROLL LINE UNTIL OVER 4 PICK >
    END 3 DROPN GRAPH >>
ERAS << ERASE >>
```

The other variables in this directory are X0 and Y0 which hold the initial values $x$ and $y$, DX the step size, and F which holds $f(x, y)$. When entering the programs, also create these variables by storing something in them; for example .1 'DX' STO. Order the menu: EUL I.EUL FSTO DRW ERAS DX X0 Y0 F.

## How to Use FIRST

Enter $f(x, y)$ as an expression in X and Y and press FSTO. Store initial values for $x$ and $y$ in X0 and Y0. Store the step size in DX (try, say, 0.1 at first). Select Euler's method by pressing EUL; select Improved Euler's method by pressing I.EUL. Then press ERAS and DRW.

You can plot a second solution on the same screen simply by selecting a new X0 and Y0 and pressing DRW without pressing ERAS. The XRNG and YRNG for the screen are set as usual in the PLOT window. The plot TYPE must be FUNCTION.

You can single-step either method to see what is happening numerically. Simply put a value for X and a value for Y on the stack. If you then press STP, the next X and Y values generated by Euler or Improved Euler (whichever you have selected) will appear on the stack.

### The Directory SYS for the HP-48S/G

Here are the programs:

FSTO << 'F' STO >>
GSTO << 'G' STO >>
XY << { X Y } 'UV' STO >>
TX << { T X } 'UV' STO >>
TY << { T Y } 'UV' STO >>
DRW << { # 0d # 0d } PVIEW DRAX X0 'X' STO Y0 'Y' STO T0 'T' STO DO
    UV 1 GET →NUM UV 2 GET →NUM R→C STP UV 1 GET →NUM UV 2
    GET →NUM R→C LINE UNTIL 0 END >>
ERAS << ERASE >>
STP << X F →NUM DT * + 'X' STO Y G →NUM DT * + 'Y' STO T DT +
    'T' STO >>

In addition to these programs there are variables X0, Y0, T0 for the initial values for $x$, $y$, $t$ and variable DT for the step size for $t$. These programs also use variables called F, G, X, Y, T, UV, which appear in the menu. After you have used the program once, you should order the menu: XY, TX, TY, DT, ERAS, DRW, FSTO, GSTO, X0, Y0, T0, T, STP, X, Y, PPAR, F, G, U.

### How to Use SYS

Enter the expression in X, Y, and T for $f(x, y, t)$ and press FSTO. Do the same for $g(x, y, t)$. Select which variables you want plotted: XY, TX, or TY. Store a step size in DT, say 0.1. Store initial values for $x$, $y$, and $t$ in X0, Y0, and T0. Press ERAS and then DRW. If you wish to plot $x$ versus $t$ and $y$ versus $t$ on the same graph, select TX and press ERAS and DRW; then select TY, do not press ERAS, and then press DRW. Plots will continue until you press ON. This will return you to the stack; press GRAPH to get the graph back.

Control XRNG and YRNG as usual on the PLOT window. To follow numerically the value of any variable, say X, press X and then press STP, then press X, then STP, and so on. The successive values of X will go on stack.

If DT is too small, the graph will be jagged and take a long time to plot. If DT is too large, the graph will consist of long straight line segments. Changing the XRNG will affect what is the best DT.

### Built-in Differential Equation Plotter for the HP-48G

The HP-48G has a built-in differential equation plotter. On the PLOT screen highlight TYPE of plot, press CHOOS, and select DIFF EQ. If you are solving a first order differential equation, $\frac{dx}{dy} = f(x, y)$, enter the expression for $f$ on line labeled $F$ (move black box to that line first). Make sure that INDEP variable name is X and solution variable name is Y. Initial values for X and Y are set on the PLOT screen; window XRNG and YRNG are set on the OPTS screen, as are the step size and even "tolerance."

The solution variable may also be a vector and the function $F$ may be vector-valued. This allows one to do systems where Y actually stands for the ordered pair $(x, y)$ and F is the ordered pair $(f(x, y, t), g(x, y, t))$. For more information see the manual.

# PART VI

## SAMPLE EXAM QUESTIONS

# Chapter 1 Exam Questions

*Problems and Solutions for Section 1.1*

1. The empirical function $W = f(t)$, given in the graph to the right, comes from the <u>Wall Street Journal</u>, September 4, 1992. From the graph, describe the domain of this function and the range of this function. In a sentence, apply the general definition of the word "function" to explain why you think that the given curve is in fact a function.

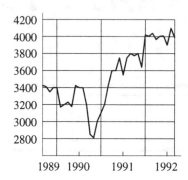

ANSWER:

Domain: September 1989 to August 1992. Range: 2810 (approx.) $\leq W \leq$ 4090 (approx.). For every date in the domain, there is a unique value of $W$.

2. Consider a ten-story building with a single elevator. From the point of view of a person on the sixth floor, sketch a graph indicating the height of the elevator as a function of time as it travels. Remember to indicate when it stops. Try to take into account all *types* of cases that can happen, but do not worry about *every* possible situation. (There are many different possible graphs that could be drawn for this.)

ANSWER:

A possible diagram: An elevator first goes from the ground floor to the third floor, then to the eighth floor, and finally back to the ground floor.

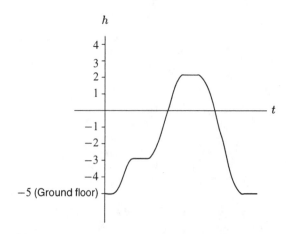

3. Draw a graph which accurately represents the temperature of the contents of a cup left overnight in a room. Assume the room is at 70° and the cup is originally filled with water slightly above the freezing point.

   ANSWER:

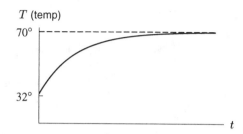

4. Suppose the Long Island Railroad train from Easthampton to Manhattan leaves at 4:30 pm and takes two hours to reach Manhattan, waits two hours at the station and then returns, arriving back in Easthampton at 10:30 pm. Draw a graph representing the distance of the train from the Farmingdale station in Easthampton as a function of time from 4:30 pm to 10:30 pm. The distance from Easthampton to Manhattan is 150 miles.

   ANSWER:

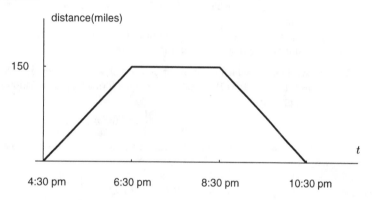

## Problems and Solutions for Section 1.2

1. Suppose we buy quantities $x_1$ and $x_2$, respectively, of two goods. The graph below shows the budget constraint $p_1x_1 + p_2x_2 = k$, where $p_1$ and $p_2$ are the prices of the two goods and $k$ is the available budget. On the graph, draw the lines that correspond to the following situations, and for each line, give the equation and the coordinates of both intercepts. Label each line clearly.

   (a) The budget is doubled, but prices remain the same.

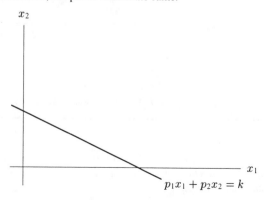

(b)  The price of the first good is doubled, but everything else remains the same (the available budget is still $k$).

ANSWER:

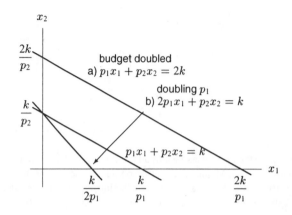

(a)  $x_2 = -\frac{p_1}{p_2}x_1 + \frac{k}{p_2}$. If the prices remain the same, the slope of the line remains the same. If the budget is doubled, push the line up, keeping the slope the same, but doubling the $x_1$ and $x_2$ intercepts.

(b)  $x_2 = -\frac{p_1}{p_2}x_1 + \frac{k}{p_2}$. When the price of the first good is doubled, we get $x_2 = -\frac{2p_1}{p_2}x_1 + \frac{k}{p_2}$. The slope of the line is double; $y$-intercept remains the same.

2.  Given a function which is linear for $x \le 2$ and also linear for $x \ge 2$. This function has the following values: $f(-4) = 3$; $f(2) = 0$; $f(4) = 6$. Find formula(s) (or equation(s)) which describe this function.

ANSWER:

For $x \le 2$, the slope is $\frac{-3}{6} = \frac{-1}{2}$ and the $y$-intercept is 1; thus $y = \frac{-1}{2}x + 1$. For $x \ge 2$, the

slope is $\frac{6}{2} = 3$. To find the $y$-intercept we substitute: $6 = 3(4) + b$, $6 - 12 = b$, so that $b = -6$. Hence, $y = 3x - 6$.

This is an example of a *piece-wise function*: $f(x) = \begin{cases} -\dfrac{1}{2}x + 1 & \text{when } x \le 2 \\ 3x - 6 & \text{when } x \ge 2 \end{cases}$

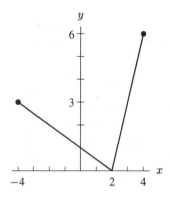

## Problems and Solutions for Section 1.3

1.  Table 1.3.1 defines three functions for $0 \le x \le 8$: $y_1 = f_1(x)$; $y_2 = f_2(x)$; and $y_3 = f_3(x)$. Identify which of the functions are linear, exponential, or neither. Write an equation for the functions which are exponential or linear.

**TABLE 1.3.1**

| $x$ | $y_1$ | $y_2$ | $y_3$ |
|---|---|---|---|
| 0 | 4.25 | 4.25 | 4.25 |
| 2 | 6.80 | 5.11 | 3.39 |
| 4 | 10.88 | 5.97 | 2.53 |
| 6 | 17.408 | 9.552 | 1.67 |
| 8 | 27.8528 | 15.2832 | 0.81 |

ANSWER:

For the $y_1$'s: $\dfrac{6.8}{2.5} = 1.6$; $\dfrac{10.88}{6.8} = 1.6$; $\dfrac{17.408}{10.88} = 1.6$; $\dfrac{27.8528}{17.408} = 1.6$. Therefore, $y_1$ is an exponential function whose $y$-intercept is 4.25; $y_1 = f_1(x) = 4.25(1.6)^x$.

For the $y_2$'s, there are no common ratios or common differences.

For the $y_3$'s, the $\Delta y$'s are: $3.39 - 4.25 = -0.86$; $2.53 - 3.39 = -0.86$; $1.67 - 2.53 = -0.86$; and $.81 - 1.67 = -0.86$. Thus $y_1$ is a linear function with slope $\dfrac{-0.86}{2} = -0.43$ and $y$-intercept 4.25; $y_3 = f_3(x) = -0.86x + 4.25$.

2.  In Table 1.3.2, we are given the population of a small country over a ten year period.

**TABLE 1.3.2**
*Population by year*

| Year | Population |
|---|---|
| 1985 | 100, 004 |
| 1987 | 108, 104 |
| 1989 | 116, 860 |
| 1991 | 126, 326 |
| 1993 | 136, 559 |
| 1995 | 147, 620 |

During this same period, each year, the farmers of this country have produced more than enough food to support its population. Table 1.3.3 gives the number of people that this country's agriculture were able to support during this same period:

**TABLE 1.3.3**  *Food production by year*

| Year | Number of people farmers can feed |
|---|---|
| 1985 | 105, 000 |
| 1987 | 115, 650 |
| 1989 | 125, 253 |
| 1991 | 134, 847 |
| 1993 | 145, 506 |
| 1995 | 155, 100 |

We are interested in determining how long the farmers will be able to produce enough food to feed this population.

(a)  Knowing that populations tend to grow exponentially and assuming that food production is linear, find equations that model these two sets of data.

(b) After studying these two sets of data, what can be said about the food supply for this population during this period?

(c) Using the equations that model population and food supply, how long will there be enough food for this population?

ANSWER:

(a) Since we are assuming the population will grow exponentially, we consider ratios of population for consecutive periods:

$$\frac{108,160}{100,004} \approx 1.081$$

$$\frac{116,986}{108,160} \approx 1.081$$

Do more if needed, but this tells us that an exponential model for this population can be given by

$$N(t) = 100,004(1.082)^{\frac{t}{2}}$$

with $t = 0$ for 1985 and $t = 2$ for 1987, etc.

To find the linear model for food produced, we find an equation of a straight line from this data. Let $F$ represent food produced. Then,

$$\frac{F - 115,650}{t - 2} = \frac{115,650 - 105,000}{2 - 0}$$

or

$$F - 115,650 = 5325(t - 2)$$

or

$$F(t) = 5325(t - 2) + 115,650$$
$$F(t) = 5325t + 105,000.$$

Again, $t = 0$ represents 1985; $t = 2$, 1987, etc.

(b) Since the number of people the farmers can feed is greater than the population on any one of the given years, one can expect a happy, healthy, growing population.

(c) Note that both $N$ and $F$ are increasing functions. Graphing both $N$ and $F$, one can see that they intersect at about $t = 20$, or during 2005. After this year, the food supply will be inadequate for the population.

## Problems and Solutions for Section 1.4

1. Give rough sketches, for $x > 0$, of the graphs of $y = x^5$, $y = x$, $y = x^{1/3}$, $y = x^0$, and $y = x^{-2}$.

ANSWER:

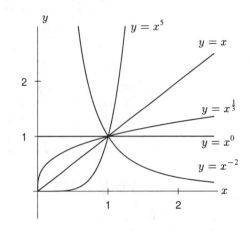

2. Consider the functions $f(x) = 10 \left(\frac{2}{3}\right)^x$ and $g(x) = \frac{1}{\sqrt{x}}$. Graph both of these functions on your graphing calculator. By zooming in on appropriate regions, you should be able to make the two graphs appear as shown in the diagrams below.

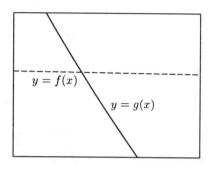
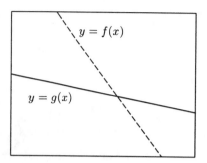

(a) Find the $x$-coordinate of the point of intersection of the two graphs indicated in the **left**-hand diagram. Give an answer accurate to within one decimal place..

(b) Find the $x$ coordinate of the point of intersection of the two graphs indicated in the **right**-hand diagram. Give an answer accurate to within one decimal place.

ANSWER:

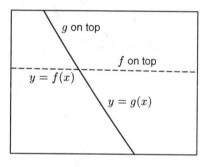
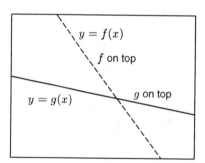

(a) The first diagram: This intersection occurs "near" $x = 0$. Try
$x$ min= 0, $x$ max= 0.1
$y$ min= 0, $y$ max= 11
Then zoom in. Get $x \approx 0.010$.

(b) The second diagram: This intersection occurs for $y$-values near zero. Try
$x$ min= 0, $x$ max= 10
$y$ min= 0, $y$ max= 1.
Then zoom. Get $x \approx 8.3$

3. (a) Use your calculator to find all the solutions to the equation

$$2^x = x^2.$$

Give your answers to one decimal place. Sketch the graphs drawn by your calculator as part of the explanation for your answer.

(b) For what values of $x$ is $2^x > x^2$?

ANSWER:

(a)

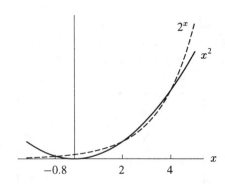

Solutions : $x = -0.8$ (by zooming), $x = 2, 4$.

(b)   $2^x > x^2$ for $-0.8 < x < 2$ or $x > 4$.

4.   On the given set of axes, graph and clearly label: (A) $y = \sqrt{x}$; (B) $y = x^{.2}$; (C) $y = x^{1.2}$; (D) $y = x^2$;
     (E) $y = x^5$; (F) $y = x^8$.

   ANSWER:

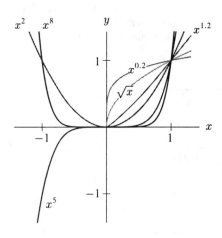

5.   A spherical cell takes in nutrients through its cell wall at a rate proportional to the area of the cell wall.
     The rate at which the cell uses nutrients is proportional to its volume.

   (a)   Write an expression for the rate at which nutrients enter the cell as a function of its radius, $r$.
   (b)   Write an expression for the rate at which the cell uses nutrients as a function of its radius,$r$.
   (c)   Sketch a possible graph showing the rate at which nutrients enter the cell against the radius $r$ (put
         $r$ along the horizontal axis). On the same axes, sketch a possible graph for the rate at which the
         cell uses nutrients.
   (d)   Show algebraically why there must be a radius $r_0$ (other than $r_0 = 0$) at which the rate at which
         nutrients are used equals the rate at which nutrients enter the cell. Mark $r_0$ on your graph.
   (e)   What happens to the cell when $r > r_0$? When $r < r_0$? What does this tell you about the radius of
         the cell in the long run?

   ANSWER:

   (a)   Rate at which nutrients enter cell $= k4\pi r^2 = Ar^2$   $(A > 0)$   $k, c$ are constants of proportion-
         ality.
   (b)   Rate at which nutrients are used $= c\frac{4}{3}\pi r^3 = Br^3$   $(B > 0)$.
   (c)

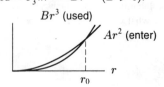

(d)   $Ar^2 = Br^3$ for $r = 0$ and $r = \dfrac{A}{B}$ so $r_0 = \dfrac{A}{B}$

(e)   When $r > r_0$, rate used > rate enter so cell shrinks.
When $r < r_0$, rate used < rate enter so cell grows.
In long run, cell's radius $\to r_0$.

## Problems and Solutions for Section 1.5

1.   Given the function $f(x) = \dfrac{2}{3x - 7}$, do the following:

(a)   Graph $f$, and from that graph, produce a graph of the inverse function of $f$.

(b)   Find an algebraic expression for the inverse of $f$ and check to see that the graph of the inverse function matches the graph found in part (a).

ANSWER:

(a)   The graph of $f$ is given in Figure 1.5.1.

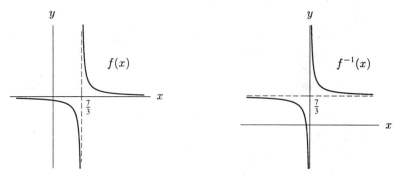

**Figure 1.5.1**                    **Figure 1.5.2**

To find the graph of the inverse of $f$, we reflect the graph of $f$ about the line $y = x$. This gives the graph shown in Figure 1.5.2.

(b)   To find the inverse of $f$ algebraically, set

$$y = \frac{2}{3x - 7}$$

and solve for $x$ in terms of $y$. This gives the following:

$$3xy - 7y = 2$$
$$3x - 7 = \frac{2}{y}$$
$$3x = \frac{2}{y} + 7$$
$$x = \frac{2}{3y} + \frac{7}{3}.$$

Rewriting this as a function with variable $x$ gives

$$h(x) = \frac{2}{3x} + \frac{7}{3}.$$

This can be checked by showing that $f\left(h(x)\right) = x$ and $h\left(f(x)\right) = x$.

## *Problems and Solutions for Section 1.6*

1. In 1909, the Danish biochemist Sören Peter Lauritz Sörensen (1868-1939) introduced the pH function as a measure of the acidity of a chemical substance: pH= $f([H^+]) = -\log_{10}[H^+]$, where $[H^+]$ in the molecular concentration of hydrogen ions (moles per liter, $M$). Sörensen determined that, for 0 <pH< 7, the substance is an acid; when pH= 7, the substance is neutral; and for pH> 7, the substance is a base or is said to be alkaline. The $[H^+]$ for blood is $3.16 \times 10^{-8} M$ and for milk is $4.0 \times 10^{-7} M$. Find the pH of blood and of milk, and categorize each as acid(s) and/or base(s). Reportedly, the worst known instance of acid rain occurred in Scotland in 1974, at which time the pH was determined to be 2.4 [Stewart, *et al.*, *College Algebra*, p. 331]. Find the hydrogen ion concentration for this acid rain.

    ANSWER:

    pH of blood $= -\log\left(3.16 \times 10^{-8}\right) = -\log 3.16 - \log 10^{-8} = -\log 3.16 + 8 \cdot \log 10$ so that the pH of blood $= -\log 3.16 + 8$.
    When we evaluate this, we get pH of blood $\approx -.4997 + 8 = 7.5003$, and blood is slightly alkaline.
    pH of milk $= -\log(4.0 \times 10^{-7}) = -\log 4 + 7 \approx -.6021 + 7 = 6.3979$, and we se that milk is mildly acidic.
    For the acid rain, $2.4 = -\log[H^+]$, or $-2.4 = \log[H^+]$, so that $10^{-2.4} \approx 3.981 \times 10^{-3} = .003981 M = [H^+]$.

2. Suppose that $N(t) = 100,000,000 \cdot 2^{t/30}$ gives the population of a certain country $t$ years after a census was taken. A historian has a collection of documents that are not dated, but do refer to the population of this country at several times. In order to help the historian date these documents, find the inverse function for the function $N$.

    ANSWER:

    To find the inverse of $N$, take the logarithm of both sides of the expression. This gives

    $$\log N = \log\left[100,000,000 \cdot 2^{\frac{t}{30}}\right]$$

    $$= \log[100,000,000] + \frac{t}{30}\log 2 \approx 8 + 0.01t$$

    Solving this for $t$ gives the desired function:

    $$t = \frac{30}{\log 2}(\log N - 8) \approx 100\log N - 797.$$

## *Problems and Solutions for Section 1.7*

1. Find an equation for the line $L$ shown below. Your answer will contain the positive constant $b$. Simplify your answer.

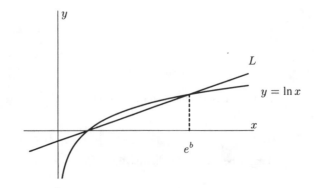

ANSWER:

The line $L$ passes through the two points on the curve $y = \ln x$ specified by $y = 0$ and $x = e^b$, that is, $(1, 0)$ (since $1 = e^0$) and $(e^b, b)$ respectively. The equation for this line is

$$\frac{y - 0}{x - 1} = \frac{b - 0}{e^b - 1},$$

so

$$y = \frac{b}{e^b - 1}(x - 1).$$

2. Here are some data from a recent Scientific American article on Old World monkeys.

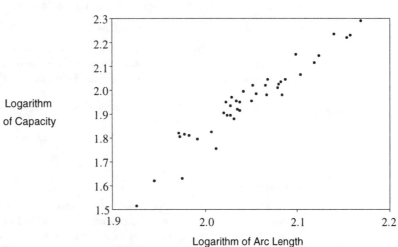

**Figure 1.7.3:** Cranial Capacity of contemporary Old World monkeys is related to arc length of skull as shown.

(a) From the data presented give an approximate formula for

$$C = \text{cranial capacity (in cm}^3)$$

as a function of

$$A = \text{arc length of skull (in cm)}.$$

[Hint: Fit a line through the data points. Logarithms are to base 10.]

(b) What type of function is $C = f(A)$ (logarithmic, exponential, trigonometric, power function,...)?

ANSWER:

(a) A line fit through the data points goes through $(2.18, 2.3)$ and $(1.9, 1.66)$, and so has slope $\frac{\Delta y}{\Delta x} = \frac{0.64}{0.28} = 2.3$. The equation is

$$y = 2.3x + b.$$

Solving for $b$ yields

$$2.3 = (2.3)2.18 + b$$
$$b \approx -2.7.$$

So $y = 2.3x - 2.7$. But $x = \log(A)$ and $y = \log(C)$, so

$$\log C = 2.3 \log A + 2.7.$$

Exponentiating both sides yields

$$C = 10^{2.3 \log A + 2.7} \approx A^{2.3}(501).$$

(b) This is a power function.

3. One of the following tables of data is linear and one is exponential. Say which is which and give an equation that best fits each table. For the exponential table you do not have to use $e$ if you do not want. An answer like $y = (3.73)(1.92)^{x/8}$ is fine.

(a)

| $x$ | 0 | 0.50 | 1.00 | 1.50 | 2.00 |
|---|---|---|---|---|---|
| $y$ | 3.12 | 2.62 | 2.20 | 1.85 | 1.55 |

(b)

| $x$ | 0 | 0.50 | 1.00 | 1.50 | 2.00 |
|---|---|---|---|---|---|
| $y$ | 2.71 | 3.94 | 5.17 | 6.40 | 7.63 |

ANSWER:

(a) This table is exponential and we find that the ratios of successive $y$-values are all 0.84 (when rounded to two decimals). An appropriate equation is therefore

$$y = 3.12(0.84)^{2x} = 3.12(0.7056)^x,$$

since $y(0) = 3.12$. (Check: When $x = 2$, $y(2) = 3.12(0.7056)^2 \approx 1.5534$.) This could equally well be written $y = 3.12e^{-0.3487x}$. Actually, there is a range of possible answers: $y = 3.12a^x$ for any $a$ between 0.7046 and 0.7059 will give the values shown in the table, when rounded to two decimals.

(b) The second table is linear. Pick a curve of the form $y = mx + b$. Since $y(0) = 2.71$, so $b = 2.71$, and $y = mx + 2.71$. But $y(1) = 5.17$, so

$$5.17 = m + 2.71$$
$$m = 2.46$$

and hence $y = 2.46x + 2.71$.

4. (a) Suppose there is an initial population of 100 rabbits on *Prosperity Island*. Assuming that the rabbits have more than enough of everything they need to live prosperously, we might expect the population to grow exponentially. If so, find a formula for $P(t)$, the number of rabbits on *Prosperity Island* at time $t$, given that after one year there are 120 rabbits on the island. (Assume $t$ is in years.) When will there be 500 rabbits on *Prosperity Island*?

(b) Next, we turn our attention to *Cramped Quarters Island*, a tiny island which, although able to support a *limited* population of rabbits, doesn't have enough space or food supplies to support unlimited exponential growth. It is suggested that if $Q(t) =$ population of rabbits on *Cramped Quarters Island* at time $t$, then the quantity $(800 - Q(t))$ will be an exponentially decaying function of $t$. Given that there were 500 rabbits at time $t = 0$, and 600 rabbits one year later, what is the general formula for $Q(t)$, the population of rabbits on *Cramped Quarters Island* at time $t$?

(c) On the axes below, make a sketch of $y = Q(t)$. Choose an appropriate scale for the $Q$ axis.

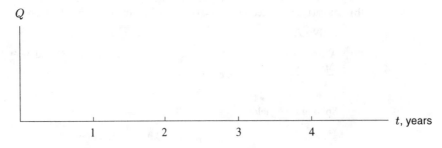

ANSWER:

(a) $P(t) = P_0 \cdot a^t$
$P(0) = P_0 = 100$
$P(1) = P_0 \cdot a^1 = 100 \cdot a = 120 \Rightarrow a = 1.2$
so $P(t) = 100 \cdot (1.2)^t$
When will there be 500 rabbits on *Prosperity Island*?
Let $t_0$ be this number. Then $P(t_0) = 500 = 100 \cdot (1.2)^{t_0}$. Therefore $5 = (1.2)^{t_0} \Rightarrow \ln 5 = t_0 \cdot \ln 1.2$
$\Rightarrow t_0 = \dfrac{\ln 5}{\ln 1.2}$

(b)  $800 - Q(t)$ is an exponential decay function.
Hence, $800 - Q(t) = f(t) = P_0 \cdot a^t$
$f(0) = 800 - Q(0) = 800 - 500 = 300 = P_0 a^t = P_0$
$f(t) = 800 - Q(1) = 800 - 600 = 200 = 300a^t \Rightarrow a = \frac{2}{3}$
$f(t) = 300 \left(\frac{2}{3}\right)^t$. So $Q(t) = 800 - 300 \left(\frac{2}{3}\right)^t$.

(c)
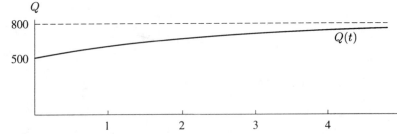

5.  An exponentially decaying substance was weighed every hour and the results are given below:

| Time | Weight (in grams) |
| --- | --- |
| 9 am | 10.000 |
| 10 am | 8.958 |
| 11 am | 8.025 |
| 12 noon | 7.189 |
| 1 pm | 6.440 |

(a)  Determine a formula of the form

$$Q = Q_0 e^{-kt}$$

which would give the weight of the substance, $Q$, at time $t$ in hours since 9 am.

(b)  What is the approximate half-life of the substance?

ANSWER:

(a)  $Q = 10e^{-kt}$ since $Q_0$ = initial value = 10.
When $t = 1$, $Q = 8.958$, so $8.958 = 10e^{-k(1)}$ and
$0.8958 = e^{-k}$ so $k = -\ln 0.8958 = 0.11$
Thus $Q = 10e^{-0.11t}$.

(b)  Half life when $Q = \frac{1}{2}Q_0$: $\frac{1}{2}Q_0 = Q_0 e^{-0.11t}$ so $\ln \frac{1}{2} = -0.11t$, so $t = 6.3$ hours.

6.  The number of bacteria in milk grows at a rate of 10% per day once the milk has been bottled. When the milk is put in the bottles, it has an average bacteria count of 500 million per bottle.

(a)  Write an equation for $f(t)$, the number of bacteria $t$ days after the milk is bottled.

(b)  Graph the number of bacteria against time. Label the axes and intercepts.

(c)  Suppose milk cannot be safely consumed if the bacteria count is greater than 3 billion per bottle. How many days will the milk be safe to drink once it has been bottled?

ANSWER:

(a)  $f(t) = 500 \times 10^6 (1.1)^t$

(b)

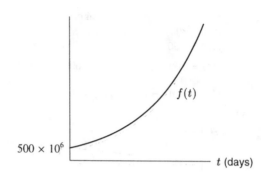

(c)  Find $t$ making $f(t) = 3 \times 10^9$
$$3 \times 10^9 = 500 \times 10^6 (1.1)^t$$

$$\frac{3000}{500} = (1.1)^y \text{ so } 6 = (1.1)^t$$

$$t = \frac{\ln 6}{\ln 1.1} \approx 18.8 \text{ days.}$$

Thus milk will be safe for 18 days; during the 19th day it will turn bad, according to this model.

7.  *Cramped Quarters Island* is a tiny island which, although able to support a limited population of rabbits, does not have enough space or food supplies to support unlimited exponential growth. It is suggested that if $Q(t)$ = population of rabbits at time $t$, then the quantity $(800 - Q(t))$ will be an exponentially decaying function of $t$. If at time $t = 0$ there were 400 rabbits, and the population was increasing at an instantaneous rate of 100 rabbits per year, find a general formula for $Q(t)$.

ANSWER:

$Q(t)$ is the population of rabbits.
$$800 - Q(t) = ae^{-kt}$$
$$Q(t) = 800 - ae^{-kt}$$
$$Q(0) = 400 = 800 - ae^{-k0}$$
$$a = 400$$
$$Q'(t) = (-a)(-k)e^{-kt} = ake^{-kt}$$
$$Q'(0) = 400k = 100 \Rightarrow k = \tfrac{1}{4} = .25$$
$$Q(t) = 800 - 400e^{-.25t}$$

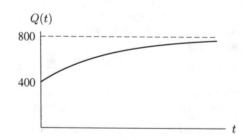

8.  In 1992, the Population Crisis Committee wrote:

Large cities in developing countries are growing much faster than cities in the industrialized world ever have. London, which in 1810 became the first industrial city to top 1 million, now has a population of 11 million. By contrast, Mexico City's population stood at only a million just 50 years ago and now is 20 million.

Assume that the instantaneous percentage growth rates of London and Mexico City were constant over the last two centuries.

(a)  How many times greater is Mexico City's percentage growth rate than London's? Show your calculations and reasoning.

(b) When were the two cities the same size? Show your calculations and reasoning.

ANSWER:

(a) Letting $\alpha$ and $\beta$ be the two growth rates for London and Mexico City, respectively, we approximate the population growth in millions by two exponentials, $e^{\alpha t}$ and $e^{\beta t}$, both of which are set to have population 1 million when $t = 0$. Since 182 and 50 are, respectively, the times that have passed since each city had 1 million people, we get

$$11 \approx 1 \cdot e^{\alpha \cdot 182} \quad \text{and} \quad 20 \approx 1 \cdot e^{\beta \cdot 50}$$

and

$$\beta = \frac{\ln 20}{50} \approx 0.0599, \alpha = \frac{\ln 11}{182} \approx 0.0132, \quad \text{and} \quad \frac{\beta}{\alpha} = \frac{182 \ln 20}{50 \ln 11} \approx 4.5.$$

(Note that these are growth rates, not percentages, but the ratio is the same as if we did it in terms of percentages.)

(b) We measure from 50 years ago (1942), when the population in London was $e^{0.0132(132)}$ and the population is Mexico City was 1 million. The functions describing population in the two cities are then:

$$\text{Mexico City : Population} = e^{0.0599t}$$
$$\text{London : Population} = e^{0.0132(132)}e^{0.0132t}$$

Setting these equal and solving, we get:

$$e^{0.0599t} = e^{0.0132(132)}e^{0.0132t}$$
$$0.0599t = 0.0132(132 + t)$$
$$t = \frac{0.0132 \cdot 132}{0.0599 - 0.0132} \approx 37.2$$

So the populations were equal 37.2 years after 1942, that is, in 1979.

9. Given that $\ln 2 = 0.69$ and $\ln 5 = 1.61$ to two decimal places, find

(a) $\ln 0.1$
(b) $\ln 100$

ANSWER:

(a)

$$\begin{aligned}
\ln 0.1 &= \ln \frac{1}{10} \\
&= \ln 1 - \ln 10 \\
&= -\ln 10 \\
&= -\ln(2 \cdot 5) \\
&= -(\ln 2 + \ln 5) \\
&= -2.30.
\end{aligned}$$

(b)

$$\begin{aligned}
\ln 100 &= \ln \left(10^2\right) \\
&= 2 \ln 10 \\
&= 2(2.30) \\
&= 4.60.
\end{aligned}$$

1. One of the graphs below shows the rate of flow, $R$, of blood from the heart in a man who bicycles for twenty minutes, starting at $t = 0$ minutes. The other graph shows the pressure, $p$, in the artery leading to a man's lungs as a function of the rate of flow of blood from the heart.

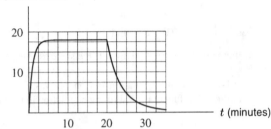

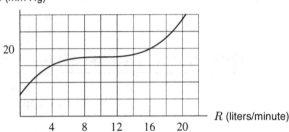

(a) Estimate $p(R(10))$ and $p(R(22))$.

(b) Explain what $p(R(10))$ represents in practical terms.

ANSWER:

(a) $p(R(10)) = p(18) = 23$ mm Hg
    $p(R(22)) = p(10) = 17.5$ mm Hg

(b) $p(R(10))$ represents the pressure in the artery at $t = 10$.

2. Given the function $y = f(x) = e^{-\frac{x^2}{2}}$:

(a) Devise functions $g(x)$ and $h(x)$ so that $f(x) = g(h(x))$.

(b) Graph the function $f(x)$; set the range of your calculator to $-3 \le x \le 3$. Copy your graph onto graph paper. Estimate the extrema (the maximum and/or minimum) point(s) and the inflection point(s) for this function.

(c) The function $N(x) = \dfrac{1}{\sqrt{2\pi}} \cdot e^{-\frac{x^2}{2}}$ is one of the cornerstones of statistics. In a sentence, briefly describe what $\dfrac{1}{\sqrt{2\pi}}$ does to $f(x)$, i.e., briefly describe the curve $N(x)$ in terms of that of $f(x)$.

ANSWER:

(a) $h(x) = -\dfrac{x^2}{2}$, the "inside" function and $g(x) = e^x$.

Then $f(x) = g(h(x)) = g\left(-\dfrac{x^2}{2}\right) = e^{-\frac{x^2}{2}}$.

(b)

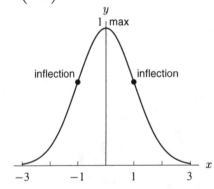

(c) The coefficient $\dfrac{1}{\sqrt{2\pi}}$ "dilates" the curve; since $\dfrac{1}{\sqrt{2\pi}} < 1$, the effect is to "squash the curve down" a bit.

This curve is the *Gaussian* or *Normal distribution*. The $\dfrac{1}{\sqrt{2\pi}}$ is chosen so that the area under the whole curve is 1. Also note that the $x$-axis is a horizontal asymptote.

3.  Given the function $m(z) = z^2$, find and simplify $m(z + h) - m(z)$.
    ANSWER:

$$
\begin{aligned}
m(z + h) - m(z) &= (z + h)^2 - z^2 \\
&= z^2 + 2zh + h^2 - z^2 \\
&= 2zh + h^2
\end{aligned}
$$

## Problems and Solutions for Section 1.9

1.  Consider the function
    $$c(x) = \cos x + 0.5 \cos 2x.$$

    (a)  Is $c(x)$ a periodic function? If so, what is its smallest period?
    (b)  Using your calculator, draw the graph of $c(x)$. Adjust the scales so you can see the patterns and symmetries clearly. Sketch your final version on the axes below, showing the scale you use, and describe what you see.
    (c)  At what points $x$ is $c(x)$ a maximum? Explain.
    (d)  Let $x_0$ be the first positive number where $c(x_0) = 0$. Find an interval containing $x_0$ whose length is $< \frac{1}{10}$. Explain briefly how you did this.
    (e)  Looking again at the symmetries in your graph in part (b), argue that the next positive number where $c(x_0) = 0$ is $2\pi - x_0$. Can you show this directly?
    (f)  In terms of $x_0$, what are all the places where $c(x) = 0$ for $-2\pi \le x \le 4\pi$?

    ANSWER:

    (a)  This is a periodic function with smallest period $2\pi$.
    (b)  This function is similar to a cosine function, except that the peaks are slightly raised, and the troughs have small bumps in them.
    (c)  $c(x)$ has a local maximum at $n\pi$, where $n$ is an integer. $c(x)$ takes on its greatest value, 1.5, at every $2\pi$.

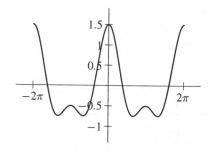

*Figure 1.9.4*

    (d)  In order to confine $x_0$ within an interval whose length is less than $\frac{1}{10}$, try picking values of $x$ and looking at the sign of $c(x)$. Start with $x = 1$, since it looks like it's near the root.

$$
\begin{aligned}
c(1) &= \cos(1) + 0.5\cos(2) \\
&\approx 0.5403 - 0.2081 > 0 \\
c(2) &= \cos(2) + 0.5\cos(4) \\
&\approx -0.4161 - 0.3268 < 0
\end{aligned}
$$

So $x_0$ is between 1 and 2.

$$c(1.5) = \cos(1.5) + 0.5\cos(3)$$
$$\approx 0.0707 - 0.495 < 0$$

So $x_0$ is between 1 and 1.5.

$$c(1.2) = \cos(1.2) + 0.5\cos(2.4)$$
$$\approx 0.3624 - 0.3686 < 0$$
$$c(1.1) = \cos(1.1) + 0.5\cos(2.2)$$
$$\approx 0.4536 - 0.2942 > 0$$

So $x_0$ is between 1.1 and 1.2.

(e) Since $c(x)$ is even, there will be a root at $-x_0$. Since this function has period $2\pi$, there will be a root at $-x_0 + 2\pi$. From the graph, it is clear that this is the next root of $c(x)$.

(f) $x_0, -x_0, 2\pi - x_0, x_0 - 2\pi, x_0 + 2\pi, 4\pi - x_0$

2. At high tide, the water level is 10 feet below a certain pier. At low tide the water level is 26 feet below the pier. Assuming sinusoidal behavior, sketch a graph of $y = f(t) =$ the water level, relative to the pier, at time $t$ (in hours) if at $t = 0$ the water level is $-18$ feet and falling, until it reaches the first low tide at $t = 3$. Based on your sketch and the information provided above, give a formula for $f(t)$.

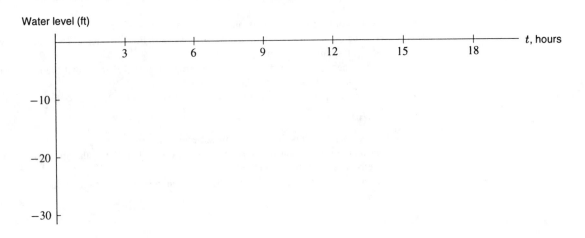

ANSWER:

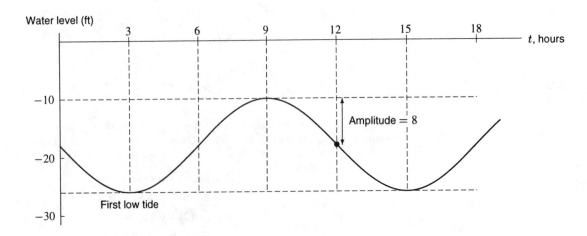

$$f(t) = A\sin(B(t + C)) + D$$

$$\text{period} = 12 \text{ hrs} \qquad \frac{2\pi}{B} = 12 \qquad B = \frac{\pi}{6}$$

$$f(t) = 8\sin\left(\frac{\pi}{6}(t + 6)\right) - 18$$

$$= 8\sin\left(\frac{\pi}{6}t + \pi\right) - 18$$

$$= -8\sin\frac{\pi}{6}t - 18$$

3. In nature, the population of two animals, one of which preys on the other (such as foxes and rabbits) are observed to oscillate with time, and are found to be well approximated by a trigonometric function. If the population of foxes is given by the graph below:

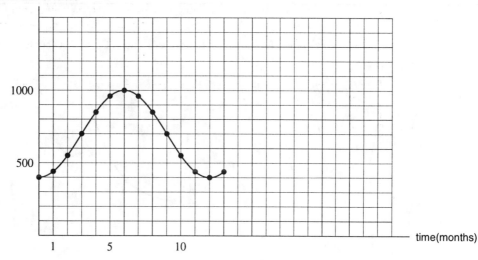

Number of foxes

(a) Find the amplitude.
(b) Find the period.
(c) Give a formula for the function.
(d) Give an estimate for three times when the population is 500.

ANSWER:

(a) $\dfrac{1000 - 400}{2} = 300$

(b) Period=12 months

(c) Average value = 700 and graph looks like an upsidedown cosine, so $F = 700 - 300\cos(kt)$
    since $k(12) = 2\pi$, $k = \dfrac{\pi}{6}$ so $F = 700 - 300\cos\left(\dfrac{\pi t}{6}\right)$

(d) First time is between $t = 1$ and $t = 2$, so let's say about $t \approx 1.5$. From graph, next values are $t \approx 10.5$ and then $t \approx 13.5$ months

4. One of the functions below is a quadratic, one is a cubic, and one is a trigonometric function. Which is which? Why? [Note: You don't have to find formulas for these functions.]

| $x$ | $f(x)$ |
|-----|--------|
| 0.2 | −0.42 |
| 0.4 | −0.65 |
| 0.6 | 0.96 |
| 0.8 | −0.15 |
| 1.2 | 0.84 |

| $x$ | $g(x)$ |
|-----|--------|
| 1.3 | 0.41 |
| 1.7 | 0.81 |
| 2.5 | 0.65 |
| 3.0 | −0.10 |
| 3.5 | −1.35 |

| $x$ | $h(x)$ |
|-----|--------|
| 0.5 | −1.13 |
| 1.2 | 0.13 |
| 1.8 | 0.03 |
| 2.0 | 0.00 |
| 2.2 | 0.05 |

ANSWER:

$f(x)$ changes direction three times, so it cannot be cubic or quadratic, and thus it is trigonometric. $h(x)$ changes direction twice, so it cannot be a quadratic, and thus it must be cubic. This leaves only $g(x)$ (which changes direction only once), so it must be a quadratic.

## Problems and Solutions for Section 1.10

1. Find a possible formula for each of the following functions. Check that your formula fits the data points.

(a)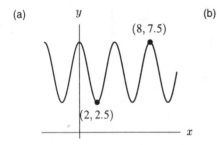

(b)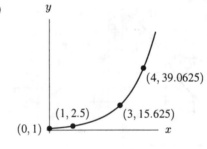

(c)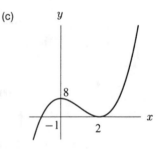

ANSWER:

(a) This function looks like a cosine function with period 4 displaced upward by 5 with amplitude 2.5. A possible formula is

$$5 + 2.5 \cos\left(\frac{2\pi x}{4}\right).$$

(b) Notice that $f(1)/f(0) = f(4)/f(3) = 2.5$. This suggests that $f$ is exponential. In fact, $f(x) = 2.5^x$ fits this data.

(c) This is a cubic with double zero at 2 and another at −1. So let $f(x) = C(x - 2)^2(x + 1)$. If $f(0) = 8$, then $C(-2)^2(1) = 8$, so we have $C = 2$.

2. (a) Using the standard viewing rectangle ($-10 \leq x \leq 10, -10 \leq y \leq 10$), I graph a cubic polynomial and see two more or less vertical lines.

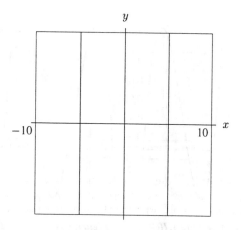

*Figure 1.10.5*

Need there be another root? Explain. Sketch some of the possibilities for the complete graph. Explain.

(b)  Once again, using the standard viewing rectangle, I graph $y = x^2 - e^{0.1x}$ and I see what appears to be a parabola.

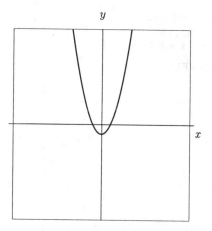

*Figure 1.10.6*

Is this all there is to the graph? Sketch what you think the complete picture should be. Explain.
ANSWER:

(a)  There must be another real root. A cubic polynomial can have one real root, a real root and a double root, or three real roots. Since two roots are shown in the picture, of which neither is a double, there must be another. These are some possibilities:

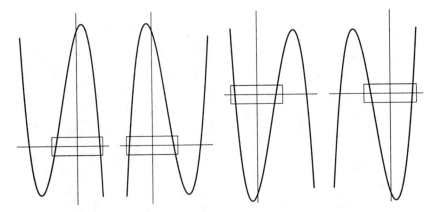

*Figure 1.10.7*      *Figure 1.10.8*      *Figure 1.10.9*      *Figure 1.10.10*

(b)   As $x$ approaches negative infinity, $e^{0.1x}$ approaches 0, the graph becomes closer and closer to pure parabolic as we move out leftwards from $x = 0$.

As $x$ approaches infinity, $e^{0.1x}$ approaches infinity. In fact, $e^{0.1x}$ increases so fast with $x$ that it will eclipse the $x^2$ term. There will be thus a downward turn somewhere to the right of $x = 0$, and the curve will cross the $x$-axis and head for negative infinity.

3.   Give rough sketches of the graphs of the following functions. In each case, give a scale along the $x$-axis and $y$-axis.

(a)   $y = 4 + 3\sin 2x$

(b)   $y = \log_{10}(x - 3)$

(c)   $y = -5(x + 2)x^2(x - 1)$

ANSWER:

(a)

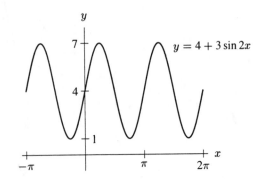

(b)

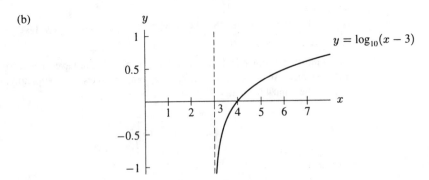

(c)

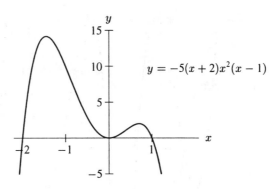

$y = -5(x + 2)x^2(x - 1)$

4. Give a possible function for each curve.

(a)

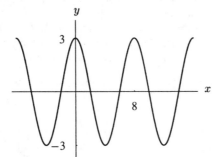

(b)

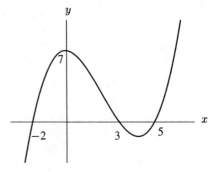

(c)

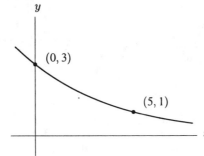

(d)

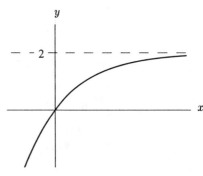

ANSWER:

(a) This graph is periodic with amplitude 3 and period 8 and has a maximum at $x = 0$. So a reasonable solution is $y = 3\cos\left(\frac{\pi}{4}x\right)$.

(b) This curve appears to be a cubic polynomial with roots at $x = -2, 3$ and 5. Thus $y = k(x + 2)(x - 3)(x - 5)$ is a first guess. Since $y(0) = 7$,

$$7 = k(2)(-3)(-5)$$
$$k = \frac{7}{30}$$

So, $y = \frac{7}{30}(x + 2)(x - 3)(x - 5)$ is a possible answer.

(c) This appears to be an exponential decay curve of the form $y = Ak^{-x}$. Since $y(0) = 3$, $y = 3k^{-x}$. Since $y(5) = 1$, we have

$$1 = 3k^{-5}$$
$$k = \left(\frac{1}{3}\right)^{-\frac{1}{5}}$$

So, $y = 3\left(\frac{1}{3}\right)^{\frac{1}{5}x} = 3^{\left(1 - \frac{x}{5}\right)}$ is a possible answer.

(d)   This graph appears to be of the form $y = a(1 - e^{-kx})$. As $x \to \infty$, $y \to a$, and the graph approaches 2, so $y = 2(1 - e^{-kx})$. Any positive $k$ will work, since no scale is indicated for the $x$-axis.

5.   For each of the graphs below, find an equation which defines the function. In (D), the numerator is a linear function.

(a)

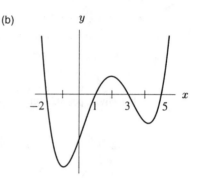

(b)

(c)

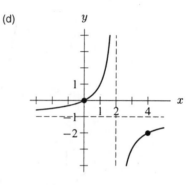

(d)

ANSWER:

(a)   $y = -\log_{10} x$ which is the $pH$ curve from problem 7!

(b)   This is a 4-th degree polynomial whose roots are $-2$, $1$, $3$, $5$. Therefore, $y = K(x + 2)(x - 1)(x - 3)(x - 5) = K(x^4 - 7x^3 + 5x^2 + 4x - 30)$, where $K >$ is a constant greater than 0. We don't have enough information to find out anything more.

(c)   This is a sine curve with amplitude 2, period $8\pi$ and vertical shift 2. Thus $y - 2 = 2\sin\left(\dfrac{x}{4}\right)$.

(d)   Since $x = 2$ is the vertical asymptote, $x - 2$ can be the denominator. We are told the numerator is linear, so $y = \dfrac{ax + b}{x - 2}$.

From the fact that the $y$-intercept is 0, we have $y = \dfrac{b}{-2} = 0$, and thus $b = 0$; now $y = \dfrac{ax}{x - 2}$, where "$a$" is constant. We can find "$a$" by substitution: $-2 = \dfrac{4a}{4 - 2} = \dfrac{4a}{2} = 2a$, so that $a = -1$.

Finally, we have $y = \dfrac{-x}{x - 2}$.

## Review Problems and Solutions for Chapter 1

For Problems 1–2, decide whether each statement is true or false, and provide a short explanation or a counterexample.

1.  The function described by the following table of values is exponential:

| $x$ | 5.2 | 5.3 | 5.4 | 5.5 | 5.6 |
|---|---|---|---|---|---|
| $f(x)$ | 27.8 | 29.2 | 30.6 | 32.0 | 33.4 |

ANSWER:

FALSE. The function is linear; for every increase of 0.1 in $x$, there is an increase of 1.4 in $f(x)$.

2.  A quantity $Q$ growing exponentially according to the formula $Q(t) = Q_0 5^t$ has a doubling time of $\frac{\ln 2}{\ln 5}$.

ANSWER:

TRUE. To calculate the doubling time, $T$, we use $2Q_0 = Q_0 5^T$ which gives $T = \frac{\ln 2}{\ln 5}$.

3.  Match the following graphs with the formulas.

I.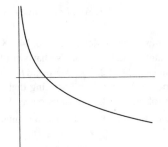

II.

III.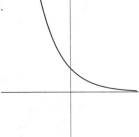

IV.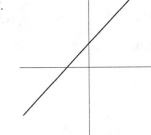

V.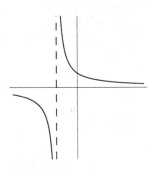

(a) $\ln(e^x) + 1$

(b) $-2 \ln x$

(c) $e^{-x}$

(d) $x^5 + 2x^4 - x^3 - 2x^2 + 5$

(e) $\dfrac{1}{x+1}$

ANSWER:

I.   This curve has the appearance of an upside-down ln curve and crosses the $x$-axis at a positive $x$-value. Thus (b) is the corresponding equation.

II.   This curve has four "wiggles" in it and thus looks like it corresponds to a degree 5 polynomial. Hence, (d) is the correct equation.

III.   This curve is always positive, decreasing, and concave up. we conclude that (c) is the corresponding equation.

IV.   This is a linear function. Equation (a), $\ln(e^x) + 1$ is actually a linear function in disguise, since $\ln(e^x) = x$. Thus, (a) is the correct equation.

V.   This graph approaches 0 as $x \to \pm\infty$ and has a vertical asymptote at $x = -1$. Thus, (e) is the correct answer.

4. Give expressions for $f(x), g(x), h(x)$ which agree with the following table of values.

| $x$ | $f(x)$ | $g(x)$ | $h(x)$ |
|---|---|---|---|
| 0 | $-7$ | 0 | $-$ |
| 1 | $-4$ | 2 | 5 |
| 2 | $-1$ | 8 | 2.50 |
| 3 | 2 | 18 | $1.66\ldots$ |
| 4 | 5 | 32 | 1.25 |
| 5 | 8 | 50 | 1 |

ANSWER:

All the values of $f(x)$ jump by 3 for a change in $x$ of 1, so $f(x)$ is linear with slope 3. Since $f(0) = -7$, we have $f(x) = 3x - 7$.

The differences between successive values of $g(x)$ are as follows: 2, 6, 10, 14, 18. These differences increase linearly, so it seems that $g''(x)$ is a constant, namely 4. Thus we have $g(x) = 2x^2 + bx + c$. Since $g(0) = 0, c = 0$, and $g(x) = 2x^2 + bx$. Since $g(1) = 2, 2 = 2 + b$ and $b = 0$, so $g(x) = 2x^2$. [Note: there is also an easier way to get the same result, namely by noticing that the values in the $g$ column, 0, 2, 8, 18 $\ldots$ are exactly twice the values of the well known function, $x^2$.]

$h(x)$ is a decreasing, concave up function that is infinite when $x = 0$ and equal to 1 when $x = 5$. $h(x) = \frac{5}{x}$ fits the requirements.

5. You are offered two jobs starting on July $1^{\text{st}}$ of 1994. Firm A offers you \$40,000 a year to start and you can expect an annual raise of 4% every July $1^{\text{st}}$. At firm B you would start at \$30,000 but can expect an annual 6% increase every July $1^{\text{st}}$. On July $1^{\text{st}}$ of which year would the job at firm B first pay more than the job at firm A?

ANSWER:

After $n$ July $1^{\text{st}}$'s, Firm $A$ pays $40000(1.04)^n$, and Firm $B$ pays $30000(1.06)^n$. So they offer equal salaries when

$$40000(1.04)^n = 30000(1.06)^n,$$

or

$$\frac{(1.06)^n}{(1.04)^n} = \frac{4}{3} \approx 1.333,$$

or

$$\left(\frac{1.06}{1.04}\right)^n = 1.333.$$

But $1.06/1.04 \approx 1.0192$, so $(1.0192)^n = 1.3333$. Taking logs of both sides yields

$$n \ln 1.0192 = \ln 1.3333$$
$$n = \frac{\ln 1.3333}{\ln 1.0192} \approx 15.1.$$

So when $n = 16$, in the year 2010, Firm $B$ offers more than Firm $A$.

6. You have \$500 invested in a bank account earning 8.2% compounded annually.

   (a) Write an equation for the money $M$ in your account after $t$ years.
   (b) How long will it take to triple your money?
   (c) Suppose the interest were compounded monthly instead, that is you earned $\frac{8.2}{12}$% interest each month. What interest would you then earn for 1 year?

   ANSWER:

   (a) $M = 500(1.082)^t$.

(b) To triple your money, set $M = 1500$, so

$$\frac{1500}{500} = (1.082)^t$$
$$3 = e^{(\ln 1.082)t}$$
$$\ln 3 = t \ln 1.082$$
$$t = \frac{\ln 3}{\ln 1.082}$$
$$\approx 13.9 \text{ years}$$

(c) If interest is compounded monthly, then we get $M = 500 \left(1 + \frac{0.082}{12}\right)^{12t}$, where $t$ is still measured in years. So $M \approx 500(1.0068333)^{12t}$. After $t = 1$ year,

$$M \approx 500(1.0068333)^{12}$$
$$\approx 500(1.08516)$$
$$\approx 542.58$$

so the interest earned is \$42.58.

# Chapter 2 Exam Questions

*Problems and Solutions for Section 2.1*

1. For any number $r$, let $m(r)$ be the slope of the graph of the function $y = (2.1)^x$ at the point $x = r$.

   (a) Complete the table to the right:

   | $r$ | 0 | 1 | 2 | 3 | 4 |
   |---|---|---|---|---|---|
   | $m(r)$ | | | 3.27 | 6.87 | 14.43 |

   (b) Explain in a few complete sentences what you did to fill in this table, and why you did it. (If you include pictures, make sure they are carefully labeled.)

   (c) What you have done in part (a) gives you some points on the graph of the function $m(r)$. Graph the points and guess the general shape of the graph of the function $m(r)$ by "fitting a curve" through this data. Give the equation of the curve.

   ANSWER:

   (a)

   | $r$ | 0 | 1 | 2 | 3 | 4 |
   |---|---|---|---|---|---|
   | $m(r)$ | 0.74 | 1.56 | 3.27 | 6.87 | 14.43 |

   (b) The slope of the tangent line to $2.1^x$ at $x = 1$ is approximately the same as that of the secant line through $x = 1$ and $x = 1.001$:

   $$m(1) \approx \frac{(2.1)^{1.001} - (2.1)^1}{0.001} = 1.56.$$

   Similarly,

   $$m(0) \approx \frac{(2.1)^{0.001} - (2.1)^0}{0.001} = 0.74.$$

   (c) For comparison, let's tabulate $y = (2.1)^x$ along with $m$:

   | $r$ | 0 | 1 | 2 | 3 | 4 |
   |---|---|---|---|---|---|
   | $m(r)$ | 0.74 | 1.56 | 3.27 | 6.87 | 14.43 |
   | $y(r)$ | 1 | 2.1 | 4.41 | 9.26 | 19.45 |
   | $\frac{m}{y}$ | 0.74 | 0.74 | 0.74 | 0.74 | 0.74 |

   We see that the $m$ values are directly proportional to the $y$ values, with a ratio of approximately 0.74. (Which happens to be $\ln 2.1$.) So $m(r) = \ln 2.1 (2.1)^r$.

2. (a) If $x(V) = V^{1/3}$ is the length of the side of a cube in terms of its volume, $V$, then calculate the average rate of change of $x$ with respect to $V$ over the intervals $0 < V < 1$ and $1 < V < 2$.

   (b) What might we conclude about this rate as the volume $V$ increases? Is it increasing? Decreasing?

   ANSWER:

   (a) average rate of change of $x = \dfrac{1^{\frac{1}{3}} - 0^{\frac{1}{3}}}{1 - 0} = 1$ for $0 < V < 1$.

   average rate of change of $x = \dfrac{2^{\frac{1}{3}} - 1^{\frac{1}{3}}}{2 - 1} \approx 0.26$ for $1 < V < 2$.

   (b) We conclude that as $V$ increases, the rate of change of $x$ decreases.

3. If the graph of $y = f(x)$ is shown below, arrange in ascending order (i.e., smallest first, largest last):

$$f'(A) \qquad f'(B) \qquad f'(C) \qquad \text{slope } AB \qquad \text{the number } 1 \qquad \text{the number } 0$$

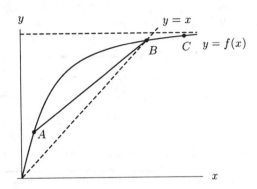

ANSWER:

By eye, we can see that $f'(C) < f'(B) < f'(A)$. We can also see that $f'(B) < \text{slope } AB < f'(A)$, so we have $f'(C) < f'(B) < \text{slope } AB < f'(A)$. Finally, we note that all the slopes on this graph are positive, and that $f'(A)$ is the only slope that is greater than the slope of $y = x$, namely 1. So we have $0 < f'(C) < f'(B) < \text{slope } AB < 1 < f'(A)$.

## Problems and Solutions for Section 2.2

1. Given the following data about a function, $f$,

| $x$ | 3 | 3.5 | 4 | 4.5 | 5 | 5.5 | 6 |
|---|---|---|---|---|---|---|---|
| $f(x)$ | 10 | 8 | 7 | 4 | 2 | 0 | -1 |

   (a) Estimate $f'(4.25)$ and $f'(4.75)$.
   (b) Estimate the rate of change of $f'$ at $x = 4.5$.
   (c) Find, approximately, an equation of the tangent line at $x = 4.5$.
   (d) Use the tangent line to estimate $f(4.75)$.
   (e) Estimate the derivative of $f^{-1}$ at 2.

   ANSWER:

   (a) $f'(4.25) \approx \frac{f(4.5) - f(4)}{4.5 - 4} = \frac{4-7}{0.5} = -6$
   $f'(4.75) \approx \frac{f(5) - f(4.5)}{5 - 4.5} = \frac{2-4}{0.5} = -4$
   (b) $f''(4.5) \approx \frac{f'(4.75) - f'(4.25)}{0.5} = \frac{-4+6}{0.5} = 4$
   (c) $f'(4.5) \approx \frac{f(5) - f(4.5)}{0.5} = -4$, thus $y - 4 = -4(x - 4.5)$ is the equation of the tangent line.
   (d) $f(4.75) \approx f(4.5) + .25 \cdot f'(4.5) \approx 3$
   (e) $(f^{-1}(2))' \approx \frac{f^{-1}(4) - f^{-1}(2)}{4 - 2} = \frac{4.5 - 5}{2} = -\frac{1}{4}$.

2. (a) Explain how the average rate of change of a function $f$ can be used to find the instantaneous rate of change of $f$ at a point $x_0$.
   (b) Give a geometric interpretation of the instantaneous rate of change.
   ANSWER:

   (a) By taking points $x_1, x_2, \ldots$ closer and closer to $x_0$ and calculating the average rate of change of $f$ over the interval $[x_0, x_n]$, we get a sequence which approaches the instantaneous rate of change of $f$ at $x_0$.
   (b) The instantaneous rate of change at a given point is the slope of a tangent to the curve at that point.

3.  (a)  Estimate $f'(0)$ when $f(x) = 2^{-x}$.
    (b)  Will your estimate be larger or smaller than $f'(0)$? Explain.

    ANSWER:

    (a)  To estimate $f'(0)$, find the average slope over intervals that get smaller and smaller but still contain $x = 0$:

| Interval Size | Average Slope |
|---|---|
| 0.1 | $\dfrac{f(0.1)-f(0)}{0.1} \approx -0.670$ |
| 0.01 | $\dfrac{f(0.01)-f(0)}{0.01} \approx -0.691$ |
| 0.001 | $\dfrac{f(0.001)-f(0)}{0.001} \approx -0.693$ |

    $f'(0)$ appears to be about $-0.693$.

    (b)  The average slopes in the chart above seem to approach a limiting value (which turns out to be $\ln \frac{1}{2} \approx -0.69315$) from above; this indicates that our estimate of $f'(0)$ is probably an overestimate.

4.  Given the following data about a function $f$,

| $x$ | 3.0 | 3.2 | 3.4 | 3.6 | 3.8 |
|---|---|---|---|---|---|
| $f(x)$ | 8.2 | 9.5 | 10.5 | 11.0 | 13.2 |

    (a)  Estimate $f'(3.2)$ and $f'(3.5)$.
    (b)  Give the average rate of change of $f$ between $x = 3.0$ and $x = 3.8$.
    (c)  Give the equation of the tangent line at $x = 3.2$.

    ANSWER:

    (a)  Estimate the slope at 3.2 by finding the average slope over the interval $[3.2, 3.4]$:

    $$\text{over } [3.2, 3.4], \text{ slope } = \frac{10.5 - 9.5}{0.2} = 5$$

    To estimate the slope at 3.5, we have to look at the average slope over $[3.4, 3.6]$, which is $\frac{11.0 - 10.5}{0.2} = 2.5$.

    (b)  The average rate of change is $\frac{13.2-8.2}{3.8-3.0} = 6.25$.
    (c)  At $x = 3.2$, $f(x) = 9.5$ and the slope $\approx 5$ by part (a). So

    $$y - 9.5 = 5(x - 3.2)$$
    $$y = 9.5 + 5x - 16$$
    $$= 5x - 6.5$$

5.  Let $f(x) = \log(\log(x))$. (This is the "common log" which uses "base 10.") Our goal is to approximate the derivative of this function at the point $x = 10$. Give an UPPER BOUND (call it "U") and a LOWER BOUND (call it "L") for $f'(10)$ that agree up to three decimal places. Explain how you know that $U$ is an upper bound for $f'(10)$ and that $L$ is a lower bound for $f'(10)$. Include a sketch to explain your reasoning. You may assume the graph of $y = f(x)$ is concave down. Note: An "upper bound" for $f'(10)$ is simply a number which is larger than $f'(10)$.

    ANSWER:

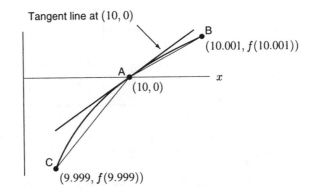

Tangent line at $(10, 0)$

B $(10.001, f(10.001))$

A $(10, 0)$

$x$

C $(9.999, f(9.999))$

Note: The figure is not drawn to scale.

Since the graph of $f$ is concave down, the slope of the line joining points $C$ and $A$ will be larger than the slope of the tangent line at point $A$ and similarly, the slope of the line joining the points $A$ and $B$ will be smaller than the slope of the tangent line at $A$. Since the slope of the tangent line at $A$ is $f'(10)$, we get:

$$\underbrace{\frac{\log(\log(10.001)) - \overbrace{\log(\log(10))}^{0}}{0.001}}_{L} < f'(10) < \frac{\overbrace{\log(\log(10))}^{0} - \log(\log(9.999))}{0.001} = U$$

$$L \approx 0.0188598173 \qquad U \approx .0188625224$$

After rounding, they agree to $0.01886$, which is better than the required accuracy.

6. For $f(x) = \log x$, estimate $f'(1)$ by finding the average slope over intervals which get smaller and smaller but still contain the value $x = 1$.

   ANSWER:

   Taking average slopes over smaller and smaller intervals to the right of $x = 1$, we obtain the following table:

| Interval Length | Average Slope |
|:---:|:---:|
| 0.1 | $\dfrac{f(1.1) - f(1)}{0.1} \approx 0.414$ |
| 0.01 | $\dfrac{f(1.01) - f(1)}{0.01} \approx 0.432$ |
| 0.001 | $\dfrac{f(1.001) - f(1)}{0.001} \approx 0.434$ |
| 0.0001 | $\dfrac{f(1.0001) - f(1)}{0.0001} \approx 0.434$ |

   Thus, $f'(1)$ appears to be about $0.434$.

7. There is a function used by statisticians, called the error function, which is written

$$y = \text{erf}(x).$$

Suppose you have a statistical calculator, which has a button for this function. Playing with your calculator, you discover the following:

| $x$ | $\mathrm{erf}(x)$ |
|---|---|
| 1 | 0.29793972 |
| 0.1 | 0.03976165 |
| 0.01 | 0.00398929 |
| 0 | 0 |

(a) Using this information alone, give an estimate for $\mathrm{erf}'(0)$, the derivative of erf at $x = 0$. Only give as many decimal places as you feel reasonably sure of, and explain why you gave that many decimal places.

(b) Suppose that you go back to your calculator, and find that

$$\mathrm{erf}(0.001) = 0.000398942.$$

With this extra information, would you refine the answer you gave in (a)? Explain.

ANSWER:

(a) Since $\mathrm{erf}'(0) = \lim_{h \to 0} \dfrac{\mathrm{erf}(h) - \mathrm{erf}(0)}{h - 0} = \lim_{h \to 0} \dfrac{\mathrm{erf}(h)}{h}$, we approximate $\mathrm{erf}'(0)$ by $\dfrac{\mathrm{erf}(h)}{h}$ where $h$ is small. As $\dfrac{\mathrm{erf}(0.1)}{0.1}$ and $\dfrac{\mathrm{erf}(0.01)}{0.01}$ agree in the first two decimal places, it seems safe to estimate $\mathrm{erf}'(0) = 0.39$.

(b) The new value for $\mathrm{erf}(0.001)$ gives us agreement out to four decimal places between $\dfrac{\mathrm{erf}(0.01)}{0.01}$ and $\dfrac{\mathrm{erf}(0.001)}{0.001}$, so we can refine our answer to 0.3989.

8. Each of the quantities below can be represented in the picture. For each quantity, state whether it is represented by a length, a slope or an area. Then using the letters on the picture, make clear exactly which length, slope or area represents it. [Note: The letters $P, Q, R$, etc., represent points.]

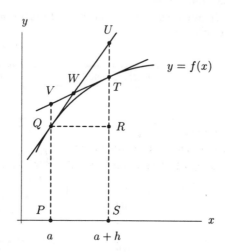

(a) $f(a + h) - f(a)$
(b) $f'(a + h)$
(c) $f'(a)h$
(d) $f(a)h$

ANSWER:

(a) $f(a + h) - f(a)$ is represented by the length $TR$.
(b) $f'(a + h)$ is the slope of the line $TV$.
(c) $f'(a)h$ is the length $RU$.
(d) $f(a)h$ is the area of the rectangle $PQRS$.

9. Given the following table of values for a Bessel function, what is your best estimate for the derivative at $x = 0.5$?

| $x$ | 0 | 0.1 | 0.2 | 0.3 | 0.4 | 0.5 | 0.6 | 0.7 | 0.8 | 0.9 | 1.0 |
|---|---|---|---|---|---|---|---|---|---|---|---|
| $J_0(x)$ | 1.0 | .9975 | .9900 | .9776 | .9604 | .9385 | .9120 | .8812 | .8463 | .8075 | .7652 |

ANSWER:

We can approximate $J_0'(0.5)$ by the difference quotient with $h = 0.1$ to the right of 0.5:.

$$J_0'(0.5) \approx \frac{J_0(0.6) - J_0(0.5)}{0.1} = \frac{0.9120 - 0.9385}{0.1} = -0.265.$$

However, to obtain a better approximation, we approximate $J_0'(0.5)$ by the average of the difference quotients with $h = 0.1$ to the left and right of 0.5.

$$J_0'(0.5) \approx \frac{1}{2}\left(\frac{J_0(0.5) - J_0(0.4)}{0.1} + \frac{J_0(0.6) - J_0(0.5)}{0.1}\right)$$

$$= \frac{1}{2}\left(\frac{0.9385 - 0.9604}{0.1} + \frac{0.9120 - 0.9385}{0.1}\right) = -0.242.$$

## Problems and Solutions for Section 2.3

1. Which of the functions below could be the derivative of which of the others? (Hint: try all combinations.)

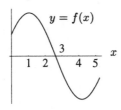
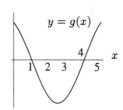
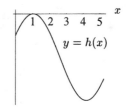

ANSWER:

$g(x)$ could be the derivative of $h(x)$ or $f(x)$

2. Below is the graph of a function $f$. Sketch the graph of its derivative $f'$ on the same axes.

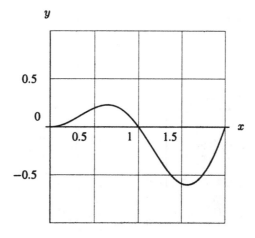

ANSWER:

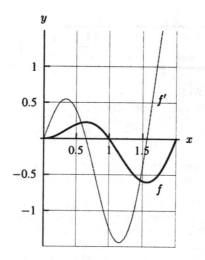

3.  Sketch the graph of the derivative, $y = f'(x)$, for each of the functions $y = f(x)$ whose graphs are given below.

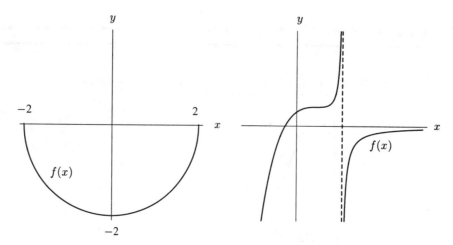

ANSWER:

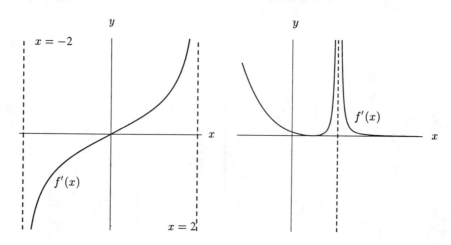

4. Consider the function $y = f(x)$ graphed below. (Notice that $f(x)$ is defined for $-5 < x < 6$, *except* $x = 2$.)

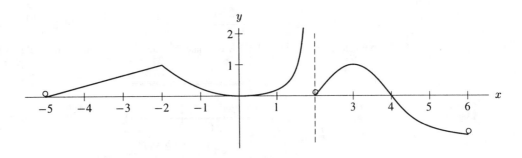

(a) For what values of $x$ (in the domain of $f$) is $f'(x) = 0$?
(b) For what values of $x$ (in the domain of $f$) is $f'(x)$ positive?
(c) For what values of $x$ (in the domain of $f$) is $f'(x)$ negative?
(d) For what values of $x$ (in the domain of $f$) is $f'(x)$ undefined?
(e) Based on your answers to the above questions, make a sketch of $y = f'(x)$ on the axes below. Make your sketch as precise as possible.

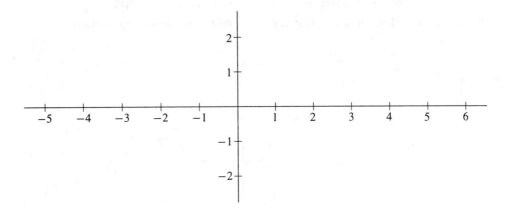

ANSWER:

(a) $x = 0, 3$
(b) $x \in (-5, -2), \quad x \in (0, 2), \quad x = (2, 3)$
(c) $x \in (-2, 0), \quad x \in (3, 6)$
(d) $x = -2$
(e)

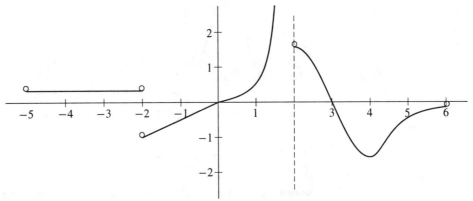

5.  Estimate the value of $f'(x)$ for the function $f(x) = 10^x$.

    ANSWER:

    $$f'(x) = \lim_{h \to 0} \frac{f(x+h) - f(x)}{h} = \lim_{h \to 0} \frac{10^{x+h} - 10^x}{h} = 10^x \lim_{h \to 0} \frac{10^h - 1}{h}.$$

    So far, our calculation is exact. We now estimate the limit by substituting small values of $h$;

    | $h$ | $\frac{10^h - 1}{h}$ |
    |---|---|
    | 1 | 9 |
    | 0.1 | 2.589 |
    | 0.01 | 2.329 |
    | 0.001 | 2.305 |
    | 0.0001 | 2.303 |
    | 0.00001 | 2.303 |

    So $f'(x)$ appears to be approximately equal to $(2.303)10^x$.

6.  Sketch the graph of the derivative of the function whose graph is shown:

    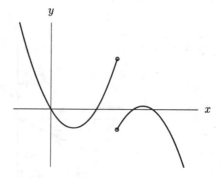

    ANSWER:

    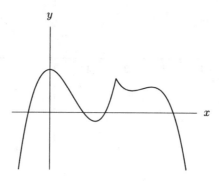

7.  The following graph is of $y = f(x)$. Draw $f'(x)$ and $f^{-1}(x)$ on the same axes.

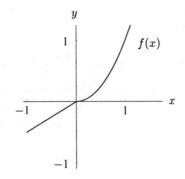

ANSWER:

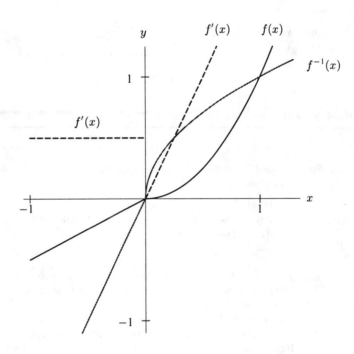

8.  The graph of $f(x)$ is given in Figure 2.3.11.

    (a)  Sketch the graph of $f'(x)$ on the same axes.
    (b)  Where does $f'(x)$ change its sign?
    (c)  Where does $f'(x)$ have a local maximum or minimum?

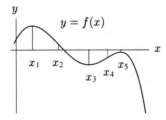

*Figure 2.3.11*

ANSWER:

(a)

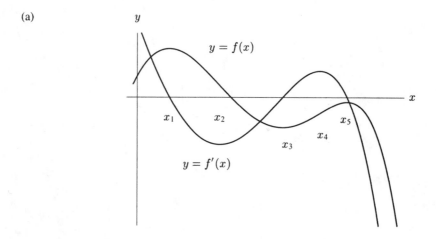

(b)   At $x_1$, $x_3$, $x_5$.
(c)   At $x_2$, $x_4$.

## Problems and Solutions for Section 2.4

1.   Suppose that $f(T)$ is the cost to heat my house, in dollars per day, when the outside temperature is $T$ degrees Fahrenheit.

   (a)   What does $f'(23) = -0.17$ mean?
   (b)   If $f(23) = 7.54$ and $f'(23) = -0.17$, approximately what is the cost to heat my house when the outside temperature is $20°$F?

   ANSWER:

   (a)   $f'(23) = -0.17$ means that when the temperature outside is 23 degrees, the cost of heating the house will decrease by a rate of approximately 17 cents per day for each degree above 23. Since we know nothing about how $f(T)$ behaves at temperatures other than $T = 23$, it is impossible to know over which range of temperatures this approximation is valid. It seems reasonable to assume, however, that $f(T)$ will be relatively smooth over a range of a few degrees.
   (b)   If the temperature goes down by $3°$ (i.e., to $20°$), then the cost will increase by about $(-3)(-0.17) = 0.51$, resulting in a cost of $\$7.54 + \$0.51 = \$8.05$.

2.   To study traffic flow along a major road, the city installs a device at the edge of the road at 4:00 a.m. The device counts the cars driving past, and records the total periodically. The resulting data is plotted on a graph, with time (in hours) on the horizontal axis and the number of cars on the vertical axis. The graph is shown below; it is the graph of the function

   $$C(t) = \text{Total number of cars that have passed by after } t \text{ hours.}$$

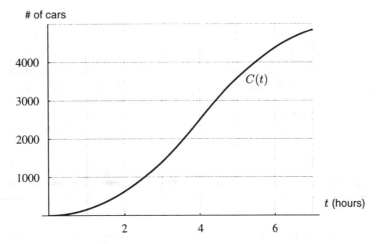

**# of cars**

*Figure 2.4.12:* Traffic Along Speedway

(a)  When is the traffic flow greatest?

(b)  From the graph, estimate $C'(3)$.

(c)  What is the meaning of $C'(3)$? What are its units? What does the value of $C'(3)$ you obtained in (b) mean in practical terms?

ANSWER:

(a)  Traffic flow is greatest when the slope of $C(t)$ is greatest, which occurs at about $t = 4$. Since $t$ is in hours past 4:00 a.m., the flow is greatest at about 8:00 a.m.

(b)  $C'(3) \approx 1000$

(c)  $C'(3)$ tells us how many cars per hour are flowing past at 7:00 a.m. The value we obtained above for $C'(3)$ tells us that traffic flow at that time is about 1000 cars per hour.

3.  Every day the Office of Undergraduate Admissions receives inquiries from eager high school students (e.g. "Please, please send me an application", etc.) They keep a running account of the number of inquiries received each day, along with the total number received until that point. To the right is a table of *weekly* figures from about the end of August 1989 to about the end of October 1989.

| Week of | Inquiries That Week | Total for Year |
|---------|---------------------|----------------|
| 8/28–9/01 | 1085 | 11,928 |
| 9/04–9/08 | 1193 | 13,121 |
| 9/11–9/15 | 1312 | 14,433 |
| 9/18–9/22 | 1443 | 15,876 |
| 9/25–9/29 | 1588 | 17,464 |
| 10/02–10/06 | 1746 | 19,210 |
| 10/09–10/13 | 1921 | 21,131 |
| 10/16–10/20 | 2113 | 23,244 |
| 10/23–10/27 | 2325 | 25,569 |

(a)  One of these columns can be interpreted as a rate of change. Which one? Of what? Explain.

(b)  Based on the table write a formula that gives approximately the total number of inquiries received by a given week. Explain.

(c)  Using your answer in part (b), roughly how many inquiries will the admissions office receive in 1989?

(d)  The actual number of inquiries in 1989 was about 34,000. Discuss this, using your knowledge of how people apply to college.

ANSWER:

(a)  The second column – Inquiries That Week – is the weekly rate of change of the total for the year since, for example, $13{,}121 - 11{,}928 = 1193$, 1193 is the difference between the total number of inquiries as of 9/04 and 9/11

(b)  We have that the ratio of consecutive entries in the second column (total applicants for the year) is always about 1.1. So if $T$ is the total number of applicants then we can try the exponential model

$$T(t) = (11{,}928)(1.1)^t$$

with $t = 0$ corresponding to the week of 8/28 to 9/01.

(c)   There are about 18 weeks from the start ($t = 0$) until the end of the year. Putting $t = 18$ into the formula for $T$ above gives $T = 66{,}319$ for the total number of applications for the year.

(d)   Since most students send for applications in October and November to apply by the first of January, requests should fall off in November, not continue to rise as our formula suggests. So the true figure (34,000) should be much less than the calculated figure (66,319).

## Problems and Solutions for Section 2.5

1.  Esther is a swimmer who prides herself in having a smooth backstroke. Let $s(t)$ be her position in an Olympic size pool, as a function of time ($s(t)$ is measured in meters, $t$ is seconds). (The Olympic size pool is 50 meters long.)

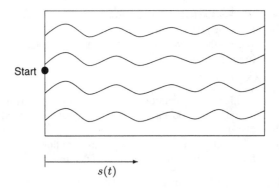

Start

$s(t)$

Below we list some values of $s(t)$, for a recent swim.

| $t$ | 0 | 3.0 | 8.6 | 14.6 | 20.8 | 27.6 | 31.9 | 38.1 | 45.8 | 53.9 | 60 |
|---|---|---|---|---|---|---|---|---|---|---|---|
| $s(t)$ | 0 | 10 | 20 | 30 | 40 | 50 | 40 | 30 | 20 | 10 | 0 |

(a)   Sketch possible graphs for Esther's position and velocity. Put scales on your axes.

(b)   Find Esther's average speed and average velocity over the whole swim.

(c)   Based on the data, can you say whether or not Esther's instantaneous speed was ever greater than 3 meters/second? Why?

(d)   Give a brief qualitative description of the graph of Esther's position (i.e., describe where the position is increasing, decreasing, concave up or down). Explain these qualitative features in terms of Esther's swimming behavior.

ANSWER:

(a)

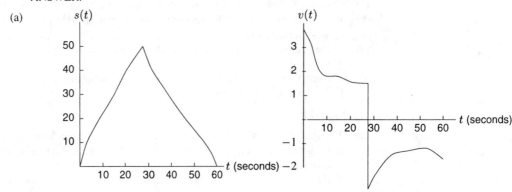

(b)   Average speed $= \dfrac{\text{total distance}}{\text{total time}} = \dfrac{100}{60}$ m/s $= 1.67$ m/s

Average velocity $= \dfrac{\text{total displacement}}{\text{total time}} = \dfrac{0}{60}$ m/s $= 0$ m/s (because she finishes in the same place she started)

(c)   Yes, because her average velocity over the first 3 seconds is $\frac{10}{3}$ m/s $> 3$ m/s.

(d)   Position is increasing up to the 50 meter marker, where she turns around, and then decreasing as she comes back. Position is concave down at first, because she starts out fast and then settles down to a steady speed. At steady speed, position graph is a straight line. Near the other end, the graph is concave down again. She starts fast in the opposite direction and then slows down, making the graph concave up. At the very end, she speeds up in a last minute sprint, making the graph concave down.

2.   The graph below represents the *rate of change* of a function $f$ with respect to $x$; i.e., it is a graph of $f'$.

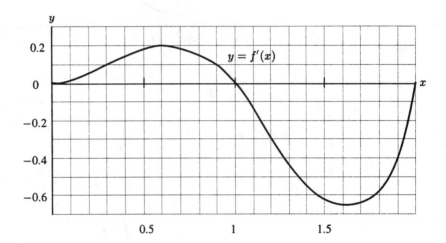

You are told that $f(0) = 0$. On what intervals is $f$ increasing? On what intervals is it decreasing? On what intervals is the graph of $f$ concave up? Concave down? Is there any value $x = a$ other than $x = 0$ in the interval $0 \leq x \leq 2$ where $f(a) = 0$? If not, explain why not, and if so, give the approximate value of $a$.

ANSWER:

$f$ is increasing where $f'$ is positive, namely from 0 to 1, and is decreasing where $f'$ is negative, between 1 and 2. $f$ is concave up where $f'$ is increasing, namely on the intervals $[0, 0.6]$ and $[1.6, 2]$ and concave down on the interval $[0.6, 1.6]$. Finding an $a$, $0 \leq a \leq 2$, such that $f(a) = 0$ is equivalent to finding an $a$ such that

$$\int_0^a f'(x)\, dx = 0$$

We see that at $x = 1.4$, $\int_0^{1.4} f'(x)\, dx$ is approximately zero, since the area above the $x$-axis between 0 and 1 cancels the area below the $x$-axis between 1 and 1.4, so $a \approx 1.4$.

3.   On the axes below, sketch a smooth, continuous curve (i.e., no sharp corners, no breaks) which passes through the point $P(3, 4)$, and which clearly satisfies the following conditions:

- Concave up to the left of $P$
- Concave down to the right of $P$
- Increasing for $x > 0$
- Decreasing for $x < 0$
- Does *not* pass through the origin.

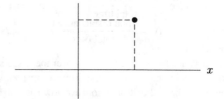

ANSWER:

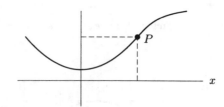

4. Given the following function:

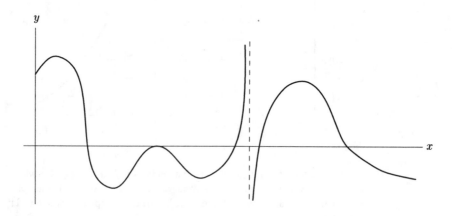

(a) Indicate intervals where it is increasing, decreasing, concave up and concave down.
(b) Sketch the graph of the derivative function.

ANSWER:

(a)

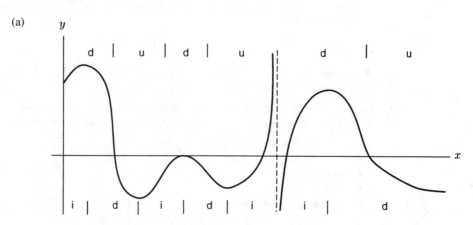

For the above figure the increasing and decreasing intervals are indicated by: d=decreasing and i=increasing. The concavity is indicated by: d=down, u=up.

(b)

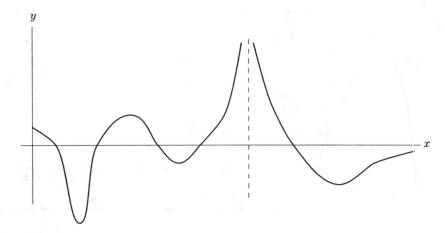

5.  A function defined for all $x$ has the following properties:

    - $f$ is increasing.
    - $f$ is concave down.
    - $f(5) = 2$.
    - $f'(5) = 1/2$.

    (a)  Sketch a possible graph for $f(x)$.
    (b)  How many zeros does $f(x)$ have and where are they located? Justify your answer.
    (c)  Is it possible that $f'(1) = \frac{1}{4}$? Justify your answer.

    ANSWER:

    (a)

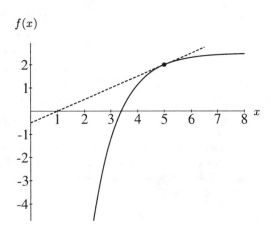

    (b)  The function has exactly one zero because it is increasing everywhere. Since $f(5) = 2$, there cannot be a zero to the right of $x = 5$. The line tangent to the function at the point $(5, 2)$ crosses the $x$-axis at $x = 1$. Since the function is concave down, its graph must lie below such a line and thus the function must have a zero between 1 and 5.
    (c)  Since $f(x)$ is concave down everywhere, $f'(1) > f'(5)$. But $\frac{1}{4} < \frac{1}{2}$, so $f'(1) = \frac{1}{4}$ is impossible.

6.  Assume that $f$ and $g$ are differentiable functions defined on all of the real line. Mark the following TRUE or FALSE.

    (a)  It is possible that $f > 0$ everywhere $f' > 0$, and $f'' < 0$ everywhere.
    (b)  $f$ can satisfy: $f'' > 0$ everywhere, $f' < 0$ everywhere, and $f > 0$ everywhere.
    (c)  $f$ and $g$ can satisfy: $f'(x) > g'(x)$ for all $x$, and $f(x) < g(x)$ for all $x$.
    (d)  If $f'(x) = g'(x)$ for all $x$ and if $f(x_0) = g(x_0)$ for some $x_0$, then $f(x) = g(x)$ for all $x$.
    (e)  If $f'' < 0$ everywhere and $f' < 0$ everywhere then $\lim_{x \to +\infty} f(x) = -\infty$.
    (f)  If $f'(x) > 0$ for all $x$ and $f(x) > 0$ for all $x$ then $\lim_{x \to +\infty} f(x) = \infty$.

ANSWER:

(a) FALSE.
(b) TRUE.
(c) TRUE.
(d) TRUE.
(e) TRUE.
(f) FALSE.

7. Suppose a function is given by a table of values as follows:

| $x$ | 1.1 | 1.3 | 1.5 | 1.7 | 1.9 | 2.1 |
|-----|-----|-----|-----|-----|-----|-----|
| $f(x)$ | 12 | 15 | 21 | 23 | 24 | 25 |

(a) Estimate the instantaneous rate of change of $f$ at $x = 1.7$.
(b) Write an equation for the tangent line to $f$ at $x = 1.7$ using your estimate found in (a).
(c) Use your answer in (b) to predict a value for $f$ at $x = 1.8$. Is your prediction too large or too small? Why?
(d) Is $f''$ positive or negative at $x = 1.7$? How can you tell? Can you estimate its value?

ANSWER:

(a) We approximate the instantaneous rate of change of $f(x)$ at $x = 1.7$ by the slope of the line joining the points $(1.7, 23)$ and $(1.9, 24)$, which is $\frac{1}{0.2} = 5$.
(b) The equation of a line with slope 5 passing through the point $(1.7, 23)$ is

$$y - 23 = 5(x - 1.7)$$
$$y = 23 + 5x - 8.5$$
$$= 14.5 + 5x.$$

(c) At $x = 1.8$, we predict that

$$y = 14.5 + 5 \cdot (1.8)$$
$$= 23.5.$$

Since the curve appears to be concave down over the interval $x \geq 1.3$, the line joining $(1.7, 23)$ and $(1.9, 24)$ lies *below* the curve, and hence 23.5 is an underestimate.

(d) $f''$ appears to be negative. To estimate the value of $f''(1.7)$, we first estimate values of $f'(1.6)$ and $f'(1.8)$:

$$f'(1.6) \approx \frac{f(1.7) - f(1.5)}{1.7 - 1.5} = 10 \quad \text{and}$$
$$f'(1.8) \approx \frac{f(1.9) - f(1.7)}{1.9 - 1.7} = 5.$$

Now,

$$f''(1.7) \approx \frac{f'(1.8) - f'(1.6)}{1.8 - 1.6} = \frac{5 - 10}{0.2} = -25.$$

8. A certain function $f$ is decreasing and concave down. In addition, $f'(3) = -2$ and $f(3) = 5$.

(a) Sketch the graph of $f$.
(b) Estimate $f(2)$, namely give two values you're sure $f(2)$ is between.
(c) Estimate the zeros of $f$. (First say how many there are and why.)

ANSWER:

(a)

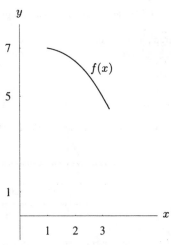

(b)　Since $f$ is concave down, it lies below any of its tangent lines (except at the point of contact). The tangent line at $(3, 5)$ has the equation $y = -2x + 11$. Hence $f(2) < -2(2) + 11 = 7$. Since $f$ is decreasing, $f(2) > f(3) = 5$. Thus we know that $5 < f(2) < 7$.

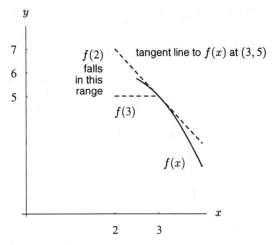

(c)　Since $f$ is decreasing, it can cross the $x$-axis only once, so there is only one zero. Since the curve lies everywhere below the tangent line $y = -2x + 11$ (considered in Part (b)), and this tangent line crosses the $x$-axis at $x = 5.5$, we know that $f(x)$ must cross the $x$-axis somewhere between $x = 3$ and $x = 5.5$. See Figure. The root can thus lie anywhere in the interval from 3 to 5.5.

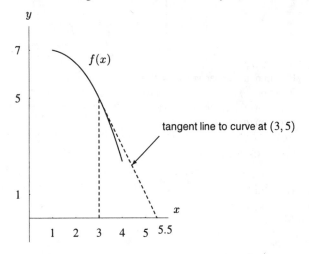

For Problems 9–10, circle the correct answer(s) or fill in the blanks. No reasons need be given.

9. Each graph in the right-hand column below represents the *second* derivative of some function shown in the left-hand column. Match the functions and their second derivatives.

| Functions | Second Derivatives |
|---|---|
| (a) 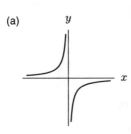 | (i) 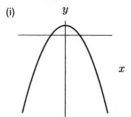 |
| (b) 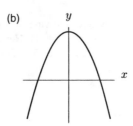 | (ii) 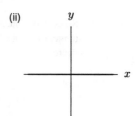 |
| (c 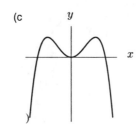 | (iii) 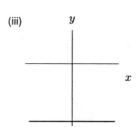 |
| (d) 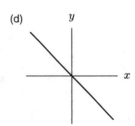 | (iv) 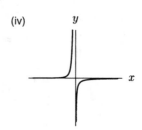 |

Function (a) has second derivative_____ .
Function (b) has second derivative_____ .
Function (c) has second derivative_____ :
Function (d) has second derivative_____ :

ANSWER:

(a)   (iv)
(b)   (iii)
(c)   (i)
(d)   (ii)

10. The cost of mining a ton of coal is rising faster every year. Suppose $C(t)$ is the cost of mining a ton of coal at time $t$.

(a) Which of the following must be positive? (Circle those which are.)
   (i) $C(t)$
   (ii) $C'(t)$
   (iii) $C''(t)$

(b) Which of the following must be increasing? (Circle those which are.)
   (i) $C(t)$
   (ii) $C'(t)$
   (iii) $C''(t)$

(c) Which of the following must be concave up? (Circle those which are.)
   (i) $C(t)$
   (ii) $C'(t)$
   (iii) $C''(t)$

ANSWER:

(a) $C(t), C'(t), C''(t)$ positive
(b) $C(t), C'(t)$ increasing
(c) $C(t)$ concave up.

## Review Problems and Solutions for Chapter 2

1. Let $f(x) = x^{\sin(x)}$.

(a) Using your calculator, estimate $f'(2)$.
   Don't forget to set your calculator to radian mode.
(b) Find the linear approximation for $f(x)$ near $x = 2$.
(c) Using the computer, graph $f(x)$ and its linear approximation together on the same screen. For what range of values do you think your approximation is reasonably accurate? Explain how you chose your answer.
(d) Now graph $f(x)$ and $g(x) = x^x$ on the same axes. Describe what you see, including any particularly interesting features. Can you explain those features?

ANSWER:

(a) We use shrinking intervals to the right of $x = 2$ to approximate $f'(2)$:

| Interval size, $h$ | $\dfrac{f(x+h) - f(x)}{h}$ |
|---|---|
| 0.1 | $\dfrac{f(2.1) - f(2)}{0.1} \approx 0.192$ |
| 0.01 | $\dfrac{f(2.01) - f(2)}{0.01} \approx 0.300$ |
| 0.001 | $\dfrac{f(2.001) - f(2)}{0.001} \approx 0.311$ |
| 0.0001 | $\dfrac{f(2.0001) - f(2)}{0.0001} \approx 0.312$ |

Hence, $f'(2)$ appears to be about $0.312$.

(b)   The linear approximation, $h(x)$, for $f(x)$ near $x = 2$ is given by

$$h(x) \approx f(2) + (x - 2)f'(2) = 1.878 + (x - 2)0.312 = 1.254 + 0.312x.$$

(c)

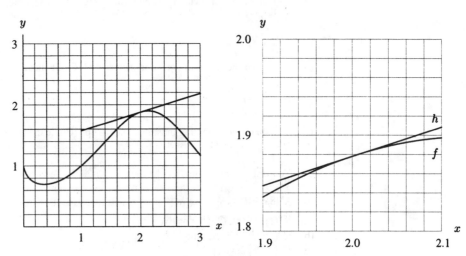

The graph on the right is an enlargement of the region $1.9 < x < 2.1$ and $1.8 < y < 2.0$. From the graph we guess that the linear approximation found is accurate only over the region $1.97 < x < 2.04$. This is because the two curves agree fairly closely over this region.

(d)

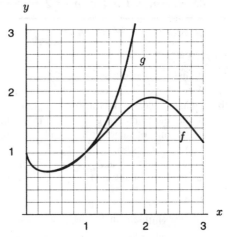

The curves $x^x$ and $x^{\sin x}$ agree closely for $0 < x < 1$. This is because the exponents of these two functions, namely $x$ and $\sin x$ agree fairly well over $0 < x < 1$.

2.   Alone in your dim, unheated room you light one candle rather than curse the darkness. Disgusted by the mess, you walk directly away from the candle, cursing. The temperature (in degrees Fahrenheit) and illumination (in % of one candle power) decrease as your distance (in feet) from the candle increases. In fact, you have tables showing this information!

| distance(feet) | Temp. (°F) |
|:---:|:---:|
| 0 | 55 |
| 1 | 54.5 |
| 2 | 53.5 |
| 3 | 52 |
| 4 | 50 |
| 5 | 47 |
| 6 | 43.5 |

| distance(feet) | illumination |
|:---:|:---:|
| 0 | 100 |
| 1 | 85 |
| 2 | 75 |
| 3 | 67 |
| 4 | 60 |
| 5 | 56 |
| 6 | 53 |

You are cold when the temperature is below 40°. (You are from California.) You are in the dark when the illumination is at most 50% of one candle power.

(a) Two graphs are sketched below. One is temperature as a function of distance and one is illumination as a function of distance. Which is which? Explain.

(b) What is the average rate at which the temperature is changing when the illumination drops from 75% to 56%?

(c) You can still read your watch when the illumination is about 65%, so somewhere between 3 and 4 feet. Can you read your watch at 3.5 feet? Explain.

(d) Suppose you know that at 6 feet the instantaneous rate of change of the temperature is −4.5° F/ft and the instantaneous rate of change of illumination is −3% candle power/ft. Estimate the temperature and the illumination at 7 feet.

(e) Are you in the dark before you are cold, or vice-versa?

ANSWER:

(a) The first graph plots illumination versus distance. We can see this in the chart because illumination drops rapidly at first, then begins to level off.

The second graph is a plot of temperature versus distance. This can be seen on the chart as temperature drops slowly at first, then greatly with distance from the candle.

(b) $\dfrac{47 - 53.5}{5 - 2} = -2.17°\,\text{F/ft}.$

(c) If we want to find the brightness at 3.5 feet from the candle, let's average the brightness at 3 and 4 feet to get 63.5%. However, since this curve is *concave up*, 63.5% is an *overestimate*. So we cannot read the watch.

(d) If, at 6 feet from the candle, the instantaneous rate of change is −4.5°F/ft, then an estimate for temperature at 7 feet might be $43.5 - 4.5 = 39°$F. Since this curve is concave down, this extrapolation is an *overestimate*. If, at 6 feet from the candle, the instantaneous rate of change is −3% candle power / ft, then an estimate for the illumination at 7 feet might be $53 - 3 = 50\%$ candle power/ft. Since this concave up, this extrapolation is an *underestimate*.

(e) At 7 feet from the candle, the temperature is less than 39° F and the illumination is greater than 50%. You are cold, but you are not yet dark. You thus become cold before you become dark.

3. Two politicians, named $A$ and $B$, carefully inspect a table of values, $x$ versus $y$. $A$ claims that the table is linear, while $B$ claims it is exponential.

(a) You look at the table and agree with $A$. Explain what you saw in the table.
(b) You look at the table and agree with $B$. Explain what you saw in the table.
(c) You look at the table and realize that neither is *exactly* right, but *both* of them are *approximately* correct. Explain why this can be so. Referring to the derivative might be appropriate.

ANSWER:

(a) For each change in $x$, the corresponding change in $y$ is proportional with the same constant of proportionality.

(b) Each time $x$ changes by a certain amount, the ratio of the corresponding $y$-values is the same.

(c) The table could be approximately linear and approximately exponential if the exponential function used were approximately linear. This could happen if we used a portion of an exponential graph and had zoomed in sufficiently so that the exponential looked almost straight.

# Chapter 3 Exam Questions

## Problems and Solutions for Section 3.1

1. Consider a sports car which accelerates from 0 ft/sec to 88 ft/sec in 5 seconds (88 ft/sec = 60 mph). The car's velocity is given in the table below.

| $t$ | 0 | 1 | 2 | 3 | 4 | 5 |
|------|---|----|----|----|----|----|
| $V(t)$ | 0 | 30 | 52 | 68 | 80 | 88 |

(a) Find upper and lower bounds for the distance the car travels in 5 seconds.

(b) In which time interval is the average acceleration greatest? Smallest?

ANSWER:

(a) Since $v(t)$ is increasing, a lower bound is given by the left-hand sum, and an upper bound is given by the right-hand sum.

$$\text{lower bound} = 0 + 30 + 52 + 68 + 80 = 230 \text{ feet};$$
$$\text{upper bound} = 30 + 52 + 68 + 80 + 88 = 318 \text{ feet}.$$

(b) In the first interval it is greatest. In the last interval it is smallest.

2. The graph shown below is that of the velocity of an object (in meters/second).

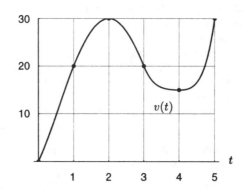

(a) Find an upper and a lower estimate of the total distance traveled from $t = 0$ to $t = 5$ seconds.

(b) At what times is the acceleration zero?

ANSWER:

(a) $v(0) = 0, v(1) = 20, v(2) = 30, v(3) = 20, v(4) = 15, v(5) = 30.$

Since this function is increasing over $[0, 2]$, decreasing over $[2, 4]$, and increasing over $[4, 5]$, we need to break the function into three parts in order to determine an overestimate and an underestimate of the distance travelled.

$$\text{Over } [0, 2], \text{ lower bound} = 0 + 20 = 20,$$
$$\text{upper bound} = 20 + 30 = 50.$$
$$\text{Over } [2, 4], \text{ lower bound} = 20 + 15 = 35,$$
$$\text{upper bound} = 30 + 20 = 50.$$
$$\text{Over } [4, 5], \text{ lower bound} = 15,$$
$$\text{upper bound} = 30.$$

So, adding the upper and lower bounds for the separate intervals, we get

$$\text{lower bound on distance traveled} = 20 + 35 + 15 = 70 \text{ meters};$$
$$\text{upper bound on distance traveled} = 50 + 50 + 30 = 130 \text{ meters}.$$

(b)  $v' = 0$ at $t = 2$ and $t = 4$.

## Problems and Solutions for Section 3.2

1.  Estimate $\int_8^{10} \ln x \, dx$ with accuracy 0.1. Show why you chose the $\Delta x$ that you did.
    ANSWER:
    Since $\ln x$ is increasing on [8,10],

    $$\text{LEFT}(n) < \int_8^{10} \ln x \, dx < \text{RIGHT}(n),$$

    and

    $$|\text{RIGHT}(n) - \text{LEFT}(n)| \le |\ln 10 - \ln 8|\Delta x$$

    We need $0.224 \,\Delta x < 0.1$, so we take $\Delta x = \frac{1}{3}, n = 6$, and we find $\text{LEFT}(6) \approx 4.35 < \int_8^{10} \ln x \, dx <$ $\text{RIGHT}(6) \approx 4.43$, so $\int_8^{10} \ln x \, dx \approx 4.39$ with an accuracy of 0.1.

2.  Consider the region $A$ bounded above by the graph of $f(x) = e^{-x^2}$, bounded below by the graph of $g(x) = e^{x^2} - 1$, and bounded on the left by the $y$-axis.

    (a)  Sketch and label the curves $f(x)$ and $g(x)$ and shade the region $A$. Find (approximately if necessary) and label the coordinates of the three corner points of $A$.
    (b)  By just looking at your sketch in Part (a), decide whether the area of $A$ is more or less than 0.7. Is it more or less than 0.3? Give a graphical justification of your answers.
    (c)  Express the area of the region $A$ as an integral, or as a sum or difference of integrals. Approximate the value(s) of the integral(s) with an accuracy that allows you to decide whether the area of $A$ is more or less than 0.5. Explain what you are doing.
    (d)  Name the possible sources of error in your calculation of the area of $A$ in part (b).

    ANSWER:

    (a)

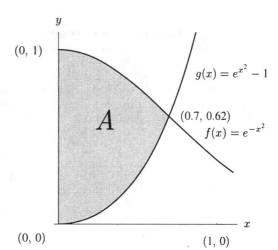

(b)   The area of $A$ is more than 0.3 but less than 0.7. To visualize this, draw a triangle connecting all three "corners" of the area. If we take the base of the triangle to be the left side of the area then:

$$A \approx \frac{1}{2}(1)(x) = \frac{x}{2}$$

Since $x \approx 0.7$, $A \approx 0.35 < 0.7$. Not only is this approximation of A greater than 0.3, we also know it is less than the actual value of A. Thus $A > 0.3$.

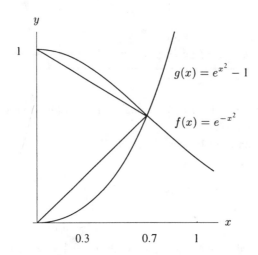

(c)

$$\int_0^{0.7} e^{-x^2}dx - \int_0^{0.7} (e^{x^2} - 1)dx = \int_0^{0.7} \left( e^{-x^2} - e^{x^2} + 1 \right) dx$$

We can approximate the value of this integral with left and right Riemann sums, dividing the region $[0, 0.7]$ into fourteen subdivisions. Then

$$0.441235 = \text{RIGHT} < A < \text{LEFT} = 0.492219,$$

which shows that the exact value of $A$ is less than 0.5.

(d)   The sources of error from this method are the extra space in $A$ not included in the triangle, and our approximation for the point of intersection of the functions $f$ and $g$.

## Problems and Solutions for Section 3.3

1.   Each of the quantities below can be represented in the picture. For each quantity, state whether it is represented by a length, slope, or an area. Then using letters on the picture, make clear exactly which length, slope or area represents it. [Note: The letters $P, Q, R$, etc., represent points.]

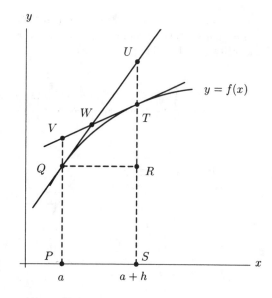

(a)  $f(a + h) - f(a)$
(b)  $f'(a + h)$
(c)  $f'(a)h$
(d)  $f(a)h$
(e)  State whether the quantity

$$\frac{1}{h} \int_a^{a+h} f(x)\, dx$$

is represented by a length or area in the picture. Draw the length or shade the area in the picture above.

ANSWER:

(a)  length $TR$
(b)  slope $TV$
(c)  length $UR$
(d)  area $PQRS$
(e)  The average of $f$ over the interval $[a, a + h]$ is a length.

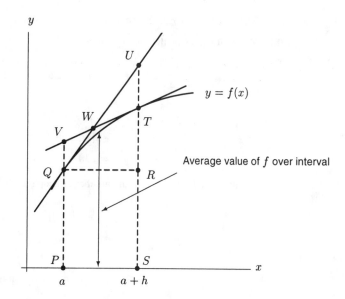

**Breakfast at Cafeteria Charlotte**

2. Below is the graph of the rate $r$ in arrivals/minute at which students line up for breakfast. The first people arrive at 6:50 a.m. and the line opens at 7:00 a.m.

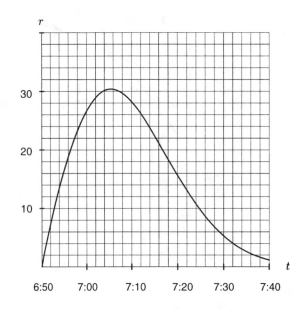

Suppose that once the line is open, checkers can check peoples' meal cards at a constant rate of 20 people per minute. Use the graph and this information to find an estimate for the following:

(a) The length of the line (i.e. the number of people) at 7:00 when the checkers begin.

(b) The length of the line at 7:10.

(c) The length of the line at 7:20.

(d) The rate at which the line is growing in length at 7:10.

(e) The length of time a person who arrives at 7:00 has to stand in line.

(f) The time at which the line disappears.

ANSWER:

(a) The length of the line at 7 : 00 will simply be the number of people who arrived before 7 : 00 a.m. This is just $\int_{6:50}^{7:00} r \, dt$. By counting squares, this turns out to be 150 students.

(b) This will simply be the [number of people who have arrived] - [number of people checked]

$$= \int_{6:50}^{7:10} r \, dt - 10(20)$$
$$= \int_{6:50}^{7:00} r \, dt + \int_{7:00}^{7:10} r \, dt - 200$$
$$\approx 150 + 280 - 200$$
$$= 230.$$

(c) Similarly, at 7 : 29 we have the number of people in line

$$= \int_{6:50}^{7:20} r \, dt - 400$$
$$= 430 + \int_{7:10}^{7:20} r \, dt - 400$$
$$\approx 430 + 220 - 400$$
$$= 250.$$

(d) At 7 : 10, the rate of arrivals is about 28 people per minute. The checking rate is 20 people per minute, so the line is growing at a rate of 8 people per minute.

(e) A person who arrives at 7 : 00 has about 150 people waiting in front of her. At a checking rate of 20 people per minute, she will spend approximately 7.5 minutes in line.

(f) The total number of arrivals, from the graph, $\int_{6:50}^{7:40} r\, dt$, appears to be about 800. At a checking rate of 20 people per minute, this will take 40 minutes, beginning at 7 : 00 a.m. So the line will disappear at 7 : 40 a.m.

3. (a) Explain, using words and pictures, how you would decide whether or not the quantity

$$\frac{2}{\pi} \int_0^{\frac{\pi}{2}} \sin t\, dt$$

is greater than, less than, or equal to 0.5 <u>without</u> doing any calculations. (Please be as concise as possible.)

(b) Which of the following best approximates $\dfrac{2}{\pi} \int_0^{\frac{\pi}{2}} \sin t\, dt$? Circle one. No explanation needed.

   0.35        0.4        0.45        0.5        0.55        0.6    .    0.65

ANSWER:

(a)

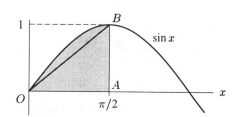

        Compare the areas:

area $OAB$ < area under sine curve

$\frac{2}{\pi} \times$ area $OAB < \frac{2}{\pi} \times$ area under sine curve.

$\frac{2}{\pi} \times \frac{1}{2} \times 1 \times \frac{\pi}{2} < \frac{2}{\pi} \int_0^{\frac{\pi}{2}} \sin t\, dt$

$.5 < \frac{2}{\pi} \int_0^{\frac{\pi}{2}} \sin t\, dt$

(b) 0.65

4. (a) The average value of a function $g$ on $0 \le x \le 1$ is a constant $\bar{g}$ given by

$$\bar{g} = \frac{1}{1-0} \int_0^1 g(x)\, dx = \int_0^1 g(x)\, dx.$$

Show that

$$\int_0^1 \bar{g} g(x)\, dx = \bar{g}^2.$$

(b) Since $(g(x) - \bar{g})^2 \ge 0$ (being a square), we have

$$0 \le \int_0^1 (g(x) - \bar{g})^2\, dx.$$

Use this and part (a) to show that

$$\left( \int_0^1 g(x)\, dx \right)^2 \le \int_0^1 (g(x))^2\, dx.$$

ANSWER:

(a)

$$\int_0^1 \overline{g} g(x)\, dx = \overline{g} \int_0^1 g(x)\, dx = (\overline{g})^2.$$

Notice that $\overline{g}$ is a constant and therefore can be factored out of the integral.

(b)  Since $\int_0^1 (g(x) - \bar{g})^2 \, dx \geq 0$ and

$$\int_0^1 (g(x) - \bar{g})^2 \, dx = \int_0^1 \left( (g(x))^2 - 2\bar{g}g(x) + \bar{g}^2 \right) \, dx$$

$$= \int_0^1 (g(x))^2 \, dx - 2\bar{g} \int_0^1 g(x) \, dx + \bar{g}^2 \int_0^1 \, dx$$

$$= \int_0^1 (g(x))^2 \, dx - 2\bar{g}^2 + \bar{g}^2$$

$$= \int_0^1 (g(x))^2 \, dx - \bar{g}^2,$$

we have

$$\int_0^1 (g(x))^2 \, dx - \bar{g}^2 \geq 0$$

i.e.,  $$\int_0^1 (g(x))^2 \, dx \geq \left( \int_0^1 g(x) \, dx \right)^2.$$

5.

$A$                                                    $B$

A car is moving along a straight road from $A$ to $B$, starting from $A$ at time $t = 0$. Below is the velocity (positive direction is from $A$ to $B$) plotted against time.

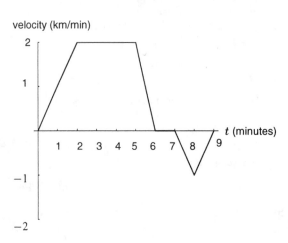

(a)  How many kilometers away from $A$ is the car at time $t = 2, 5, 6, 7$, and 9?
(b)  Carefully sketch a graph of the acceleration of the car against time. Label your axes.

ANSWER:

(a)  Since distance is found by integrating velocity, we find the area under the curve:
    $t = 2$, the distance from $A$ is $\frac{1}{2}(2)(2) = 2$
    $t = 5$, the distance from $A$ is $2 + 3(2) = 8$
    $t = 6$, the distance from $A$ is $8 + \frac{1}{2}(1)(2) = 9$
    $t = 7$, the distance from $A$ is 9
    $t = 9$, the distance from $A$ is $9 - \frac{1}{2}(2)(1) = 8$

(b)

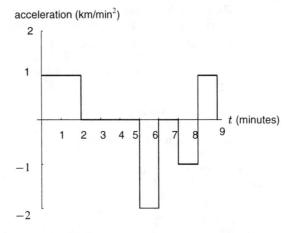

6.  A shop is open from 9am–7pm. The function $r(t)$, graphed below, gives the rate at which customers arrive (in people/hour) at time $t$. Suppose that the salespeople can serve customers at a rate of 80 people per hour.

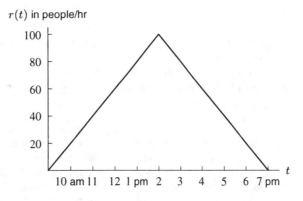

(a)  When do people have to start waiting in line before getting served? Explain clearly how you get your answer.

(b)  When is the line longest, and how many people are in the line then? Explain your answer.

(c)  When does the line vanish? Justify your answer.

ANSWER:

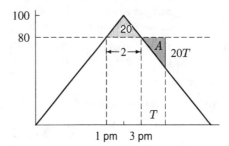

(a)  The line starts forming when people arrive faster than they can be served, which happens when $r(t) > 80$. This happens first when $t \geq 1$ pm.

(b)  The line builds up from 1pm to 3pm. After 3pm, the rate of arrivals falls <u>below</u> 80 and so the line starts to shrink again. The line is longest at 3pm, and the number in line is the shaded area above line at 80, i.e., length of line $= \frac{1}{2} \cdot 2 \cdot 20 = 20$ people.

(c) The line vanishes when an extra number served (over and above new arrivals) equals the 20 people in line before. This occurs when area is marked $A = 20$, slope of $r(t)$ (for $2 \leq t \leq$ 7pm) is $\dfrac{-100}{5} = -20$. Thus, if $T$ is the time beyond 3pm when the line vanishes, Area $= \dfrac{1}{2} \cdot T \cdot 20T = 10T^2 = 20$ so $T = \sqrt{2}$ or 1.41 hours $\approx$ 1 hour and 25 minutes, so around 4:25pm.

7. To the right is the graph of the *velocity*, in feet per second, of a hat that is thrown up in the air from ground level. Positive velocity means upward motion.
[Note that this is the graph of *velocity*, not distance.]

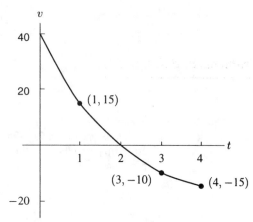

(a) When does the hat reach the top of its flight and about how high is it then?
(b) About how high is the hat at time $t = 4$?
(c) About what is the average velocity, $0 \leq t \leq 4$?
(d) About how big is the average *speed*, $0 \leq t \leq 4$?

ANSWER:

(a) At the top of its flight, the velocity of the hat (the derivative of its height) is zero and this occurs when $t = 2$. Since the hat starts at ground level, the height it reaches is the area under the velocity graph between $t = 0$ and $t = 2$, which we approximate by the trapezoid rule with $n = 2$ as $\frac{40+15}{2} + \frac{15+0}{2} = 35$ feet. Since the graph is concave up, this is an overestimate.

(b) We now subtract the area from $t = 2$ to $t = 4$ to the value obtained above for the area between $t = 0$ and $t = 2$, giving a total distance of $\approx 35 + \frac{0-10}{2} + \frac{-10-15}{2} = 17.5$ feet.

(c) The average velocity is given by $\frac{\text{total displacement}}{\text{total time}} \approx \frac{17.5}{4} \approx 4.4$ ft/sec.

(d) Speed is defined as $|v|$, so the average speed is given by

$$\frac{\int_0^4 |v|\, dt}{4} = \frac{\int_0^2 v\, dt + \int_2^4 (-v)\, dt}{4} = \frac{35 + 17.5}{4} \approx 13.1 \text{ ft/sec}.$$

8. Rashmi and Tia both go running from 7:00am to 8:00am. Both women increase their velocity throughout the hour, both beginning at a rate of 8 mi/hr. at 7:00am and running at a rate of 15 mi/hr by 8:00am. Rashmi's velocity increases at an increasing rate and Tia's velocity increases at a decreasing rate.

(a) Who has run the greater distance in the hour? Explain your reasoning clearly and convincingly.
(b) Who has the greatest average velocity, Rashmi or Tia, or do they have the same average velocity?

ANSWER:

(a) Consider the graphs of the two velocities:

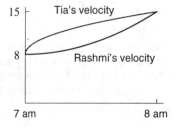

Then, total distance covered $= \displaystyle\int_7^8 (\text{velocity})dt = $ (area under curve between 7 and 8).

Area under Tia's curve is larger so she has covered more distance.

(b)  average velocity = (total distance covered)/(time it took to cover it)

Since both spend one hour running and Tia covered more ground, her average velocity must be greater!

N.B. Average velocity is <u>not</u> defined to be $\dfrac{\text{change in velocity}}{\text{change in time}}$ !! That would be average acceleration.

## Problems and Solutions for Section 3.4

1.  (a)  The acceleration of an object is given by the graph shown below. Make a graph of the velocity function $v$, of this object if $v(0) = 0$.

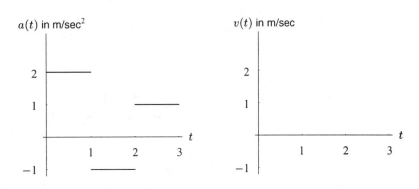

(b)  What is the relationship between the total change in $v(t)$ over the interval $0 \le t \le 3$ and $a(t)$?

ANSWER:

(a)

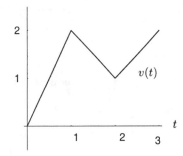

(b)  $\displaystyle\int_0^3 a(t)\, dt = v(3) - v(0)$

Check this:

$$\int_0^3 a(t)\, dt = 2 - 1 + 1 = 2; \qquad v(3) - v(0) = 2 - 0 = 2.$$

2.  Suppose $f(t)$ is given by the graph to the right. Complete the table of values of the function $F(x) = \int_0^x f(t)\, dt$.

| $x$ | $F(x)$ |
|-----|--------|
| 0   |        |
| 1   |        |
| 2   |        |
| 3   |        |
| 4   |        |
| 5   |        |
| 6   |        |

ANSWER:

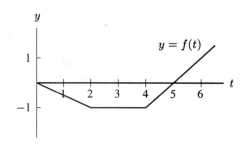

| $x$ | $F(x)$ |
|-----|--------|
| 0   | 0 |
| 1   | $-\frac{1}{4}$ |
| 2   | $-1$ |
| 3   | $-2$ |
| 4   | $-3$ |
| 5   | $-\frac{7}{2}$ |
| 6   | $-3$ |

## Review Problems and Solutions for Chapter 3

For Problems 1–3, circle the correct answer(s) or fill in the blanks. No reasons need be given.

1. Suppose $A$ = the area under the curve $y = e^{-x^2}$ over the interval $-1 \le x \le 1$. Which of the following is true?

   (a)  $A = F(1) - F(-1)$, where $F(x) = \dfrac{e^{-x^2}}{-2x}$.

   (b)  $1.495 < A$.

   (c)  $1.492 < A < 1.495$.

   (d)  $1.487 < A < 1.492$.

   ANSWER:

   (c) Use calculator; $A = 1.49365$.

2. If $r(t)$ represents the rate at which a country's debt is growing, then the increase in its debt between 1980 and 1990 is given by

   (a)  $\dfrac{r(1990) - r(1980)}{1990 - 1980}$

   (b)  $r(1990) - r(1980)$

   (c)  $\dfrac{1}{10} \displaystyle\int_{1980}^{1990} r(t)\,dt$

   (d)  $\displaystyle\int_{1980}^{1990} r(t)\,dt$

   (e)  $\dfrac{1}{10} \displaystyle\int_{1980}^{1990} r'(t)\,dt$

ANSWER:

(d) Fundamental Theorem

3. The graph of $f''$ is shown below.

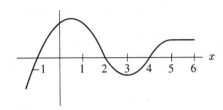

If $f$ is increasing at $x = -1$, which of the following <u>must</u> be true? (Circle all that apply.)

(a) $f'(2) = f'(4)$
(b) $f'(4) > f'(-1)$
(c) $f'(4) > 0$
(d) $f(5) = f(6)$

ANSWER:

$f$ increasing at $x = -1$ means $f'(-1) > 0$.

(a) false: $f'(4) - f'(2) = \displaystyle\int_2^4 f''(t)\,dt < 0$

(b) true: $f'(4) - f'(-1) = \displaystyle\int_{-1}^4 f''(t)\,dt > 0$

(c) true: $f'(4) > f'(-1) > 0$
(d) false: $f'(t) > 0$ for all $t > -1$ so $f(6) > f(5)$.

For Problems 4–6, decide whether each statement is true or false, and provide a short explanation or a counterexample.

4. $\displaystyle\int_{-1}^1 \sqrt{1 - x^2}\,dx = \frac{\pi}{2}$.

ANSWER:

TRUE. The integral represents the area under the upper half of the circle radius 1 centered at the origin. The area is thus $\frac{\pi}{2}$.

5. If a function is concave UP, then the left-hand Riemann sums are always less than the right-hand Riemann sums with the same subdivisions, over the same interval.

ANSWER:

FALSE. On the example below, the function is concave up, yet the left-hand sum is clearly larger than the right-hand sum.

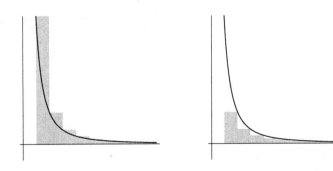

6. If $\int_a^b f(x)\,dx = 0$, then $f$ must have at least one zero between $a$ and $b$ (assume $a \neq b$).

ANSWER:

TRUE, if we allow only continuous functions. FALSE, if we allow discontinuous functions. The function shown below has no roots, yet $\int_{-2}^{4} f(x)\,dx = 0$.

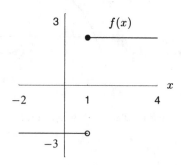

# Chapter 4 Exam Questions

*Problems and Solutions for Section 4.1*

1. Consider the function $f(x) = x^3 - 4x^2 + 9$.

   (a) Give the equations of the tangent line at $x = 1$ and the tangent line at $x = 2$.

   (b) Estimate $f(1.5)$ first using the tangent line at $x = 1$ and then using the tangent line at $x = 2$.

   (c) The estimate using $x = 1$ is slightly better. Explain why.

   ANSWER:

   (a) $f'(x) = 3x^2 - 8x$. Then $f'(1) = -5$ is the slope of the tangent line at $x = 1$, and $f'(2) = -4$ is the slope of the tangent line at $x = 2$. The equations of these lines are

   $$y = -5x + 11 \qquad \text{(tangent line at } (1, 6))$$

   $$y = -4x + 9 \qquad \text{(tangent line at } (2, 1))$$

   (b) Substituting 1.5 in for $x$, the first tangent line equation gives $f(1.5) \approx -5(1.5) + 11 = 3.5$. The second equation gives $f(1.5) \approx -4(1.5) + 9 = 3$. (The actual value is 3.375.)

   (c)

   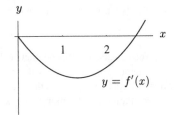

   The error in the local linearization depends on how much $f'$ is changing. (There would be no error if $f'$ were constant, for then $f$ would itself be linear.) From the graph we can see that $f'$ is more nearly constant between 1 and 1.5 than between 1.5 and 2, so we'd expect $f$ to deviate more from its linearization at 2 than from its linearization at 1. Alternatively we may note that $f''(x) = 6x - 8$, whence $|f''(1)| < |f''(2)|$, so $f'$ is changing more rapidly near 2 than near 1.

2. Given $f(x) = x^3 - 6x^2 + 9x - 5$,

   (a) Find the slope of the tangent line to the curve at $x = -2$.

   (b) What is the equation of this tangent line?

   (c) Find all points where the curve has a horizontal tangent.

   ANSWER:

   (a) $f(x) = x^3 - 6x^2 + 9x - 5$, so $f'(x) = 3x^2 - 12x + 9$. At $x = -2$, the slope is 45.

   (b) The tangent line passes through $(-2, -55)$, so its equation is

   $$y + 55 = 45(x + 2) \qquad \text{or} \qquad y = 45x + 35.$$

   (c) The line tangent to the curve $y = f(x)$ is horizontal when its slope, $f'(x)$, is zero. This happens when $3x^2 - 12x + 9 = 3(x - 1)(x - 3) = 0$, that is, when $x = 1$ or $x = 3$.

3. Decide whether the following statement is true or false and provide a short explanation or counterexample: The 10th derivative of $f(x) = x^{10}$ is 0.

   ANSWER:

   FALSE. The tenth derivative of $f(x) = x^{10}$ is 10! (10 factorial).

## Problems and Solutions for Section 4.2

1. Consider the graph $y = e^x$.
   (a) Find the equation of the tangent line to the graph at $(a, e^a)$.
   (b) Find the $x$- and $y$-intercepts of the line in part (a).
   (c) Show that the highest $y$-intercept of *any* tangent line is $y = 1$. (You may give a geometric argument as long as you say clearly what properties of the graph you are using.)

   ANSWER:

   (a) The slope of the tangent line at $(a, e^a)$ is $\dfrac{dy}{dx}\Big|_{x=a} = e^a$, so the equation of the tangent line is

   $$\frac{y - e^a}{x - a} = e^a$$
   $$y - e^a = xe^a - ae^a$$
   $$y = e^a(x - a + 1)$$

   (b) At $x = 0$, $y = e^a(1 - a)$. At $y = 0$, $x = a - 1$.
   (c) The formula of part (b) gives the $y$-intercept for the line tangent to any point of the graph of $y = e^x$. So the maximum $y$-intercept is attained wherever $e^a(1 - a)$ is largest.

   To find where $e^a(1 - a)$ is maximized, we examine the derivative: $\dfrac{d}{da}e^a(1 - a) = -ae^a$. This clearly has only one root, at $a = 0$, and is negative for all $a > 0$; so the maximum $y$-intercept is $e^a(1 - a)\Big|_{a=0} = 1$.

   You can also see this geometrically. Since the graph of $y = e^x$ is concave up, the tangent line at any point $(a, e^a)$ lies below the curve. So the $y$-intercept of any tangent line will be at or below where the curve $y = e^x$ hits the $y$-axis, i.e. at $(0, 1)$. Thus the tangent line at $(0, 1)$ has the largest $y$-intercept, namely 1, among all possible tangent lines.

2. If $P$ dollars are invested at an annual rate of $r\%$, then in $t$ years this investment grows to $F$ dollars, where

   $$F = P\left(1 + \frac{r}{100}\right)^t.$$

   (a) Assuming $P$ and $r$ are constant, find $\dfrac{dF}{dt}$. In practical terms (in terms of money), what does this derivative mean?
   (b) Solve the given equation for $P$. Assuming $F$ and $r$ are constant, find $\dfrac{dP}{dt}$. What is its sign? Why is this sign reasonable?

   ANSWER:

   (a) $\frac{dF}{dt} = P(1 + \frac{r}{100})^t \ln(1 + \frac{r}{100})$, which gives the rate at which the total amount of money grows.
   (b) $P = F(1 + \frac{r}{100})^{-t}$, so $\frac{dP}{dt} = -F(1 + \frac{r}{100})^{-t} \ln(1 + \frac{r}{100})$. The sign is negative, indicating that given the amount one wants to end up with, increasing the amount of time for which the money is invested decreases the amount one must put it initially to get the desired return.

## Problems and Solutions for Section 4.3

1. Consider the following table of data for the function $f$.

   | $x$ | 5.0 | 5.1 | 5.2 | 5.3 | 5.4 |
   |------|------|------|------|------|------|
   | $f(x)$ | 9.2 | 8.8 | 8.3 | 7.7 | 7.0 |

(a) Estimate $f'(5.1)$.

(b) Give an equation for the tangent at $x = 5.1$.

(c) What is the sign of $f''(5.1)$? Explain your answer.

(d) Is this the table of data linear? Exponential? Quadratic? Explain your answer.

(e) Suppose $g$ is a function such that $g(5.1) = 10$ and $g'(5.1) = 3$. Find $h'(5.1)$ where

    (i)  $h(x) = f(x)g(x)$

    (ii)  $h(x) = f(x)/g(x)$.

ANSWER:

(a)

$$f'(5.1) \approx \frac{f(5.2) - f(5.1)}{0.1} = \frac{8.3 - 8.8}{0.1} = -5.$$

(b) $y - 8.8 = -5(x - 5.1)$, so $y = -5x + 34.3$ is the equation for the tangent line.

(c) The sign of $f''(5.1)$ is negative because the derivative is decreasing (becoming more negative) here. To see this, compare

$$\big(f(5.1) - f(5.0)\big)/0.1 = -4$$

with

$$\big(f(5.2) - f(5.1)\big)/0.1 = -5$$

(d) The table is quadratic because the derivative of $f$ is linear: $f'(5) \approx -4$, $f'(5.1) \approx -5$, $f'(5.2) \approx -6$, and so on. Overall, the change in the derivative is linearly related to the change in $x$. Thus $f'(x) = ax + b$, for some $a$ and $b$, so $f(x) = ax^2/2 + bx + C$ for some $a$, $b$, and $C$.

(e) (i) Since

$$h'(x) = f'(x)g(x) + f(x)g'(x),$$

$$h'(5.1) = f'(5.1)g(5.1) + f(5.1)g'(5.1) = (-5)10 + (8.8)3 = -23.6.$$

    (ii)  Since

$$h'(x) = \frac{g(x)f'(x) - f(x)g'(x)}{(g(x))^2},$$

$$h'(5.1) = \frac{(10)(-5) - (8.8)3}{(10)^2} = -0.764.$$

## *Problems and Solutions for Section 4.4*

1. The table to the right gives values for functions $f$ and $g$, and their derivatives.

(a) Find $\dfrac{d}{dx}(f(x)g(x))$ and $\dfrac{d}{dx}\left(\dfrac{f(x)}{g(x)}\right)$ at $x = -1$.

(b) Find $\dfrac{d}{dx}f(g(x))$ and $\dfrac{d}{dx}g(f(x))$ at $x = 0$.

| $x$ | $-1$ | $0$ | $1$ | $2$ | $3$ |
|-----|------|-----|------|------|------|
| $f$ | 3 | 3 | 1 | 0 | 1 |
| $g$ | 1 | 2 | 2.5 | 3 | 4 |
| $f'$ | $-3$ | $-2$ | $-1.5$ | $-1$ | 1 |
| $g'$ | 2 | 3 | 2 | 2.5 | 3 |

ANSWER:

(a)

$$\frac{d}{dx}\big(f(x)g(x)\big)\bigg|_{x=-1} = f(x)g'(x) + f'(x)g(x)\bigg|_{x=-1}$$

$$= 3(2) + (-3)1 = 3.$$

$$\frac{d}{dx}\left(\frac{f(x)}{g(x)}\right)\bigg|_{x=-1} = \frac{f'(x)g(x) - f(x)g'(x)}{\big(g(x)\big)^2}\bigg|_{x=-1}$$

$$= \frac{(-3)(1) - (3)(2)}{1^2} = -9.$$

(b)

$$\frac{d}{dx}\left(f(g(x))\right)\Big|_{x=0} = f'(g(x))g'(x)\Big|_{x=0}$$

$$= f'(2)(3) = -1(3) = -3.$$

$$\frac{d}{dx}\left(g(f(x))\right)\Big|_{x=0} = g'(f(x))f'(x)\Big|_{x=0}$$

$$= g'(3)(-2) = 3(-2) = -6.$$

2. A table of values for a function $F$ near $x = 3$ and tables of values for a function $G$ near $x = 3$ and near $x = 7$ are given below.

| $x$ | 2.9 | 3.0 | 3.1 |
|-----|-----|-----|-----|
| $F(x)$ | 6.7 | 7.0 | 7.3 |

| $x$ | 2.9 | 3.0 | 3.1 |
|-----|-----|-----|-----|
| $G(x)$ | 5.2 | 5.0 | 4.8 |

| $x$ | 6.9 | 7.0 | 7.1 |
|-----|-----|-----|-----|
| $G(x)$ | 1.95 | 2.0 | 2.05 |

(a) Find $F'(3), G'(3), G'(7)$.
(b) If $H(x) = F(x)G(x)$, find $H'(3)$.
(c) If $H(x) = F(x)/G(x)$, find $H'(3)$.
(d) If $H(x) = G(F(x))$, find $H'(3)$.

ANSWER:

(a)

$$F'(3) \approx \frac{F(3.1) - F(3.0)}{3.1 - 3.0} = \frac{7.3 - 7.0}{0.1} = 3$$

$$G'(3) \approx \frac{G(3.1) - G(3.0)}{3.1 - 3.0} = \frac{4.8 - 5.0}{0.1} = -2$$

$$G'(7) \approx \frac{G(7.1) - G(7.0)}{7.1 - 7.0} = \frac{2.05 - 2.00}{0.1} = \frac{1}{2}$$

(b) $H'(3) = F'(3)G(3) + F(3)G'(3) = 3 \cdot 5 + 7 \cdot (-2) = 1.$
(c) $H'(3) = \frac{F'(3)G(3) - G'(3)F(3)}{G^2(3)} = \frac{29}{25}.$
(d) $H'(3) = G'(F(3))F'(3) = G'(7)F'(3) = \frac{1}{2} \cdot 3 = \frac{3}{2}.$

3. The volume of a certain tree is given by $V = \frac{1}{12\pi}C^2h$, where $C$ is the circumference of the tree at the ground level and $h$ is the height of the tree. If $C$ is 5 feet and growing at the rate of 0.2 feet per year, and if $h$ is 22 feet and is growing at 4 feet per year, find the rate of growth of the volume $V$.

ANSWER:

We have

$$V = \frac{1}{12\pi}C^2h,$$

so

$$\frac{dV}{dt} = \frac{1}{12\pi}\left(2Ch\frac{dC}{dt} + C^2\frac{dh}{dt}\right).$$

Since we are given that $C = 5$, $\frac{dC}{dt} = 0.2$, $h = 22$ and $\frac{dh}{dt} = 4$, we get:

$$\frac{dV}{dt} = \frac{1}{12\pi}(2 \cdot 5 \cdot 22(0.2) + 25 \cdot 4) \approx 3.82 \text{ ft}^3/\text{yr}.$$

4. Let $f(x)$ and $g(x)$ be two functions. Values of $f(x)$, $f'(x)$, $g(x)$, and $g'(x)$ for $x = 0$, 1, and 2 are given in the table below. Use the information in the table to answer the questions that follow.

| $x$ | $f(x)$ | $f'(x)$ | $g(x)$ | $g'(x)$ |
|-----|--------|---------|--------|---------|
| 0   | 1      | $-1$    | 2      | 5       |
| 1   | $-1$   | 2       | 4      | 0       |
| 2   | 7      | 3       | 11     | 0.5     |

(a) If $H(x) = e^{f(x)} + \pi x$, then $H'(0) =$

    (i)  $\dfrac{1}{e} + \pi$

    (ii)  $e^x + \pi x$

    (iii)  $e + \pi$

    (iv)  $e$

    (v)  $\pi - e$

(b) If $J(x) = [f(x)]^2$, then $J'(1) =$

    (i)  1

    (ii)  $-2$

    (iii)  4

    (iv)  $-4$

    (v)  2

(c) If $K(x) = f(g(x))$, then $K'(0) =$

    (i)  15

    (ii)  35

    (iii)  $-5$

    (iv)  $-1$

    (v)  7

ANSWER:

(a) $H'(x) = e^{f(x)} \cdot f'(x) + \pi$

$H'(0) = e^{f(0)} \cdot f'(0) + \pi = e^1 \cdot (-1) + \pi$

(e) $\pi - e$

(b) $J'(x) = 2f(x) \cdot f'(x)$

$J'(1) = 2f(1) \cdot f'(1)$

(d) $-4$

(c) $K'(x) = f'(g(x)) \cdot g'(x)$

$K'(0) = f'(g(0)) \cdot g'(0)$

$\qquad = f'(2) \cdot g'(0) \qquad$ (a) 15

$\qquad = 3 \cdot 5 = 15$

5. (a) What is the instantaneous rate of change of the function $f(x) = e^{-x^2}$ at $x = 0$? at $x = 1$? at $x = 2$?

(b) Use the information from part (a) to sketch the graph of the function for $x \geq 0$.

ANSWER:

(a) $f'(x) = -2x e^{-x^2}$; $f'(0) = 0$; $f'(1) = -2e^{-1}$; $f'(2) = -4e^{-4}$

(b)

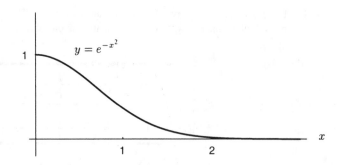

$y = e^{-x^2}$

6. (a) Find the equation of the tangent line to $f(x) = e^{-3x}$ at $x = 2$.
   (b) Use it to approximate the value of $f(2.2)$.
   (c) Find the point where the tangent line crosses the $x$-axis.

   ANSWER:

   (a) Since $f'(x) = -3e^{-3x}$, $f'(2) = -3e^{-6}$. Moreover, $f(2) = e^{-6}$. The tangent line to the graph of $f$ at $x = 2$ goes through $(2, e^{-6})$ and has slope $-3e^{-6}$. The equation of the tangent line is then

   $$y - e^{-6} = -3e^{-6}(x - 2)$$
   $$y = -3e^{-6}x + 7e^{-6}$$

   (b) $f(2.2) \approx -3e^{-6}(2.2) + 7e^{-6} = 0.4e^{-6} = 0.00099.$
   (c) The tangent line crosses the $x$-axis when $y = 0$; that is, when $x = 7/3$.

7. Find a point on the graph of $y = e^{3x}$ at which the tangent line passes through the origin.

   ANSWER:

   Call the desired point $(q, e^{3q})$. Then the slope of the tangent line at this point is $3e^{3q}$, and the equation of the tangent line at $(q, e^{3q})$ is $y - e^{3q} = 3e^{3q}(x - q)$. We know that this line passes through $(0, 0)$, so we have $-e^{3q} = 3e^{3q}(-q)$; $q = \frac{1}{3}$. So the desired point is $\left(\frac{1}{3}, e\right)$

## Problems and Solutions for Section 4.5

1. Find the derivatives:

   (a) $\dfrac{d}{dt} e^{2(t-1)}$

   (b) $\dfrac{d}{d\theta} \left(\theta \sin(\theta^2)\right)$

   ANSWER:

   (a) $\dfrac{d}{dt} e^{2(t-1)} = 2e^{2(t-1)}$

   (b) $\dfrac{d}{d\theta} \left(\theta \sin(\theta^2)\right) = \sin(\theta^2) + \theta \left(2\theta \cos(\theta^2)\right) \sin(\theta^2) + 2\theta^2 \cos(\theta^2)$

2. (a) Find a function $F(x)$ such that $F'(x) = x^4 + \sin x$ and $F(0) = 5$.
   (b) Sketch the graph of a function $G(x)$ whose *derivative* $G'(x) = g(x)$ has the graph drawn below.

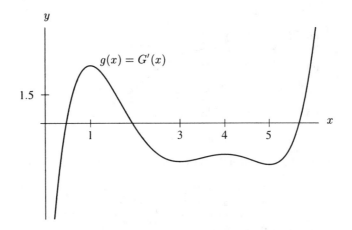

ANSWER:

(a) The anti-derivative of $F'(x) = x^4 + \sin x$ is $\frac{x^5}{5} - \cos x + C$. Since $F(0) = 5$, $\frac{0^5}{5} - \cos(0) + C = 5$, and $C = 6$. So,

$$F(x) = \frac{x^5}{5} - \cos x + 6.$$

(b)

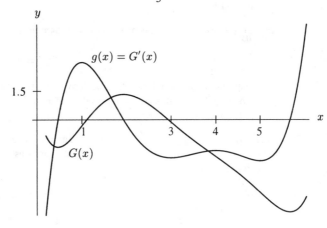

3. A particle moves in such a way that $x(t) = 4t^2 + 7 \sin t$.

   (a) What is the instantaneous rate of change at $t = 0$?
   (b) What is the instantaneous rate of change at $t = \frac{\pi}{2}$?
   (c) What is the average rate of change between $t = 0$ and $t = \frac{\pi}{2}$?

   ANSWER:

   (a) The derivative is $x'(t) = 8t + 7 \cos t$, so the instantaneous rate of change at $x = 0$ is $x'(0) = 7$.
   (b) $x'(\frac{\pi}{2}) = 4\pi$.
   (c) The average rate of change over $\left[0, \frac{\pi}{2}\right]$ is given by

$$\frac{x\left(\frac{\pi}{2}\right) - x(0)}{\frac{\pi}{2} - 0} = \frac{\left(\pi^2 + 7\right) - 0}{\frac{\pi}{2}} = \frac{2\left(\pi^2 + 7\right)}{\pi} \approx 10.74.$$

4. Differentiate each of the following:

   (a) $f(x) = x^{\frac{3}{4}} - x^{\frac{4}{3}} + x^{-\frac{4}{3}}$
   (b) $f(w) = \sqrt{w^2 + 5}$
   (c) $f(z) = e^{z^2}/(z^2 - 3)$
   (d) $f(x) = xe^{-x}$
   (e) $f(\theta) = \sin(2\theta^3 + 1)$
   (f) $f(x) = (x + \sin x)^\pi$

ANSWER:

(a) $f'(x) = \frac{3}{4}x^{-\frac{1}{4}} - \frac{4}{3}x^{\frac{1}{3}} - \frac{4}{3}x^{-\frac{7}{3}}$

(b) $f'(x) = x(-e^{-x}) + e^{-x} = e^{-x}(1-x)$

(c) $f'(w) = \frac{1}{2}(w^2+5)^{-\frac{1}{2}} \cdot 2w = \dfrac{w}{\sqrt{w^2+5}}$

(d) $f'(\theta) = \cos(2\theta^3+1) \cdot 6\theta^2 = 6\theta^2 \cos(2\theta^3+1)$

(e) $f'(z) = \dfrac{(z^2-3)(2ze^{z^2}) - 2z(e^{z^2})}{(z^2-3)^2} = \dfrac{2z(z^2-4)e^{z^2}}{(z^2-3)^2}$

(f) $f'(x) = \pi(x+\sin x)^{\pi-1}(1+\cos x)$

5. Find the equation of the tangent line to the curve given by $f(x) = x\sin x$ at the point $x = \pi/4$.

ANSWER:

$$f'(x) = x\cos x + \sin x; f'(\frac{\pi}{4}) = \frac{\pi}{4} \cdot \frac{\sqrt{2}}{2} + \frac{\sqrt{2}}{2} = \frac{\sqrt{2}}{2}(\frac{\pi}{4}+1). \text{ Since } f(\frac{\pi}{4}) = \frac{\pi\sqrt{2}}{8}, \text{ the}$$

equation of the line is $y - \dfrac{\pi\sqrt{2}}{8} = \dfrac{\sqrt{2}}{2}(\dfrac{\pi}{4}+1)(x - \dfrac{\pi}{4})$.

6. Consider the two functions $f(x) = -\cos^2(x)$ and $g(x) = \sin^2(x)$.

   (a) Show that $f' = g'$.
   (b) Use part (a) to derive the famous trigonometric identity $1 = \sin^2(x) + \cos^2(x)$.
       [Hint: what can you conclude about two functions whose derivatives are the same?]

   ANSWER:

   (a) $\dfrac{d}{dx}(-\cos^2 x) = -2\cos x(-\sin x) = 2\cos x \sin x$, and $\dfrac{d}{dx}\sin^2 x = 2\sin x \cos x$. So,

   $$f' = g'.$$

   (b) Since these functions have the same derivatives, they must differ by only a constant. So $-\cos^2 x = \sin^2 x + C$. Since this holds for all values of $x$, set $x = 0$. Then $-\cos^2(0) = \sin^2(0) + C$ and $C = -1$. So $\sin^2 x + \cos^2 x = 1$.

7. When hyperventilating, a person breathes in and out extremely rapidly. A spirogram is a machine that draws a graph of the volume of air in a person's lungs as a function of time. During hyperventilation, the spirogram trace might be represented by

$$V = 3 - 0.05\cos(200\pi t)$$

where $V$ is the volume of the lungs in liters and $t$ is the time in minutes.

   (a) What are the maximum and minimum volumes of air in the lungs?
   (b) What is the period of this function?
   (c) Sketch the graph of one period of this function, starting at $t = 0$. Put scales on the $V$ and $t$ axes.
   (d) Find the maximum rate (in liters/minute) of flow of air during inspiration (i.e. breathing in). This is called the *peak inspiratory flow*.
   (e) Find the average rate of flow of air during inspiration. This is called the *mean inspiratory flow*.

   ANSWER:

   (a) Since $\cos(200\pi t)$ varies between $-1$ and $1$, $V$ varies between 2.95 and 3.05.
   (b) The period of this function is $\frac{2\pi}{200\pi} = \frac{1}{100}$ min $\approx 0.66$ sec.
   (c)

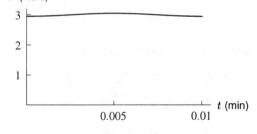

The following graph represents the same information, but it is shifted up and the $V$ scale is stretched to emphasize the change in the curve with time.

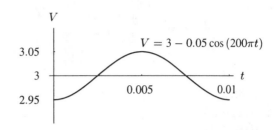

(d)   The rate of flow is $\frac{dV}{dt} = 10\pi \sin(200\pi t)$, whose maximum is $10\pi$ liters/minute, exactly halfway through inspiration.

(e)   The *mean inspiratory flow* is

$$\frac{\int_0^{0.005} 10\pi \sin(200\pi t)\, dt}{0.005} = 20 \text{ liters/minute.}$$

## Problems and Solutions for Section 4.6

1.   If $P$ dollars is invested at an annual interest rate of $r\%$, then at $t$ years this investment grows to $F$ dollars, where

$$F = P\left(1 + \frac{r}{100}\right)^t.$$

Find $\dfrac{dF}{dr}$. (Assume $P$ and $t$ are constant.) In terms of money, what does this derivative tell you?

ANSWER:

$$\begin{aligned}
\frac{dF}{dr} &= \frac{d}{dr}P(1 + \frac{r}{100})^t \\
&= Pt(1 + \frac{r}{100})^{t-1}\frac{d}{dr}\left(1 + \frac{r}{100}\right) \quad \text{(using the chain rule)} \\
&= \frac{Pt}{100}\left(1 + \frac{r}{100}\right)^{t-1}
\end{aligned}$$

The derivative tells me how much extra money I will get for a small increase in the interest rate.

2.   Find the derivatives of the following functions.

(a) $f(x) = x \ln x - x$

(b) $g(t) = \sin 3t - \cos 5t$

(c) $R(p) = \dfrac{e^p}{1 + e^p}$

(d) $H(x) = \sqrt{1 - x^2}$

ANSWER:

(a)

$$\begin{aligned}
f(x) &= x \ln x - x \\
f'(x) &= \ln x + x \cdot \frac{1}{x} - 1 \\
&= \ln x + 1 - 1 \\
&= \ln x
\end{aligned}$$

(b)

$$\begin{aligned}
g(t) &= \sin 3t - \cos 5t \\
g'(t) &= 3\cos 3t + 5\sin 5t
\end{aligned}$$

(c)                    (d)

$$R(p) = \frac{e^p}{1 + e^p}$$

$$R'(p) = \frac{e^p(1 + e^p) - e^p e^p}{(1 + e^p)^2}$$

$$= \frac{e^p + e^{2p} - e^{2p}}{(1 + e^p)^2} = \frac{e^p}{(1 + e^p)^2}$$

$$H(x) = \sqrt{1 - x^2}$$

$$H'(x) = \frac{1}{2}(1 - x^2)^{-\frac{1}{2}} \cdot (-2x)$$

$$= \frac{-x}{\sqrt{1 - x^2}}$$

3.   Find $f'(x)$

    (a)   $f(x) = e^{3x} \cos 5x$

    (b)   $f(x) = \sin \sqrt{\ln x + 7}$

    (c)   $f(x) = \dfrac{x + 1}{x^2 + 3}$

    ANSWER:

    (a)   $f'(x) = 3e^{3x} \cos 5x + 5e^{3x}(-\sin 5x) = e^{3x}(3 \cos 5x - 5 \sin 5x).$

    (b)   $f'(x) = \cos(\sqrt{\ln x + 7}) \cdot \dfrac{1}{2} \dfrac{1}{\sqrt{\ln x + 7}} \cdot \dfrac{1}{x} = \dfrac{\cos \sqrt{\ln x + 7}}{2x\sqrt{\ln x + 7}}.$

    (c)   $f'(x) = \dfrac{(x^2 + 3) - 2x(x + 1)}{(x^2 + 3)^2} = \dfrac{-x^2 - 2x + 3}{(x^2 + 3)^2}.$

4.   Perform the indicated differentiation. Please do not simplify your answers!

    (a)   $\dfrac{d}{dx}\left[\dfrac{x^2 + 1}{x^2 - 1}\right]$

    (b)   $\dfrac{d}{dx}[e^x \sin x]$

    (c)   $\dfrac{d}{dx}\left[4e^{(3x^2 + 7x)}\right]$

    (d)   $\dfrac{d}{dx}[\arctan x + x - \sqrt{x}]$

    (e)   $\dfrac{d}{dx}\left[(\ln x)^2 - \ln(x^2)\right]$

    ANSWER:

    (a)   $\dfrac{d}{dx}\left[\dfrac{x^2 + 1}{x^2 - 1}\right] = \dfrac{2x(x^2 - 1) - 2x(x^2 + 1)}{(x^2 - 1)^2}$

    (b)   $\dfrac{d}{dx}[e^x \sin x] = e^x \sin x + e^x \cos x$

    (c)   $\dfrac{d}{dx}\left[4e^{(3x^2 + 7x)}\right] = 4(6x + 7)e^{(3x^2 + 7x)}$

    (d)   $\dfrac{d}{dx}[\arctan x + x - \sqrt{x}] = \dfrac{1}{1 + x^2} + 1 - \dfrac{1}{2\sqrt{x}}$

    (e)   $\dfrac{d}{dx}[(\ln x)^2 - \ln(x^2)] = \dfrac{2 \ln x}{x} - \dfrac{2}{x}$

5.   (a)   Find an equation for the tangent line to the curve, $y = \ln x$, which passes through the origin. [Hint: Make a sketch.]

    (b)   Consider the equation $\ln x = mx$ where $m$ is some constant (positive, negative, or zero). For which values of $m$ will this equation have no solution? For which values of $m$ will this equation have one solution? For which values of $m$ will this equation have two solutions?

    [Note: If you were unable to answer part (a), you may refer to the slope of the line as "$m_0$".]

    ANSWER:

    (a)   Slope of tangent $= \dfrac{y_0}{x_0}$

            Slope of $y = \ln x$ at $x_0$ is $\dfrac{1}{x_0}$

These must be the same: $\dfrac{y_0}{x_0} = \dfrac{1}{x_0}$

$\underline{y_0 = 1 = \ln x_0} \quad \Rightarrow \quad \underline{x_0 = e}$

Slope of tangent $= \dfrac{y_0}{x_0} = \dfrac{1}{e}$

$\underline{\text{Tangent: } y = \dfrac{1}{e} \cdot x}$

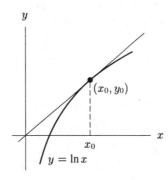

(b)   $m > \dfrac{1}{e}$ (no solution)

   $m = \dfrac{1}{e}$   and   $m \le 0$ (one solution)

   $0 < m < \dfrac{1}{e}$ (two solutions)

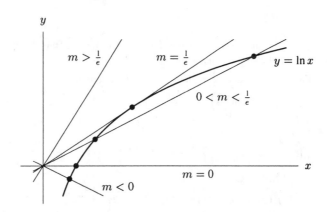

6.   Find, without simplifying your answers:

   (a)   $\dfrac{d}{dx}\left(\ln(x^2 e^x)\right)$        (b)   $\dfrac{d}{d\theta}\left(\dfrac{\cos\theta}{\sin\theta}\right)$        (c)   $\dfrac{d}{dz}\left(\sqrt{1 + 2^{3z}}\right)$

   ANSWER:

   (a)   $\dfrac{d}{dx}(\ln(x^2 e^x)) = \dfrac{d}{dx}\left(\ln(x^2) + \ln(e^x)\right) = \dfrac{d}{dx}(2\ln x + x) = \dfrac{2}{x} + 1$

   (b)   $\dfrac{d}{d\theta}\left(\dfrac{\cos\theta}{\sin\theta}\right) = \dfrac{-\sin\theta \cdot \sin\theta - \cos\theta\cos\theta}{\sin^2\theta} = -\dfrac{1}{\sin^2\theta}$

   (c)   $\dfrac{d}{dz}\left(\sqrt{1 + 2^{3z}}\right) = \dfrac{d}{dz}\left(\sqrt{1 + e^{3z\ln 2}}\right) = \dfrac{3 \cdot \ln 2 \cdot 2^{3z}}{2\sqrt{1 + 2^{3z}}}$

7.   Let $a$ be a positive constant (i.e., $a > 0$). The equation

$$a^x = 1 + x$$

has the solution $x = 0$, for all $a$. Are there any solutions for $x > 0$? How does your answer depend on the value of $a$? You may explore with the computer or calculator by trying various different values of $a$ to help answer this question, and you will get partial credit for an answer which simply reports on the results of this exploration, but to receive full credit you must include an exact answer with justification.

ANSWER:

The derivative of $a^x$ is $(\ln a)a^x$, so the slope of $a^x$ at $x = 0$ is $\ln a$, and the slope increases without bound after that. The graph of $y = 1 + x$ is a straight line with slope 1. Hence if $\ln a \geq 1$, the graph of $a^x$ is always above the graph of $1 + x$, since it is always increasing at a greater rate (see Figure 4.6.1). If $\ln a < 1$, then $a^x$ starts out with slope less than the slope of $y = 1 + x$ but eventually overtakes it (see Figure 4.6.2), so there is a solution to $a^x = 1 + x$ with $x > 0$.

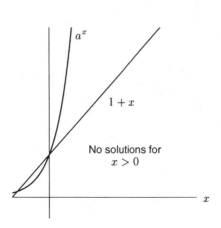

**Figure 4.6.1**: $a = 10$

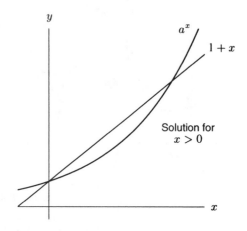

**Figure 4.6.2**: $a = 1.5$

Now, $\ln a > 1$ if $a > e$ and $\ln a < 1$ if $a < e$. Thus the equation $a^x = 1 + x$ has a solution for $x > 0$ whenever $a < e$.

8. Find the derivatives of each of the following functions.

   (a)  $f(x) = \sin(2x) \cdot \sin(3x)$
   (b)  $f(x) = e^{-(1-x)^2}$
   (c)  $f(x) = \dfrac{1 + x}{2 + 3x + 4x^2}$
   (d)  $f(x) = \ln(\cos x)$

   ANSWER:

   (a)  $f'(x) = 3\cos(3x)\sin(2x) + 2\cos(2x)\sin(3x)$
   (b)  $f'(x) = 2(1 - x)e^{-(1-x)^2}$
   (c)  $f'(x) = -\dfrac{1 + 8x + 4x^2}{(2 + 3x + 4x^2)^2}$
   (d)  $f'(x) = -\tan x$

9. Differentiate the following functions

   (a)  $f(x) = \sqrt{x} + \dfrac{1}{\sqrt[3]{x}}.$
   (b)  $g(t) = 2^{2(t-1)}.$
   (c)  $h(\theta) = \theta \sin(\theta^2).$
   (d)  $f(y) = \ln\dfrac{1 + y}{1 - y}.$

   ANSWER:

(a)  $f(x) = \sqrt{x} + \dfrac{1}{\sqrt[3]{x}}$

$$\begin{aligned}
\frac{df}{dx} &= \frac{d}{dx}\left(\sqrt{x} + \frac{1}{\sqrt[3]{x}}\right) \\
&= \frac{d}{dx}(x^{\frac{1}{2}}) + \frac{d}{dx}(x^{-\frac{1}{3}}) \\
&= \frac{1}{2}x^{-\frac{1}{2}} + \left(-\frac{1}{3}\right)x^{-\frac{4}{3}} \\
&= \frac{1}{2\sqrt{x}} - \frac{1}{3x\sqrt[3]{x}}
\end{aligned}$$

(b)  $g(t) = 2^{2(t-1)} = e^{2(t-1)\ln 2}$

By the chain rule, 
$$\begin{aligned}
\frac{dg}{dt} &= \frac{d}{dt}e^{2(t-1)\ln 2} \\
&= (2\ln 2)e^{2(t-1)\ln 2} \\
&= (2\ln 2)2^{2(t-1)} \\
&= 2^{2t-1}\ln 2
\end{aligned}$$

(c)  $h(\theta) = \theta\sin(\theta^2)$

By the product rule, 
$$\begin{aligned}
\frac{dh}{d\theta} &= \frac{d}{d\theta}\left(\theta\sin(\theta^2)\right) \\
&= \sin(\theta^2)\frac{d}{d\theta}(\theta) + \theta\frac{d}{d\theta}(\sin(\theta^2)) \\
&= \sin(\theta^2) + \theta\frac{d}{d\theta}(\sin(\theta^2)) \quad \text{(using the chain rule)} \\
&= \sin\theta^2 + \theta(\cos\theta^2)\frac{d}{d\theta}\theta^2 \\
&= \sin\theta^2 + \theta(\cos\theta^2)2\theta \\
&= 2\theta^2\cos\theta^2 + \sin\theta^2
\end{aligned}$$

(d)  $f(y) = \ln\dfrac{1+y}{1-y}$

$$\begin{aligned}
\frac{df}{dy} &= \frac{d}{dy}\ln\left(\frac{1+y}{1-y}\right) \\
&= \frac{d}{dy}\ln(1+y) - \frac{d}{dy}\ln(1-y) \\
&= \frac{1}{1+y}\frac{d}{dy}(1+y) - \frac{1}{1-y}\frac{d}{dy}(1-y) \\
&= \frac{1}{1+y} + \frac{1}{1-y} = \frac{2}{1-y^2}
\end{aligned}$$

10.  What is the instantaneous rate of change of the function $f(x) = x\ln x$ at $x = 1$? at $x = 2$? What do these values suggest about the concavity of the function between 1 and 2?

ANSWER:

At any point $x$ the derivative $f'(x)$ is $1\ln x + x\frac{1}{x} = 1+\ln x$, so $f'(1) = 1$, and $f'(2) = 1+\ln 2 > 1$. The derivative of $f$ appears to be increasing between 1 and 2; this observation suggests that $f$ is concave up on this interval.

**410**

1. Find the indicated derivatives.

   (a) $f(x) = 4x^3 - 3x^2 + 2x - 8$. Find $f'(x)$.

   (b) $y = u\sqrt{u+1}$, $u = 2x^2 + 3$. Find $\dfrac{dy}{du}$, and $\dfrac{dy}{dx}$.

   (c) $y = e^{\cos^2\theta}$. Find $\dfrac{dy}{d\theta}$.

   (d) $p(x) = \ln((x-a)(x-b)(x-c))$. $a, b, c$ are constants. Find $p'(x)$.

   (e) $x = \dfrac{\sin t}{1 + \cos t}$. Find $\dfrac{dx}{dt}$.

   (f) $(x+y)^2 = (2x+1)^3$. Find $\dfrac{dy}{dx}$. (Use implicit differentiation. Your answer will involve both $x$ and $y$.)

   ANSWER:

   (a) $f'(x) = 12x^2 - 6x + 2$.

   (b) $\dfrac{dy}{du} = u\left(\dfrac{1}{2}(u+1)^{-\frac{1}{2}}\right) + (u+1)^{\frac{1}{2}} = (u+1)^{-\frac{1}{2}}\left(\dfrac{3}{2}u + 1\right)$. Since $u = 2x^2 + 3$, and $\dfrac{du}{dx} = 4x$,

   $$\dfrac{dy}{dx} = \dfrac{dy}{du}\dfrac{du}{dx} = (2x^2+4)^{-\frac{1}{2}}\left(\dfrac{3}{2}(2x^2+3)+1\right)(4x).$$

   (c) $\dfrac{dy}{d\theta} = -2\cos\theta\sin\theta e^{\cos^2\theta}$.

   (d) $p(x) = \ln((x-a)(x-b)(x-c)) = \ln(x-a) + \ln(x-b) + \ln(x-c)$. Hence,

   $$p'(x) = \dfrac{1}{x-a} + \dfrac{1}{x-b} + \dfrac{1}{x-c}$$

   (e) $\dfrac{dx}{dt} = \dfrac{\cos t(1+\cos t) - \sin t(-\sin t)}{(1+\cos t)^2} = \dfrac{\cos t + \cos^2 t + \sin^2 t}{(1+\cos t)^2} = \dfrac{1}{1+\cos t}$.

   (f)
   $$2(x+y)\left(1+\dfrac{dy}{dx}\right) = 3(2x+1)^2(2)$$
   $$(x+y) + \dfrac{dy}{dx}(x+y) = 3(2x+1)^2$$
   $$\dfrac{dy}{dx} = \dfrac{3(2x+1)^2 - x - y}{x+y}$$

2. Suppose that $xy^2 + \sin y + x^3 = 8$.

   (a) Find $\dfrac{dy}{dx}$.

   (b) Give a table of estimates of values of $y$ for $x$ near 2. (Use $x = 1.98, 1.99, 2.00, 2.01$.)

   ANSWER:

   (a) We differentiate implicitly:
   $$y^2 + x\left(2y\dfrac{dy}{dx}\right) + \cos y\dfrac{dy}{dx} + 3x^2 = 0$$
   so
   $$\dfrac{dy}{dx} = -\dfrac{3x^2 + y^2}{2xy + \cos y}$$

   (b) At $(2,0)$, $\frac{dy}{dx} = -12$. Hence the line $y = -12x + 24$ is tangent to the given curve at $(2,0)$. Using this approximation we obtain the following table:

   | $x$ | 1.98 | 1.99 | 2.00 | 2.01 |
   |---|---|---|---|---|
   | $y$ | 0.24 | 0.12 | 0.00 | −0.12 |

   These aren't very good estimates however; the actual values (rounded) are $0.18, 0.10, 0.00$ and $-0.22$.

3. Consider the following three equations:

   (a)  $y^2 - 2\cos x = 2$,

   (b)  $x \sin y + y = 2$,

   (c)  $\ln|y/(1-y)| = 0.71x + \ln 2$.

Assuming each of the above equations implicitly defines $y$ as a function of $x$, find $\dfrac{dy}{dx}$ for each equation.

   ANSWER:

(a)

$$y^2 - 2\cos x = 2$$
$$2y\frac{dy}{dx} + 2\sin x = 0$$
$$\frac{dy}{dx} = -\frac{\sin x}{y}.$$

(b)

$$x\sin y + y = 2$$
$$\sin y + x\cos y\frac{dy}{dx} + \frac{dy}{dx} = 0$$
$$\frac{dy}{dx} = -\frac{\sin y}{x\cos y + 1}.$$

(c)

$$\ln\left|\frac{y}{1-y}\right| = 0.71x + \ln 2$$
$$\ln|y| - \ln|1-y| = 0.71x + \ln 2$$
$$\left(\frac{1}{y} + \frac{1}{1-y}\right)\frac{dy}{dx} = 0.71$$
$$\frac{dy}{dx} = 0.71y(1-y).$$

4. The part of the graph of $\sin(x^2 + y) = x$ that is near $(0, \pi)$ defines $y$ as a function of $x$ implicitly.

   (a)  Is this function increasing or decreasing near 0? Explain how you know.

   (b)  Does the graph of this function lie above or below its tangent line at $(0, \pi)$? Explain how you know.

   ANSWER:

   (a)  To check whether the function increases or decreases near 0 we simply check the sign of $\frac{dy}{dx}$ near 0. Implicit differentiation of the function with respect to $x$ gives

$$\cos(x^2 + y)\left(2x + \frac{dy}{dx}\right) = 1$$
$$\frac{dy}{dx} = \frac{1}{\cos(x^2 + y)} - 2x$$
$$\left.\frac{dy}{dx}\right|_{x=0\ y=\pi} = \frac{1}{\cos(0^2 + \pi)} - 2(0) = \frac{1}{-1} - 0 = -1.$$

In fact $\frac{dy}{dx}$ is negative near 0, so the function decreases near $(0, \pi)$.

   (b)  We check concavity of the function at 0 by finding

$$\frac{d^2y}{dx^2} = \frac{d}{dx}\left(\frac{1}{\cos(x^2 + y)} - 2x\right)$$
$$= -\frac{1}{\cos^2(x^2 + y)} \cdot (-\sin(x^2 + y)) \cdot \left(2x + \frac{dy}{dx}\right) - 2$$

$$= \frac{\sin(x^2 + y)}{\cos^2(x^2 + y)}\left(2x + \frac{1}{\cos(x^2 + y)} - 2x\right) - 2$$

$$= \frac{\sin(x^2 + y)}{\cos^3(x^2 + y)} - 2$$

At $(0, \pi)$, $\frac{d^2y}{dx^2} = -2$, so the function is concave down here, and hence lies *below* its tangent line.

5. The purpose of this problem is to sketch the implicit function $x^3 + y^3 = -8$.

   (a) Find all the $y$-values for which $x = 0$.
   (b) Calculate $dy/dx$.
   (c) Use parts (a) and (b), and a computer or calculator, to sketch this implicit function. Explain what program you used, and what you did, and copy the sketch of the implicit function from the computer or calculator to your paper.

   ANSWER:

   (a) If $x = 0$, $y^3 = -8$, so $y = -2$.

   (b) Using implicit differentiation, we find that $3x^2 + 3y^2\frac{dy}{dx} = 0$, so $\frac{dy}{dx} = -\frac{x^2}{y^2}$.

   (c)

   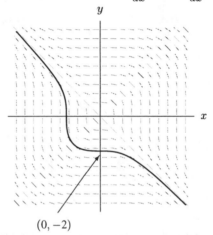

   $(0, -2)$

   The curve above was found by entering $\frac{dy}{dx} = -\frac{x^2}{y^2}$ into a program that draws slope fields and then getting the program to draw the solution curve passing through the point $(0, -2)$.

## Problems and Solutions for Section 4.8

1. (a) Find the best linear approximation to $f(x) = (1 + x)^{\frac{1}{2}}$ at $x = 0$.
   (b) Use a calculator or a computer to plot $f(x)$ and your linear approximation. Describe what program you used, what you did, and how this confirms that your linear approximation is reasonable.

   ANSWER:

   (a) We know that $f(0) = 1$, and $f'(x) = \frac{1}{2}(1 + x)^{-\frac{1}{2}}$, so $f'(0) = \frac{1}{2}$. The best linear approximation to $f(x)$ at $x = 0$ is the tangent line with slope $\frac{1}{2}$ through the point $(0, 1)$, which is the line $y = \frac{1}{2}x + 1$.

   (b) We plot the functions $f(x) = (1 + x)^{1/2}$ and $g(x) = \frac{1}{2}x + 1$ to get the graph below. From the graph, we see that these two functions are very close near $x = 0$.

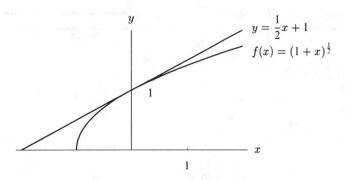

2. The graph of $f(x)$ is shown in Figure 4.8.3.

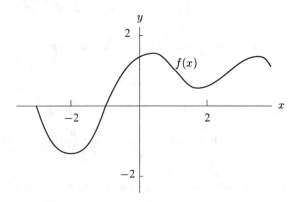

*Figure 4.8.3*

(a) List in increasing order (from smallest to largest)

$$f'(2), f(0), f'(-0.9), \text{ the number } 1, f''(0), f''(1).$$

(b) Suppose we want to estimate $f(1.5)$ by using tangent line approximations at $x = 0, 1$ and $2$. Which tangent line yields the best approximation?

ANSWER:

(a) $f'(2)$ is certainly positive, and appears to be about $\frac{1}{2}$. $f(0)$ is greater than 1, but less than 2. $f'(-0.9)$ is approximately 2. $f''(0)$ is negative. $f''(1)$ looks like it is about 0, since there is an inflection point near $x = 1$. So we have:

$$f''(0) < f''(1) < f'(2) < 1 < f(0) < f'(-0.9)$$

(b)

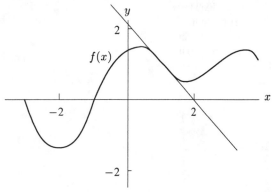

From the graph we see that $f(1.5)$ can be best approximated using the tangent line at $(1, f(1))$ because the tangent line at $(1, f(1))$ appears to pass through $(1.5, f(1.5))$. (The graph between $(1, f(1))$ and $(1.5, f(1.5))$ is almost linear.)

*Review Problems and Solutions for Chapter 4*

1. Differentiate:

   (a) $f(x) = \dfrac{x^2 + 1}{x^2 - 1}$

   (b) $f(x) = 2^x \tan x$

   (c) $f(x) = \sqrt{(\ln x)^2 + 5}$

   ANSWER:

   (a) Use the quotient rule,

   $$\frac{d}{dx}\left(\frac{x^2+1}{x^2-1}\right) = \frac{(x^2-1)(2x) - (x^2+1)(2x)}{(x^2-1)^2} = \frac{2x^3 - 2x - 2x^3 - 2x}{(x^2-1)^2} = \frac{-4x}{(x^2-1)^2}.$$

   (b) Since $\frac{d}{dx}(2^x) = 2^x \ln 2$, we can use the product rule:

   $$\frac{d}{dx}(2^x \tan x) = 2^x \frac{1}{\cos^2 x} + 2^x (\ln 2) \tan x.$$

   (c) Repeated application of the chain rule yields

   $$\frac{d}{dx}\sqrt{(\ln x)^2 + 5} = \frac{1}{2\sqrt{(\ln x)^2 + 5}}\frac{d}{dx}\big((\ln x)^2 + 5\big) = \frac{(2\ln x)/x}{2\sqrt{(\ln x)^2 + 5}} = \frac{\ln x}{x\sqrt{(\ln x)^2 + 5}}$$

For Problems 2–4, circle the correct answer(s) or fill in the blanks. No reasons need be given.

2. If $f(x) = (\ln 2)^x$, then $f'(2)$ is

   (a) $2\ln 2$

   (b) $(\ln 2)^3$

   (c) approximately $-0.176$

   (d) approximately $-0.173$

   ANSWER:

   (c) $f'(x) = (\ln 2)^x \ln \ln 2$ so $f'(2) = (\ln 2)^2 \cdot \ln \ln 2 = -0.176$

3. The function $D(v)$ in the figure below gives the air resistance, or drag (in pounds), on a blunt object as a function of its velocity. (Notice that the curve rises sharply near $v = 700$ miles/hour, the speed of sound. This represents the "sound barrier.") If a blunt object traveling 725 miles/hour is accelerating at the constant rate of 7000 miles/hour$^2$, at approximately what rate (in pounds/hour) is the drag increasing at that moment? Circle the *closest* answer.

   (a) 6000 lb/hr

   (b) 8 lb/hr

   (c) 700 lb/hr

   (d) 60,000 lb/hr

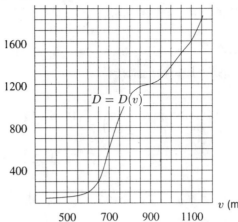

ANSWER:

(d) Slope of curve at $V = 725$ is $\dfrac{dD}{dV} \approx 8$ lb/mph.

By chain rule $\dfrac{dD}{dt} = \dfrac{dD}{dV} \cdot \dfrac{dV}{dt} = 8 \cdot 7000 \approx 56{,}000.$

4. The slope of the tangent line to the curve $y \cos x + e^y = 7$ at $\left(\frac{\pi}{2}, \ln 7\right)$ is

(a) 0

(b) 7

(c) $\dfrac{(\ln 7)}{7}$

(d) $\dfrac{(7 + \ln 7)}{7}$

(e) None of the above.

ANSWER:

(c) $y' \cos x - y \sin x + e^y y' = 0$ so $y' = \dfrac{y \sin x}{\cos x + e^y} = \dfrac{\ln 7 \cdot \sin\left(\frac{\pi}{2}\right)}{\cos \frac{\pi}{2} + e^{\ln 7}} = \dfrac{\ln 7}{7}$

5. Find derivatives of the following functions. <u>Do not</u> simplify your answers.

(a) $\dfrac{(z^2 + 1)^2}{z}$

(b) $\sin(\theta \cos \theta)$

(c) $\dfrac{t}{e^t} + e^2$

(d) $\dfrac{\sqrt{x}}{x} - \sqrt{x^2 + 1}$

(e) $\arctan\left(\dfrac{92}{x}\right)$

ANSWER:

(a) $\dfrac{d}{dz}\left(\dfrac{z^4 + 2z^2 + 1}{z}\right) = \dfrac{d}{dz}\left(z^3 + 2z + \dfrac{1}{z}\right) = 3z^2 + 2 - \dfrac{1}{z^2}$

(b) $\dfrac{d}{d\theta}(\sin(\theta \cos \theta)) = \cos(\theta \cos \theta) \cdot [\cos \theta - \theta \sin \theta]$

(c) $\dfrac{d}{dt}(te^{-t} + e^2) = e^{-t} - te^{-t}$

(d) $\dfrac{d}{dx}\left(x^{-\frac{1}{2}} - (x^2 + 1)^{\frac{1}{2}}\right) = -\dfrac{1}{2}x^{-\frac{3}{2}} - \dfrac{1}{2}(x^2 + 1)^{-\frac{1}{2}} \cdot 2x$

(e) $\dfrac{d}{dx}\left(\arctan\left(\dfrac{92}{x}\right)\right) = \dfrac{1}{1 + \left(\frac{92}{x}\right)^2} \cdot \left(\dfrac{-92}{x^2}\right)$

6. Find derivatives of the following functions. You need not simplify:

  (a) $\cos(x^2 + 1)$

  (b) $\dfrac{e^{-x}}{1 + x^3}$

  (c) $2^e - \dfrac{2}{x} + \sqrt{1 - x}$

  ANSWER:

  (a) $\dfrac{d}{dx}\cos(x^2 + 1) = -2x\sin(x^2 + 1).$

  (b)

  $$\dfrac{d}{dx}\left(\dfrac{e^{-x}}{1 + x^3}\right) = \dfrac{(1 + x^3)\frac{d}{dx}(e^{-x}) - (e^{-x})\frac{d}{dx}(1 + x^3)}{(1 + x^3)^2}$$

  $$= \dfrac{-e^{-x}(1 + 3x^2 + x^3)}{(1 + x^3)^2}.$$

  (c) $\dfrac{d}{dx}\left(2^e - \dfrac{2}{x} + \sqrt{1 - x}\right) = 2x^{-2} - \dfrac{1}{2}(1 - x)^{-\frac{1}{2}}.$

7. Differentiate each of the following:

  (a) $f(x) = (x + \sin x)^e$

  (b) $g(x) = e^{(x + \sin x)}$

  (c) $F(z) = \dfrac{\tan z}{\ln z}$

  (d) $P(w) = 5^w w^{-\frac{5}{2}}$

  (e) $R(\theta) = \sqrt{\theta}\cos(\theta^2).$

  ANSWER:

  (a) By the chain rule, $f'(x) = e(x + \sin x)^{e-1}(1 + \cos x).$

  (b) $g'(x) = e^{(x + \sin x)}(1 + \cos x).$

  (c) Using the quotient rule,

  $$F'(z) = \dfrac{\frac{1}{\cos^2 z}\ln z - (\tan z)\frac{1}{z}}{(\ln z)^2}.$$

  (d) $P'(w) = 5^w \ln 5 w^{-\frac{5}{2}} + 5^w\left(-\dfrac{5}{2}w^{-\frac{7}{2}}\right)$

  (e) $R'(\theta) = \dfrac{1}{2\sqrt{\theta}}\cos(\theta^2) - \sqrt{\theta}\cdot 2\theta\sin(\theta^2).$

8. Find the derivatives of the following functions:

  (a) $f(x) = x^2\ln(x^2)$

  (b) $g(x) = \dfrac{x^2 + 4}{x^2 - 4}$

  (c) $h(x) = (x^2 + 1)\arctan x$

  (d) $m(x) = \sin(\cos(e^{3x}))$

  ANSWER:

  (a) $\dfrac{d(x^2\ln(x^2))}{dx} = (x^2)\left(\dfrac{2x}{x^2}\right) + 2x\ln(x^2) = 2x + 2x\ln(x^2) = 2x(1 + 2\ln x).$

  (b) $\dfrac{d\left(\frac{x^2+4}{x^2-4}\right)}{dx} = \dfrac{(x^2 - 4)2x - (x^2 + 4)2x}{(x^2 - 4)^2} = \dfrac{-16x}{(x^2 - 4)^2}.$

  (c) $\dfrac{d((x^2 + 1)\arctan x)}{dx} = (x^2 + 1)\cdot\dfrac{1}{x^2 + 1} + 2x\arctan x = 1 + 2x\arctan x.$

  (d) $\dfrac{d(\sin(\cos(e^{3x})))}{dx} = \cos(\cos(e^{3x}))\cdot(-\sin(e^{3x}))\cdot 3e^{3x} = -3e^{3x}\sin(e^{3x})\cos(\cos(e^{3x})).$

9. Find $\dfrac{dy}{dx}$ if:

  (a) $y = xe^{-3x}$

  (b) $y = \cos^2(3x - 1)$

(c) $y = \dfrac{1}{x^2 + 1}$

ANSWER:

(a) $\dfrac{d(xe^{-3x})}{dx} = x(-3e^{-3x}) + e^{-3x} = -3xe^{-3x} + e^{-3x}$

(b) $\dfrac{d(\cos^2(3x - 1))}{dx} = 2\cos(3x-1)(-\sin(3x-1))(3) = -6\sin(3x-1)\cos(3x-1) = -3\sin(6x - 2)$

(c) $\dfrac{d(\frac{1}{x^2+1})}{dx} = \dfrac{d((x^2 + 1)^{-1})}{dx} = -(x^2 + 1)^{-2}(2x) = \dfrac{-2x}{(x^2 + 1)^2}$

10. Differentiate:

(a) $x^2\sqrt{1 - x}$

(b) $\sin\dfrac{1}{x}$

(c) $e^{e^x}$

ANSWER:

(a) $\dfrac{d}{dx}(x^2\sqrt{1 - x}) = \sqrt{1 - x}\,\dfrac{d}{dx}(x^2) + x^2\dfrac{d}{dx}(\sqrt{1 - x}) = 2x\sqrt{1 - x} - \dfrac{1}{2\sqrt{1 - x}} \cdot x^2$

(b) $\dfrac{d}{dx}\sin\left(\dfrac{1}{x}\right) = \cos\left(\dfrac{1}{x}\right) \cdot \left(-\dfrac{1}{x^2}\right) = -\dfrac{1}{x^2}\cos\left(\dfrac{1}{x}\right)$

(c)

$$\dfrac{d}{dx}e^{(e^x)} = \dfrac{de^{e^x}}{de^x} \cdot \dfrac{de^x}{dx}$$
$$= e^{e^x} \cdot e^x = e^{x + e^x}$$

11. Let $f(x) = x^4 - 4x + 2$.

(a) How many zeros does $f$ have? Justify your answer.
(b) Approximate one of the zeros by first getting an initial estimate and then improving it by using Newton's Method *once*.
(c) An initial estimate of $x = 1$, or $x$ very near to 1, doesn't work well for Newton's Method. Why?
(d) Suppose we wished to solve $f(x) = b$ instead (same $f$). For which values of $b$ would there be no solutions? For which values of $b$ would there be one solution? For which two solutions? For which more than two solutions?

ANSWER:

(a) Since $f'(x) = 4x^3 - 4$ has only one zero, at $x = 1$, the function $f$ has only one critical point. Therefore, $f$ can have at most two roots. Since $f$ changes sign ($f(0) = 2$, $f(1) = -1$ and $f(2) = 10$) it must cross the $x$ axis twice, so it has two zeros, one between 0 and 1, the other between 1 and 2.
(b) Try the initial estimate $x_0 = 0$. Use the improved value of the root, $x_1 = x_0 - f(x_0)/f'(x_0)$, with $f(0) = 2$, $f'(0) = -4$ to get $x_1 = 0 - \frac{2}{-4} = \frac{1}{2}$, a better estimate.
(c) If we try the above method with $x_0$ close to 1, $f'(x_0)$ will be close to 0, so the fraction $f(x_0)/f'(x_0)$ will be very large indeed. So $x_1 = x_0 - f(x_0)/f'(x_0)$ will be far from the true value of the root. Geometrically, the slope of the tangent to the graph of $f$ is very flat near $x = 1$, so the point at which such a tangent line intersects the $x$-axis is far away.
(d) Since $f(x)$ has only one critical point, a minimum at $(1, -1)$, and $f(x) \to \infty$ when $x \to \pm\infty$, we see that $f$ will attain the value $b$ twice if $b > -1$, once for $b = -1$, and not at all for $b < -1$. There can never be more than two roots.

$b > -1$ $b = -1$

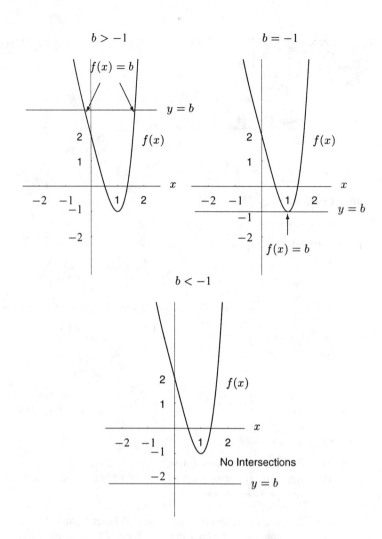

$b < -1$

No Intersections

12. Sketch the graphs of $g(x) = x$ and $h(x) = e^{-x}$ for $x \geq 0$. Use Newton's method to estimate the location of the point of intersection of the two curves correct to four decimal places.

    ANSWER:

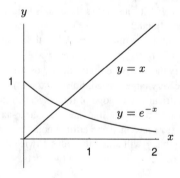

We want to find the point where $x = e^{-x}$. This is really the same as finding the roots of $f(x) = x - e^{-x}$. The iteration formula for Newton's method is given by

$$x_{n+1} = x_n - \frac{f(x_n)}{f'(x_n)},$$

where $x_n$ is the $n^{\text{th}}$ iterated approximation of the root of $f(x)$. We use an initial estimate of $x_0 = 0.5$. $f'(x) = 1 + e^{-x}$, so

$$x_1 = 0.5 - \frac{0.5 - e^{-0.5}}{1 + e^{-0.5}}$$
$$= 0.5 - \frac{-0.10653}{1.60653}$$
$$= 0.56631.$$

Similarly,

$$x_2 = 0.56714,$$
$$x_3 = 0.56714.$$

This is correct to four decimal places. The point of intersection is thus $(0.56714, 0.56714)$.

13. The purpose of this problem is to find all the roots of $f(x) = 3x^3 + 2x^2 - 4x + 1$ *exactly*.

   (a) Use a computer or a calculator to obtain all the roots of $f(x)$ to 5 decimal places. Do this using both the bisection method and Newton's method. Explain what program you used, and what you did, paying particular attention to the number of iterations, bracketing and initial values. How do you *know* you have found *all* the roots?

   (b) If you have done part (a) correctly, then one of the approximate roots you have obtained should suggest an exact root. Which one, and how did you confirm that the root was exact?

   (c) Based on the information you have obtained in part (b), find exact expressions for all the roots.

   ANSWER:

   (a) Using a computer or calculator root-finding program, we find that the roots are at $0.33333, 0.61803$, and $-1.61803$. Since a cubic can have at most three roots, and we have found three roots, we must have found all of them.

   (b) It seems likely that $0.33333$ is, in fact, $\frac{1}{3}$. Substituting $x = \frac{1}{3}$ into the function, we obtain $0$, so $x = \frac{1}{3}$ is indeed an exact root of the polynomial.

   (c) Since we know that $\frac{1}{3}$ is an exact root, we know that $(3x - 1)$ is a factor of $f(x)$. Thus $f = (3x - 1)(x^2 + x - 1)$. We then use the quadratic formula to find the roots of the second factor to give us the other two roots of $f(x)$, which turn out to be $\frac{-1+\sqrt{5}}{2}$ and $\frac{-1-\sqrt{5}}{2}$.

# Chapter 5 Exam Questions

*Problems and Solutions for Section 5.1*

1. Below is the graph of the *derivative* of a function $f$, i.e., it is a graph of $y = f'(x)$.

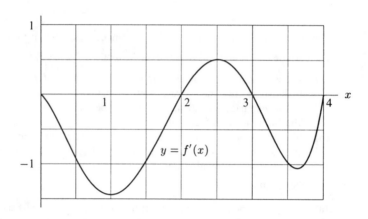

   (a) State the intervals on which $f$ is increasing and on which it is decreasing.
   (b) Say where the local maxima and minima of $f$ occur, and for each one say whether it is a local maximum or a local minimum.
   (c) Where in the interval $0 \le x \le 4$ does $f$ achieve its global maximum?
   (d) Suppose that you are told that $f(0) = 1$. Estimate $f(2)$.
   (e) Still assuming that $f(0) = 1$, write down an exact expression for $f(2)$.

   ANSWER:

   (a) The function $f$ is increasing between 2 and 3, since the derivative is positive there. It is decreasing everywhere else.
   (b) The point $x = 0$ is a local maximum, $x = 2$ is a local minimum, $x = 3$ is a local maximum, $x = 4$ is a local minimum.
   (c) The global maximum occurs at $x = 0$.
   (d) $f(2) \approx -0.5$; this is calculated as

   $$1 - (\text{the area between the } x\text{-axis and the curve, from 0 to 2}).$$

   Note that each grid square has area 0.25.

   (e) $f(2) = \displaystyle\int_0^2 f'(x)dx + 1$.

2. Starting at time $t = 0$, water is poured *at a constant rate* into an empty vase (pictured below). It takes ten seconds for the vase to be filled completely to the top. Let $h = f(t)$ be the depth of the water in the vase at time $t$. On the axes provided, sketch a graph of $h = f(t)$. On your graph, indicate the region(s) where the function is concave up, and where it is concave down. Finally, label the point (on the curve) at which $f'(t)$ is largest.

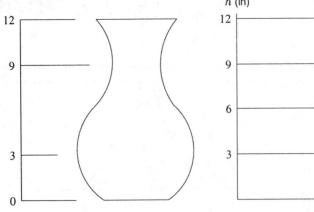

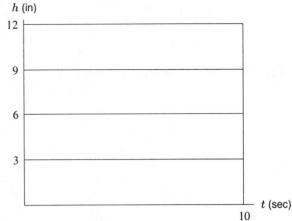

ANSWER:

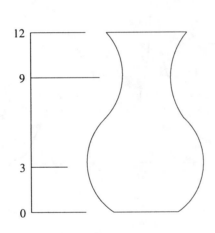

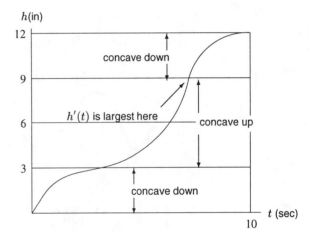

The rate of increase of $h$ is greatest when the cross sectional area of the vase at length $h$ is the smallest. Since the vase gets wider as $h$ increases from 0 to 3, the value of $h'(t)$ gets smaller. This means that the graph is concave down between $h = 0$ and $h = 3$. For $3 < h < 9$, the vase gets narrower as we go up, so $h'(t)$ increases over this interval, so the graph is concave up and then the vase widens from $h = 0$ to $h = 12$, so it's concave down there.

Finally, $h'(t)$ is greatest when the vase is narrowest. This occurs at $h = 9$.

3.  Given the following graph, label all points where the function has a maximum, a minimum, a horizontal tangent, a vertical tangent, a point of inflection or a point where $f$ is not defined.

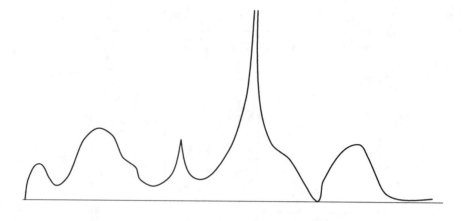

ANSWER:

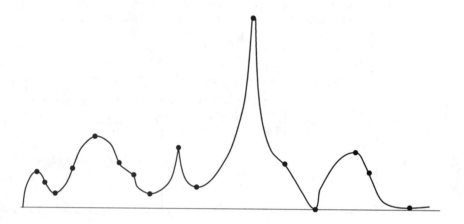

4. A water tank is constructed in the shape of a sphere seated atop a circular cylinder. If water is being pumped into the tank at a constant rate, sketch the graph of the height of the water as a function of time. Be sure to indicate the location of all "interesting" points, including any critical points where the function has horizontal slope or is not differentiable, and points of inflection.

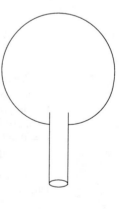

ANSWER:

Mark the points $a, b, c$ in the picture as shown:

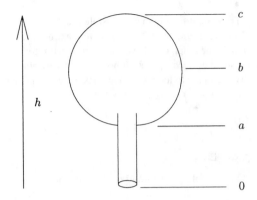

From $h = 0$ to $h = a$ the height increases linearly with time since the radius, and hence the cross-sectional area of the cylinder, does not change over this interval. From $a$ to $b$, height will be an increasing but concave down function of $t$; between $a$ and $b$, the radius grows and $\frac{dh}{dt}$ must slow down accordingly. Similarly, over the interval $[b, c]$, $h(t)$ will be increasing, but concave up.

The points $a$, $b$, and $c$ are of interest. At $h = b$, the slope $\frac{dh}{dt}$ is a minimum, since the radius is at its largest, so concavity changes. (We also knew from the discussion above that concavity changes on either side of $b$.) Hence, we have an inflection point when $h = b$. At $h = c$, the radius has shrunk to zero; hence $\frac{dh}{dt}$ must be infinite at that point only. When $h = a$, $\frac{d^2h}{dt^2}$ does not exist. This is true because $\frac{d^2h}{dt^2} = 0$ over $[0, a]$, and beginning at $h = a$, $\frac{d^2h}{dt^2}$ immediately takes on negative values that are not infinitely close to 0 (due to downward concavity). This discontinuity in the second derivative is reflected in a "kink" in the graph of $\frac{dh}{dt}$ vs. $t$, but cannot be seen in the graph of $h$ vs. $t$. Here is the complete picture:

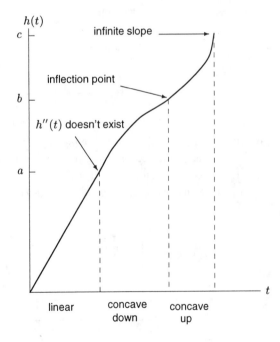

5. (a) Sketch the graph of a continuous function with the following properties:
   - $f(0) = 1$,
   - $|f'(x)| < 0.5$,
   - $f''(x) < 0$, for $x < 0$,

**424**

- $f'(2) = 0$.

(There are infinitely many possible graphs.)

(b)  Does your graph in (a) have a local maximum for $x < 0$?

(c)  Could the graph of $f$ have a local maximum for $x < 0$ and still satisfy the given four conditions? If so, draw such a graph. If not, explain why not.

(d)  Which of the following are inconsistent with the four conditions in part (a)? (Explain each answer.)

    (i)  $\displaystyle\lim_{x \to -\infty} f(x) = 0$,

    (ii)  $f(2) = 3$,

    (iii)  $f''(2) = 0$.

ANSWER:

(a)  One possible graph would be the following.

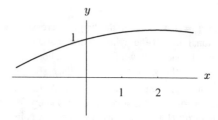

(b)  No.

(c)  Yes.

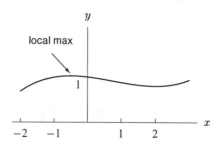

(d)  (i)  Inconsistent. Since $f''(x) < 0$ for $x < 0$, $f(x)$ can either cross the $x$-axis to the left of $x = 0$ and approach $-\infty$, or approach $\infty$ or a positive constant as $x \to -\infty$; it cannot approach 0.

    (ii)  Inconsistent. Since $f(0) = 1$ and $|f'(x)| < 0.5$, the most that $f(3)$ could be is $1 + 2(0.5) = 2$.

    (iii)  Consistent. We could have a picture like the following:

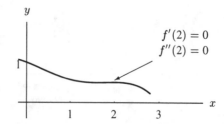

6.  Given below are the graphs of two functions $f(x)$ and $g(x)$.

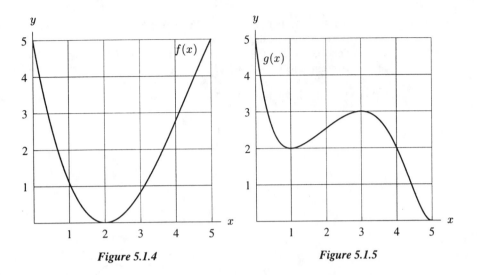

*Figure 5.1.4*          *Figure 5.1.5*

Let $h(x) = f(g(x))$. Use the graphs to answer the following questions about $h$.

(a) Find (approximately) the critical points of $h$ and classify them.

(b) Where is $h$ increasing? Decreasing?

(c) On the axes below sketch a graph of $h$.

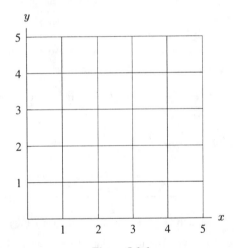

*Figure 5.1.6*

ANSWER:

(a) Note that $h'(x) = f'(g(x))g'(x)$. So $h'(x) = 0$ whenever $f'(g(x)) = 0$ or $g'(x) = 0$. But $g'(x) = 0$ for $x = 3$ or $x = 1$ and $f'(x) = 0$ when $x = 2$, so $f'(g(x)) = 0$ when $g(x) = 2$, i.e., when $x = 4$. Thus the critical points of $h$ are at $x = 1$, $x = 3$ and $x = 4$.

    The critical point of $h$ at $x = 3$ is a maximum since, for $x$ slightly greater or less than 3, $g(x) < g(3)$, and since $f$ is increasing near $g(3) = 3$, $f(g(x)) < f(g(3))$.

    The critical point of $h$ at $x = 4$ is a global, hence local, minimum because $h(4) = 0$ and $h(x) \geq 0$ for all $x$ (since $f(x) \geq 0$ for all $x$).

    The critical point of $h$ at $x = 1$ is a minimum, since $g(x) \geq g(1)$ for $x$ near 1, and $f(g(x)) \geq f(g(1))$ for $x$ near 1 also, since $f$ is increasing near $g(1) = 3$.

(b) For $0 < x < 1$, $g'(x) < 0$ and $3 < g(x) < 5$, so $f'(g(x)) > 0$ and $h'(x) = f'(g(x))g'(x) < 0$. Hence $h$ is decreasing on $[0, 1]$.

For $1 < x < 3$, $g'(x) > 0$ and $3 < g(x) < 5$, so $f'(g(x)) > 0$ and $h'(x) = f'(g(x))g'(x) > 0$. Hence $h$ is increasing on $[1, 3]$.

For $3 < x < 4$, $g'(x) < 0$ and $2 < g(x) < 5$, so $f'(g(x)) > 0$ and $h'(x) = f'(g(x))g'(x) < 0$. Hence $h$ is decreasing on $[3, 4]$.

For $4 < x < 5$, $g'(x) < 0$ and $0 < g(x) < 2$, so $f'(g(x)) < 0$ and $h'(x) = f'(g(x))g'(x) > 0$. Hence $h$ is increasing on $[4, 5]$.

(c)

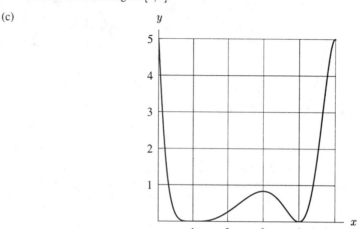

**Figure 5.1.7**: Graph of $h(x) = f(g(x))$

7. Let $f(x)$ be a function with positive values and let $g = \sqrt{f}$.

   (a) If $f$ is increasing at $x = x_0$, what about $g$?
   (b) If $f$ is concave down at $x = x_1$, what about $g$?
   (c) If $f$ has a local maximum at $x = x_2$, what about $g$?

   ANSWER:

   (a) $\dfrac{dg}{dx} = \dfrac{d(\sqrt{f})}{dx} = \dfrac{f'}{2\sqrt{f}}$. If $f$ is increasing at $x = x_0$, then $f'(x_0) > 0$. Thus, $g'(x_0) = \dfrac{f'(x_0)}{2\sqrt{f(x_0)}} > 0$, and so $g$ is increasing at $x = x_0$.

   (b) $\dfrac{d^2 g}{dx^2} = \dfrac{d\left(\frac{f'}{2\sqrt{f}}\right)}{dx} = \dfrac{f''}{2\sqrt{f}} + f' \cdot \left(-\dfrac{1}{4}f^{-\frac{3}{2}} \cdot f'\right) = \dfrac{f'' - (f')^2/(2f)}{2\sqrt{f}}$. If $f$ is concave down at $x = x_1$, then $f''(x_1) < 0$. Since $f(x_1)$ and $(f'(x_1))^2$ are positive,
   $$g''(x_1) = \dfrac{f''(x_1) - (f'(x_1))^2/(2f(x_1))}{2\sqrt{f(x_1)}}$$ is negative, and so $g$ is concave down at $x = x_1$.

   (c) If $f$ has a local maximum at $x = x_2$, then $f'(x_2) = 0$, $f'$ is positive for $x$ slightly smaller than $x_2$, and $f'$ is negative for $x$ slightly larger than $x_2$. Recall that $g'(x) = \dfrac{f'(x)}{2\sqrt{f(x)}}$, and so $g'(x)$ has the same sign as $f'(x)$ for all $x$ (since $2\sqrt{f(x)}$ is always positive). Consequently, $g'(x_2) = 0$, $g'$ is positive for $x$ slightly smaller than $x_2$, and $g'$ is negative for $x$ slightly larger than $x_2$. Therefore, $g$ has a local maximum at $x = x_2$.

8. Let $f$ be a function. Is the following sentence true or false?

   *The inflection points of $f$ are the local extrema of $f'$.*

   Explain your answer in a couple of short, clear sentences. You may assume that the second derivative of $f$ is defined and continuous everywhere.

   ANSWER:

   This is true. If $x = p$ is an inflection point, then $f''$ changes sign at $x = p$, so since $f''$ is defined and continuous everywhere, we have $f''(p) = 0$. Hence $p$ is a critical point of the derivative function $f'$. Since $f''$ changes sign at $p$, an inflection point is a local extremum of $f'$, by the first derivative test applied to $f'$.

9. **Lunch at Cafeteria Charlotte**

   Below is the graph of the rate $r$ at which people arrive for lunch at Charlotte.

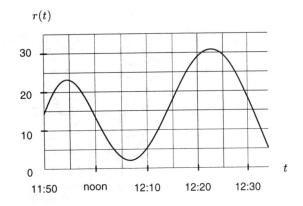

$r(t)$

30

20

10

0

11:50    noon    12:10    12:20    12:30    $t$

Checkers start at 12:00 noon and can pass people through at a constant rate of 5 people/minute. Let $f(t)$ be the length of the line (i.e. the number of people) at time $t$. Suppose that at 11:50 there are already 150 people lined up. Using the graph together with the information above, answer the following. Explain your answers.

(a)  Find and classify all critical points of $f$.

(b)  When is $f$ increasing? decreasing?

(c)  When is $f$ concave up? concave down?

(d)  Sketch the graph of $f$. Label the important points.

(e)  When is the line longest? shortest?

ANSWER:

(a)  This problem compares two rates, the rate of people arriving in line, shown by the graph of $r(t)$ and the rate at which they are checked through, a constant rate of 5 people/minute starting at 12:00 noon. To compare these rates draw the line $r = 5$ starting from 12:00. Since $f'(t) = r(t) = -5$ and the line $r = 5$ cuts the graph of $r(t)$ at approximately $12 : 03$, $12 : 10$ and $12 : 34$, these are the critical points of $f(t)$. The point $t = 12 : 03$ is a local maximum since $f'$ changes from positive to negative there. Likewise, $t = 12 : 10$ is a local minimum and $t = 12 : 34$ is a local maximum.

Symbolically, we could write

$$f(t) = \int_0^t r(x)\,dx + 150, \qquad 0 \le t \le 10,$$

where $t = 0$ is $11 : 50$ and $t$ is measured in minutes, and for $t \ge 10$

$$f(t) = 150 + \int_0^{10} r(x)\,dx + \int_{10}^t \left(r(x) - 5\right)\,dx$$

$$= 150 + \int_0^t r(x)\,dx - \int_{10}^t 5\,dx$$

$$= 150 + \int_0^t r(x)\,dx - (5t - 50)$$

$$= \int_0^t r(x)\,dx - 5t + 200$$

(b)  $f$ is increasing when $r(t) > 5$, and that happens before 12:03 and from 12:10 until 12:34. $f$ is decreasing when $r(t) < 5$, which is the case between 12:03 and 12:10.

(c)  We get the concavity of $f$ by finding where $f''$ is positive and where it's negative. Since $f'' = r'$, $f$ is concave up when $r' > 0$, which happens before 11:55 and between 12:07 and 12:23. $f$ is concave down when $r' < 0$, which takes place between 11:55 and 12:07 and between 12:23 and 12:34.

428

(d)

$f(t)$

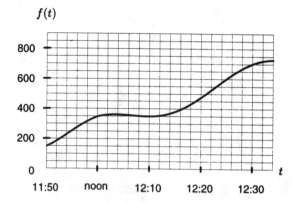

(e)   To answer the question, we check the critical points and the endpoints of $f$. $f(11:50) = 150$; $f(12:03) = 361$; $f(12:10) = 349$; $f(12:34) = 727$, so the line is longest at 12:34 and shortest at 11:50.

10.   Consider $f(x) = x^2 e^{-x}$ for $-1 \le x \le 3$.

(a)   Show that $f'(x) = e^{-x}(2x - x^2)$ and that $f''(x) = e^{-x}(x^2 - 4x + 2)$.
(b)   For which $x$ is $f$ increasing? For which is $f$ decreasing?
(c)   Find the values of $x$ where $f(x)$ is the greatest; where $f(x)$ is the least.
(d)   Find all values of $x$ where there is a point of inflection.
(e)   Find the values of $x$ where $f$ is increasing most rapidly; where $f$ is decreasing most rapidly.
(f)   Sketch the graph of $f$.

ANSWER:

(a)

$$f'(x) = x^2 \frac{d(e^{-x})}{dx} + \frac{d(x^2)}{dx} e^{-x} = x^2(-e^{-x}) + 2xe^{-x}$$
$$= (2x - x^2)e^{-x}.$$

$$f''(x) = (2x - x^2)\frac{d(e^{-x})}{dx} + \frac{d(2x - x^2)}{dx} e^{-x} = (x^2 - 2x)e^{-x} + (2 - 2x)e^{-x}$$
$$= (x^2 - 4x + 2)e^{-x}.$$

(b)   $f$ is increasing when $f'$ is positive: that is, when $(2x - x^2)e^{-x} > 0$. Since $e^{-x} > 0$, we just need the condition $2x - x^2 > 0$, which is equivalent to $x(2 - x) > 0$. This holds for $0 < x < 2$. $f'$ will be negative, and consequently $f$ will be decreasing, when $x < 0$ or $x > 2$.

(c)   The maximum and minimum of $f$ will occur at critical points or the endpoints of our interval $[-1, 3]$. By part (b), $f'(x) = 0$ when $x = 0$ or $x = 2$. Since $f(0) = 0$, $f(2) = 4e^{-2}$, $f(-1) = e$, $f(3) = 9e^{-3}$, we can see that $f(x)$ is the greatest for $x = -1$ and the least for $f(0) = 0$.

(d)   $f$ can have a point of inflection only where $f''(x) = e^{-x}(x^2 - 4x + 2) = 0$, that is, when $x^2 - 4x + 2 = 0$ (since $e^{-x} > 0$). The solutions to this equation are $x = 2 \pm \sqrt{2}$. Only $x = 2 - \sqrt{2}$ lies in the interval $-1 \le x \le 3$. Since the sign of the second derivative changes from positive to negative across $x = 2 - \sqrt{2}$, $(2 - \sqrt{2}, (2 - \sqrt{2})^2 e^{-(2-\sqrt{2})})$ is an inflection point.

(e)   The function $f$ increases (or decreases) most rapidly where $f'$ is greatest (or least). The only critical point of $f'$ on $-1 \le x \le 3$ occurs at $x = 2 - \sqrt{2}$. It is a maximum (since $f''$ changes sign from positive to negative across $x = 2 - \sqrt{2}$). Now, $f'(-1) = -3e$, $f'(3) = -3e^{-3}$, so $f'(-1)$ is the global minimum for $f'$. Hence $f$ is increasing most rapidly at $x = 2 - \sqrt{2}$, and decreasing most rapidly at $x = -1$.

(f)

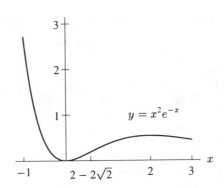

$$y = x^2 e^{-x}$$

$-1$    $2 - 2\sqrt{2}$    $2$    $3$

11.  Given $f(x) = x^4 - 4x^3 - 8x^2 + 1$ on the interval $[-5, 5]$, find all the maxima and minima and points of inflection. Use this information to sketch the curve.

ANSWER:

To find the maxima and minima of $f$ on $[-5, 5]$, we need to check critical points and endpoints. To find the critical points, set $f'(x) = 0$.

$$\begin{aligned}
f'(x) &= 4x^3 - 12x^2 - 16x \\
&= 4x(x^2 - 3x - 4) \\
&= 4x(x - 4)(x + 1).
\end{aligned}$$

So critical points occur where $x = 0, 4$ and $-1$.

$$f''(x) = 12x^2 - 24x - 16$$

Since $f''(0) = -16 < 0$, $(0, 1)$ is a local maximum point.
Since $f''(-1) = 20 > 0$, $(-1, -2)$ is a local minimum point.
Since $f''(4) = 80 > 0$, $(4, -127)$ is a local minimum point.
As for the end points, we have $f(-5) = 926$ and $f(5) = -74$. Therefore, $(-5, 926)$ is a global maximum and $(4, -127)$ is a global minimum.

To find the inflection points, set $f''(x) = 0$. Then $3x^2 - 6x - 4 = 0$, so

$$\begin{aligned}
x &= \frac{6 \pm \sqrt{36 - 4(-4)(3)}}{6} \\
&= 1 \pm \frac{\sqrt{21}}{3} \\
&\approx 1 \pm 1.528 \\
&= 2.528 \text{ or } -0.528
\end{aligned}$$

Since the second derivative changes sign across these $x$-values (we can see this because $f''(-1) = 20$, $f''(0) = -16$ and $f''(3) = 20$), they are the $x$-coordinates of inflection points.

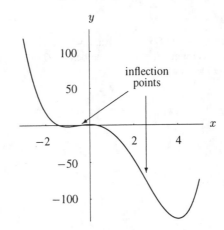

12. Consider the function $f(x) = x + 2\cos x$, for $0 \le x \le 2\pi$.

   (a) Find where $f$ is increasing and where $f$ is decreasing.
   (b) Find the largest and smallest values of $f$ in decimal form.
   (c) Find all points of inflection.
   (d) Find where $f$ is increasing most rapidly.
   (e) Sketch the graph of $f$.
   (f) How many roots are there for $f(x) = 1$ in the given interval $0 \le x \le 2\pi$? How many for $f(x) = 2$? How many for $f(x) = 3$? Explain your answers with pictures.

   ANSWER:

   (a) $f(x) = x + 2\cos x$, and $f'(x) = 1 - 2\sin x$. $f$ increases when $f' > 0$, i.e. when $1 - 2\sin x > 0$, or when $\sin x < \frac{1}{2}$. This is true for $0 \le x < \frac{\pi}{6}$, and $\frac{5\pi}{6} < x \le 2\pi$. $f$ decreases when $f' < 0$, i.e. when $1 - 2\sin x < 0$, or when $\sin x > \frac{1}{2}$. This is true for $\frac{\pi}{6} < x < \frac{5\pi}{6}$.

   (b) The largest and smallest values of any function $f$ over an interval occur either at the critical points of $f$ or at the endpoints of the interval. $f'(x) = 0$ when $\sin x = \frac{1}{2}$, namely when $x = \frac{\pi}{6}, \frac{5\pi}{6}$.

   $$f\left(\frac{\pi}{6}\right) = \frac{\pi}{6} + 2\left(\frac{\sqrt{3}}{2}\right) \approx 2.26$$

   $$f\left(\frac{5\pi}{6}\right) = \frac{5\pi}{6} + 2\left(-\frac{\sqrt{3}}{2}\right) \approx 0.89$$

   Now check endpoints: $f(0) = 2$, while $f(2\pi) = 2 + 2\pi \approx 8.28$. Thus the largest value of $f$ is 8.28 and the smallest value is 0.89.

   (c) Inflection points can only occur when $f''(x) = -2\cos x = 0$. This is true for $x = \pi/2, 3\pi/2$. Since $f''(x)$ changes sign at both $x = \pi/2$ and $x = 3\pi/2$, these are in fact inflection points.

   (d) The maxima of $f'$ will occur at the critical points of $f'$ (namely $x = \pi/2$ and $3\pi/2$) or at the endpoints (namely $x = 0$ and $2\pi$). Now, $f'(0) = 1$, $f'(\pi/2) = -1$, $f'(3\pi/2) = 3$, and $f'(2\pi) = 1$, so $f$ increases most rapidly at $x = 3\pi/2$.

   (e)

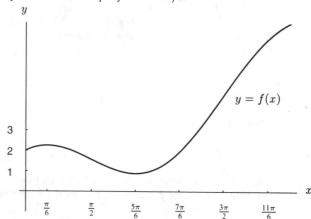

   (f) A solution to $f(x) = $ constant will occur whenever the graph of $y = f(x)$ intersects the graph $y = $ constant. As can be seen below, $f(x) = 1$ has 2 solutions, $f(x) = 2$ has 3 solutions, and $f(x) = 3$ has 1 solution.

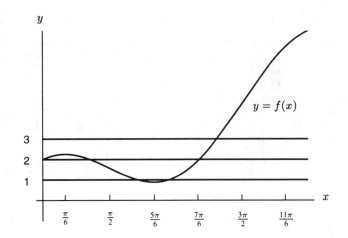

13. The graph of $f'$ is shown below. (The graph of $f$ is not shown.) Use the graph of $f'$ to answer the following questions.

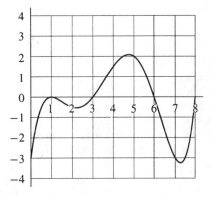

(a) On which intervals, if any, is $f$ increasing?

(b) At which values of $x$ does $f$ have a local maximum? A local minimum?

(c) On which intervals, if any, is $f$ concave up?

(d) Which values of $x$, if any, correspond to inflection points on the graph of $f$?

(e) Sketch a graph of $f''$. (Your graph need only have the right general shape. You do not need to put units on the vertical axis.)

(f) Assume that $f(0) = 0$. Sketch a graph of $f$. (Your graph need only have the right general shape. You do not need to put units on the vertical axis.)

ANSWER:

(a) $3 < x < 6$

(b) Local max at $x = 6$; local min at $x = 3$.

(c) $0 < x < 1$ and $2.1 < x < 4.9$ and $7.2 < x < 8$.

(d) $x = 1, 2.1, 4.9, 7.2$

(e)

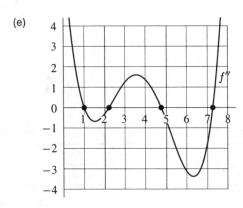

(f)

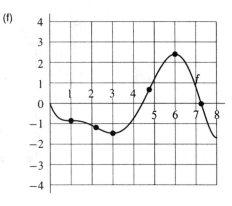

---

## Problems and Solutions for Section 5.2

1.  Let

    $$f(x) = e^{-\frac{x^2}{b}},$$

    where $b$ is a positive constant.

    (a)  Using a computer or a calculator, sketch a graph of $f$. By choosing various different values of $b$, observe how the shape of the graph changes when $b$ is made larger or smaller. Describe your observation in a clear, concise sentence that would make sense to someone who can not see your graph.

    (b)  Find the inflection points of $f$, in terms of $b$.

    (c)  Use your answer to (b) to explain mathematically the effect of varying $b$ that you observed in (a).

    ANSWER:

    (a)  The graph, which is a bell shaped curve with height 1 and centered at $x = 0$, becomes more spread out horizontally as $b$ is increased, while retaining the same central height of 1.

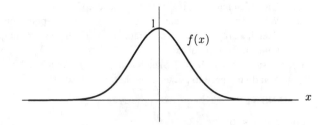

    (b)  To find the inflection points, we need to find the second derivative.

    $$f'(x) = e^{-\frac{x^2}{b}} \cdot \left(-\frac{2x}{b}\right)$$

    $$f''(x) = \left(e^{-\frac{x^2}{b}} \cdot \frac{-2x}{b}\right) \cdot \left(-\frac{2x}{b}\right) + e^{-\frac{x^2}{b}} \cdot \left(-\frac{2}{b}\right)$$

    $$= e^{-\frac{x^2}{b}} \left(\frac{4x^2}{b^2} - \frac{2}{b}\right)$$

Setting this equal to 0, we get

$$e^{-\frac{x^2}{b}}\left(\frac{4x^2}{b^2} - \frac{2}{b}\right) = 0$$

since $e^{-\frac{x^2}{b}}$ is never 0.

$$\left(\frac{4x^2}{b^2} - \frac{2}{b}\right) = 0$$

$$\frac{4x^2}{b^2} = \frac{2}{b}$$

$$2x^2 = b$$

$$x = \pm\sqrt{\frac{b}{2}}$$

Since $f''(x)$ changes sign on either side of the points $x = \sqrt{\frac{b}{2}}$ and $x = -\sqrt{\frac{b}{2}}$, these are indeed inflection points.

(c)  As $b$ increases, the inflection points move farther out from the $y$ axis. This explains the horizontal spreading observed in (a).

2.  Consider the two-parameter family of curves

$$y = ax + \frac{b}{x}.$$

Assume that $a > 0, b > 0$.

(a)  For three (reasonable) choices of $a$ and $b$ with $a < b$, $a = b$, $a > b$, respectively, sketch the three curves. (You may use your calculator. Label your choices of $a$ and $b$.)

(b)  For the family

$$y = ax + \frac{b}{x},$$

determine the critical points, critical values, local and global maxima or minima and concavity in terms of the parameters $a$ and $b$. (In the general case, not just for your curves in part (a)).

(c)  In words and in sketches explain how the sizes of $a$ and $b$ influence the shape of $y = ax + \frac{b}{x}$.

(d)  From part (b) deduce the famous inequality between the arithmetic and the geometric mean:

If $a$ and $b$ are positive numbers, then: $\sqrt{ab} \leq \dfrac{a+b}{2}$.

ANSWER:

(a)  Graphs for $a < b$, $a = b$, $a > b$

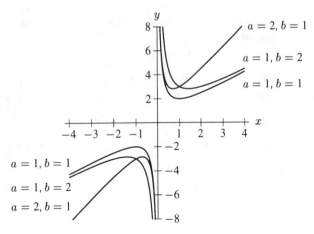

(b)  Solving $y' = a - \dfrac{b}{x^2} = 0$, we get only two critical points: $x = \sqrt{\dfrac{b}{a}}$ and $x = -\sqrt{\dfrac{b}{a}}$. The coordinates of the critical points are thus $(\sqrt{\dfrac{b}{a}}, 2\sqrt{ab})$, and $(-\sqrt{\dfrac{b}{a}}, -2\sqrt{ab})$. Now, $y'' = 2\dfrac{b}{x^3}$.

Since $y''(\sqrt{\frac{b}{a}}) > 0$, the graph has a local minimum at $(\sqrt{\frac{b}{a}}, 2\sqrt{ab})$. Since $y''(-\sqrt{\frac{b}{a}}) < 0$, the graph has a local maximum at $(-\sqrt{\frac{b}{a}}, -2\sqrt{ab})$. As $x \to 0^+$, $y \to +\infty$ and as $x \to 0^-$, $y \to -\infty$. Therefore, we see that $x = 0$ is an asymptote and that there are no global maxima or minima. Finally, since $y'' > 0$ for $x > 0$ and $y'' < 0$ for $x < 0$, the graph is concave up for $x > 0$ and concave down for $x < 0$. No inflection point.

(c)    $a$ and $b$ do not influence the concavity of $y = ax + \frac{b}{x}$. Let's consider the effect on the critical points at $(\sqrt{\frac{b}{a}}, 2\sqrt{ab})$ and $(-\sqrt{\frac{b}{a}}, -2\sqrt{ab})$ of varying $a$ and $b$. If $a$ is held fixed, increasing $b$ causes the graph to move farther from the $x$-axis and the critical points to move farther from the $y$-axis. If $b$ is held fixed, increasing $a$ causes the graph to move farther from the $x$-axis and the critical points to move closer to the $y$-axis. Or, the larger the *ratio* of $b$ to $a$, the further out from the $y$-axis the critical points will be, and the larger the *product* of $a$ and $b$, the further from the $x$-axis the critical points will be.

(d)    From Part (b) we know that the curve $y = ax + \frac{b}{x}$ attains a local minimum $y = 2\sqrt{ab}$ at $x = \sqrt{\frac{b}{a}}$. Since the curve has no other critical points for $x > 0$ and as $x \to 0^+$ or $x \to +\infty$, $y \to +\infty$, we see that $2\sqrt{ab}$ is a global minimum of $y = ax + \frac{b}{x}$ for $x > 0$. We therefore have:

$$2\sqrt{ab} \le ax + \frac{b}{x} \quad \text{for } x > 0.$$

Let $x = 1$. We get:

$$2\sqrt{ab} \le a + b$$
$$\sqrt{ab} \le \frac{a + b}{2}.$$

3.    The purpose of this problem is to explain the graph of $f(x) = \dfrac{1}{1 + ae^{-x}}$ for $a > 0$.

(a)    Use the computer to graph the function $f(x)$ for $a > 0$. Do this for various values of $a$. Based on what you see, write down what you think happens to the graph of $f(x)$ as $a$ increases. Pay particular attention to what happens to any asymptotes, maxima, minima, and points of inflection.

(b)    It is claimed that if $x$ represents time, then $f(x)$ is related to the number of people on Earth. Briefly explain why this might be reasonable.

(c)    Forget what you did in parts (a) and (b). Calculate $f'(x)$ and $f''(x)$.

(d)    Using the results you obtained in part (c) confirm that the statements you made in part (a) are accurate.

ANSWER:

(a)    There are no vertical asymptotes; there are horizontal asymptotes at $y = 1$ and $y = 0$ for all values of $a$. $f(x)$ approaches 1 as $x$ approaches infinity, and $f(x)$ approaches 0 as $x$ approaches negative infinity. The graph is strictly increasing, so there are no maxima or minima. The point of inflection, which always has a $y$-value of $\frac{1}{2}$, moves to the right as $a$ increases. It seems that all curves in the family $\dfrac{1}{1 + ae^{-x}}$, $a > 0$ are just horizontally shifted versions of one another.

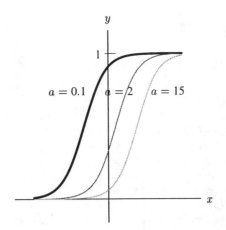

(b)  At first, $f(x)$ increases very slowly, but its rate of increase is growing. This continues until its rate of increase is quite large, at which point it starts slowing down. Here, $f(x)$ is still increasing, but more and more slowly, until the graph is practically level. Similarly, the world's population has always been increasing, but at different rates. When the population was small, so was the rate of increase. Over time, the population has grown larger and so has the rate of increase of population. Theoretically, if the population gets too large, the rate at which it is increasing will start decreasing, as the effects of overpopulation become significant. The asymptote as $x$ approaches infinity corresponds to the maximum population the Earth can support.

(c)  $f' = \dfrac{ae^{-x}}{(1 + ae^{-x})^2}, \qquad f'' = \dfrac{ae^{-x}(ae^{-x} - 1)}{(1 + ae^{-x})^3}.$

(d)  For all $x$, $f'$ is positive, so $f$ is always increasing. The second derivative of $f$ is zero when $x = \ln a$, which gives a $y$ value of $\frac{1}{2}$, so the inflection point is $(\ln a, \frac{1}{2})$, and does move to the right as $a$ increases.

4.  Consider the one-parameter family of functions

$$f(x) = ax(1 - x), \qquad a > 0,$$

for $0 \le x \le 1$. As simple as this family is, it exhibits many remarkable properties which have been studied intensively over the last several years.

(a)  Sketch several members of the family for $a$ in the range $1 < a < 5$. Also sketch the line $y = x$. Label your choices of $a$. (Remember, take $0 \le x \le 1$).

(b)  Find the local and global maxima and minima of $f(x)$ in terms of $a$.

(c)  What is the largest value of $a$ such that we have $f(x) \le 1$ for all $0 \le x \le 1$?

(d)  In terms of $a$, find all points $x$ in $0 \le x \le 1$ where $f(x) = x$. These are called the "fixed points" of the function. How can you spot the fixed points from your sketches in Part (a)?

(e)  If $x_0$ is a fixed point of $f(x) = ax(1 - x)$ and $x_0 \ne 0$, show that $f(x) < x$ for $x > x_0$. Prove this using calculus and also relate it to your sketches in Part (a).

ANSWER:

(a)

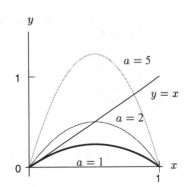

(b)

$$f'(x) = \frac{d}{dx}\left(ax(1-x)\right)$$
$$= \frac{d}{dx}(ax - ax^2)$$
$$= a - 2ax.$$

So if $f'(x) = 0, a - 2ax = 0$. Then $2x = 1$ (since $a$ cannot be 0) and $x = \frac{1}{2}$. Thus $\frac{1}{2}$ is the only critical point. Checking endpoints, $f(0) = f(1) = 0$ are global minima, and $f(\frac{1}{2}) = \frac{a}{4}$ is a maximum, since $f''(x) = -2a < 0$.

(c)   Since $\frac{a}{4}$ is the maximum of $f$, $f$ is less than or equal to 1 for all $0 < x < 1$, provided $a \le 4$. The largest value occurs when $a = 4$.

(d)   $f(x) = x$ means that $ax(1-x) = x$, so $x(a(1-x) - 1) = 0$, and thus $x = 0$ or $x = 1 - \frac{1}{a}$. The fixed points are where each curve intersects the line $y = x$.

(e)   From Part (d), we see that $x_0 = 1 - \frac{1}{a}$. For $x > x_0 = 1 - \frac{1}{a}$,

$$f(x) = ax(1-x)$$
$$< ax(1-x_0) \quad \text{because we are considering } x > x_0$$
$$= ax(\frac{1}{a}) \quad \text{because } x_0 = 1 - \frac{1}{a}$$
$$= x.$$

In Part (a), the curve lies below the line $y = x$ after the point of intersection. Another way of doing this is as follows:

Note that $f'(x) = a - 2ax$. If $x > x_0$, we have

$$x > 1 - \frac{1}{a}$$
$$-2ax < -2a(1 - \frac{1}{a})$$
$$a - 2ax < a - 2a + 2$$
$$f'(x) < -a + 2$$

But since $a$ is at least 1, $f'(x)$ can be at most 1, when $a = 1$. So the slope of $f$ is less than the slope of the line $y = x$ for $x > x_0$, and hence $f(x) < x$ for $x > x_0$. This can also be seen on the graph.

5.   Given the following data about the second derivative of a function $f$,

| $x$ | 0 | 1 | 2 | 3 |
|---|---|---|---|---|
| $f''(x)$ | 1 | $-1$ | $-3$ | $-5$ |

which of the following types of function could $f$ be? (Circle all that apply.) Assume $b > 0$. The other constants can be positive or negative.

(a)   $ae^{bx}$

(b)   $e^{-x^2/b}$

(c)   A quadratic (i.e., $ax^2 + bx + c$).

(d)   A cubic (i.e., $ax^3 + bx^2 + cx + d$)

(e)   $\sin(bx)$.

ANSWER:

The data in the table suggests that $f'(x)$ is a linear function. We expect $f(x)$ to be a cubic.

6.

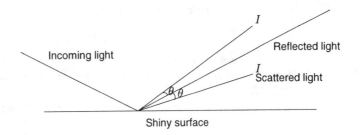

Incoming light

Reflected light

$I$

Scattered light

$\theta$ $\theta$

Shiny surface

When light strikes a shiny surface, much of it is reflected in the direction shown. However some of it may be scattered on either side of the reflected light. If the intensity (brightness) of the scattered light at the angle $\theta$ (shown in the picture) is $I$, the Phong model says that

$$I = k \cos^n(\theta)$$

where $k$ and $n$ are positive constants depending on the surface. Thus this function gives an idea of how "spread-out" the scattered light is.

(a)  Sketch graphs $I$ against $\theta$ for $0 \leq \theta \leq \frac{\pi}{2}$ for various values of $k$ and $n$.
(b)  Explain in words what effect the parameter $k$ has on the shape of the graph.
(c)  Explain in words what effect the parameter $n$ has on the shape of the graph. In particular, what is the difference between the ways in which surfaces with small $n$ and surfaces with large $n$ scatter light?
(d)  If $k$ remains fixed, what happens to the graph of $I$ against $\theta$ as $n \rightarrow \infty$? What does this tell you about how $I$ depends on $\theta$ in this case?

ANSWER:

(a)  $n = 1$, various $k$'s

$k = 1$, various $n$'s.

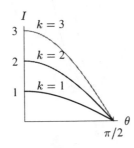

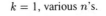
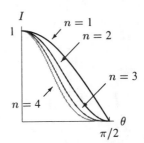

(b)  Stretches graph upward ($k > 1$), shrinks ($k < 1$).
(c)  Value of $I$ drops to 0 more quickly as $n$ increases. Surfaces with small $n$ scatter light more, those with large $n$ scatter less light.
(d)  It drops more and more sharply from the vertical intercept:

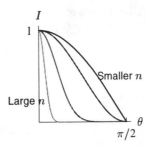

As $n \rightarrow \infty$, less light is scattered. In the limit, $I = k$ when $\theta = 0$ and $I = 0$ elsewhere. This mans that no light is scattered–we have a perfectly reflecting surface.

7.  Consider the one-parameter family of functions given by

$$e^{Ax} + e^{-Ax}, \text{ where } A > 0.$$

Use calculus to draw a graph of members of the family. Show what happens as $A$ gets very small and very large. Be sure to label critical points and points of inflection, if any.

ANSWER:

Consider the general curve $f(x) = e^{Ax} + e^{-Ax}$. To find the maxima and minima of this function, set

$$f'(x) = \frac{d}{dx}\left(e^{Ax} + e^{-Ax}\right) = 0$$
$$Ae^{Ax} - Ae^{-Ax} = 0$$
$$e^{Ax} = e^{-Ax}.$$

This is true only when $x = 0$. To find concavity, take the second derivative:

$$f''(x) = \frac{d}{dx}\left(Ae^{Ax} - Ae^{-Ax}\right) = A^2\left(e^{Ax} + e^{-Ax}\right).$$

Since this quantity is positive for all $x$ and any $A$, any curve in this family is concave up and has a minimum at the point $(0, 2)$. Since there is no change in the concavity, there are no inflection points. This function is also even, as we can see by replacing $x$ with $-x$ in the original function: $f(-x) = e^{-Ax} + e^{Ax} = f(x)$. We also know that the greater $A$ is, the greater is the curvature or concavity. We obtain the following family of curves:

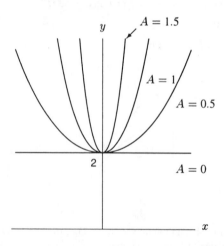

8.  For the function $y = axe^{-bx}$, choose $a$ and $b$ so that $y$ has a critical point at $x = 2$ and a maximum value of 7.

ANSWER:

To find the critical points of $y = axe^{-bx}$, set

$$y' = 0$$
$$ae^{-bx} - abxe^{-bx} = 0$$
$$a(1 - bx)e^{-bx} = 0$$

There is thus a critical point at $x = \frac{1}{b}$. Since

$$y'' = -abe^{-bx} - ab(1 - bx)e^{-bx}$$
$$= -ab(2 - bx)e^{-bx},$$

$y''(\frac{1}{b}) = -abe^{-1} < 0$, and so there is indeed a local maximum at $x = \frac{1}{b}$. $b$ must then be $\frac{1}{2}$, and since $y(2) = 2ae^{-1} = 7$, $a = \frac{7}{2}e$.

9. (a) Find the family of all quadratic functions that have zeros at $x = 1$ and $x = 5$. (Your answer will contain one arbitrary constant.)

(b) Use your answer to (a) to find the family of all cubic functions, $f$, that have critical points at $x = 1$ and $x = 5$.

(c) For all cubics, $f$, in this family, find

(i) $p$, the $x$-coordinate of the point of inflection;

(ii) $f''(p)$, where $p$ is the $x$-coordinate of the point of inflection;

(iii) $f'(1)$.

(d) From the list below, check off the data you would like to be told in order to specify the cubic $f$ uniquely. Don't ask for more or less information than you need. (There are many possible answers. Just give one choice or one set of choices.) Briefly explain your answer.

___$f(0)$

___$f(p)$ where $p$ is the point of inflection

___$f'(p)$ where $p$ is the point of inflection

___$f'(0)$

ANSWER:

(a) $y = D(x - 1)(x - 5)$, where $D$ is an arbitrary constant, is the family of all quadratic functions having zeros at $x = 1$ and $x = 5$.

(b) The derivative of a cubic with critical points at 1 and 5 is a quadratic with zeros at 1 and 5. So a cubic with this kind of derivative is an antiderivative of $D(x - 1)(x - 5)$.

$$f(x) = \int D(x - 1)(x - 5)\,dx$$

$$= D \int x^2 - 6x + 5\,dx$$

$$= \frac{Dx^3}{3} - 3Dx^2 + 5Dx + C$$

(c) (i) $f''(x) = 2Dx - 6D$. This is zero when $D(x - 3) = 0$, so $p = 3$ is the $x$-coordinate of the point of inflection.

(ii) $f''(3) = 0$

(iii) $f'(1) = 0$, since $f$ has a critical point at $x = 1$.

(d) Since the expression found for $f$ in (b) has two arbitrary constants, we need two conditions to fix $f$ uniquely. Any two conditions from $f(0)$, $f'(0)$, $f(p)$ and $f'(p)$ will work, except for the two $f'(0)$ and $f'(p)$, since neither of these two will fix $C$.

## Problems and Solutions for Section 5.3

1. Find the best possible upper and lower bounds for the function $f(x) = xe^{-x}$ for $x \geq 0$, i.e., find numbers $A$ and $B$ such that

$$A \leq xe^{-x} \leq B, \quad x \geq 0.$$

The numbers $A$ and $B$ should be as close together as possible.

ANSWER:

First find the critical points. Set $f'(x) = 0$ to obtain:

$$f'(x) = e^{-x} - xe^{-x} = 0,$$

$$e^{-x}(1 - x) = 0.$$

Since $e^{-x}$ never equals 0, $x = 1$ is a critical point. Since $f'$ is positive to the left of $x = 1$ and is negative to the right of $x = 1$, there is a local maximum at $x = 1$. $f(0) = 0$ and as $x \to \infty$, $f(x) \to 0$. So the lower bound of $f(x)$ is 0 and the upper bound is $f(1) = e^{-1}$. So $0 \leq xe^{-x} \leq e^{-1}$ for $x \geq 0$.

2. Find two positive numbers whose sum is 8 such that the sum of the cube of the first and the square of the second is a minimum.

   ANSWER:

   Let $x, y$ be the two positive numbers such that $x + y = 8$; we wish to minimize $x^3 + y^2$. Since $y = 8 - x$, we need to minimize $x^3 + (8 - x)^2$. Differentiating and setting this derivative equal to zero,

   $$3x^2 + 2(8 - x)(-1) = 0$$
   $$3x^2 - 16 + 2x = 0.$$

   Using the quadratic formula, we obtain:

   $$x = \frac{-2 \pm \sqrt{4 - 4(3)(-16)}}{6}$$
   $$= -\frac{1}{3} \pm \frac{7}{3} = -\frac{8}{3},\ 2.$$

   But $x$ must be positive, so $x = 2, y = 6$. Comparing values of $x^3 + y^2$ at the critical points, namely $x = 2, y = 6$, and the endpoints, namely $x = 0, y = 8$ and $x = 8, y = 0$, we see that $x = 2, y = 6$ is in fact the global minimum.

3. A landscape architect plans to enclose a 3000 square-foot rectangular region in a botanical garden. She will use shrubs costing \$25 per foot along three sides and fencing costing \$20 per foot along the fourth side. Find the dimensions that minimize the total cost.

   ANSWER:

   A rectangle with area 3000 ft$^2$ has dimensions of $x$ ft by $\frac{3000}{x}$ ft. The cost of lining three sides of the rectangle with shrubs will be $25(2x + \frac{3000}{x})$ dollars, and the cost of lining the remaining side with a fence is $20 \cdot \frac{3000}{x}$ dollars. Therefore, the total cost incurred will be $C(x) = 50x + \frac{75000}{x} + \frac{60000}{x} = 50x + \frac{135000}{x}$ dollars. To minimize the cost, set $C'(x) = 0$, to obtain:

   $$C'(x) = 50 - \frac{135000}{x^2} = 0$$
   $$x^2 = \frac{135000}{50}$$
   $$x = \sqrt{2700} \approx \pm 52.0 \text{ ft.}$$

   Since we are only interested in positive distances, we discard $x \approx -52.0$ ft. Now, $x \approx 52.0$ ft is a possible minimum. Since $C''(52.0) = \frac{2 \cdot 135000}{52.0^3} > 0$, $x \approx 52.0$ ft is indeed a minimum. The dimensions of the plot are then $\approx 52.0$ ft by $\frac{3000}{52.0} \approx 57.7$ ft.

4. A rectangular sheet of paper is to contain 72 square inches of printed matter with 2 inch margins at top and bottom and 1 inch margins on the sides. What dimensions for the sheet will use the least paper?

   ANSWER:

   Let $x$ be the length of the side of the printed matter. Then $\frac{72}{x}$ is the length of the top edge of the printed matter.

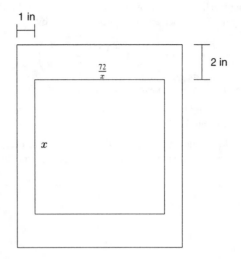

The area of the sheet is given by $A(x) = (\frac{72}{x} + 2)(x + 4)$. To minimize $A(x)$, set $A'(x) = -\frac{288}{x^2} + 2 = 0$. Since $x = 12$ is the only positive (and hence reasonable) solution to this equation and since $A''(12)$ is positive, $x = 12$ must minimize the area. Thus, the piece of paper must be 16 inches high and 8 inches wide.

5. What point of the parabola whose equation is $y = x^2$ is nearest to the point $(6, 3)$?

ANSWER:

We wish to minimize the distance between a point $(x, x^2)$ on the parabola $y = x^2$ and the point $(6, 3)$. Using the distance formula we note that $d(x)$, the distance from the parabola to $(6, 3)$, equals $\sqrt{(x - 6)^2 + (x^2 - 3)^2}$. This will be minimized if and only if its square is also minimized. We will call this $f(x)$.

$$f(x) = (x - 6)^2 + (x^2 - 3)^2$$
$$= (x^2 - 12x + 36) + (x^4 - 6x^2 + 9)$$
$$= x^4 - 5x^2 - 12x + 45.$$
$$f'(x) = 4x^3 - 10x - 12$$

To find critical points, set $f'(x) = 0$,
$$4x^3 - 10x - 12 = 0$$
$$2x^3 - 5x - 6 = 0$$
$$(x - 2)(2x^2 + 4x + 3) = 0.$$

There is only one real solution, $x = 2$; the other two roots are complex. Thus $(2, 4)$ is a critical point since the derivative is zero at $x = 2$. Since points on the parabola move away from $(6, 3)$ for large $x$, this critical point minimizes the distance. Alternatively, $f''(x) = 12x^2 - 10$, so $f''(2) = 48 - 10 = 38 > 0$, so $(2, 4)$ is a minimum. $(2, 4)$ is closest to $(6, 3)$ since $x = 2$ is the only critical point.

6. A single cell of a bee's honey comb has the shape shown to the right. The surface area of this cell is given by

$$A = 6hs + \frac{3}{2}s^2 \left( \frac{-\cos\theta}{\sin\theta} + \frac{\sqrt{3}}{\sin\theta} \right)$$

where $h$, $s$, $\theta$ are as shown in the picture.

(a) Keeping $h$ and $s$ fixed, for what angle, $\theta$, is the surface area minimal?

(b) Measurements on bee's cells have shown that the angle actually used by bees is about $\theta = 55°$. Comment.

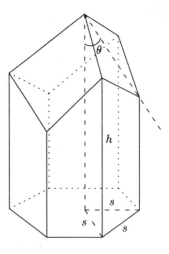

ANSWER:

(a) To minimize $A$ with $h$ and $s$ fixed we have to find $\frac{dA}{d\theta}$.

$$\frac{dA}{d\theta} = \frac{3}{2}s^2 \frac{d}{d\theta} \left( \frac{\sqrt{3} - \cos\theta}{\sin\theta} \right)$$

$$= \frac{3}{2}s^2 \left( \frac{\sin^2\theta - \cos\theta(\sqrt{3} - \cos\theta)}{\sin^2\theta} \right)$$

$$= \frac{3}{2}s^2 \left( \frac{\sin^2\theta - \sqrt{3}\cos\theta + \cos^2\theta}{\sin^2\theta} \right)$$

$$= \frac{3}{2}s^2 \left( \frac{1 - \sqrt{3}\cos\theta}{\sin^2\theta} \right)$$

Set $\frac{dA}{d\theta} = \frac{3}{2}s^2 \left( \frac{1 - \sqrt{3}\cos\theta}{\sin^2\theta} \right) = 0$. Then $1 - \sqrt{3}\cos\theta = 0$ and $\cos\theta = \frac{1}{\sqrt{3}}$, so $\theta \approx 54.7°$ is a critical point of $A$. Since

$$\frac{d^2A}{d\theta^2}\bigg|_{\theta=54.7} = \frac{3}{2}s^2 \left( \frac{\sqrt{3}\sin^3\theta - 2\sin\theta\cos\theta(1 - \sqrt{3}\cos\theta)}{\sin^4\theta} \right) \bigg|_{\theta=54.7}$$

$$\approx \frac{3}{2}s^2(2.122) > 0,$$

$\theta = 54.7$ is indeed a minimum.

(b) Since $55°$ is very close to $54.7°$, we conclude that bees attempt to minimize the surface areas of their honey combs.

## Problems and Solutions for Section 5.4

1. The cost $C(q)$ (in dollars) of producing a quantity of $q$ of a certain product is shown in the graph below.

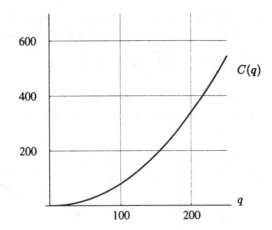

Suppose that the manufacturer can sell the product for $2 each (regardless of how many are sold), so that the total revenue from selling a quantity $q$ is $R(q) = 2q$. The difference

$$\pi(q) = R(q) - C(q)$$

is the total profit. Let $q_0$ be the quantity that will produce the maximum profit.

You are told that $q_0$ can be found by finding the point on the graph where $C'(q_0) = 2$.

(a)  Draw the graph of $R$ on the figure above and then explain why this rule makes sense graphically.
(b)  Now give a mathematical explanation of the rule, using what you know about maxima and minima.

ANSWER:

(a)

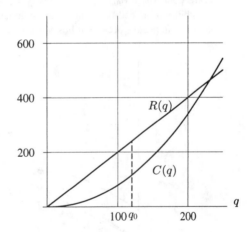

Graphically this makes sense, because the point where the separation between $R(q)$ and $C(q)$ is greatest is the point where the slopes of the two lines are equal (namely 2).

(b)  Mathematically, to maximize $\pi(q)$, first find the first derivative,

$$\pi'(q) = R'(q) - C'(q)$$
$$= 2 - C'(q).$$

Now set $\pi'(q) = 0$. We know $q_0$ where $C'(q_0) = 2$ is a critical point. Since $\pi'(q) = -C''(q)$ and the graph of $C(q)$ is concave up, $\pi''(q) \leq 0$. Hence $q_0$ is a local maximum. Since $\pi''(q) \leq 0$ for all $q$, $q_0$ is the global maximum.

2.  Given below is the graph of the cost $C(q)$ of producing the quantity $q$ and the revenue $R(q) = pq$ of selling the quantity $q$, where $p$ is the price per unit ($p$ is a constant).

(a)  Show graphically where the quantity $q_0$ is such that the average cost per unit, $a(q) = \frac{C(q)}{q}$, is a minimum. Explain what you are doing.

(b) Show graphically where the quantity $q_1$ is such that your profit $R(q) - C(q)$ is a maximum. Explain the relationship between $C'(q_1)$ and $p$ that should be evident in your picture.

(c) Which is larger, $C'(q_0)$ or $C'(q_1)$? If you want to maximize profit, should you minimize your average cost? Explain your answer.

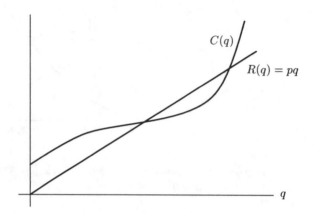

ANSWER:

(a) The quantity $a(q) = C(q)/q$ is the slope of a line joining the point $(q, C(q))$ to the origin. So to minimize $a(q)$ we must search among lines that join the origin to a point on the graph of $C$ and find the one $L$ of least slope. From the figure, we can see that the line $L$ will be tangent to $C$ at the point $(q_0, C(q_0))$. The quantity $q_0$ is the one which minimizes $a(q)$. (We can exclude the possibility of an end-point minimum by looking at the given figure.) Also, notice that $C$ will be concave up near $q_0$ because it lies above its tangent $L$.

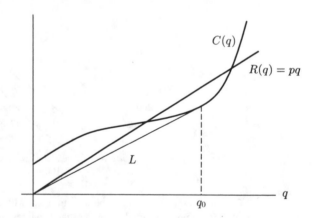

This result can also be obtained analytically. We find that $a'(q) = \left(qC'(q) - C(q)\right)/q^2$. If $q_0$ is a critical point for $a$, then $a'(q_0) = 0$, so $q_0 C'(q_0) - C(q_0) = 0$, which leads to $C'(q_0) = C(q_0)/q_0$; i.e. the slope of the tangent at $(q_0, C(q_0))$ is the same as the slope of the line joining $(q_0, C(q_0))$ to the origin, which is exactly what we found above. This will be a minimum point if $a''(q_0) > 0$. Since $a''(q) = C''(q)/q - 2\left(qC'(q) - C(q)\right)/q^3$, we find $a''(q_0) = C''(q_0)/q_0$. Since $q_0 > 0$, we shall have $a''(q_0) > 0$ if and only if $C''(q_0) > 0$; i.e., $C$ is concave up at $q_0$. The geometric argument gives much clearer insight into the problem.

(b) The profit $\pi$ will be maximized at a point $q_1$ where $\pi'(q_1) = 0$. (Again we rely on the picture to exclude the possibility of an end-point maximum.) So $\pi'(q_1) = R'(q_1) - C'(q_1) = 0$, giving $p = C'(q_1)$. Hence the profit $\pi$ is maximized at the point $q_1$ where the tangent $M$ to $C$ is parallel to the graph of $R(q)$.

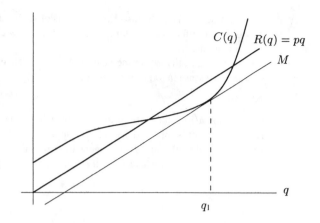

(c) The picture shows that the slope of $L$ is less than the slope of $M$, so $C'(q_0) < C'(q_1)$. Thus if we decide to minimize average cost (by setting $q = q_0$), we will *not* in general have maximized profit (which requires $q = q_1$).

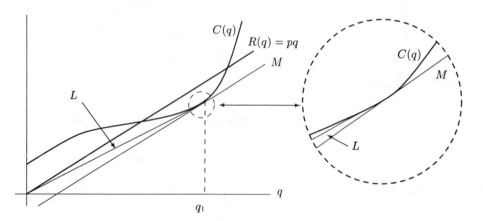

The enlargement shows that since $C$ is concave up in this region, $q_0 < q_1$.

3. The cost $C(q)$ (in dollars) of producing a quantity $q$ of a certain product is shown in the graph below.

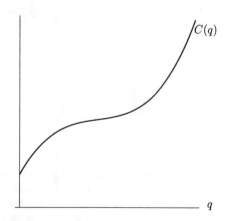

The *average cost* is $a(q) = \frac{C(q)}{q}$.

(a) Interpret $a(q)$ graphically, as the slope of a line in the sketch above.

(b) Based on the graphical interpretation in (a), find on the graph the quantity $q_0$ where $a(q)$ is minimal.

(c) Now suppose that the fixed costs (i.e., the costs of setting up before production starts) are doubled. How does this affect the cost function? Sketch the new cost function on the same set of axes as the original one.

(d) Let $q_1$ be the quantity where the new $a(q)$ is minimal. Where is $q_1$ in relation to $q_0$? Does your answer make sense in terms of economics?

ANSWER:

(a) The function $a(q)$ is the slope of the line through $(0,0)$ and $(q, C(q))$.

(b) The average cost is minimized when the slope of the line joining $(0,0)$ to $(q, C(q))$ is minimal. This occurs when the line $L$ is tangent to the graph of $C(q)$, as drawn in Figure 5.4.8. Thus $(q_0, C(q_0))$ is the point where $L$ touches the graph of $C(q)$.

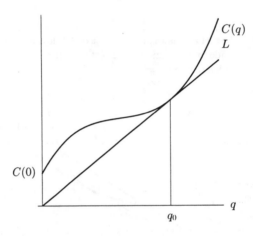

Figure 5.4.8

(c) The cost function is shifted up by $C(0)$.

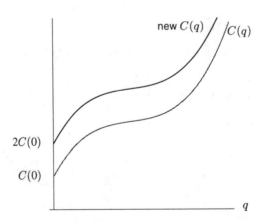

(d) Suppose $M$ is the tangent line which gives the new minimal value of $a(q)$. From the figure, we can see that $M$ is steeper than $L$. Since $C$ is concave up, $M$ touches the cost graph to the right of $q_0$. Thus $q_1 > q_0$. In practical terms, this means that if the start up costs are double, the manufacturer must make more of the product to minimize the average cost. This makes economic sense.

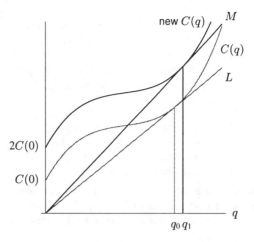

*Figure 5.4.9*

## Problems and Solutions for Section 5.5

1. A wire of length $L$ is cut into two pieces. [We allow the possibility that one of the pieces has zero length.] The first piece is bent into a circle, the second into a square. How long should the piece of wire that is bent into a *circular* shape be in order to *maximize* the *sum* of the areas of the *two* shapes? How long should that piece be if you want to *minimize* the sum of the areas? [For full points, you must explain in detail *why* the length you suggest will indeed result in a maximum or minimum for the sum of the areas of the two shapes.]

   ANSWER:

   $x$ = length bent into the circle.

   $L - x$ = length bent into the square.

   $x$ = circle of circumference $x \Rightarrow x = 2\pi r$

   $$r = \frac{x}{2\pi}, \text{ so area of circle} = \frac{\pi}{4\pi^2}x^2 = \frac{x^2}{4\pi}$$

   $$x \Rightarrow \text{ Area} = \left(\frac{L-x}{4}\right)^2$$

   Let $A(x)$ = sum of areas.

   $$A(x) = \frac{\pi}{4\pi^2}x^2 + \frac{1}{16}(L-x)^2 = \frac{1}{4\pi}x^2 + \frac{1}{16}(L-x)^2, x \in [0, L]$$

   Now find a max/min of $A(x)$ on $[0, L]$:

   $$\frac{dA}{dx} = \frac{2}{4\pi}x + \frac{2}{16}(L-x)(-1) = \frac{1}{2\pi}x - \frac{1}{8}(L-x) = \left(\frac{1}{2\pi} + \frac{1}{8}\right)x - \frac{1}{8}L$$

   $$\frac{dA}{dx} = 0 \text{ when } \frac{1}{2\pi}x + \frac{1}{8}x = \frac{1}{8}L \Rightarrow x = \frac{L}{1 + \frac{4}{\pi}} = \frac{L\pi}{\pi + 4}$$

   $$\frac{d^2A}{dx^2} = \left(\frac{1}{2\pi} + \frac{1}{8}\right) > 0 \text{ for all } x, \text{ i.e. the length } L\pi/(\pi+4) \text{ will give a minimum area. Consider}$$
   the endpoints: $A(0) = L^2/16$, $A(L) = L^2/4\pi > A(0)$. Therefore, the absolute maximum area occurs when $x = L$.

**448**

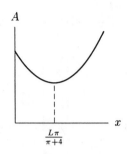

$$\frac{L\pi}{\pi+4}$$

2. A rectangular building is to cover 20,000 square feet. Zoning regulations require 20 foot frontages at the front and the rear and 10 feet of space on either side. Find the dimensions of the smallest piece of property on which the building can be legally constructed.

   ANSWER:

   Assume that the front of the building is $x$ feet long. Then the sides of the building must be $\frac{20000}{x}$ feet long. The dimensions of the property will thus be $x + 20$ and $\frac{20000}{x} + 40$. The area of the plot will be:

   $$A(x) = (x + 20)\left(\frac{20000}{x} + 40\right) = 20000 + \frac{400000}{x} + 800 + 40x$$

   Differentiating and setting this equal to zero,

   $$A'(x) = -\frac{400000}{x^2} + 40 = 0$$
   $$40 = \frac{400000}{x^2}$$
   $$x^2 = 10000$$
   $$x = 100$$

   (No negative roots allowed!) The property will thus have dimensions $120' \times 240'$.

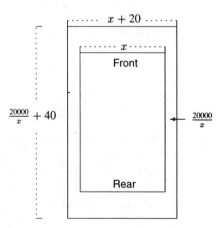

3. The regular air fare between Boston and San Francisco is $500. An airline flying 747s with a capacity of 380 on this route observes that they fly with an average of 300 passengers. Market research tells the airlines' managers that each $20 fare reduction would attract, on average, 20 more passengers for each flight. How should they set the fare to maximize their revenue? Why?

   ANSWER:

   Suppose we lower the fare by $x$ dollars. Then the revenue generated at this fare will be:

   $$r(x) = (500 - x)(300 + x),$$

where $x$ is the discount in dollars. (For every dollar decrease in fare, another person will fly.) To maximize revenue, we examine the critical points of $r$:

$$\frac{dr}{dx} = \frac{d}{dx}\left((500-x)(300+x)\right)$$
$$= -(300+x) + (500-x)$$
$$= 200 - 2x.$$

So, $\frac{dr}{dx} = 0$ when $x = 100$. But this is too high, since when $x = 100$, the number of people on the plane is 400. So the maximum must occur when $x = 80$ or 0 (the endpoints.) When $x = 80$, $r(x) = 420 \cdot 380 = 159{,}600$; when $x = 0$, $r(x) = 300 \cdot 500 = 150{,}000$. Hence, the airline would do best to fill up its planes at $420.

4. The purpose of this problem is to find the $x$-value which produces the shortest distance from the point $(0,0)$ to the curve $y = e^x$.

   (a) Use the computer. Plot the curve $y = e^x$ and a circle of radius $a$ centered at $(0,0)$. By varying $a$, estimate the value of $x$ which gives the shortest distance from $(0,0)$ to the curve. What is your estimate? Explain what you did.

   (b) Using calculus, confirm that the statement you made in part (a) is accurate. (You may need to use a computer or a calculator to find roots.) What is your estimate for $x$, accurate to 5 decimal places? Explain what method you used to get this accuracy.

   ANSWER:

   (a) When $a = 0.78$, the circle barely touches the curve $e^x$. They touch at $x \approx -0.43$, so that value of $x$ gives us the point on the curve closest to the the origin.

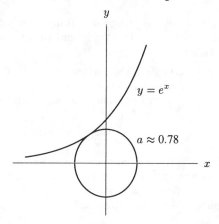

   (b) The distance from the point $(x, e^x)$ to the origin is $D(x) = \sqrt{x^2 + (e^x)^2} = \sqrt{x^2 + e^{2x}}$, so, in order to find the closest $e^x$ comes to the origin, we want to minimize $D(x)$. By taking the derivative and solving for a root (using a root-finding program), we find that $x = -0.42630$ gives the desired minimum.

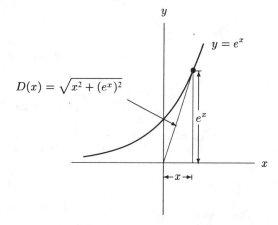

5.  If you throw a stone into the air at an angle of $\theta$ to the horizontal, it moves along the curve

$$y = x \tan\theta - \frac{x^2}{2k}(1 + \tan^2\theta)$$

where $y$ is the height of the stone above the ground, $x$ is the horizontal distance, and $k$ is a positive constant.

   (a)  If the angle $\theta$ is fixed, what value of $x$ gives the maximum height? (Your answer will contain $k$ and $\theta$.) Explain how you know this $x$-value gives a maximum.

   (b)  Suppose the stone is to be thrown over a wall at a fixed horizontal distance $\ell$ away from you. If you can vary $\theta$, what is the highest wall that the stone can go over? (Your answer will contain $k$ and $\ell$.) You do <u>not</u> need to justify that your answer is a maximum.

   ANSWER:

   (a)  $\dfrac{dy}{dx} = \tan\theta - \dfrac{2x}{2k}(1 + \tan^2\theta) = 0$ gives $x = \dfrac{k\tan\theta}{1 + \tan^2\theta}$.

   This value gives a maximum because curve is an upside down parabola.

   (b)  When $x = \ell$, $y = \ell\tan\theta - \dfrac{\ell^2}{2k}(1 + \tan^2\theta)$

   $\dfrac{dy}{d\theta} = \dfrac{\ell}{\cos^2\theta} - \dfrac{\ell^2}{2k}\left(\dfrac{2\tan\theta}{\cos^2\theta}\right) = 0$ when $\dfrac{\ell}{k}\,\dfrac{(k - \ell\tan\theta)}{\cos^2\theta} = 0$ so $\tan\theta = \dfrac{k}{\ell}$.

   Thus height is $y = \ell \cdot \dfrac{k}{\ell} - \dfrac{\ell^2}{2k}\left(1 + \dfrac{k^2}{\ell^2}\right) = k - \dfrac{1}{2k}(\ell^2 + k^2) = \dfrac{k^2 - \ell^2}{2k}$

6.  A rectangle with its base on the $x$-axis is inscribed in the region bounded by the curve $f(x) = x^2$, the $x$-axis and the line $x = 4$. Find the dimensions of the rectangle with maximal area.

   ANSWER:

   Choose a rectangle that has one corner at $(4, 0)$. If the other vertical side of the rectangle intersects the $x$-axis at $(x, 0)$, then the length of the base of the rectangle is $4 - x$, and the height is $x^2$. The area will thus be $(4 - x)x^2$. To maximize this, set the derivative equal to 0. This gives

$$\frac{d}{dx}(4x^2 - x^3) = 8x - 3x^2 = x(8 - 3x) = 0.$$

There are two roots to this equation, $x = 0$ and $x = 8/3$. The root $x = 0$ corresponds to the rectangle of height 0 lying along the $x$-axis, and it certainly does not maximize the area. Since the second derivative of the area, $8 - 6x$ is negative when $x = 8/3$, area is indeed maximized when $x = 8/3$. Thus the base has length $\approx 1.33$ and the height is $\approx 7.11$.

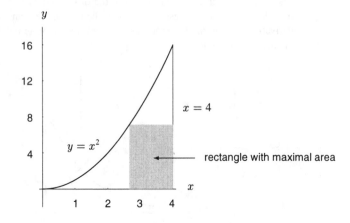

7. A submarine can travel 30 mi/hr submerged and 60 mi/hr on the surface. The submarine must stay submerged if within 200 miles of shore. Suppose that this submarine wants to meet a surface ship 200 miles off shore. The submarine leaves from a port 300 miles along the coast from the surface ship. What route of the type sketched below should the sub take to minimize its time to rendezvous?

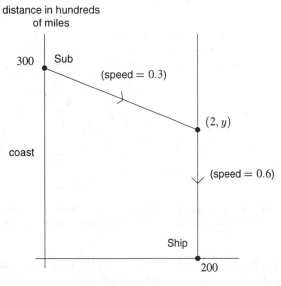

**Figure 5.5.10**

ANSWER:

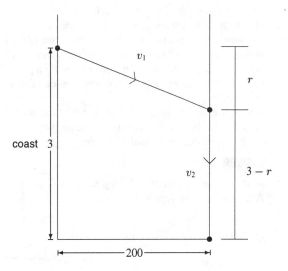

We wish to minimize $t = t_1 + t_2$, where $t_1$ is spent traveling with speed 0.3, and $t_2$ is spent traveling with speed 0.6. Let $r = 3 - y$. We know (by the Pythagorean Theorem) that the distance travelled at the slow speed is $\sqrt{4 + r^2}$, so we have

$$
\begin{aligned}
t &= t_1 + t_2 \\
&= \frac{\sqrt{4 + r^2}}{0.3} + \frac{3 - r}{0.6} \\
&= \frac{1}{0.6}\left(2\sqrt{4 + r^2} + 3 - r\right)
\end{aligned}
$$

So $\dfrac{dt}{dr} = \dfrac{1}{0.6}(2r(4+r^2)^{-\frac{1}{2}} - 1)$, which is zero when $r = \dfrac{2}{\sqrt{3}}$.

$$\text{Since } \left.\dfrac{d^2t}{dr^2}\right|_{r=\frac{2}{\sqrt{3}}} = \dfrac{1}{0.3}\left((4+r^2)^{-\frac{1}{2}} + r\cdot(-\dfrac{1}{2})(4+r^2)^{-\frac{3}{2}}\cdot 2r\right)\Big|_{r=\frac{2}{\sqrt{3}}}$$

$$= \dfrac{1}{0.3}\left((4+r^2)^{-\frac{1}{2}} - r^2(4+r^2)^{-\frac{3}{2}}\right)\Big|_{r=\frac{2}{\sqrt{3}}}$$

$$= \dfrac{1}{0.3}\left(\dfrac{4}{(4+r^2)^{\frac{3}{2}}}\right)\Big|_{r=\frac{2}{\sqrt{3}}}$$

$$= \dfrac{1}{0.3}\left(\dfrac{4}{\left(\frac{10}{3}\right)^{\frac{3}{2}}}\right) > 0,$$

$r = \dfrac{2}{\sqrt{3}}$ is indeed a minimum. So $y$ should be equal to $3 - \dfrac{2}{\sqrt{3}}$ for the submarine to minimize time.

## Review Problems and Solutions for Chapter 5

1.  One fine day you take a hike up a mountain path. Using your trusty map you have determined that the path is approximately in the shape of the curve

$$y = 4(x^3 - 12x^2 + 48x + 36)$$

Here $y$ is the elevation in feet above sea level and $x$ is the horizontal distance in miles you have traveled, but your map only shows the path for 7 miles, horizontal distance.

(a)  How high above sea level do you start your hike?
(b)  How high above sea level are you after 7 miles?
(c)  Use your calculator to draw an informative graph of the path (i.e. One that looks like a cubic.) and sketch your answer. Show the scale you use. (Take your answers in parts (a) and (b) into account!)
(d)  Where on the path is a nice flat place to stop for a picnic? Explain.
(e)  Estimate the elevation after 7.5 horizontal miles. (You do not know the shape of the path explicitly after 7 miles!)
(f)  If your friend, who is *not* in "good shape" followed this path for 15 miles total, in horizontal distance, the day before, does it make sense that the equation for the elevation continues to hold much beyond the 7 mile mark? Explain.

ANSWER:

(a)  At the start of the hike, $x = 0$, so $y = 4(36) = 144$ feet.
(b)  After 7 miles, $x = 7$, so $y = 508$ feet.
(c)

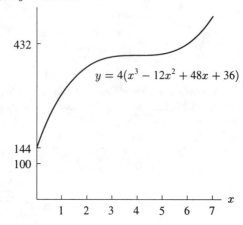

(d) A flat place occurs when the elevation is neither increasing nor decreasing, i.e., when $\dfrac{dy}{dx} = 4(3x^2 - 24x + 48) = 0$. This happens when $x = \dfrac{24 \pm \sqrt{24^2 - 4 \cdot 3 \cdot 48}}{6} = 4$, so stop about 4 miles along for a picnic.

(e) When $x = 7$, $\dfrac{dy}{dx} = 4(3(7)^2 - 24(7) + 48) = 108$. Local linearization yields

$$y(7.5) \approx y(7) + 0.5(y'(7))$$
$$= 508 + (0.5)(108)$$
$$= 562 \text{ feet.}$$

(f) No, since according to the equation $y(15) = 5724$, my friend would have to hike over a mile up, which is not easy. Beyond the seventh mile, the equation says things go uphill quickly. So if he does walk for 15 miles and is also out of shape, then in all likelihood the equation does not apply beyond the 7 mile point.

For Problems 2–4, decide whether each statement is true or false, and provide a short explanation or a counterexample.

2. If $f'' = 0$ at $x = 0$, then the graph of $f$ changes concavity at $x = 0$.

   ANSWER:

   FALSE. The graph of $f(x) = x^4$ has $f''(0) = 0$, but it is concave up everywhere.

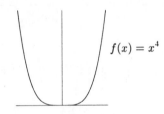

3. If $f' > 0$ on an interval, the function is concave UP on the interval.

   ANSWER:

   FALSE. The graph of $f(x) = x^3$ has $f' > 0$ for all $x \neq 0$, even though it is concave down for $x < 0$.

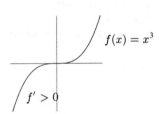

4. If $f$ is always decreasing and concave down, then $f$ must have at least one root.

   ANSWER:

   FALSE. The function $f(x) = -e^x$ is always decreasing and concave down and it has no roots.

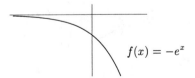

5.  Given the function $f(x) = x^2 e^{-2x}$, find all the maxima, minima and points of inflection and use this information to sketch the graph.

    ANSWER:

$$f(x) = x^2 e^{-2x}$$
$$f'(x) = 2xe^{-2x} - 2x^2 e^{-2x} = 2(x - x^2)e^{-2x}$$
$$f''(x) = 2(1 - 2x)e^{-2x} - 4(x - x^2)e^{-2x} = 2(1 - 4x + 2x^2)e^{-2x}.$$

The zeros of these functions are as follows:

| | | |
|---|---|---|
| $f(x)$ | is zero at | $x = 0.$ |
| $f'(x)$ | is zero at | $x = 0$ and $x = 1.$ |
| $f''(x)$ | is zero at | $x = 1 + \frac{1}{\sqrt{2}}$ and $x = 1 - \frac{1}{\sqrt{2}}.$ |

So the critical points of $f(x)$ are at 0 and 1, and its possible inflection points are at $1 + \frac{1}{\sqrt{2}}$ and $1 - \frac{1}{\sqrt{2}}$. We now need to classify these points, and learn what the graph looks like. We make a table of the approximate values of $f$, $f'$, and $f''$ at these points, and their signs on the intervals between:

| $x$ | $f(x)$ | $f'(x)$ | $f''(x)$ | |
|---|---|---|---|---|
| $(-\infty, 0)$ | + | − | + | |
| $0$ | 0 | 0 | 2 | zero, minimum |
| $(0, 1 - \frac{1}{\sqrt{2}})$ | + | + | + | |
| $1 - \frac{1}{\sqrt{2}}$ | 0.0478 | 0.2306 | 0 | inflection point |
| $(1 - \frac{1}{\sqrt{2}}, 1)$ | + | + | − | |
| $1$ | 0.1353 | 0 | −0.2707 | maximum |
| $(1, 1 + \frac{1}{\sqrt{2}})$ | + | − | − | |
| $1 + \frac{1}{\sqrt{2}}$ | 0.0959 | −0.0794 | 0 | inflection point |
| $(1 + \frac{1}{\sqrt{2}}, \infty)$ | + | − | + | |

Notice that the table tells us that $f''(x)$ does indeed change sign across $x = 1 + \frac{1}{\sqrt{2}}$ and $x = 1 - \frac{1}{\sqrt{2}}$, so these are inflection points.

Using the information in the table, we now draw the graph:

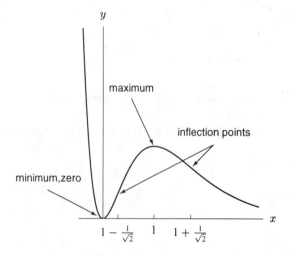

6. Draw the graph of a polynomial of degree four that has a local minimum at $(-3, -27)$ and inflection points at $(-1, -11)$ and the origin.

ANSWER:

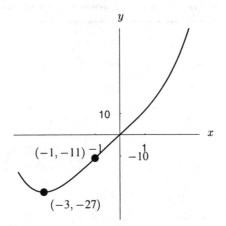

# Chapter 6 Exam Questions

*Problems and Solutions for Section 6.1*

1. Sketch a function that represents the total area between $f(x)$ and the $x$-axis from 0 to $a$.

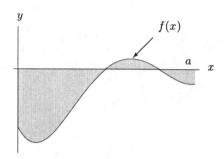

[Hint: This is not the same as $\int_0^a f(x)\,dx$.]

ANSWER:

We recall that since the area is always non-negative, the area between $f(x)$ and the $x$-axis from 0 to $a$ is $\int_0^a |f(x)|\,dx$. We therefore obtain the graph below:

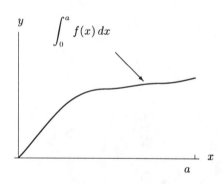

2. If $f$ is given as below, sketch two functions $F$, such that $F' = f$. In one case, have $F(0) = 0$ and in the other, have $F(0) = -1$.

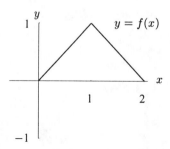

ANSWER:

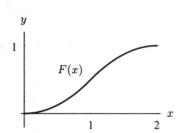 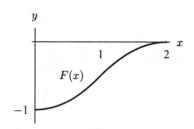

3. Match the following functions with their antiderivatives:

Function             Antiderivative

(a) 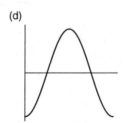    (I)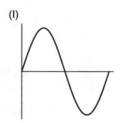

(b) 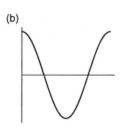    (II)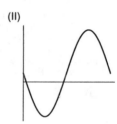

(c) 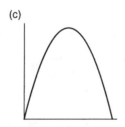    (III)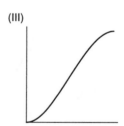

(d) 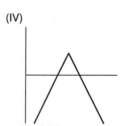    (IV)

ANSWER:

(a) ⟶ IV
(b) ⟶ I
(c) ⟶ III
(d) ⟶ II

4. A young girl who aspires to be a rocket scientist launches a model rocket from the ground at time $t = 0$. The rocket travels straight up in the air, and the following graph shows the upward velocity of the rocket as a function of time:

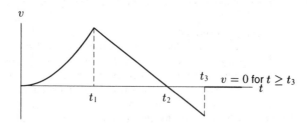

Let $h$ be the height (or vertical displacement) of the rocket, let $a$ be the acceleration of the rocket, and let $h = 0$ be the ground level from which the rocket was launched. Recall that the first derivative of displacement is velocity and that the first derivative of velocity is acceleration.

(a) Sketch a graph of the acceleration of the rocket as a function of time.

(b) Sketch a graph of the height of the rocket as a function of time.

(c) Let $v(t)$ be the function that gives the velocity of the rocket at time $t$. From the graph of the rocket's velocity, which is larger, $\left|\int_0^{t_2} v(t)dt\right|$ or $\left|\int_{t_2}^{t_3} v(t)dt\right|$? What do you know about the sign of $\int_0^{t_3} v(t)dt$? What does this mean physically?

(d) Write a story about what happened to the rocket. In particular, describe what could explain the features of the graphs of the height, velocity, and acceleration at times $t_1$, $t_2$, and $t_3$.

ANSWER:

(a)

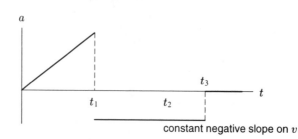

(b)

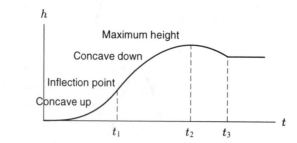

(c) The area under $v(t)$ from $t = 0$ to $t = t_2$ is <u>larger</u> than the area above $v(t)$ from $t = t_2$ to $t = t_3$. Therefore,

$$\left|\int_0^{t_2} v(t)dt\right| > \left|\int_{t_2}^{t_3} v(t)dt\right|$$

Since $\int_0^{t_2} v(t)dt > 0$ and $\int_{t_2}^{t_3} v(t)dt < 0$, we can conclude that

$$\int_0^{t_3} v(t)dt = \int_0^{t_2} v(t)dt + \int_{t_2}^{t_3} v(t)dt > 0$$

Because $\int_0^{t_3} v(t)dt$ is the height of the rocket after $t_3$ time units (and $h = $ (constant after time $t_3$), the rocket came to rest somewhere above the ground. (It landed on a roof, got caught in a tree, etc.)

(d) A possible explanation:

The engine on the rocket fired from $t = 0$ to $t = t_1$ yielding increasing upward acceleration (increasing probably because of less mass/less drag/etc.) At $t = t_1$, the engine stopped (ran out of fuel, perhaps), and there was constant negative acceleration (due to gravity) from $t = t_1$ to $t = t_3$. Since the velocity was still positive (upward) until time $t_2$, the rocket continued to ascend. At time $t = t_2$, it was at its maximum height ($v(t_2) = h'(t_2) = 0$). At time $t_3$, the velocity suddenly went to zero, implying the rocket hit something and stayed put thereafter. From part (c), whatever the rocket hit was above the level from which it was launched.

5. You decide to take a trip down a stretch of road that runs straight east and west. The following table gives your eastward velocity (in miles per minute) measured at one-minute intervals for the first ten minutes of your trip.

| Time (min) | 0 | 1 | 2 | 3 | 4 | 5 | 6 | 7 | 8 | 9 | 10 |
|---|---|---|---|---|---|---|---|---|---|---|---|
| Velocity (mi/min) | 0.00 | 0.53 | 0.90 | 1.13 | 1.20 | 1.13 | 0.90 | 0.53 | 0.00 | −0.68 | −1.50 |

(a) Sketch a graph of your velocity as a function of time, and give a description of what happened in words.

(b) Sketch a graph of your acceleration as a function of time. (This only needs to be a sketch. You don't have to calculate any values of acceleration.)

(c) Sketch a graph of your total eastward distance from your starting place as a function of time. (Again, this only needs to be a sketch.)

(d) What is your best estimate of the total eastward distance of your car from your starting position after ten minutes? You may do this by any means of your choosing, but explain your method.

ANSWER:

(a)

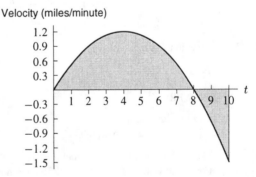

You begin driving east, increasing your speed for four minutes, when you reached a peak speed of 1.2 mi/min. During the next four minutes, you continued east, but began slowing down, and at eight minutes, you reversed direction and began going west.

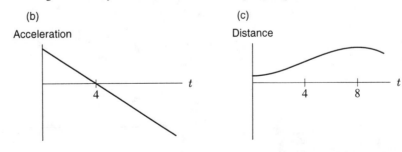

(d) The total distance can be represented as the area under the velocity function (geometric representation). Since the velocity graph looks like an upside down parabola, approximate it by $v(t) = kt(8 - t)$. When $t = 4, v = 1.2$, so $1.2 = 16k$. Thus $k = 0.075$. To find distance traveled, integrate from 0 to 10, as follows.'

$$\int_0^{10} 0.075t(8 - t)\, dt = 0.075 \cdot \left(4t^2 - \frac{t^3}{3}\right)\Big|_0^{10}$$

$$= 0.075 \cdot (400 - 333.3) \approx 5 \text{ miles}$$

## Problems and Solutions for Section 6.2

1. (a) Find the derivative of $\dfrac{x}{\sqrt{a^2 + x^2}}$. Be sure to simplify your answer as much as possible.

   (b) Use part (a) to find an antiderivative of $\dfrac{1}{(a^2 + x^2)^{\frac{3}{2}}}$.

   ANSWER:

   (a) Use the product rule (or the quotient rule):

   $$\frac{d}{dx}x(a^2 + x^2)^{-1/2} = (a^2 + x^2)^{-1/2} - \frac{1}{2}x(a^2 + x^2)^{-3/2}(2x)$$

   $$= (a^2 + x^2)^{-3/2}\left(a^2 + x^2 - x^2\right)$$

   $$= \frac{a^2}{(a^2 + x^2)^{3/2}}.$$

   (b) By part (a),

   $$\int \frac{a^2}{(a^2 + x^2)^{\frac{3}{2}}}\, dx = \frac{x}{\sqrt{a^2 + x^2}} + C$$

   $$\int \frac{1}{(a^2 + x^2)^{\frac{3}{2}}}\, dx = \frac{1}{a^2} \cdot \frac{x}{\sqrt{a^2 + x^2}} + C'.$$

2. Find a function $F$ such that:

   (a) $F'(x) = x^3 - \dfrac{1}{\sqrt{x}}$

   (b) $F'(x) = \sin x + \dfrac{1}{x}$

   ANSWER:

   (a) $F(x) = \frac{1}{4}x^4 - 2\sqrt{x} + C$

   (b) $F(x) = -\cos x + \ln|x| + C$

3. (a) Sketch the graphs of $y = e^x$ and $y = ex$.

   (b) For which values of $x$ is $e^x > ex$? Explain how you can be certain of your answer.

   (c) Find the average value of the difference between $e^x$ and $ex$ on the interval between $x = 0$ and $x = 2$.

   ANSWER:

   (a)

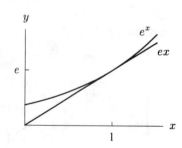

(b)   The equation of the tangent line of $y = e^x$ at $x = 1$ is $y - e^1 = e^1(x - 1)$, i.e. $y = ex$. Since $y'' = (e^x)'' = e^x > 0$ for all $x$, the graph is concave up for all $x$, and lies above its tangent line $y = ex$. Hence $e^x \geq ex$ for all $x$.

(c)   The average difference is given by

$$\frac{1}{2 - 0} \int_0^2 (e^x - ex)\,dx = \frac{1}{2}\left(e^x\Big|_0^2 - \frac{e}{2}x^2\Big|_0^2\right) = \frac{1}{2}(e^2 - 1 - 2e).$$

4.   Decide whether the following statement is true or false and provide a short explanation or counterexample.

An antiderivative of $2x\cos x$ is $x^2\sin x$.

ANSWER:

FALSE. The derivative of $x^2\sin x$ is $2x\sin x + x^2\cos x$, not $2x\cos x$.

5.   Find the total area bounded between the curve $f(x) = x^3 - 5x^2 + 4x$ and the $x$-axis.

ANSWER:

Since $x^3 - 5x^2 + 4x = x(x - 4)(x - 1)$, the roots of $f(x)$ are 0, 1, and 4. As the magnitude of $x$ gets large, for $x > 4$ and $x < 0$, $f(x)$ goes to $\infty$ and $-\infty$ respectively, and thus the area between $f(x)$ and the $x$-axis is unbounded in these regions.

Between $x = 0$ and $x = 1$, $f(x)$ is positive, and the area it bounds over this interval will be

$$\int_0^1 f(x)\,dx = \int_0^1 (x^3 - 5x^2 + 4x)\,dx$$

$$= \frac{x^4}{4} - \frac{5}{3}x^3 + 2x^2\Big|_0^1 \approx 0.5833.$$

Between $x = 1$ and $x = 4$, $f(x)$ drops below the $x$-axis, and the area it bounds over the interval will be:

$$-\int_1^4 f(x)\,dx = -\frac{x^4}{4} + \frac{5}{3}x^3 - 2x^2\Big|_1^4 \approx 11.2500.$$

Thus the total bounded area is $\approx 11.25 + 0.5833 = 11.8333$

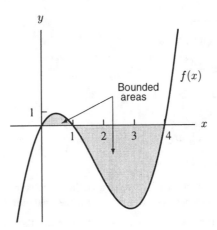

[Note that simply taking the integral $\int_0^4 f(x)\,dx$ does not give the area bounded by the curve $f(x)$, because area, as we have defined it, is a positive quantity. What we have done above is to calculate the area using $\int_0^4 |f(x)|\,dx$]

6. A factory is dumping pollutants into a lake continuously at the rate of $\dfrac{t^{\frac{2}{3}}}{60}$ tons per week, where $t$ is the time in weeks since the factory commenced operations.

(a) After one year of operation, how much pollutant has the factory dumped into the lake?

(b) Assume that natural processes can remove up to 0.15 ton of pollutant per week from the lake and that there was no pollution in the lake when the factory commenced operations one year ago. How many tons of pollutant have now accumulated in the lake? (Note: The amount of pollutant being dumped into the lake is never negative.)

ANSWER:

(a)

$$\text{amount dumped} = \int_0^{52\text{weeks}} \overbrace{\frac{1}{60}(t^{\frac{2}{3}})}^{\text{rate}} \overbrace{dt}^{\text{time}}$$

$$= \frac{1}{60} \cdot \frac{3}{5} t^{\frac{5}{3}} \Big|_0^{52}$$

$$= .01 t^{\frac{5}{3}} \Big|_0^{52} = .01(52)^{\frac{5}{3}} = 7.24 tons$$

(b) Natural processes will remove all pollutants until the dumping rate exceeds 0.15 tons/week. This will occur when $\dfrac{t^{\frac{2}{3}}}{60} = 0.15 \Rightarrow t = (9)^{\frac{3}{2}} = 27$ weeks. So we need to compute the difference between amount dumped and amount removed for the last 25 weeks of the year:

$$\int_{27}^{52} \left( \underbrace{\frac{1}{60}t^{\frac{2}{3}}}_{\substack{\text{dumping} \\ \text{rate}}} - \underbrace{0.15}_{\substack{\text{removal} \\ \text{rate}}} \right) dt = \left( .01 t^{\frac{5}{3}} - .15t \right) \Big|_{27}^{52}$$

$$= 1.06 tons$$

7. Find an antiderivative of each of the following functions.

(a) $\pi + x^2 + \dfrac{1}{\pi x^2}$

(b) $\sqrt{x} - \dfrac{1}{x\sqrt{x}}$

(c) $\cos(2\theta)$

(d) $e^t + e^3$

(e) $\dfrac{2}{x} + \dfrac{x}{2}$

ANSWER:

(a) $\pi x + \dfrac{x^3}{3} - \dfrac{x^{-1}}{\pi} + C$

(b) $\dfrac{2}{3} x^{\frac{3}{2}} + 2x^{-\frac{1}{2}} + C$

(c) $\dfrac{1}{2}\sin(2\theta) + C$

(d) $e^t + e^3 t + C$

(e) $2\ln|x| + \dfrac{x^2}{4} + C$

8. Suppose the rate at which ice in a skating pond is melting is given by $dV/dt = 4t + 2$, where $V$ is the volume of the ice in cubic feet, and $t$ is the time in minutes.

(a) Write a definite integral which represents the amount of ice that has melted in the first 4 minutes.

(b) Evaluate the definite integral in part (a).

ANSWER:

(a) Amount of ice melted in the first four minutes $= \displaystyle\int_0^4 \frac{dV}{dt}\, dt = \int_0^4 (4t + 2)\, dt.$

(b) $\displaystyle\int_0^4 (4t+2)\,dt = (2t^2 + 2t)\Big|_0^4 = 40 \text{ ft}^3.$

## Problems and Solutions for Section 6.3

1.  A car is going 80 feet per second and the driver puts on the brakes, bringing the car to a stop in 5 seconds. Assume the deceleration of the car is constant while the brakes are on.

    (a)  What is the acceleration (really deceleration) of the car?
    (b)  How far does the car travel from the time the brakes are applied until it stops?
    (c)  Suppose the car is traveling twice as fast and the brakes are applied with the same force as before. How far does the car travel before it stops?
    (d)  Suppose the brakes are twice as strong (can stop the car twice as fast). How far does the car travel if its speed is 80 feet per second? How far if its speed is 160 feet per second?

    ANSWER:

    (a)  Using $v = v_0 + at$, where $v_0 = 80$ ft/sec, we can find $a$ by using the condition that $v = 0$ when $t = 5$. So since $0 = 80 + 5a$, $a = -16\text{ft/sec}^2$.
    (b)  Remember that distance traveled is the integral of velocity with respect to time. So

    $$d = \int_0^5 (80 - 16t)\,dt = 80t - 8t^2 \Big|_0^5$$
    $$= 400 - 200 = 200 \text{ ft}.$$

    (c)  Now, $v_0 = 2 \cdot 80 = 160$, so $v = 160 - 16t$. The car will come to a stop when $t = 10$. So

    $$d = \int_0^{10} (160 - 16t)\,dt = 160t - 8t^2 \Big|_0^{10}$$
    $$= 1600 - 800 = 800 \text{ ft}.$$

    (This is four times as great as the prior stopping distance.)
    (d)  If the brakes are twice as strong, then the deceleration will be twice as great, so $v = 80 - 32t$. The car will come to a stop when $v = 0$, that is, when $t = 80/32 = 2.5$ sec. So

    $$d = \int_0^{2.5} (80 - 32t)\,dt = 80t - 16t^2 \Big|_0^{2.5}$$
    $$= 200 - 100 = 100 \text{ ft}.$$

    Finally, if $v_0 = 160$, then $v = 160 - 32t$; the car will come to a stop when $t = 5$. So

    $$d = \int_0^5 (160 - 32t)\,dt = 160t - 16t^2 \Big|_0^5$$
    $$= 800 - 400 = 400 \text{ ft}.$$

2.  A ball is dropped from a window 100 feet above the ground. Assume that its acceleration is $a(t) = -32 \text{ ft/sec}^2$ for $t \geq 0$.

    (a)  Find the velocity of the ball as a function of time $t$.
    (b)  Find its height above the ground as a function of time $t$.
    (c)  After how many seconds does it hit the ground?

    ANSWER:

    (a)  Let $v(t)$ be the velocity of the ball as a function of time $t$. $\dfrac{d(v(t))}{dt} = a(t) = -32$. Integrating $a(t)$ gives $v(t) = -32t + C$. When $t = 0$, we know that $v(0) = 0$, so $C = 0$. Hence $v(t) = -32t$ ft/sec.

(b) Let $s(t)$ be the height above the ground as a function of time $t$. $\dfrac{d(s(t))}{dt} = v(t) = -32t$. Integrating $v(t)$ yields $s(t) = -16t^2 + C$. Since $s(0) = 100$, we get $C = 100$. Thus, $s(t) = -16t^2 + 100$ feet.

(c) The ball lands when $s(t) = 0$. Set $s(t) = -16t^2 + 100 = 0$ to obtain:

$$16t^2 = 100$$
$$t = \frac{5}{2} \text{ sec.}$$

[Note that we discard the root $t = -\frac{5}{2}$ sec as not physically meaningful.]

Thus, the ball hits the ground after 2.5 seconds.

3. On planet Janet the gravitational constant $g$ is $-15$ feet per second per second: that is, for every second an object falls it picks up an extra 15 feet per second of velocity downward. A ball is thrown upward at time $t = 0$ at 60 feet per second.

    *from ground level*

(a) When does the ball reach the peak of its flight?

(b) Find the peak height of the ball by giving equations for the ball's acceleration $a$, then its velocity $v$ (including computation of the antidifferentiation constant $C$), then its position $s$.

(c) Find the peak height instead by left and right sums for $v(t)$. (First give a table of values for $v$.)

(d) Find the peak height instead by graphing $v$ versus $t$ and recalling how distance traveled is related to the graph of velocity.

(e) On planet Nanette, $g$ is $\frac{1}{3}$ as great as on Janet. Use the method in Part (d) to find the peak height (same initial velocity of 60 feet per second.)

ANSWER:

(a) The ball reaches its peak when the velocity is 0. $\frac{dv}{dt} = -15$, so $v = -15t + C$, but the initial velocity $v(0) = 60$ so $C = 60$. Since $v(t) = -15t + 60$ is 0 when $t = 4$, the ball reaches its peak after 4 seconds.

(b) Since $a = -15$ and $v = -15t + 60$, we have

$$s(t) = \int_0^t v(x)\, dx = -\frac{15}{2}t^2 + 60t + C.$$

Since the ball is thrown from the ground level, $C = 0$. The peak height, occurring at $t = 4$, is therefore $s(4) = -15\frac{t^2}{2} + 60t \Big|_0^4 = 120$ ft.

(c)

| $t$ | 0 | 1 | 2 | 3 | 4 |
|---|---|---|---|---|---|
| $v(t)$ | 60 | 45 | 30 | 15 | 0 |

A left-hand sum is LEFT(4) $= 60 + 45 + 30 + 15 = 150$ ft., and the corresponding right-hand sum is RIGHT(4) $= 45 + 30 + 15 + 0 = 90$ ft., with $\Delta t = 1$ sec. These sums approximate the integral of the velocity of the ball, which is the the distance it travels.

(d) The distance traveled equals the area under the graph of velocity between $t = 0$ and $t = 4$. Since the area is just that of a triangle, it is equal to $bh/2 = 4(60)/2 = 120$ ft. See Figure 6.3.11.

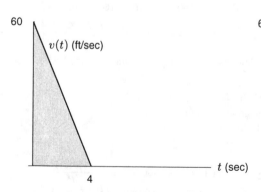

Figure 6.3.11: Ball on Planet Janet

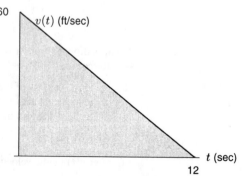

Figure 6.3.12: Ball on Planet Nanette

(e)   On Nanette, $v = 60 - 5t$, and so the ball will reach its peak at $t = 12$. The area under the curve is thus $12(60)/2 = 360$ ft., so the peak height is 360 ft. See Figure 6.3.12

4.   A ball is thrown vertically upwards from the top of a 320-foot cliff with initial velocity of 128 feet per second. Find:

(a)   how long it takes to reach its peak;
(b)   its maximum height;
(c)   how long it takes until impact;
(d)   the velocity upon impact.

   ANSWER:

   Taking upwards as the positive direction, the velocity of the ball is $v(t) = v_0 + at = 128 - 32t$, so the displacement (which is the integral of velocity) is $s(t) = \int v(t)\, dt = 128t - 16t^2 + C$. Since $s(0) = 320$, $C = 320$ and $s(t) = 128t - 16t^2 + 320$.

(a)   The peak is reached when the velocity is zero:

$$128 - 32t = 0$$
$$t = 4 \text{ s.}$$

(b)   $s(4) = 576$ ft.
(c)   The ball hits the ground at the base of the cliff when $s(t) = 0$:

$$128t - 16t^2 + 320 = 0$$
$$t^2 - 8t - 20 = 0$$
$$t = -2, 10.$$

   We discard the meaningless negative root and conclude that the ball lands after 10 seconds.
(d)   $v(10) = -192$ ft/sec. (That is, 192 ft/sec downwards.)

5.   Assuming the 440 feet is accurate and you neglect air resistance, determine the accuracy of the following paragraph:

### MY JOURNEY BENEATH THE EARTH

*Condensed from "A Wolverine is Eating My Leg"*

   Tim Cahill:
   I am in Ellison's Cave, about to rappel down Incredible Pit, the second-deepest cave pit in the continental United States. The drop is 440 feet, about what you'd experience from the top of a 40-story building. If you took the shaft in a free fall, you'd accelerate to more than 100 miles an hour and then—about five seconds into the experience—you'd decelerate to zero. And die.

   ANSWER:

   Assuming that depth is the positive number that gives the distance below the Earth's surface, and that $g = 32$ ft/sec$^2$, we have $v(t) = 32t$ since $v(0) = 0$, and $d(t) = 16t^2$ since $d(0) = 0$.

   When $d = 440$, we have $t^2 = \frac{440}{16} = 27.5$, so $t \approx 5.24$ sec. The maximum speed reached will occur at the bottom of the cave, where $t \approx 5.24$, so $v_{max} \approx 32 \cdot 5.24 \approx 168$ ft/sec. Converting this to mph, we get 168 ft/sec $\cdot$ 3600 sec/hour $\cdot \frac{1}{5280}$ miles/foot $\approx 115$ mph. The paragraph is accurate!

6.   (a)   A function $g$ is known to be linear on the interval from $-\infty$ to 2 (inclusive) and also linear on the interval from 2 to $\infty$ (again inclusive.) Furthermore, $g(1) = 2$, $g(2) = 0$, $g(4) = 8$. What are $g(0), g(3)$?
   (b)   Another function $f$ satisfies $f(0) = 0$ and $f' = g$. What are $f(2), f(3)$?
   (c)   Give formulas that express $f(t)$ directly in terms of $t$.
   ANSWER:

(a)   For $x \leq 2$, $g$ is of the form $g(x) = mx + b$, because $g$ is linear. The equations $g(1) = m + b = 2$ and $g(2) = 2m + b = 0$ give $m = -2$, $b = 4$ so $g(x) = -2x + 4$ when $x \leq 2$. Using a similar method for $x \geq 2$ with the points $(2, 0)$ and $(4, 8)$, we get $g(x) = 4x - 8$ for $x \geq 2$. Thus,

$$g(0) = -2(0) + 4 = 4$$
$$g(3) = 4(3) - 8 = 4.$$

(b) For $x \leq 2$, $f(x) = \displaystyle\int g(x)\,dx = -x^2 + 4x + C$. Since $f(0) = 0$, $f(x) = -x^2 + 4x$ for $x \leq 2$.

For $x \geq 2$, $f(x) = \displaystyle\int g(x)\,dx = 2x^2 - 8x + C$. From the work we've just done, we know that

$f(2) = -(2)^2 + 4(2) = 4$, so since $f(2) = 4 = 2(2)^2 - 8(2) + C$, we know that $C = 12$. Thus, $f(3) = 2(3)^2 - 8(3) + 12 = 6$.

(c) $f(t) = -t^2 + 4t$ for $t < 2$; $f(t) = 2t^2 - 8t + 12$ for $t \geq 2$.

7. The police observe that the skidmarks made by a stopping car are 200 ft long. Assuming the car decelerated at a constant rate of 20 ft/sec$^2$, skidding all the way, how fast was the car going when the brakes were applied?

ANSWER:

We are given that $\frac{dv}{dt} = -20$ so, integrating, $v = v_0 - 20t$, where $v_0$ is the speed when the brakes were first applied. Integrating this to get an expression for distance, we have $s = s_0 + v_0 t - 10t^2$. $s_0 = 0$ since we start measuring distance from the place the brakes were first applied. When $v = 0$, $t = \frac{v_0}{20}$, and

$s = 200$ so $200 = \frac{v_0^2}{20} - 10\frac{v_0^2}{400}$ so $v_0 = \sqrt{200 \cdot 40} = 89.44$ ft/sec.

## Problems and Solutions for Section 6.4

1. For $-1 \leq x \leq 1$, define

$$F(x) = \int_{-1}^{x} \sqrt{1 - t^2}\,dt.$$

(a) What does $F(1)$ represent geometrically?
(b) What is the value of $F(-1)$? $F(0)$?
(c) Find $F'(x)$.

ANSWER:

(a) $F(1)$ represents the area bounded by $y = \sqrt{1 - x^2}$ and $y = 0$ between $x = -1$ and $x = 1$, which is really the area of a semicircle of radius 1.

(b)

$$F(-1) = \int_{-1}^{-1} \sqrt{1 - t^2}\,dt = 0.$$

$$F(0) = \int_{-1}^{0} \sqrt{1 - t^2}\,dt$$

$$= \int_{0}^{1} \sqrt{1 - u^2}\,du \quad (\text{substitute } u = -t)$$

$$= \frac{1}{2}\left( u\sqrt{1 - u^2}\,\Big|_{0}^{1} + \int_{0}^{1} \frac{1}{\sqrt{1 - u^2}}\,du \right) \quad (\text{using integral table})$$

$$= \frac{1}{2}\left( u\sqrt{1 - u^2}\,\Big|_{0}^{1} + \arcsin u\,\Big|_{0}^{1} \right) \quad (\text{again using integral table})$$

$$= \frac{1}{2}\left( 0 + \frac{\pi}{2} \right)$$

$$= \frac{\pi}{4}.$$

Note that this is $\dfrac{1}{4}$ the area of a circle, radius 1.

(c) Using the Fundamental Theorem, $F'(x)$ will simply be $\sqrt{1 - x^2}$.

2. Evaluate each of the following:

(a) $\displaystyle \int (x^2 + e^{3x})(x^3 + e^{3x})^{\frac{4}{5}}\, dx$

(b) $\displaystyle \int \frac{\cos(\ln x)\,dx}{x}$

(c) $\displaystyle \int \frac{8e^{-2w}}{6 - 5e^{-2w}}\, dw$

(d) $\displaystyle \frac{d}{dx} \int_e^x \log_5\left(t^{21}\right) \sin(\sqrt{t})\, dt.$

ANSWER:

(a) Substitute $w = x^3 + e^{3x}$, and $dw = (3x^2 + 3e^{3x})\,dx$; then the integral becomes

$$\frac{1}{3} \int w^{4/5}\, dw = \frac{5}{27} w^{9/5} + C = \frac{5}{27}(x^3 + e^{3x})^{9/5} + C.$$

(b) Substitute $w = \ln x$ and $dw = \frac{1}{x}dx$. Then the integral becomes

$$\int \cos w\, dw = \sin w + C = \sin(\ln x) + C.$$

(c) Set $u = 6 - 5e^{-2w}$ and $du = 10e^{-2w}\, dw$. The integral becomes

$$\frac{4}{5} \int \frac{du}{u} = \frac{4}{5} \ln|u| + C = \frac{4}{5} \ln|6 - 5e^{-2w}| + C.$$

(d) Let $\log_5(t^{21}) \sin \sqrt{t}$ be the derivative of some function $f(t)$. Then we have:

$$\frac{d}{dx} \int_e^x \log_5(t^{21}) \sin \sqrt{t}\, dt = \frac{d}{dx} \int_e^x f'(t)\, dt$$

$$= \frac{d}{dx}\left(f(t)\Big|_e^x\right)$$

$$= \frac{d}{dx}\left(f(x) - f(e)\right)$$

But $f(e)$ is just a constant, so we have

$$\frac{d}{dx}\left(f(x) - f(e)\right) = \frac{d}{dx} f(x) = f'(x) = \log_5(x^{21}) \sin \sqrt{x}$$

3. Given below is the graph of a function $f$.

(a) Draw a graph of $f'$, the derivative of $f$.

(b) Draw a graph of $\displaystyle \int_0^x f(t)\, dt.$

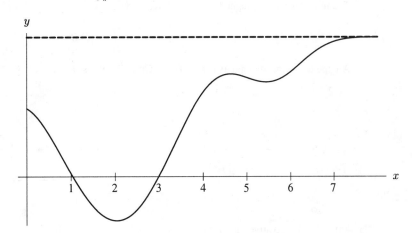

ANSWER:

(a)
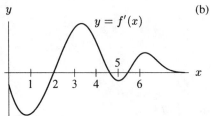
$y = f'(x)$

(b)
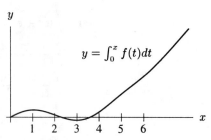
$y = \int_0^x f(t)dt$

4.  Given the graph of $f$ below, draw a graph of the function $\int_0^x f(t)\, dt$.

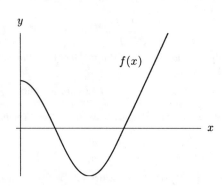

$f(x)$

ANSWER:

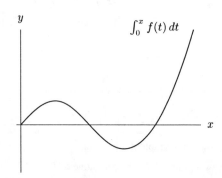

$\int_0^x f(t)\, dt$

5.  The function $f(t)$ is graphed below and we define

$$F(x) = \int_0^x f(t)dt.$$

Are the following statements true or false? Give a brief justification of your answer.

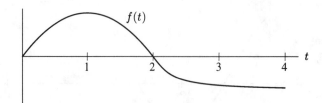

$f(t)$

(a)  $F(x)$ is positive for all $x$ between 2 and 3.

(b)  $F(x)$ is decreasing for all $x$ between 1 and 3.

(c)  $F(x)$ is concave down for $x = \dfrac{1}{2}$.

ANSWER:

(a)  **True**. Although $f(t)$ is negative there, the area below the curve (between 2 and 3) is so much smaller than the area between 0 and 2 that the integral $\displaystyle\int_0^x f(t)\,dt = \underbrace{\int_0^2 f(t)\,dt}_{\text{large } +} + \underbrace{\int_2^x f(t)\,dt}_{\text{small } -}$ is

positive for $2 \le x \le 3$.

(b)  **False**. $F$ is increasing $1 \le x \le 2$, because $f$ is positive there.
$F$ is decreasing $2 \le x \le 3$ because $f$ is negative there.

(c)  **False**. At $x = \dfrac{1}{2}$, $F' = f$ is increasing so $F$ is concave up.

6.  Let $F(x) = \displaystyle\int_0^x \sin t\,dt$, and $G(x) = \displaystyle\int_0^x \sin^2 t\,dt$ and consider the quantities

$$G\left(\frac{\pi}{2}\right), \qquad F(\pi), \qquad G(\pi), \qquad F(2\pi).$$

(a)  Show how each quantity can be represented on a graph.

(b)  Use the graph to rank these quantities in ascending (i.e., increasing) order.

ANSWER:

(a)

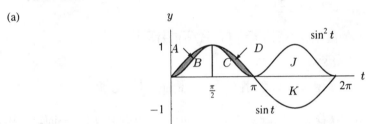

**Figure 6.4.13**

In the above graph, divide the area under the curves into regions $A, B, C, D, J,$ and $K,$ with positive area. We can now see that

$$G(\frac{\pi}{2}) = B$$
$$F(\pi) = A + B + C + D$$
$$G(\pi) = B + C$$
$$F(2\pi) = A + B + C + D - K$$

(b)  $A + B + C + D = K$, so $F(2\pi) = 0$. Therefore,

$$F(2\pi) < G(\frac{\pi}{2}) < G(\pi) < F(\pi).$$

# Chapter 7 Exam Questions

## Problems and Solutions for Section 7.1

1. Evaluate the following indefinite integrals:

   (a) $\int 4x^5\, dx$    (b) $\int \dfrac{x^2 - x + 1}{x}\, dx$    (c) $\int e^x \cos(e^x)\, dx$

   ANSWER:

   (a) $\displaystyle\int 4x^5\, dx = \frac{2}{3}x^6 + C.$

   (b) $\displaystyle\int \frac{x^2 - x + 1}{x}\, dx = \int \left(x - 1 + \frac{1}{x}\right) dx = \frac{x^2}{2} - x + \ln|x| + C.$

   (c) Let $u = e^x$, $du = e^x\, dx$. Substituting, we get

   $$\int \cos(e^x)e^x\, dx = \int \cos u\, du = \sin u + C = \sin(e^x) + C.$$

2. Find antiderivatives of the following functions:

   (a) $x^2 - \dfrac{3}{x} + \dfrac{2}{x^3}$

   (b) $\left(x + \sqrt{\sin(2x) + 3}\right)\left(x - \sqrt{\sin(2x) + 3}\right)$

   ANSWER:

   (a) $\displaystyle\int \left(x^2 - \frac{3}{x} + \frac{2}{x^3}\right) dx = \frac{x^3}{3} - 3\ln|x| - \frac{1}{x^2} + C.$

   (b) $\displaystyle\int (x + \sqrt{\sin(2x + 3)})(x - \sqrt{\sin(2x + 3)})\, dx = \int (x^2 - \sin(2x + 3))\, dx = \frac{x^3}{3} + \frac{1}{2}\cos(2x + 3) + C.$

## Problems and Solutions for Section 7.2

1. Compute:

   (a) $\displaystyle\int_{-R}^{R} \frac{\sin x}{1 + x^4}\, dx$

   (b) $\displaystyle\int_{0}^{R} \frac{1}{(4 + x)^2}\, dx$

   ANSWER:

   (a) Since $\dfrac{\sin x}{1 + x^4}$ is an odd function, the integral from $-R$ to $R$ is zero.

   (b)

   $$\int_{0}^{R} \frac{1}{(4 + x)^2}\, dx$$

   $$= -\frac{1}{4 + x}\bigg|_{0}^{R} = -\frac{1}{4 + R} - \left(-\frac{1}{4}\right)$$

   $$= \frac{1}{4} - \frac{1}{4 + R}$$

**Problems and Solutions for Section 7.3** ━━━━━━━━━━

1. Find the following indefinite integrals:

   (a) $\int e^{-0.5t}\sin 2t\,dt$

   (b) $\int (\ln x)^2 dx$ (Hint: Integrate by parts.)

   ANSWER:

   (a) $\int e^{-\frac{t}{2}}\sin 2t\,dt$; use formula #8 from the table with $a = -\frac{1}{2}, b = 2$:

   $$\int e^{-\frac{t}{2}}\sin 2t\,dt = \frac{1}{\frac{1}{4}+4}e^{-\frac{t}{2}}\left(-\frac{1}{2}\sin 2t - 2\cos 2t\right) + C$$
   $$= -\frac{4}{17}e^{-\frac{t}{2}}\left(\frac{1}{2}\sin 2t + 2\cos 2t\right) + C$$

   (b) $\int (\ln x)^2 dx$.

   Let $u = (\ln x)^2$. Then $du = \dfrac{2\ln x}{x}dx$.
   Let $dv = dx$. Then $v = x$.

   $$\int u\,dv = uv - \int v\,du \Rightarrow \int (\ln x)^2 dx = x(\ln x)^2 - \int x\left(\frac{2\ln x}{x}\right)dx$$
   $$= x(\ln x)^2 - \int 2\ln x\,dx, \text{ use #4 from the table for } \int \ln x\,dx:$$
   $$= x(\ln x)^2 - 2[x\ln x - x] + C = x(\ln x)^2 - 2x\ln x + 2x + C$$

2. Calculate the following integrals:

   (a) $\int \sec^2\theta\,d\theta \quad \left[\text{Note: } \sec\theta = \dfrac{1}{\cos\theta}\right]$

   (b) $\int ze^{3z^2+1}\,dz$

   (c) $\int y\sec^2 y\,dy$

   (d) $\int \dfrac{dt}{1+\sqrt{t}}$

   (e) $\int \dfrac{dx}{(b+ax)^2} \quad a, b \text{ constants}$

   ANSWER:

   (a) $\int \sec^2\theta\,d\theta = \tan\theta + C$ (since $\dfrac{d}{d\theta}\tan\theta = \sec^2\theta$).

   (b) Let $w = 3z^2 + 1$. Then $dw = 6z\,dz$ so $z\,dz = dw/6$. Then

   $$\int ze^{3z^2+1}\,dz = \frac{1}{6}\int e^w\,dw$$
   $$= \frac{1}{6}e^w + C$$
   $$= \frac{1}{6}e^{3z^2+1} + C.$$

(c) Let $u = y$, $v' = \sec^2 y$, $u' = 1$, $v = \tan y$. Then, through integration by parts,

$$\int y \sec^2 y \, dy = y \tan y - \int \tan y \, dy = y \tan y - \int \frac{\sin y}{\cos y} \, dy$$

$$= y \tan y + \ln|\cos y| + C. \quad (\text{Set } z = \cos y, \, dz = \sin y \, dy.)$$

(d) Let $u = 1 + \sqrt{t}$. Then $(u - 1)^2 = t$ so $2(u - 1) \, du = dt$. Then

$$\int \frac{dt}{1 + \sqrt{t}} = 2 \int \left( \frac{u - 1}{u} \right) du$$

$$= 2 \int \left( 1 - \frac{1}{u} \right) du$$

$$= 2u - 2 \ln|u| + C$$

$$= 2(1 + \sqrt{t}) - 2 \ln(1 + \sqrt{t}) + C.$$

(e) Let $u = b + ax$. Then $du = a \, dx$ so $dx = \dfrac{du}{a}$. Then

$$\int \frac{dx}{(b + ax)^2} = \frac{1}{a} \int \frac{du}{u^2}$$

$$= -\frac{1}{a} u^{-1} + C$$

$$= -\frac{1}{a(b + ax)} + C.$$

3. For each of the functions $f(x)$ below, find a function $F(x)$ with the property that $F'(x) = f(x)$ and also $F(0) = 0$.

(a) $f(x) = x \cdot \sin(2x)$
(b) $f(x) = x^2 \cdot e^{2x}$
(c) $f(x) = x^2 \cdot (4 + x^3)^{10}$

ANSWER:

(a) By Table #15, $(p(x) = x, a = 2)$

$$\int x \sin(2x) dx = -\frac{1}{2} x \cos(2x) + \frac{1}{4} \sin(2x) + C$$

(or by parts with $u = x$, $dv = \sin(2x)dx$)), we get $du = dx$, $v = -\frac{\cos 2x}{2}$

$F(x)$ is of the form $-\dfrac{1}{2} x \cos(2x) + \dfrac{1}{4} \sin(2x) + C$

$F(0) = 0$ implies $0 = F(0) = -\dfrac{1}{2} 0 \cos(2 \cdot 0) + \dfrac{1}{4} \sin(2 \cdot 0) + C = C$. Therefore

$$F(x) = -\frac{1}{2} x \cos(2x) + \frac{1}{4} \sin(2x)$$

(b) By Table #15, $(p(x) = x^2, a = 2)$

$$\int x^2 e^{2x} dx = \frac{1}{2} e^{2x} \cdot x^2 - \frac{1}{4} e^{2x} \cdot 2x + \frac{1}{8} e^{2x} \cdot 2 + C = F(x)$$

$$0 = F(0) = \frac{1}{4} + C, \text{ so } C = -\frac{1}{4}$$

$$F(x) = e^{2x} \left( \frac{1}{2} x^2 - \frac{1}{2} x + \frac{1}{4} \right) - \frac{1}{4}$$

(or use by parts two times, starting with $u = x^2$, $v' = e^{2x}$).

(c) $\displaystyle\int x^2 (4 + x^3)^{10} dx$; use substitution with $w = x^3 + 4$, $\dfrac{dw}{dx} = 3x^2$

$$\int x^2 (4 + x^3)^{10} \, dx = \int w^{10} \frac{dw}{3} = \frac{1}{33} w^{11} + C = \frac{1}{33} (4 + x^2)^{11} + C = F(x)$$

$$0 = F(0) = \frac{1}{33}(4-0)^{11} + C = \frac{4^{11}}{33} + C \Rightarrow C = -\frac{4^{11}}{33}$$

Therefore $F(x) = \frac{1}{33}\left[(4+x^2)^{11} - 4^{11}\right]$

4. Integrate:

(a) $\displaystyle\int \frac{x^3+1}{x^2}\,dx$

(b) $\displaystyle\int_0^2 \frac{x^2}{x^3+1}\,dx$

(c) $\displaystyle\int \frac{\sqrt{\ln x}}{x}\,dx$

(d) $\displaystyle\int \sin(3x)e^{\cos 3x}\,dx$

ANSWER:

(a)
$$\int \frac{x^3+1}{x^2}\,dx = \int \left(x + \frac{1}{x^2}\right)\,dx = \frac{x^2}{2} - \frac{1}{x} + C$$

(b) Set $u = x^3 + 1$, $du = 3x^2\,dx$, to get:
$$\int_0^2 \frac{x^2}{x^3+1}\,dx = \frac{1}{3}\int_1^9 \frac{du}{u} = \frac{1}{3}\ln|u|\bigg|_1^9 = \frac{1}{3}\ln 9 \approx 0.7324.$$

(c) Set $u = \ln x$, $du = 1/x\,dx$, to get:
$$\int \frac{\sqrt{\ln x}}{x}\,dx = \int \sqrt{u}\,du = \frac{2}{3}u^{\frac{3}{2}} + C = \frac{2}{3}(\ln x)^{\frac{3}{2}} + C.$$

(d) Set $u = \cos 3x$, $du = -3\sin 3x\,dx$, to get:
$$\int \sin(3x)e^{\cos(3x)}\,dx = -\frac{1}{3}\int e^u\,du = -\frac{1}{3}e^u + C = -\frac{1}{3}e^{\cos(3x)} + C.$$

5. Find the following integrals. Show your work.

(a) $\displaystyle\int \left(\frac{1}{x+1} - \frac{1}{(x+1)^2}\right)\,dx$

(b) $\displaystyle\int x\cos 2x\,dx$

ANSWER:

(a) We substitute $y = x + 1$, $dy = dx$, giving
$$\int \frac{1}{y}\,dy - \int \frac{1}{y^2}\,dy = \ln|y| + \frac{1}{y} + C = \ln|x+1| + \frac{1}{x+1} + C.$$

(b) Integrating by parts with $u = x$, $v' = \cos 2x$,
$$\int x\cos 2x\,dx = \frac{1}{2}x\sin 2x - \int \frac{1}{2}\sin 2x\,dx = \frac{1}{2}x\sin 2x + \frac{1}{4}\cos 2x + C.$$

## Problems and Solutions for Section 7.4

1. Use the table of antiderivatives to evaluate each of the following:

(a) $\displaystyle\int \frac{dx}{x^2 - 6x + 10}$

(b) $\displaystyle\int \frac{dx}{\sqrt{x^2 - 6x + 10}}$

(c) $\displaystyle\int \frac{x^2}{x^2 + 5}\,dx$

(d) $\displaystyle\int \frac{dt}{\sqrt{9 - 5t^2}}$

(e) $\displaystyle\int e^{4x}\cos 3x\,dx$

ANSWER:

(a)

$$\int \frac{dx}{x^2 - 6x + 10} = \int \frac{dx}{(x-3)^2 + 1}$$

Let $u = x - 3$, $du = dx$, to obtain:

$$\int \frac{dx}{(x-3)^2 + 1} = \int \frac{du}{u^2 + 1}$$
$$= \arctan u + C$$
$$= \arctan(x - 3) + C.$$

(b)

$$\int \frac{dx}{\sqrt{x^2 - 6x + 10}} = \int \frac{dx}{\sqrt{(x-3)^2 + 1}}$$

Let $u = x - 3$, $du = dx$, to obtain:

$$\int \frac{dx}{\sqrt{(x-3)^2 + 1}} = \int \frac{du}{\sqrt{u^2 + 1}}$$
$$= \int \ln|u + \sqrt{u^2 + 1}| + C$$
$$= \int \ln|x - 3 + \sqrt{(x-3)^2 + 1}| + C.$$

(c)

$$\int \frac{x^2}{x^2 + 5}\, dx = \int \frac{x^2 + 5 - 5}{x^2 + 5}\, dx$$
$$= \int \left(1 - \frac{5}{x^2 + 5}\right) dx$$
$$= x - \sqrt{5}\arctan \frac{x}{\sqrt{5}} + C.$$

(d)

$$\int \frac{dt}{\sqrt{9 - 5t^2}} = \int \frac{dt}{\sqrt{5(\frac{9}{5} - t^2)}}$$
$$= \frac{1}{\sqrt{5}} \int \frac{dt}{\sqrt{\frac{9}{5} - t^2}}$$
$$= \frac{1}{\sqrt{5}} \arcsin\left(\frac{t}{\frac{3}{\sqrt{5}}}\right) + C$$
$$= \frac{1}{\sqrt{5}} \arcsin \frac{t\sqrt{5}}{3} + C.$$

(e)

$$\int e^{4x} \cos 3x\, dx = \frac{1}{4^2 + 3^2} e^{4x}(4\cos 3x + 3\sin 3x) + C$$
$$= \frac{1}{25} e^{4x}(4\cos 3x + 3\sin 3x) + C.$$

2.  Find the following indefinite integrals:

    (a) $\displaystyle\int \frac{1}{x^2 + x - 6}\,dx$

    (b) $\displaystyle\int \cos^3 \beta\, d\beta$

    ANSWER:

    (a) $\displaystyle\int \frac{1}{(x^2 + x - 6)}\,dx = \int \frac{1}{(x+3)(x-2)}\,dx$

    From the table on p. 362, use #26 with $a = -3$, $b = 2$.

    $-\dfrac{1}{5}(\ln|x + 3| - \ln|x - 2|) + C$

    (b) $\displaystyle\int \cos^3 \beta\, d\beta$

    Use #18 from the table: $= \dfrac{1}{3}\cos^2 \beta\, \sin \beta + \dfrac{2}{3}\displaystyle\int \cos \beta\, d\beta + \text{constant}$

    $\dfrac{1}{3}\cos^2 \beta\, \sin \beta + \dfrac{2}{3}\sin \beta + C$

3.  Consider the semicircle of radius 3 pictured below.

    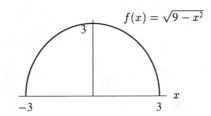

    $f(x) = \sqrt{9 - x^2}$

    (a) Write a definite integral in terms of $f(x)$ that gives the area of the semicircle.
    (b) Based solely on your knowledge of *geometry*, what is the value of this definite integral?
    (c) Evaluate the indefinite integral.
    (d) Find the area of the semicircle by substituting the limits, then compare this result with your answer in Part (b).

    ANSWER:

    (a) $\displaystyle\int_{-3}^{3} \sqrt{(9 - x^2)}\,dx$

    (b) $\dfrac{1}{2} \cdot \pi r^2 = \dfrac{9}{2} \cdot \pi$

    (c) Use #30 with $a = 3$:

    $$\int \sqrt{(9 - x^2)}\,dx = \frac{1}{2} \cdot \left[ x\sqrt{(9 - x^2)} + 9 \cdot \int \frac{1}{\sqrt{(9x^2 + x - 6)}}\,dx \right] + \text{constant}$$

    To integrate this integral, use #28 with $a = 3$:

    $$= \frac{1}{2} \cdot \left[ x\sqrt{(9 - x^2)} + 9\arcsin\left(\frac{x}{3}\right) \right] + C$$

    (d) $\dfrac{1}{2} \cdot \left[ x\sqrt{(9 - x^2)} + 9\arcsin\left(\dfrac{x}{3}\right) \right]\Big|_{-3}^{3} = \dfrac{9}{2} \cdot [\arcsin(1) - \arcsin(-1)]$

    $$= \frac{9}{2} \cdot \frac{\pi}{2} - \frac{9}{2} \cdot \left(-\frac{\pi}{2}\right) = \frac{9}{2} \cdot \pi$$

4.  Calculate the following integrals.

    (a) $\int \cos(7\theta)\,d\theta$

    (b) $\displaystyle\int \frac{e^x}{1 + e^{2x}}\,dx$

(c) $\displaystyle\int \frac{t+5}{t^2+10t+77}dt$

(d) $\displaystyle\int \frac{2dx}{x^2+4x+3}$

(e) $\int \sin\left(\sqrt{y}\right)dy$

ANSWER:

(a) Set $u=7\theta$ so $\dfrac{du}{7}=d\theta$ i.e. $\displaystyle\int \cos(7\theta)d\theta = \frac{1}{7}\int \cos u\,du = \frac{1}{7}\sin(7\theta)+C.$

(b) Set $u=e^x$ so $du=e^x dx$ i.e. $\displaystyle\int \frac{e^x}{1+e^{2x}} = \int \frac{1}{1+u^2} = \tan^{-1}(e^x)+C.$

(c) Set $u=t^2+10t+77$ so $du=2(t+5)dt$ i.e. $\dfrac{du}{2}=(t+5)dt$. Hence

$$\int \frac{t+5}{t^2+10t+77}dt = \frac{1}{2}\int \frac{1}{u}du = \frac{1}{2}\ln|t^2+10t+77|+C.$$

(d) Notice that $x^2+4x+3 = x^2+4x+4-1 = (x+2)^2-1$. Letting $u=x+2$, $du=dx$ we get

$$\int \frac{2dx}{x^2+4x+3} = \int \frac{2dx}{(x+2)^2-1} = 2\int \frac{1}{u^2-1}du = 2\int \frac{1}{(u-1)(u+1)}du$$
$$= 2\int \frac{du}{(u-1)(u-(-1))}.$$

By the tables (or by decomposing into partial fractions!), the last integral equals ($a=1,b=-1$):

$$\int \frac{du}{(u-1)(u-(-1))} = 2\frac{1}{1-(-1)}\left(\ln|u-1|-\ln|u+1|\right)+C,$$

or, going back to $x$,

$$\int \frac{2dx}{x^2+4x+3} = \ln|x+1|-\ln|x+3|+C.$$

(e) Let $x=\sqrt{y}$ so $dx = \dfrac{1}{2\sqrt{y}}dy$ or $2\sqrt{y}dx = dy$. But since $\sqrt{y}=x$, we have $dy=2x\,dx$ so $\int \sin\left(\sqrt{y}\right)dy = 2\int x\sin(x)dx$. Integrating by parts with $u=x$, $u'=1$, $v'=\sin x$, $v=-\cos x$ gives

$$2\int x\sin x\,dx = 2\left[-x\cos x + \int \cos x\,dx\right] = 2(\sin x - x\cos x)+C,$$

or

$$\int \sin\sqrt{y}\,dy = 2\left(\sin\sqrt{y}-\sqrt{y}\cos\sqrt{y}\right)+C.$$

## Problems and Solutions for Section 7.5

1. The following are some of the values for a function known as the Gudermannian function, $G(x)$.

| $x$ | 0 | 0.1 | 0.2 | 0.3 | 0.4 | 0.5 | 0.6 | 0.7 | 0.8 | 0.9 | 1.0 |
|---|---|---|---|---|---|---|---|---|---|---|---|
| $G(x)$ | 0 | 0.100 | 0.199 | 0.296 | 0.390 | 0.480 | 0.567 | 0.649 | 0.726 | 0.798 | 0.866 |

Use these values to approximate the value of

$$\int_0^1 G(x)\,dx.$$

ANSWER:

Since $G(x)$ is increasing, LEFT(10) is an underestimate and RIGHT(10) is an overestimate. We therefore approximate $\int_0^1 G(x)\,dx$ by $\text{TRAP}(10) = \dfrac{\text{LEFT}(10) + \text{RIGHT}(10)}{2}$.

$$\text{LEFT}(10) = 0.1(0 + 0.100 + \ldots + 0.798) = 0.421$$
$$\text{RIGHT}(10) = 0.1(0.100 + 0.199 \ldots + 0.866) = 0.507$$
$$\text{TRAP}(10) = \frac{\text{LEFT}(10) + \text{RIGHT}(10)}{2} = 0.464$$

2. The following numbers are the left, right, trapezoidal, and midpoint approximations to $\int_0^1 f(x)\,dx$, where $f(x)$ is as shown. (Each uses the same number of subdivisions.)

   I)   0.36735
   II)  0.39896
   III) 0.36814
   IV)  0.33575

   (a) Which is which? How do you know?

   (b) Write $A < \int_0^1 f(x)\,dx < B$, where $B - A$ is as small as possible.

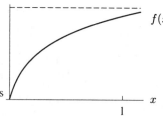

   ANSWER:

   (a) $f$ is increasing and concave down, so we expect to have

   $$\text{LEFT}(n) < \text{TRAP}(n) < \text{MID}(n) < \text{RIGHT}(n).$$

   Thus (IV) is left, (I) is trapezoid, (III) is midpoint and (II) is right.

   (b) We know the true value is between those given by the trapezoid and midpoint rules since the curve is concave down, so

   $$0.36735 < \int_0^1 f(x)\,dx < 0.36814.$$

3. Compute the following integrals. If you provide an approximation, it should be rounded to three decimal places and you must explain how you got it and how you know it has the desired accuracy.

   (a) $\displaystyle\int_2^3 \frac{1}{\ln x}\,dx$

   (b) $\displaystyle\int_0^3 x\sqrt{16 + x^2}\,dx$

   ANSWER:

   (a) Using left- and right-hand sums with $n = 1200$, the left-hand sum is 1.11864 and the right-hand sum is 1.11820. Since these sums differ by only $0.00044 < 0.0005$, and since $\frac{1}{\ln x}$ is monotonically decreasing between 2 and 3,

   $$\int_2^3 \frac{1}{\ln x}\,dx \approx 1.11842$$

   is correct to 3 decimal places.

(b)   Let $u = 16 + x^2$. So $du = 2x\,dx$. By substituting, we get

$$\frac{1}{2} \int \sqrt{u}\,du = \frac{1}{2} \cdot \frac{2}{3} u^{\frac{3}{2}} + C$$

$$= \frac{1}{3}(16 + x^2)^{\frac{3}{2}} + C$$

So

$$\int_0^3 x\sqrt{16 + x^2}\,dx = \frac{1}{3}(16 + x^2)^{\frac{3}{2}} \Big|_0^3$$

$$= \frac{1}{3}(25)^{\frac{3}{2}} - \frac{1}{3}(16)^{\frac{3}{2}}$$

$$= \frac{1}{3} \cdot 125 - \frac{1}{3} \cdot 64$$

$$= \frac{61}{3}$$

4.   The table to the right shows the velocity $v(t)$ of a falling object at various times (time $t$ measured in seconds, velocity $v(t)$ measured in m/sec).

| $t$ | 0 | 1 | 2 | 3 |
|---|---|---|---|---|
| $v(t)$ | 17 | 23 | 28 | 32 |

(a)   Due to air resistance, the object's acceleration is decreasing. What does this tell you about the shape of the graph of $v(t)$?

(b)   Find upper and lower bounds for the distance the object fell in these three seconds. The bounds should be less than three meters apart. Illustrate your reasoning on a sketch.

ANSWER:

(a)   $v(t)$ will be concave down.

(b)   Find a left-hand sum, a right-hand sum, and a trapezoidal sum with $\Delta t = 1$.

$$\text{LEFT}(3) = 1 \cdot (17 + 23 + 28) = 68\text{m}$$

$$\text{RIGHT}(3) = 1 \cdot (23 + 28 + 32) = 83\text{m}$$

$$\text{TRAP}(3) = \frac{68 + 83}{2} = 75.5\text{m}$$

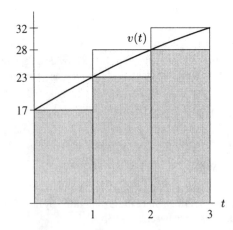

Because this curve is concave down, the trapezoid rule gives an underestimate of 75.5; the right-hand sum produces an overestimate of 83. These are not close enough! For a closer overestimate try the following. Use two intervals; the first of length 2 and the second of length 1.

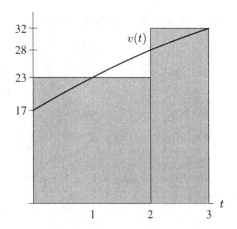

Using the midpoint rule with the first interval gives an overestimate; using the right-hand rule with the second interval also gives an overestimate. Such a sum gives $2 \cdot 23 + 32 = 78$ as an overestimate. So the distance fallen is between 75.5 and 78 meters.

5. For each of the definite integrals below, confine the value of an integral to an interval of size 0.1. For each of your answers, explain carefully which method you used to obtain it, and show how you know your answer is as accurate as required.

(a) $\displaystyle\int_{\frac{\pi}{2}}^{\frac{5\pi}{2}} e^{\sin x}\, dx$

(b) $\displaystyle\int_{0}^{10} \ln\left(x^2 + 1\right) dx$

ANSWER:

(a) To find $\displaystyle\int_{\pi/2}^{5\pi/2} e^{\sin x}\, dx$ to within 0.1, we first note that $e^{\sin x}$ is decreasing over $\left[\frac{\pi}{2}, \frac{3\pi}{2}\right]$ and increasing over $\left[\frac{3\pi}{2}, \frac{5\pi}{2}\right]$. In fact, since the function is symmetric about $\frac{3\pi}{2}$, we can say that

$$\int_{\frac{\pi}{2}}^{\frac{5\pi}{2}} e^{\sin x}\, dx = 2 \cdot \int_{\frac{\pi}{2}}^{\frac{3\pi}{2}} e^{\sin x}\, dx$$

Since $e^{\sin x}$ is decreasing over $\left[\frac{\pi}{2}, \frac{3\pi}{2}\right]$, a left-hand sum will be an overestimate and a right-hand sum will be an underestimate. We want the error for an estimate of $\displaystyle\int_{\pi/2}^{5\pi/2} e^{\sin x}\, dx$ to be less than 0.05. Set

$$|f(b) - f(a)| \cdot \frac{b-a}{n} = \left(e^{\sin \frac{3\pi}{2}} - e^{\sin \frac{\pi}{2}}\right) \cdot \frac{\pi}{n} \le 0.05$$

So, $n \ge \dfrac{e^{\sin \frac{3\pi}{2}} - e^{\sin \frac{\pi}{2}}}{0.05} \cdot \pi \approx 147.7$. Hence use $n = 150$. Approximate $\int_{\pi/2}^{3\pi/2} e^{\sin x}\, dx$ with $n = 150$ to obtain:

$$\text{LEFT}(150) \approx 4.00 \text{ (rounding up)}$$
$$\text{RIGHT}(150) \approx 3.95 \text{ (rounding down)}.$$

So $3.95 < \displaystyle\int_{\pi/2}^{3\pi/2} e^{\sin x}\, dx < 4.00$. Hence $7.90 < \displaystyle\int_{\pi/2}^{5\pi/2} e^{\sin x}\, dx < 8.00$.

(b) To estimate $\int_{0}^{10} \ln(x^2 + 1)\, dx$, note that $\ln(x^2 + 1)$ is increasing over the interval $[0, 10]$, so a left-hand sum will be an underestimate and a right-hand sum will be an overestimate. To find the number of divisions necessary, set

$$0.1 \ge |\ln 101 - \ln 1| \cdot \frac{10}{n}.$$

So $n \geq 461$. Thus use $n = 500$ to obtain:

$$\text{LEFT}(500) \approx 29.04 \text{ (rounding down)}$$
$$\text{LEFT}(500) \approx 29.14 \text{ (rounding up)}$$

So $29.04 < \int_0^{10} \ln(x^2 + 1) \, dx < 29.14$.

6.  Suppose that a computer takes $10^{-6}$ seconds to add two numbers together, and it takes $10^{-5}$ seconds to multiply two numbers together. The computer is asked to integrate the function $f(x) = 3 \cdot x^2$ from 0 to 1 using left hand sums with $n$ divisions. As a function of $n$, introduce the time, $T(n)$, used by the computer to do the calculation. Compute $T(n)$. (The computer figures $x^2$ as $x \cdot x$.)

    ANSWER:

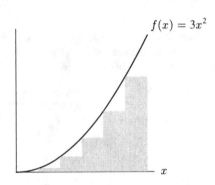

$f(x) = 3x^2 = 3 \cdot x \cdot x$.

The time the computer takes to evaluate one interval (i.e., to multiply twice) $= 10^{-5} + 10^{-5} = 2 \times 10^{-5}$.

The time the computer takes to evaluate $n$ such intervals $= (2 \times 10^{-5}) \times n$.

If there are $n$ intervals, then the computer will have to add $(n - 1)$ times. The time the computer will take to do all the additions $= (n - 1) \times 10^{-6}$.

Therefore the time taken for the entire calculation is

$$T(n) = (2 \times 10^{-5}) \times n + (n - 1) \times 10^{-6}.$$

7.  (a)  Find the exact value of $\int_1^{10} x \sqrt[3]{x - 1} \, dx$. (An exact value is one like $\sqrt{7}$, $\ln 10$, $\tan(\pi + 1)$.)

    (b)  You want to estimate $\int_0^2 \cos(\theta^2) d\theta$ by finding values, $A$ and $B$, which differ by less than 0.0001 and such that

    $$A < \int_0^1 \cos(\theta^2) d\theta < B.$$

    Explain how you found $A$ and $B$, and justify your assertion that they lie on either side of the integral.

    ANSWER:

    (a)  Let $w = \sqrt[3]{x - 1}$, then $w^3 + 1 = x$ so $3w^2 dw = dx$. When $x = 1$, $w = 0$; when $x = 10$, $w = \sqrt[3]{9}$.

    $$\int_1^{10} x \sqrt[3]{x - 1} \, dx = \int_0^{\sqrt[3]{9}} (w^3 + 1) \cdot w \cdot 3w^2 dw = 3 \int_0^{\sqrt[3]{9}} w^6 + w^3 dw = \frac{3w^7}{7} + \frac{3w^4}{4} \Big|_0^{\sqrt[3]{9}}$$
    $$= \frac{3}{7}(9)^{\frac{7}{3}} + \frac{3}{4}\left(9^{\frac{4}{3}}\right)$$

    Note: To get the exact value, you need to use the Fundamental Theorem.

(b)  Graph of $y = \cos(\theta^2)$ is decreasing and concave down for $0 \le \theta \le 1$. (Draw it on the calculator and see.) Thus Trap < True < Midpt; we'll take Trap = $A$, Mid = $B$.

With $n = 50$, get Trap = .90447 = $A$, Mid = .90455 = $B$, so

$$\underbrace{0.90447}_{A} < \int_0^1 \cos(\theta^2)d\theta < \underbrace{0.90455}_{B}$$

8.  Last Monday we hired a typist to work from 8am to 12 noon. His typing speed decreased between 8am and his 10am cup of coffee, and increased again afterwards, between 10am and noon. His instantaneous speed (measured in characters per second) was measured each hour and the results are given below:

| Time  | 8am | 9 | 10 | 11 | 12 |
|-------|-----|---|----|----|----|
| Speed | 6   | 4 | 1  | 3  | 5  |

You want to estimate the total number of characters typed between 8am and 12 noon.

(a)  Make an upper and a lower estimate using Riemann sums. Represent each estimate on a sketch.
(b)  Use the trapezoidal approximation to make a better estimate. Represent this estimate on a sketch.
(c)  A good typist types at an average speed of at least four characters per second. Use your answer to (b) to decide if we got a good typist. Show your reasoning.

ANSWER:

(a)

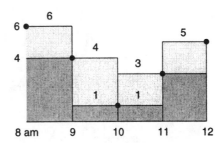

Hour = 3600 seconds.
Upper sum = $(6 + 4 + 3 + 5)3600 = 64800$ chars. (dotted rectangle).
Lower sum = $(4 + 1 + 1 + 3)3600 = 32400$ chars.

(b)

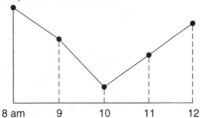

$$\text{Trapezoid} = \frac{\text{Left+Right}}{2} = 48600 \text{ chars.}$$

(c)  Average = $\dfrac{48600}{4(3600)} = 3.375$ char/sec doesn't look good. Even using the highest estimate,

rate = $\dfrac{64800}{4(3600)} = 4.5$ char/sec, only a bit above 4 char/sec, so the rate is probably not above 4 char/sec. We probably didn't hire a good typist.

9.  Consider the following definite integrals:

(a)  $\displaystyle\int_0^{\frac{2}{5}} \frac{1}{4 + 25x^2}\, dx$

(b)  $\displaystyle\int_{\frac{-\pi}{4}}^{\frac{\pi}{4}} \sin^2 \theta\, d\theta$

(i)  Evaluate these integrals using the fundamental theorem of calculus. Write your answer both in analytical form, e.g., $\pi + \ln \frac{2}{3} - \arctan \sqrt{5}$, and in decimal form, e.g., $1.58587.\dots$

(ii) Obtain a numerical approximation of both integrals correct to two decimal places, and compare the numerical results with the decimal results in part (a). Explain what kind of sum you are using (left sum, trapezoids, etc.), and how many subdivisions were necessary.

ANSWER:

(a) (i) $\displaystyle\int \frac{dx}{4+25x^2} = \frac{1}{25}\int \frac{dx}{\frac{4}{25}+x^2}$. Apply V-24 with $a^2 = \frac{4}{25} \Rightarrow a = \frac{2}{5}$

$$= \frac{1}{25}\left[\frac{5}{2}\arctan\frac{5}{2}x\right] + C = \frac{1}{10}\arctan\frac{5}{2}x + C.\ \text{Thus,}$$

$$\int_C^{\frac{2}{5}} \frac{dx}{4+25x^2} = \frac{1}{10}\arctan\frac{5}{2}x\Big|_0^{\frac{2}{5}} = \frac{1}{10}(\arctan 1 - \arctan 0) = \frac{\pi}{40} \approx 0.0785$$

(ii) Apply IV-57 with $n > 2$:

$$\int \sin^2\theta\, d\theta = -\frac{1}{2}\sin\theta\cos\theta + \frac{1}{2}\int d\theta = -\frac{1}{2}\sin\theta\cos\theta + \frac{1}{2}\theta + C$$

Thus

$$\int_{-\frac{\pi}{4}}^{\frac{\pi}{4}} \sin^2\theta\, d\theta = \frac{1}{2}\left[-\sin\theta\cos\theta + \theta\right]_{-\frac{\pi}{4}}^{\frac{\pi}{4}}$$

$$= \frac{1}{2}\left[-\left(\frac{1}{\sqrt{2}}\right)^2 + \frac{\pi}{4} - \left(-\left(-\frac{1}{\sqrt{2}}\right)\left(\frac{1}{\sqrt{2}}\right) - \frac{\pi}{4}\right)\right]$$

$$= \frac{1}{2}\left[-\frac{1}{2} + \frac{\pi}{4} - \frac{1}{2} + \frac{\pi}{4}\right] = \frac{\pi}{4} - \frac{1}{2} \approx 0.285$$

(b) (i) With $N = 20$ subdivisions, the trapezoid and midpoint are both accurate to three decimal places with

$$\underbrace{0.078545}_{\substack{\text{midpoint}\\\text{overestimate}}} \geq \int_0^{\frac{2}{5}} \frac{dx}{4+25x^2} \geq \underbrace{0.078529}_{\substack{\text{trapezoid}\\\text{underestimate}}}$$

(ii) With $N = 20$ subdivisions, the trapezoid and midpoint sums are correct to two decimal places with

$$\underbrace{0.2864}_{\substack{\text{trapezoid}\\\text{overestimate}}} \geq \int_{-\frac{\pi}{4}}^{\frac{\pi}{4}} \sin^2\theta\, d\theta \geq \underbrace{0.2849}_{\substack{\text{midpoint}\\\text{underestimate}}}$$

10. Consider the ellipse pictured below:

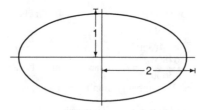

The perimeter of the ellipse is given by the following integral: $\displaystyle\int_0^{\frac{\pi}{2}} 8\sqrt{1 - \frac{3}{4}\sin^2\theta}\, d\theta$. It turns out that there is no elementary antiderivative for the function $f(\theta) = 8\sqrt{1 - \frac{3}{4}\sin^2\theta}$, and so the integral must be evaluated numerically. A graph of the integrand $f(\theta)$ is shown below.

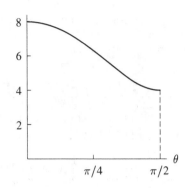

(a) On the graph above, sketch a graphical representation of the *left* Riemann sum approximation of the definite integral with $N = 4$ equal divisions of the interval from $\theta = 0$ to $\theta = \frac{\pi}{2}$. Does it appear that the left sum will overestimate or underestimate the integral?

(b) Calculate the left, right, trapezoid, and midpoint sums that approximate the definite integral with $N = 4$ equal divisions of the interval.

(c) Based on part (b), what is your best estimate of the integral, and how many decimal places of accuracy do you think you have?

(d) Look at the picture of the ellipse and decide whether your answer to part (c) seems to represent a reasonable estimate of the perimeter of the ellipse.

ANSWER:

(a)

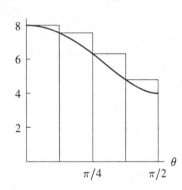

These rectangles will <u>overestimate</u> the integral.

(b) $x_0 = 0, x_1 = \frac{\pi}{8}, x_2 = \frac{\pi}{4}, x_3 = \frac{3\pi}{8}, x_4 = \frac{\pi}{2}, \Delta x = \frac{\pi}{8}$

$$\text{Left Sum} = \sum_{i=0}^{3} f(x_i)\Delta x = \big(f(x_0) + f(x_1) + f(x_2) + f(x_3)\big) \cdot \Delta x$$

$$= .3927 \cdot (8 + 7.5479 + 6.3246 + 4.7989)$$

$$= .3927 \cdot (26.6714) = 10.4738$$

$$\text{Right Sum} = \sum_{i=1}^{4} f(x_i)\Delta x = \big(f(x_1) + f(x_2) + f(x_3) + f(x_4)\big) \cdot \Delta x$$

$$= .3927 \cdot (7.5479 + 6.3246 + 4.7986 + 4)$$

$$= .3927 \cdot (22.6711) = 8.9029$$

$$\text{Trap Sum} = \sum_{i=1}^{4} \frac{1}{2} \cdot \big[f(x_{i-1}) + f(x_i)\big] \Delta x = \text{the average of the left and right sums}$$

$$= \frac{1}{2} \cdot (10.4738 + 8.9029) = 9.6884$$

$$\text{Mid Sum} = \sum_{i=1}^{4} f(z_i)\Delta x, \text{ where } z_i = \frac{1}{2} \cdot (x_i + x_{i=1})$$

$$z_1 = \frac{\pi}{16}, \quad z_2 = \frac{3\pi}{16}, \quad z_3 \frac{5\pi}{16}, \quad z_4 \frac{7\pi}{16}$$

$$= \left(f(z_1) + f(z_2) + f(z_3) + f(z_4)\right) \cdot \Delta x$$

$$= .3927 \cdot (7.88499 + 7.0132 + 5.5512 + 4.2222)$$

$$= .3927 \cdot (24.67159) = 9.6885$$

(c) 9.688. The midpoint and trapezoid sums agree to three decimal places, so there are three decimal places of accuracy.

(d) Yes. Consider the perimeter of circles, which we know how to calculate. A circle of radius 1, which fits inside the ellipse, has perimeter $2 \cdot \pi = 6.28$. A circle of radius 2, inside which the ellipse fits, has perimeter $4 \cdot \pi = 12.57$. So we know that the perimeter of the ellipse must be between these values.

11. It is desired to evaluate the following definite integral:

$$\int_1^3 \sin\left(\frac{1}{x}\right) dx$$

As it turns out, there is no antiderivative to the function $f(x) = \sin\left(\frac{1}{x}\right)$, and so it will be necessary to evaluate the integral numerically.

(a) Sketch a graph of $f(x)$ from $x = 1$ to $x = 3$. Be sure the slope and concavity of the curve are clear on your graph.

(b) Calculate the left, right, trapezoid, and midpoint sums that approximate the definite integral with $N = 4$ equal divisions of the interval $1 \leq x \leq 3$. State whether each sum is an overestimate or an underestimate of the integral, with an appropriate explanation.

(c) Based on part (b), what is your best estimate of the integral? How many decimal places of accuracy do you have?

ANSWER:

(a) Using the graphing calculator and plugging in points, we get a decreasing concave-up curve as such:

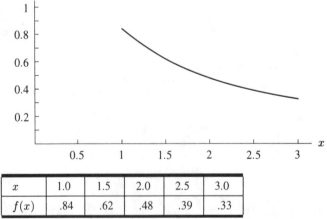

| $x$ | 1.0 | 1.5 | 2.0 | 2.5 | 3.0 |
|------|------|------|------|------|------|
| $f(x)$ | .84 | .62 | .48 | .39 | .33 |

(b) Again, using a numerical integration program, we get
LEFT=1.1643   Overestimate, as $f(x)$ is monotone decreasing in $[1, 3]$.
RIGHT=0.9072   Underestimate, as $f(x)$ is decreasing in $[1, 3]$.
TRAP=1.0358   Overestimate, as $f(x)$ is concave up in $[1, 3]$.
MID=1.0219   Underestimate, as $f(x)$ is concave up in $[1, 3]$.

(c) The best estimate is that $1.0219 < \int_1^3 \sin\left(\frac{1}{x}\right) dx < 1.0358$. Using the weighted average, we get 1.0265. There is only 1 decimal place of accuracy (as TRAP and MID agree to only 1 decimal place).

12. A drug is being administered intravenously to a patient at a constant rate of 2 mg/hr. The following table shows the rate of change of the amount of the drug in the patient's body at half-hour intervals. Initially there is none of the drug in the patient's body.

| Time (hours) | 0.0 | 0.5 | 1.0 | 1.5 | 2.0 | 2.5 | 3.0 | 3.5 | 4.0 |
|---|---|---|---|---|---|---|---|---|---|
| Rate (mg/hr) | 2.00 | 1.09 | 0.75 | 0.57 | 0.46 | 0.39 | 0.33 | 0.29 | 0.26 |

(a) Sketch a graph of the rate of change of the amount of drug in the patient's body as a function of time. Draw a smooth curve through the data points.

(b) Give a description of what is happening in words. In particular, explain why the rate of change of the amount of the drug is not simply a constant $+2$ mg/hr, which is the rate at which the drug is being administered.

(c) Sketch a graph of the total amount of the drug in the person's body as a function of time. You should be able to make this sketch just from your graph of the rate in part (a).

(d) What is your best estimate of the total amount of the drug in the patient's body after four hours? You may do this by any means of your choosing, but explain your method.

ANSWER:

(a)

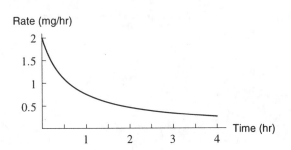

(b) The rate of change of the amount of drug in the patient's body is <u>decreasing</u> as time increases. This could be due to the drug saturating the patient's system or changed to another form as time increases.

(c) Using trapezoids to calculate area under the rate curve, we get the graph below.

| $x$ | $f(x)$ |
|---|---|
| 0.0 | 0 |
| 0.5 | 0.77 |
| 1.0 | 1.23 |
| 1.5 | 1.56 |
| 2.0 | 1.82 |
| 2.5 | 2.03 |
| 3.0 | 2.21 |
| 3.5 | 2.37 |
| 4.0 | 2.51 |

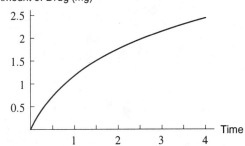

(d) Calculating the total area under the rate curve, we get
   LHS $\approx 2.94$
   RHS $\approx 2.07$
   TRAP $\approx 2.51$

13. (a) Using two subdivisions, find the left, right, trapezoid and midpoint approximations to
$$\int_0^1 (1 - e^{-x})\, dx.$$

(b) Draw sketches showing what each approximation represents.

(c) Given only the information you found in (a), what is your best estimate for the value of this integral?

ANSWER:

(a) To find $\int_0^1 (1 - e^{-x})\, dx$, try left-hand sums using two subdivisions. Let $f(x) = 1 - e^{-x}$. At $x = 0$, $f(0) = 0$ and at $x = 0.5$, $f(0.5) = 1 - e^{-0.5} \approx 0.3935$. So

$$\text{LEFT}(2) = 0.5(0 + 0.3935) = 0.1968.$$

Try right-hand sums, using two subdivisions.

At $x = 0.5$ $f(0.5) \approx 0.3935$ and at $x = 1$, $f(1) = 1 - e^{-1} \approx 0.6321$. So

$$\text{RIGHT}(2) = 0.5(0.3935 + 0.6321) = 0.5128.$$

Try midpoint sums, using two subdivisions.

At $x = 0.25$, $f(0.25) = 1 - e^{-0.25} \approx 0.2212$ and at $x = 0.75$, $f(0.75) = 1 - e^{-0.75} \approx 0.5726$. So

$$\text{MID}(2) = 0.5(0.2212 + 0.5276) = 0.3744.$$

Find the trapezoidal sum:

$$\text{TRAP}(2) = \frac{\text{LEFT}(2) + \text{RIGHT}(2)}{2} = \frac{0.1968 + 0.5128}{2} = 0.3548.$$

(b)

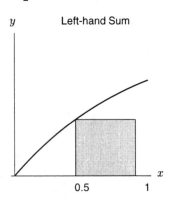

Figure 7.5.14

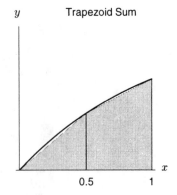

Figure 7.5.15

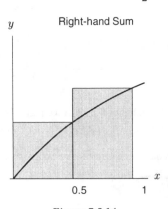

Figure 7.5.16

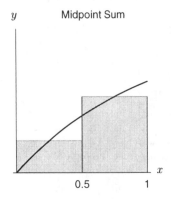

Figure 7.5.17

(c) Since the curve $1 - e^{-x}$ is concave down, the trapezoid rule must give an underestimate. By the same reasoning, the midpoint sum must provide an overestimate. A good estimate of the true area under the curve might be given by the average of these two sums, namely 0.3646.

14. Let $S(t)$ be the number of daylight hours, in Cambridge, MA, on the $t^{\text{th}}$ day of the year. During spring (from the vernal equinox, $t = 80$, to the summer solstice, $t = 173$), the graph of $S(t)$ is concave down. In the table below we list some values of $S(t)$. What is the average length of the days in spring (in hours and minutes)? Please give an upper bound and a lower bound for the answer. These bounds should differ by less than 10 minutes.

| $t$ | $S(t)$ |
|---|---|
| 80 | 12 hours 12 minutes |
| 111 | 13 hours 44 minutes |
| 142 | 14 hours 50 minutes |
| 173 | 15 hours 12 minutes |

ANSWER:

First, we convert all values of $S(t)$ into minutes for simplicity. By inspecting the values in the table, it is clear that left- and right-hand sums will not produce the needed accuracy So, to find the understimate, we approximate $\int S(t)\,dt$ by TRAP(3):

$$\int S(t)\,dt \approx \frac{1}{2}\left(\text{LEFT}(3) + \text{RIGHT}(3)\right)$$

$$= \frac{1}{2}(732 + 824 + 89 + 824 + 890 + 912) \cdot 31$$

$$= 78616$$

So $\overline{S(t)} = \dfrac{78616}{173 - 80} \approx 845.3$ minutes.

The overestimate is a bit more tricky. If we approximate $\int S(t)\,dt$ by RIGHT(3), we get $\overline{S(t)} = (824 + 890 + 912)\frac{31}{93} \approx 875.5$ minutes, but then the bounds are not within 10 minutes of each other. We would try MID(3), but we don't know the values for $S(\frac{80+111}{2})$, $S(\frac{111+142}{2})$, or $S(\frac{142+173}{2})$. The trick is to estimate $\int S(t)\,dt$ with MID(1) between $t = 80$ and $t = 142 + \text{RIGHT}(1)$ between $t = 142$ and $t = 173$. We get: $\overline{S(t)} = \frac{1}{3}(824 \times 2 + 912) \approx 854$ minutes, rounding up. Therefore, our answer is 845 minutes $< \overline{S(t)} < 854$ minutes; 14 hours 5 minutes $< \overline{S(t)} < 14$ hours 14 minutes.

15. Give an upper bound $U$ and a lower bound $L$ for

$$\int_{-0.5}^{0.3} \frac{1}{1 + x^4}\,dx$$

such that $U - L < 10^{-3}$. Explain your procedure.

ANSWER:

Since, by inspecting the graph of $\dfrac{1}{1 + x^4}$, we can tell that the function is concave down over $[-0.5, 0.3]$, TRAP($n$) will be an underestimate (a lower bound), and MID($n$) will be an overestimate (an upper bound).

$$\text{TRAP}(50) \approx 0.98789$$
$$\text{MID}(50) \approx 0.98793$$

So, $0.98789 \leq \displaystyle\int_{-0.5}^{0.3} \frac{1}{1 + x^4}\,dx \leq 0.98793$.

The difference between upper and lower bounds is $\approx 0.00004 < 0.001$.

16. Below is the graph of $y = \arctan x$:

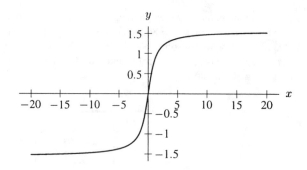

(Note that arctan is the $\boxed{\tan^{-1}}$ button on your calculator.)

(a)   For any number of subdivisions $N$ write an inequality using $\text{RIGHT}(N)$, $\text{LEFT}(N)$ and $\int_{-10}^{16} \arctan x \, dx$. Explain.

(b)   In computing $\int_{-10}^{16} \arctan x \, dx$ using left- and right-hand sums we record the following table:

| $N$ | $\text{LEFT}(N)$ | $\text{RIGHT}(N)$ |
|---|---|---|
| 2 | $-2.877$ | 35.8465 |
| 3 | $-8.2473$ | 17.474 |
| 4 | $-0.3163$ | 19.0505 |

Why do you think there are such wide variations in this table? You might want to illustrate your reasoning using the graphs below. Be sure to distinguish between the variation for different $N$ and the difference between left- and right-hand sums for a particular $N$.

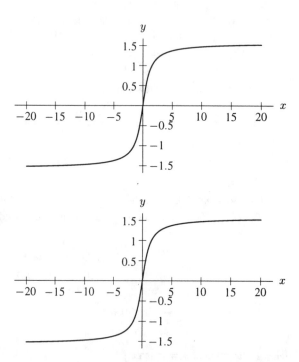

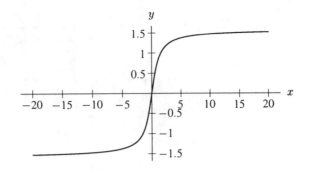

(c)  The point $x = 0$ is an inflection point for $y = \arctan x$. If we write

$$\int_{-10}^{16} \arctan x \, dx = \int_{-10}^{0} \arctan x \, dx + \int_{0}^{16} \arctan x \, dx,$$

then we can get over-estimates and under-estimates for the integrals on the right via the midpoint and trapezoidal rules. Explain.

(d)  We have the following data:

For $\displaystyle\int_{-10}^{0} \arctan x \, dx$

| $N$ | Midpoint | Trapezoid |
|---|---|---|
| 50 | $-12.40537$ | $-12.40041$ |

For $\displaystyle\int_{0}^{16} \arctan x \, dx$

| $N$ | Midpoint | Trapezoid |
|---|---|---|
| 50 | $21.363787$ | $21.35097$ |

Based on your answer to part (c) find numbers $A$ and $B$ such that

$$A \le \int_{-10}^{16} \arctan x \, dx \le B.$$

Explain. How big is $B - A$?

(e)  Evaluate $\int_{-10}^{16} \arctan x \, dx$ "symbolically" (plug in the limits but don't evaluate).

Hint: Integrate by parts using $\dfrac{d}{dx} \arctan x = \dfrac{1}{1 + x^2}$.

ANSWER:

(a)  Since $\arctan x$ is an increasing function, $\text{LEFT}(N) < \displaystyle\int_{-10}^{16} \arctan x \, dx < \text{RIGHT}(N)$ for any number of divisions N.

(b)  The general reason for the wide variation in values in the table, for different $N$, is that $\arctan x$ is steep only near $x = 0$, and is relatively flat further out. A small number of rectangles (like 2, 3, or 4) will necessarily obscure this behavior, either underestimating or overestimating it.

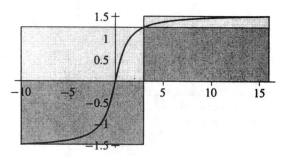

*Figure 7.5.18*: $N = 2$

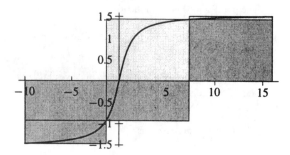

*Figure 7.5.19*: $N = 3$

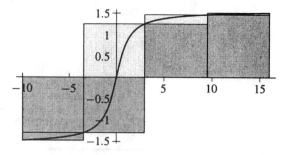

*Figure 7.5.20*: $N = 4$

With $N = 2$, for example, a right-hand sum completely ignores the behavior of the function for $x$ to the left of 3. But at $x = 3$, $\arctan x$ is already beyond the steep increase at $x = 0$! Similar problems occur for $N = 3$ and $N = 4$. As for the difference between left- and right-hand sums for a particular $N$, consider the following:

$$\text{RIGHT}(N) - \text{LEFT}(N) = ((f(b) - f(a))\frac{b - a}{N}$$

but in this case, we have

$$\text{RIGHT}(N) - \text{LEFT}(N) = (1.51 - (-1.47)) \cdot \frac{26}{N}$$

$$\approx \frac{77.5}{N}.$$

For small $N$, this will be very large.

(c)  On $[-10, 0]$, $\arctan x$ is concave up, so

$$\text{MID}(N) < \int_{-10}^{0} \arctan x \, dx < \text{TRAP}(N) \text{ for any } N.$$

On $[0, 16]$, arctan $x$ is concave down, so

$$\text{TRAP}(N) < \int_{-10}^{0} \arctan x \, dx < \text{MID}(N) \text{ for any } N.$$

So for an underestimate, we can use $\text{MID}(N)$ on $[-10, 0]$ and $\text{TRAP}(N)$ on $[0, 16]$. Vice versa for an overestimate.

(d) According to the previous part, we have

$$A = \text{underestimate} = -12.40537 + 21.35097 = 8.9456$$
$$B = \text{overestimate} = -12.40041 + 21.363787 = 8.96338$$
$$B - A = 0.01778$$

(e) Integrating by parts with $u = \arctan x$ and $v' = 1$ we get

$$\int_{-10}^{16} \arctan x \, dx = x \arctan x \Big|_{-10}^{16} - \int_{-10}^{16} \frac{x}{1 + x^2} \, dx,$$

since $v = x$ and $u' = \dfrac{dx}{1 + x^2}$. Notice that $\displaystyle\int \frac{x}{1 + x^2} \, dx = \frac{1}{2} \ln(1 + x^2) + C$. Therefore,

$$\int_{-10}^{16} \arctan x \, dx = x \arctan x \Big|_{-10}^{16} - \frac{1}{2} \ln(1 + x^2) \Big|_{10}^{16}$$

$$= 16 \arctan 16 + 10 \arctan(-10) - \frac{1}{2} \ln(1 + 16^2) + \frac{1}{2} \ln(1 + 10^2)$$

$$\approx 8.956$$

17. Consider the functions

$$f_k(x) = (1 - x)^{1/k} \quad \text{for} \quad k = 1, 2, 3.$$

(a) Sketch a graph showing these three functions for $0 \leq x \leq 1$

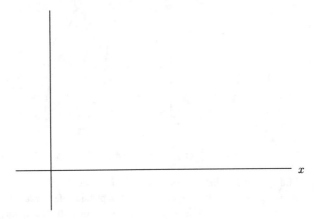

Consider the integrals

$$I_k = \int_{0}^{1} (1 - x^k)^{1/k} dx \quad k = 1, 2, 3.$$

(b) Suppose you use the midpoint and trapezoid rules to approximate each of these integrals. For each integral, does each rule give an overestimate, an underestimate, the exact value, or is it impossible to tell without knowing $n$, the number of subdivisions? (Circle one answer for each integral and give a very brief reason.)

| $I_1$ | Midpt: | Over | Under | Exact | Can't Tell |
|---|---|---|---|---|---|
| | Why? | | | | |
| | Trap: | Over | Under | Exact | Can't Tell |
| | Why? | | | | |
| $I_2$ | Midpt: | Over | Under | Exact | Can't Tell |
| | Why? | | | | |
| | Trap: | Over | Under | Exact | Can't Tell |
| | Why? | | | | |
| $I_3$ | Midpt: | Over | Under | Exact | Can't Tell |
| | Why? | | | | |
| | Trap: | Over | Under | Exact | Can't Tell |
| | Why? | | | | |

ANSWER:

(a)  The functions are shown in Figure 7.5.21.

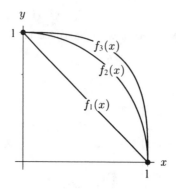

*Figure 7.5.21*

(b)  Mid($n$) and Trap($n$) give exact values of $I_1$ since, in the case of Trap($n$) it is easy to see that if $n$ is even as low as 1 the trapezoid of the trapezoid rule is exactly the triangle whose area we want. In the case of Mid($n$), if $n$ is even as low as one, the trapezoid whose oblique side is tangent to the "curve" (and whose area equals that of the midpoint rectangle) fits the triangular area exactly since the tangents of straight lines are the the the lines themselves.

For $I_2$ *and* $I_3$ we conclude that Trap($n$) underestimates and Mid($n$) overestimates as both regions are bounded above by curves which are concave down.

18.  Suppose the points $x_0, x_1, ..., x_n$ are equally spaced and $a = x_0 < x_1 < x_2 < ... < x_n = b$. Give a formula (in terms of $f$ and the $x_i$'s) for each of the following approximations to $\int_a^b f(x)dx$. (No justification needed.)

(a)  The left Riemann sum approximation.

(b)    The right Riemann sum approximation.

(c)    The trapezoid approximation.

(d)    The midpoint approximation.

ANSWER:

(a)    The left Riemann sum approximation uses the value of $f$ at the left of each interval:

$$\text{Left}(n) = \sum_{i=0}^{n-1} f(x_i)\Delta x.$$

(b)    The right Riemann sum uses the value of $f$ at the right of each interval:

$$\text{Right}(n) = \sum_{i=1}^{n} f(x_i)\Delta x.$$

(c)    The trapezoid approximation is the average of the left and right Riemann approximations:

$$\text{Trap}(n) = \frac{1}{2}\left(\text{Left}(n) + \text{Right}(n)\right)$$

$$= \frac{1}{2}\left(\sum_{i=0}^{n-1} f(x_i)\Delta x + \sum_{i=1}^{n} f(x_i)\Delta x\right)$$

$$= \sum_{i=0}^{n-1}\left(\frac{f(x_i) + f(x_{i+1})}{2}\right)\Delta x.$$

(d)    The midpoint approximation uses the value of $f$ evaluated the the midpoint of each interval:

$$\text{Mid}(n) = \sum_{i=0}^{n-1} f\left(\frac{x_i + x_{i+1}}{2}\right)\Delta x.$$

19.    TRUE/FALSE: For each statement, write whether it is true or false and give a short explanation.

(a)    For any given function, TRAP($n$) is always *more* accurate than LEFT($n$).

(b)    The midpoint rule gives *exact* answers for linear functions, no matter how many subdivisions are used.

(c)    $\displaystyle\int_0^3 \cos^{36}(x)\,dx > \pi.$

ANSWER:

(a)    FALSE. A simple counterexample is a constant function, say $f(x) = 5$, for which LEFT($n$) is just as accurate as TRAP($n$), since both are exact. For other functions, LEFT($n$) can even be more accurate than TRAP($n$). (See if you can come up with an example of such function.)

(b)    TRUE. Using MID(1) on any interval $[a, b]$ of a linear function overshoots and undershoots the exact area equally so there is exact cancellation. Consequently, for $N$ larger than 1, MID($N$) gives an exact answer on the whole interval $[a, b]$ because on each subinterval it acts as MID(1), which we know gives an exact answer.

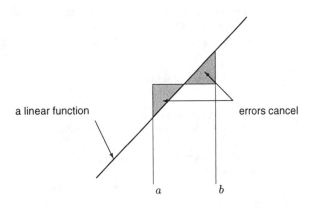

(c) FALSE. Since $-1 \le \cos x \le 1$ everywhere, $\cos^{36}(x) \le 1$ everywhere, so $\int_0^3 \cos^{36}(x)\,dx \le \int_0^3 1\,dx = 3$.

20. In the field of dynamical astronomy, integrals such as the following appear in the problem of determining trajectories of planets or spacecraft:

$$\int_0^1 \frac{1}{1 + c \cos \theta}\,d\theta$$

In this definite integral, $c$ is a constant that can go from 0 to $+\infty$ depending on the shape of the orbit. Except for some special values of $c$, there is no fundamental antiderivative for the integrand

$$f(\theta) = \frac{1}{1 + c \cos \theta}$$

(a) Sketch a graph of $f(\theta)$ with $c = 0.5$ for $0 \le \theta \le 1$.
(b) Calculate the left, right, trapezoid, and midpoint sums that approximate the definite integral for $c = 0.5$ with $N = 5$ equal divisions of the interval $0 \le \theta \le 1$. State whether each sum is an overestimate or an underestimate of the integral, with an appropriate explanation.
(c) Based on part (b), what is your best estimate of the integral? How many decimal places of accuracy do you have?

ANSWER:

(a) For $c = 0.5$, $f(\theta) = \dfrac{1}{1 + (0.5) \cos \theta}$. To graph this function, we plot a few points:

| $\theta$ | 0 | 0.2 | 0.4 | 0.6 | 0.8 | 1.0 |
|---|---|---|---|---|---|---|
| $f(\theta)$ | 0.6667 | 0.6711 | 0.6847 | 0.7079 | 0.7416 | 0.7873 |

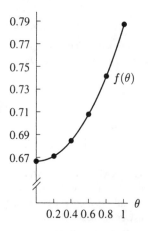

From this graph we can conclude the function is increasing and concave up.

(b) For $N = 5$ equal divisions over the interval $0 \le \theta \le 1$; $x_0 = 0$, $x_1 = 0.2$, $x_2 = 0.4$, $x_3 = 0.6$, $x_4 = 0.8$, $x_5 = 1.0$ and $\Delta x = 0.2$. The values of $f(x)$ were calculated in part (a).

$$\text{LEFT} = \sum_{i=0}^{4} f(x_i)\Delta x$$

$$= \left[ f(x_0) + f(x_1) + f(x_2) + f(x_3) + f(x_n) \right] \Delta x$$
$$= [0.6667 + 0.6711 + 0.6847 + 0.7079 + 0.7416]\,(0.2)$$
$$= 0.6944$$

Because the function is an increasing function, we can conclude that the left Riemann sum is an underestimate.

$$\text{RIGHT} = \sum_{i=1}^{2} f(x_i)\Delta x$$

$$= [f(x_1) + f(x_2) + f(x_3) + f(x_4) + f(x_5)]\Delta x$$

$$= [0.6711 + 0.6847 + 0.7079 + 0.7416 + 0.7873](0.2)$$
$$= 0.7185$$

Because the function is an increasing function, the right hand side is an overestimate.

TRAP=Average of left and right sums

$$= \frac{RHS + LHS}{2} = \frac{0.6944 + 0.7185}{2} = 0.7065$$

Because the function is concave up, the trapezoid sum will give an overestimate.

$$\text{MID} = \sum_{i=0}^{4} f\left(x_i + \frac{1}{2}\Delta x\right)\Delta x$$

$$= \left[f(0.1) + f(0.3) + f(0.5) + f(0.7) + f(0.9)\right]\Delta x$$
$$= [0.6678 + 0.6767 + 0.6950 + 0.7234 + 0.7629](0.2)$$
$$= 0.7052$$

Because the function is concave up, a MID will give us an underestimate.

(c)  Because we know that

$$\text{MID} \leq \int_0^2 f(x) \leq \text{TRAP}$$

$$\text{so } 0.7052 \leq \int_0^2 f(x) \leq 0.7065.$$

The best estimate we can make is one between these two numbers, say 0.706. This is accurate to 2 decimal places.


## *Problems and Solutions for Section 7.6*

1.  (a)  Use the trapezoid rule with $n = 4$ to approximate

$$\int_0^1 \sqrt{1 + e^{-x}}\, dx.$$

   (b)  Do the same using Simpson's rule with $n = 4$.
   (c)  Indicate how much more accurate you would expect the results to be if you used $n = 40$ in each case.

   ANSWER:

   (a)

| $x$ | $f(x)$ |
|------|---------|
| 0.00 | 1.41421 |
| 0.25 | 1.33372 |
| 0.50 | 1.26749 |
| 0.75 | 1.21341 |
| 1.00 | 1.16956 |

LEFT(4) = 1.30721
RIGHT(4) = 1.24605
TRAP(4) = 1.27663

(b)

| $x$ | $f(x)$ |
|-----|--------|
| 0.125 | 1.37204 |
| 0.375 | 1.29896 |
| 0.625 | 1.23906 |
| 0.875 | 1.19032 |

Using the table to the left, we get

$$\mathrm{MID}(4) = 1.27509$$

$$\mathrm{SIMP}(4) = \frac{1}{3}\left(2 \times \mathrm{MID}(4) + \mathrm{TRAP}(4)\right)$$
$$= 1.27560.$$

(c)  Since the trapezoid rule has error proportional to $\frac{1}{n^2}$, using $n = 40$ will be $\frac{\frac{1}{4^2}}{\frac{1}{40^2}} = 100$ times as accurate as using $n = 4$. Since the Simpson's rule has error proportional to $\frac{1}{n^4}$, using $n = 40$ will be $\frac{\frac{1}{4^4}}{\frac{1}{40^4}} = 10{,}000$ times as accurate as using $n = 4$.

2.  The table below contains numerical data for a definite integral approximated by the left-hand, midpoint, trapezoid, and Simpson's rule methods. Which column is which? Why?

| $N$ | | | | |
|-----|---------|---------|---------|---------|
| 1  | 2.4737    | −44.1930   | 0.4737    | −67.5263   |
| 3  | −39.6662  | −45.5098   | −40.3329  | −48.4316   |
| 9  | −44.8687  | −45.5261   | −45.0909  | −45.8548   |
| 27 | −45.45315 | −45.52630  | −45.62722 | −45.5629   |
| 81 | −45.518171| −45.526300 | −45.572862| −45.530364 |

ANSWER:

The second column consistently gives answers very close to the true value (which appears to be around 45.53) so it is likely to be the Simpson's rule column. We recall that $\mathrm{SIMP}(N) = \frac{1}{3}(2\,\mathrm{MID}(N) + \mathrm{TRAP}(N))$. Noting that 2nd column $= \frac{1}{3}(2 \times$ 4th column $+$ 1st column$)$, we conclude that $\mathrm{MID}(N)$ is the 4th column and $\mathrm{TRAP}(N)$ is the 1st column. The 3rd column is therefore the $\mathrm{LEFT}(N)$ column.

3.  Compute to within 0.001 the following integral: $\displaystyle\int_0^1 (1+x^2)^{-4}\,dx$. You may use a graphing calculator or a copy of the integral tables. Please justify all of your steps.

ANSWER:

First look at the function $(1+x^2)^{-4}$:

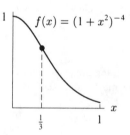

Using Left and Right sums: Left-sum overestimates and right-sum underestimates the integral, as the function is monotonic and decreasing. The number of steps we should take, $N$, should verify

$$|\mathrm{Left}(N) - \mathrm{Right}(N)| = |f(0) - f(1)|\frac{1}{N} = \left|1 - \frac{1}{1.6}\right|\frac{1}{N} < 0.001$$

so $N \ge 938$ steps. Then $\begin{cases} LHS \cong 0.47413 \quad \text{and} \\ RHS \cong 0.47507 \end{cases}$.

The integral $\simeq 0.475$ up to 0.001.

Using Trap and Midpoint: By concavity we must use TRAP on $[0, 1/3]$ and Mid on $[1/3, 1]$ to underestimate. Use Mid on $[0, 1/3]$ and Trap on $[1/3, 1]$ to overestimate. Use approximately 100 steps to estimate them, then sum-up to get $0.474588 <$ integral $< 0.474617$, well within $10^{-3}$.

(C) It is possible to compute the integral precisely:

$$I = \int_0^1 \frac{dx}{(1+x^2)^4}.$$

Put $x = \tan\theta$; then $dx = \dfrac{d\tan\theta}{d\theta} d\theta = \dfrac{1}{\cos^2\theta} d\theta$. If $x = 0$, $\theta = 0$; if $x = 1$, $\theta = \dfrac{\pi}{4}$, so substitute and get

$$I = \int_0^{\pi/4} (1 + \tan^2\theta)^{-4} \cos^{-2}\theta \, d\theta = \int_0^{\pi/4} \cos^6\theta \, d\theta$$

Use Table #18 to write it as (with $m = 6$)

$$I = \frac{1}{6}\cos^6\theta \sin\theta \Big|_0^{\frac{\pi}{4}} + \frac{5}{6}\int_0^{\frac{\pi}{4}} \cos^4\theta \, d\theta$$

$$= \frac{1}{6}\left(\frac{1}{\sqrt{2}}\right)^6 + \frac{5}{6}\left[\frac{1}{4}\cos^3\theta \sin\theta \Big|_0^{\frac{\pi}{4}} + \frac{3}{4}\int_0^{\frac{\pi}{4}} \cos^2\theta \, d\theta\right]$$

$$= \frac{1}{48} + \frac{5}{24}\frac{1}{(\sqrt{2})^4} + \frac{15}{24}\left[\frac{1}{2}\cos\theta \sin\theta \Big|_0^{\frac{\pi}{4}} + \frac{1}{2}\cdot\frac{\pi}{4}\right]$$

$$= \frac{1}{48} + \frac{5}{24}\frac{1}{4} + \frac{15}{96} + \frac{15}{192}\pi = \underline{0.4746035}$$
$$\text{true value}$$

4. Compute the following integrals. If you provide an approximation, it should be rounded to three decimal places, and you must explain how you got it and how you know it has the desired accuracy.

(a) $\displaystyle\int_2^4 (1 + \ln(x))^{-1} dx$

(b) $\displaystyle\int_0^4 x \cdot (9 + x^2)^{1/2} dx$

ANSWER:

(a) $\int_2^4 (1 + \ln x)^{-1} dx$.

 Method 1. (With Riemann sum.)
  With 100 divisions, Left= 0.97256945, Right= 0.96913832.
 With 200 divisions, Left= 0.9717084, Right= 0.9699928.
 With 1000 divisions, Left= 0.97102, Right= 0.97067.
 Therefore the answer is 0.971. We know that this is the desired answer because it is approached from both left and right.
 Method 2. (With a calculator.)

$$\int_2^4 (1 + \ln x)^{-1} dx = 0.9708.$$

(b) $\int_0^4 x \cdot (9 + x^2)^{1/2} dx$.

 Method 1. (with a calculator) The answer is 32.667.
 Method 2. (substitution)
  Let $w = 9 + x^2$.
 Then $dw = 2x \cdot dx$.
 Change the limits: when $x = 0$, $w = 9$ and when $x = 4$, $w = 25$.

$$\int_0^4 x \cdot (9 + x^2)^{1/2} \, dx = \int_9^{25} w^{1/2} \frac{dw}{2}$$

$$= \left[ \frac{1}{2} \frac{w^{3/2}}{3/2} \right]_9^{25}$$

$$= \frac{1}{3} [25^{3/2} - 9^{3/2}]$$

$$= \frac{1}{3} [125 - 27]$$

$$= 32.667.$$

Method 3. (with Riemann sums)

Trap: 32.6673

Mid: 32.666

Simp: 32.66666

Therefore the answer is 32.667. We know that this has the desired accuracy because the same value is approached by different methods.

## Problems and Solutions for Section 7.7

1. (a) Does the integral $\int_1^\infty \frac{x^2}{e^{-x} + x} \, dx$ converge? Why or why not?

   (b) If the following improper integral converges, find its value. Otherwise explain why it does not converge.

$$\int_0^\infty x^2 e^{-x} \, dx$$

ANSWER:

(a) The integral does not converge, because the integrand does not approach zero as $x$ goes to infinity.

This is because $e^{-x} \to 0$ as $x \to \infty$, and the integrand behaves like $\frac{x^2}{x} = x$, which grows without bound as $x \to \infty$.

(b) We need to integrate by parts twice to determine the indefinite integral:

$$\int x^2 e^{-x} \, dx = -x^2 e^{-x} + 2 \int x e^{-x} \, dx$$

$$= -x^2 e^{-x} + 2 \left( -x e^{-x} + \int e^{-x} \, dx \right)$$

$$= -x^2 e^{-x} + 2 \left( -x e^{-x} - e^{-x} \right)$$

$$= -e^{-x} \left( x^2 + 2x + 2 \right) + C.$$

Then,

$$\int_0^\infty x^2 e^{-x} \, dx = \lim_{a \to \infty} \int_0^a x^2 e^{-x} \, dx$$

$$= \lim_{a \to \infty} \left. -e^{-x} (x^2 + 2x + 2) \right|_0^a$$

$$= \lim_{a \to \infty} \left( -e^{-a} (a^2 + 2a + 2) + 2 \right).$$

As $a \to \infty$, $e^{-a}$ goes to 0 faster than the polynomial $a^2 + 2a + 2$ grows. So

$$\lim_{a \to \infty} \left( -e^{-a} (a^2 + 2a + 2) + 2 \right) = \lim_{a \to \infty} 2 = 2.$$

The integral thus converges to a value of 2.

2. Does the following improper integral converge? If so, find its value. $\displaystyle\int_0^1 \frac{1}{x^{\frac{1991}{1992}}}\, dx$

ANSWER:

$$\int_0^1 x^{-\frac{1991}{1992}}\, dx = \lim_{b \to 0} \int_b^1 x^{-\frac{1991}{1992}}\, dx$$

$$= \lim_{b \to 0} 1992 x^{\frac{1}{1992}}\Big|_b^1$$

$$= \lim_{b \to 0}\left(1992 - b^{\frac{1}{1992}}\right)$$

$$= 1992$$

The integral converges to 1992.

3. If the following improper integral converges, then give its value correct to three decimal places. You may do this by any means of your choosing, but show your work clearly and explain your steps.

$$\int_0^2 \frac{1}{\sqrt{1-x}}\, dx$$

ANSWER:

Let $w = 1 - x \Rightarrow dw = -dx$.

$$\int_0^1 \frac{1}{\sqrt{1-x}}\, dx$$

$$= -\int_1^0 w^{-\frac{1}{2}}\, dw = \int_0^1 w^{-\frac{1}{2}}\, dw = \lim_{b \to 0+} \int_b^1 w^{-\frac{1}{2}}\, dw$$

$$= \lim_{b \to 0+}\left[2\sqrt{w}\right]_b^1 = \lim_{b \to 0+}\left[2 - 2\sqrt{b}\right] = 2$$

The integral converges, and it equals 2.000.

4. Find the value of the following improper integrals, or, if an integral does not converge, say so explicitly.

(a) $\displaystyle\int_{-1}^0 \frac{1}{\sqrt{1+x}}\, dx$

(b) $\displaystyle\int_0^\infty \frac{1}{\sqrt{1+x}}\, dx$

ANSWER:

(a) This integral is improper because the integrand is undefined at $x = -1$.

$$\int \frac{1}{\sqrt{1+x}}\, dx = 2\sqrt{1+x} + C,$$

so $\displaystyle\int_{-1}^0 \frac{1}{\sqrt{1+x}}\, dx = \lim_{a \to -1+}\left[2\sqrt{1+x}\right]_a^0 = \lim_{a \to -1+}\left[2 - 2\sqrt{1+a}\right] = 2.$

The integral converges to 2.

(b) $\displaystyle\int_0^\infty \frac{1}{\sqrt{1+x}}\, dx = \lim_{b \to \infty}\left[2\sqrt{1+x}\right]_0^b = \lim_{b \to \infty}\left[2\sqrt{1+b} - 2\right]$

The integral diverges.

5. Do the following integrals converge? If so, calculate the value. If not, explain why not.

(a) $\displaystyle\int_0^2 \frac{dx}{(x-1)^2}$

(b) $\displaystyle\int_0^\infty xe^{-x}\, dx$

**500**

ANSWER:

(a) $\dfrac{1}{(x-1)^2}$ misbehaves at $x = 1$, as shown in Figure 7.7.22:

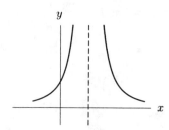

*Figure 7.7.22*

So

$$\int_0^2 \frac{1}{(x-1)^2}\,dx = \lim_{a\to 1^-}\int_0^a \frac{dx}{(x-1)^2} + \lim_{b\to 1^+}\int_b^2 \frac{dx}{(x-1)^2}$$

$$= \lim_{a\to 1^-}\left[-\left(\frac{1}{x-1}\right)\Big|_0^a\right] + \lim_{b\to 1^+}\left[-\left(\frac{1}{x-1}\right)\Big|_b^2\right]$$

$$= \lim_{a\to 1^-}\left[-\frac{1}{a-1}-1\right] + \lim_{b\to 1^+}\left[-\frac{1}{2}+\frac{1}{b-1}\right].$$

Neither limit is defined so the integral diverges.

(b)

$$\int_0^\infty xe^{-x}\,dx = \lim_{b\to\infty}\int_0^b xe^{-x}\,dx.$$

Using integration by parts with $u = x$, $u' = 1$, $v' = e^{-x}$, $v = -e^{-x}$ we have:

$$\lim_{b\to\infty}\int_0^b xe^{-x}\,dx = \lim_{b\to\infty}\left(-be^{-b}+0\right) + \lim_{b\to\infty}\int_0^b e^{-x}\,dx.$$

Since the left limit is equal to zero,

$$\int_0^\infty xe^{-x}\,dx = \lim_{b\to\infty}\int_0^b e^{-x}\,dx = \lim_{b\to\infty}\left[-e^{-x}\Big|_0^b\right] = \lim_{b\to\infty}\left[-\frac{1}{e^b}+1\right] = 1.$$

So the integral converges.

6. Doe the following integrals converge or diverge? If an integral converges, give its exact value. Justify your answer using antiderivatives.

(a) $\displaystyle\int_0^\infty xe^{-x}\,dx$

(b) $\displaystyle\int_0^2 \frac{dx}{(x-1)^{4/3}}$

ANSWER:

(a) Applying the definition of an improper integral,

$$\int_0^\infty xe^{-x}\,dx = \lim_{b\to\infty}\int_0^b xe^{-x}\,dx$$

Using integration by parts with $u = x$, $v' = e^{-x}$, $u' = 1$, $v = 1$, we have

$$\lim_{b\to\infty}\int_0^b xe^{-x}\,dx = \lim_{b\to\infty}-xe^{-x}\Big|_0^b - e^{-x}\Big|_0^b$$

$$= \lim_{b\to\infty}\left[-be^{-b}+0e^0\right] - \left[e^{-b}-e^0\right] = 1.$$

So $\displaystyle\int_0^\infty xe^{-x}dx$ converges to 1.

(b)  Since the integrand goes to infinity at $x = 1$, we can split the integral up around this point:

$$\int_0^2 \frac{dx}{(x-1)^{4/3}} = = \lim_{a\to 1-}\int_0^a \frac{dx}{(x-1)^{4/3}} + \lim_{b\to 1+}\int_b^2 \frac{dx}{(x-1)^{4/3}}$$

$$= \lim_{a\to 1-} -3\cdot\frac{1}{(x-1)^{1/3}}\Big|_0^a + \lim_{b\to 1+} -3\cdot\frac{1}{(x-1)^{1/3}}\Big|_b^2$$

$$= \lim_{a\to 1-} -3\left[\frac{1}{(a-1)^{1/3}} - \frac{1}{(-1)^{1/3}}\right] + \lim_{b\to 1+} -3\left[\frac{1}{1^{1/3}} - \frac{1}{(b-1)^{1/3}}\right],$$

which diverges.

7.  Evaluate the following integral:

$$\int_0^\infty 3z^2 e^{-z^3}\, dz.$$

ANSWER:

Applying the formula for this improper integral,

$$\int_0^\infty 3z^2 e^{-z^3}dz = \lim_{b\to\infty}\int_0^b 3z^2 e^{-z^3}dz$$

$$= \lim_{b\to\infty} -e^{-z^3}\Big|_0^b$$

$$= \lim_{b\to\infty}\left(-e^{-b^3} + e^0\right)$$

$$= 1.$$

## Problems and Solutions for Section 7.8

1.  Are the following integrals convergent or divergent? Give reasons for your answers and if the integral is convergent, please give an approximation rounded off to two decimal places. (Note: the function $f(x) = \dfrac{e^{-x}}{1+x}$ is concave up for $x \geq 0$.)

(a)  $\displaystyle\int_0^\infty \frac{1}{e^x}\, dx$       (b)  $\displaystyle\int_0^\infty \frac{e^{-x}}{1+x}\, dx$

ANSWER:

(a)  This integral is convergent:

$$\int_0^\infty \frac{1}{e^x}\, dx = \lim_{b\to\infty}\int_0^b e^{-x}\, dx = \lim_{b\to\infty} -e^{-x}\Big|_0^b = \lim_{b\to\infty}(e^0 - e^{-b}) = 1.$$

(b)  This integral is also convergent. The integrand $\frac{e^{-x}}{1+x}$ is positive and less than $e^{-x}$ for $x \geq 0$; since by (a), $\int_0^\infty e^{-x}\, dx = 1$, our integral is finite and, in particular, less than 1. As $b$ tends to infinity, $\int_0^b \frac{e^{-x}}{1+x}\, dx$ tends to 0.60 (or more precisely 0.5963); that is the value of our integral.

502

2. Does $\int_1^\infty \dfrac{2+e^{-z}}{z}dz$ converge? Explain clearly how you know.

ANSWER:

Since $\dfrac{2+e^{-z}}{z} > \dfrac{2}{z}$ and $\int_1^\infty \dfrac{2}{z}dz$ does <u>not</u> converge, neither does $\int_1^\infty \dfrac{2+e^{-z}}{z}dz$.

3. Is $\int_0^\infty \dfrac{\sin^2 x}{(1+x)^2}dx$ convergent or divergent? Give reasons for your answer and if it is convergent, give an upper bound for its value.

ANSWER:

$$\int_0^\infty \frac{\sin^2 x}{(1+x)^2}dx \le \int_0^\infty \frac{1}{(1+x)^2}dx \quad (\text{because } \sin^2 x \le 1)$$

$$= -\frac{1}{1+x}\Big|_0^\infty$$

$$= \lim_{b\to\infty}\left(-\frac{1}{1+b}+1\right) = 1.$$

It is convergent and 1 is an upper bound.

4. Does the following integral converge or diverge? Justify your answer.

$$\int_0^\infty x\cdot(x^3-3x-1)^{-1/2}dx$$

ANSWER:

For large and positive $x$,

$$\frac{x}{(x^3-3x-1)^{1/2}} \ge \frac{1}{x^{1/2}},$$

hence since $\int_0^\infty \dfrac{1}{x^{1/2}}dx$ diverges, so does $\int_0^\infty \dfrac{x}{(x^3-3x-1)^{1/2}}dx$.

5. The following improper integral may arise in the study of certain damped oscillatory motion, such as that of a pendulum that eventually comes to rest due to friction:

$$\int_0^\infty e^{-t}(1+\cos t)dt$$

(a) Show why this improper integral converges. (Hint: It is easier to do this with the comparison theorem than by finding the antiderivative and evaluating the improper integral exactly.)

(b) Based on your answer to part (a), give an upper bound on the value of the improper integral.

ANSWER:

(a) $e^{-t}(1+\cos t) \le 2e^{-t}$ for all $t \ge 0$, because $-1 \le \cos t \le 1$.

Since $\int_0^\infty 2e^{-t}dt$ converges, by comparison, $\int_0^\infty e^{-t}(1+\cos t)dt$ also converges.

(b) We can use the value of $\int_0^\infty 2e^{-t}dt$ as an upper bound on the value of $\int_0^\infty e^{-t}(1+\cos t)dt$.

$$\int_0^\infty 2e^{-t}dt = \lim_{b\to\infty}\int_0^b 2e^{-t}dt = \lim_{b\to\infty} -2e^{-t}\Big|_0^b = \lim_{b\to\infty}(-2e^{-t}+2e^0)=2$$

Since $\int_0^\infty e^{-t}(1+\cos t)dt < \int_0^\infty 2e^{-t}$, then 2 is an upper bound for $\int_0^\infty e^{-t}(1+\cos t)dt$.

## Review Problems and Solutions for Chapter 7

1. Evaluate each of the following and show *all* work:

   (a) $\displaystyle\int \sin^2 x \cos^3 x \, dx$

   (c) $\displaystyle\int \frac{x^2}{x^2 + 1} \, dx$

   (b) $\displaystyle\int x e^{-x} \, dx$

   (d) $\displaystyle\int \frac{t^2}{\sqrt{9 - t^2}} \, dt$

   ANSWER:

   (a) $\displaystyle\int \sin^2 x \cos^3 x \, dx = \int \sin^2 x (1 - \sin^2 x) \cos x \, dx = \int (\sin^2 x \cos x - \sin^4 x \cos x) \, dx =$
   $\displaystyle \frac{1}{3} \sin^3 x - \frac{1}{5} \sin^5 x + C.$

   (b) Integrate by parts with $u = x, v' = e^{-x}$, to get $\displaystyle\int x e^{-x} \, dx = -x e^{-x} + \int e^{-x} \, dx = -e^{-x}(x + 1) + C.$

   (c) $\displaystyle\int \frac{x^2}{x^2 + 1} \, dx = \int \frac{x^2 + 1 - 1}{x^2 + 1} \, dx = \int \left(1 - \frac{1}{x^2 + 1}\right) dx = x - \arctan x + C.$

   (d)

   $$\int \frac{t^2}{\sqrt{9 - t^2}} \, dt = \int \frac{-(9 - t^2) + 9}{\sqrt{9 - t^2}} \, dt$$

   $$= \int \left(-\sqrt{9 - t^2} + \frac{9}{\sqrt{9 - t^2}}\right) dt$$

   $$= -\frac{1}{2} \left(t\sqrt{9 - t^2} + 9 \int \frac{dt}{\sqrt{9 - t^2}}\right) + \left(9 \arcsin \frac{t}{3} + C\right)$$

   $$= -\frac{1}{2} t \sqrt{9 - t^2} + \frac{9}{2} \arcsin \frac{t}{3} + C'$$

   Note: The last two steps were performed using integral tables.

2. Use the results of Problem 1(a) to evaluate

   $$\int_0^{\frac{\pi}{2}} \sin^2 x \cos^3 x \, dx.$$

   ANSWER:
   $$\int_0^{\frac{\pi}{2}} \sin^2 x \cos^3 x \, dx = \left(\frac{1}{3} \sin^3 x - \frac{1}{5} \sin^5 x\right)\Bigg|_0^{\frac{\pi}{2}} = \frac{2}{15}.$$

3. Find by any method. Say briefly but clearly what you did.

   (a) $\displaystyle\int_0^1 x^3 e^{x^2} \, dx$

   (b) $\displaystyle\int_{-2}^2 f(x) \, dx$ where $f(x) = \begin{cases} 1 \text{ for } x \le 1 \\ x \text{ for } x > 1 \end{cases}$

   ANSWER:

   (a) Substituting $t = x^2, dt = 2x \, dx,$

   $$\int_{x=0}^{x=1} x^2 e^{x^2} (x \, dx) = \frac{1}{2} \int_{t=0}^{t=1} t e^t \, dt.$$

   Integrating by parts with $u = t, v' = e^t$, gives

   $$\frac{1}{2} \int_0^1 t e^t \, dt = \frac{1}{2} t e^t \Bigg|_0^1 - \frac{1}{2} \int_0^1 e^t \, dt = \frac{1}{2} e^t (t - 1) \Bigg|_0^1 = \frac{1}{2}.$$

(b) We do the integral in two pieces, using the additivity property. We get:

$$\int_{-2}^{1} 1\, dx + \int_{1}^{2} x\, dx = x\Big|_{-2}^{1} + \frac{1}{2}x^2\Big|_{1}^{2} = 3 + \frac{3}{2} = 4\tfrac{1}{2}.$$

4. Find elementary formulas for the following:

(a) $\displaystyle\int (1+x)\sin(2x)\, dx$

(b) $\displaystyle\int \frac{1+e^{2t}}{e^t}\, dt$

ANSWER:

(a)

$$\int (1+x)\sin 2x\, dx = \int \sin 2x\, dx + \int x \sin 2x\, dx$$

$$= -\frac{\cos 2x}{2} + \int x \sin 2x\, dx + C$$

In the integral $\displaystyle\int x \sin 2x\, dx$, integrate by parts, with $u = x, u' = 1$;

$v' = \sin 2x, \quad v = -\frac{1}{2}\cos 2x$

$$\int x \sin 2x\, dx = -\frac{1}{2}x\cos 2x + \int \frac{1}{2}\cos 2x\, dx$$

$$= -\frac{x\cos 2x}{2} + \frac{\sin 2x}{4} + C'$$

So,

$$\int (1+x)\sin 2x\, dx = -\frac{\cos 2x}{2} - \frac{x\cos 2x}{2} + \frac{\sin 2x}{4} + C''$$

(b)

$$\int \frac{1+e^{2t}}{e^t}\, dt = \int (e^{-t} + e^t)\, dt$$

$$= -e^{-t} + e^t + C$$

5. Integrate

(a) $\displaystyle\int x^2(2x - 1)\, dx$

(b) $\displaystyle\int \frac{\cos^3 x}{\sin x}\, dx$

(c) $\displaystyle\int \frac{x}{\cos^2 x}\, dx$

(d) $\displaystyle\int_{2}^{4} \frac{e^{2x}}{\sqrt{e^x - 1}}\, dx$

(e) Derive the reduction formula

$$\int (\ln x)^n\, dx = x(\ln x)^n - n\int (\ln x)^{n-1}\, dx.$$

ANSWER:

(a) $\displaystyle\int x^2(2x - 1)\, dx = \int 2x^3 - x^2\, dx = \frac{x^4}{2} - \frac{x^3}{3} + C.$

(b)

$$\int \frac{\cos^3 x}{\sin x}\, dx = \int \frac{\cos x \cos^2 x}{\sin x}\, dx = \int \frac{\cos x (1 - \sin^2 x)}{\sin x}\, dx$$

$$= \int \left( \frac{\cos x}{\sin x} - \cos x \sin x \right) dx.$$

Let $u = \sin x$. Then $du = \cos x\, dx$ and

$$\int \left( \frac{\cos x}{\sin x} - \cos x \sin x \right) dx = \int \left( \frac{1}{u} - u \right) du = \ln |u| - \frac{u^2}{2} + C$$

$$= \ln |\sin x| - \frac{\sin^2 x}{2} + C.$$

(c)  Integrate by parts with $u = x$ and $v' = \frac{1}{\cos^2 x}$. Then $u' = 1$, and $v = \tan x$. We get $\int \frac{x}{\cos^2 x}\, dx =$

$x \tan x - \int \tan x\, dx$. But $\int \tan x\, dx = -\ln |\cos x| + C$, so we have $x \tan x - \ln |\cos x| + C$ as the final answer.

(d)  Setting $u = e^x$ and $du = e^x\, dx$, we get $\int_2^4 \frac{e^{2x}\, dx}{\sqrt{e^x - 1}} = \int_{e^2}^{e^4} \frac{u\, du}{\sqrt{u - 1}}$. We now set $v = u - 1$,

to get $\int_{e^2}^{e^4} \frac{u\, du}{\sqrt{u - 1}} = \int_{e^2 - 1}^{e^4 - 1} \frac{v + 1}{\sqrt{v}}\, dv = \int_{e^2 - 1}^{e^4 - 1} \left( \sqrt{v} + \frac{1}{\sqrt{v}} \right) dv = \frac{2}{3} v^{\frac{3}{2}} + 2v^{\frac{1}{2}} \Big|_{e^2 - 1}^{e^4 - 1} =$

$\frac{2}{3}(e^4 - 1)^{\frac{3}{2}} + 2(e^4 - 1)^{\frac{1}{2}} - \frac{2}{3}(e^2 - 1)^{\frac{3}{2}} - 2(e^2 - 1)^{\frac{1}{2}} \approx 260.42.$

(e)  Integrate by parts with $u = (\ln x)^n$ and $v' = 1$. Then $u' = n(\ln x)^{n-1} \cdot \frac{1}{x}$ and $v = x$. We

get $\int (\ln x)^n\, dx = x(\ln x)^n - \int n(\ln x)^{n-1} \left( \frac{1}{x} \right) \cdot x\, dx$. But $\int n(\ln x)^{n-1} \left( \frac{1}{x} \right) \cdot x\, dx =$

$n \int (\ln x)^{n-1}\, dx$, to complete the proof.

6.  Evaluate each of the indefinite integrals below. Be sure to show your work.

(a)  $\displaystyle\int xe^x\, dx$

(d)  $\displaystyle\int \frac{\sin x}{\cos x}\, dx$

(b)  $\displaystyle\int \frac{e^x}{1 + e^{2x}}\, dx$

(e)  $\displaystyle\int \frac{1}{\sqrt{1 - 4x^2}}\, dx$

(c)  $\displaystyle\int \frac{1}{1 + e^x}\, dx$

ANSWER:

(a)  Using the formula for integration by parts, $\int uv'\, dx = uv - \int u'v\, dx$, with $u = x$ and $v = e^x$, we find:

$$\int xe^x\, dx = xe^x - \int e^x\, dx = xe^x - e^x + C = e^x(x - 1) + C.$$

(b)  Set $u = e^x$, $du = e^x\, dx$. Then

$$\int \frac{e^x\, dx}{1 + e^{2x}} = \int \frac{du}{1 + u^2} = \arctan u + C = \arctan(e^x) + C.$$

(c)

$$\int \frac{1}{1 + e^x}\, dx = \int \frac{1 + e^x - e^x}{1 + e^x}\, dx$$

$$= \int \left( 1 - \frac{e^x}{1 + e^x} \right) dx$$

$$= \int 1\, dx - \int \frac{e^x}{1 + e^x}\, dx.$$

In the second integral, set $u = 1 + e^x$, $du = e^x\, dx$. Substituting, we get

$$-\int \frac{e^x}{1+e^x}\, dx = -\int \frac{du}{u}$$
$$= -\ln|u| + C$$
$$= -\ln(1 + e^x) + C.$$

So $\int \frac{1}{1+e^x}\, dx = x - \ln(1 + e^x) + C'$.

(d)  Set $u = \cos x$, $du = -\sin x\, dx$. Then

$$\int \frac{\sin x}{\cos x}\, dx = -\int \frac{du}{u} = -\ln|u| + C$$
$$= -\ln|\cos x| + C.$$

(e)  Set $u = 2x$, $du = 2\, dx$. Then

$$\int \frac{1}{\sqrt{1-4x^2}}\, dx = \frac{1}{2}\int \frac{du}{\sqrt{1-u^2}} = \frac{1}{2}\arcsin u + C = \frac{1}{2}\arcsin(2x) + C.$$

7.  Calculate the following indefinite integrals. (Remember, you can always check your answers.)

(a)  $\int x^3 \cos x\, dx$

(b)  $\int \sin(\ln t)\, dt$

(c)  $\int \left( (\ln z)^2 + 3\ln z \right)\, dz$

ANSWER:

(a)  Using the Table (#16), or parts:
$$\int x^3 \cos x\, dx = x^3 \sin x + 3x^2 \cos x - 6x \sin x - 6\cos x + C$$

(b)  Parts:
$$\int \sin(\ln t)\, dt \quad = \quad t\sin(\ln t) -$$

$$u = \sin(\ln t)\quad u' = \frac{\cos(\ln t)}{t}$$
$$v = t \qquad v' = 1$$

$$\int \cos(\ln t)\, dt \quad = \quad t\sin(\ln t) - [t\cos(\ln t) + \int \sin(\ln t)\, dt]$$

Parts again
$$u = \cos(\ln t)\quad u' = \frac{-\sin(\ln t)}{t}$$
$$v = t \qquad v' = 1$$

solving $\int \sin(\ln t)\, dt = \frac{t}{2}[\sin(\ln t) - \cos\ln t)] + C$

(Alternatively, use $w = \ln t$, $t = e$, $dt = e^2 dw$ and #8 from Table.]

(c)  $\int \ln z\, dz = z\ln z - z + C$ (from Table #4)

$$\int (\ln z)^2 dz \quad = \quad z(\ln z)^2 - \int 2\ln z\, dz = z(\ln z)^2 - 2[z(\ln z) - z] + C$$

$$u = (\ln z)^2\quad u' = \frac{2\ln z}{z}$$
$$v = z \qquad v' = t$$

$$= z(\ln z)^2 - 2z\ln z + 2z + C$$

so $\int ((\ln z)^2 + 3\ln z)\, dz = z(\ln z)^2 + z\,lnz - z + C$

8. Find the following indefinite integrals:

   (a) $\displaystyle\int e^{-2x}\cos x\,dx$

   (b) $\displaystyle\int \frac{t}{t+1}\,dt$

   ANSWER:

   (a) Apply II-9 from the integral table; $u = -2, b = 1$.

   $$= \frac{1}{(-2)^2 + (1)^2}e^{-2x}[-2\cos x + \sin x] + C$$

   $$= \frac{1}{5}e^{-2x}(-2\cos x + \sin x) + C$$

   You can integrate by parts twice to get the same answer.

   (b) You have to apply long division to get the degree of the numerator to be less than the degree of the denominator.

   $$\frac{t}{t+1} = 1 - \frac{1}{t+1} \text{ Thus,}$$

   $$\int \frac{t}{t+1}\,dt = \int \left(1 - \frac{1}{t+1}\right)dt = t - \ln|t+1| + C$$

9. Find the following integrals:

   (a) $\displaystyle\int xe^x\,dx$

   (b) $\displaystyle\int (\sin t)e^{\cos t}\,dt$

   (c) $\displaystyle\int \frac{1}{4-y^2}\,dy$

   ANSWER:

   (a) Use parts or #14 of tables: $\displaystyle\int xe^x\,dx = xe^x - \int e^x\,dx = xe^x - e^x + C$

   (b) Set $w = \cos t$ and $dw = -\sin t\,dt$. $\displaystyle\int \sin te^{\cos t}\,dt = -\int e^w\,dw = -e^w + C = -e^{\cos t} + C$

   (c) Use #16 of tables: $(a = 2, b = -2)$

   $$\int \frac{dy}{4-y^2} = \int \frac{dy}{(2-y)(2+y)} = -\int \frac{dy}{(y-2)(y+2)} = -\frac{1}{4}(\ln|y-2| - \ln|y+2|) + C$$

10. Find the following indefinite integrals:

    (a) $\displaystyle\int \frac{x}{x^2-1}\,dx$

    (b) $\displaystyle\int x^2\sin x\,dx.$

    ANSWER:

    (a) $\displaystyle\int \frac{x}{x^2-1}\,dx$

    Let $w = x^2 - 1 \Rightarrow dw = 2x\,dx \Rightarrow x\,dx = \frac{1}{2}dw$

    $$= \frac{1}{2}\int \frac{dw}{w} = \frac{1}{2}\ln|w| + C$$

    $$= \frac{1}{2}\ln|x^2 - 1| + C$$

**508**

(b) $\displaystyle\int x^2 \sin x \, dx$

Apply Formula III-15 from the table of integrals, letting
$p(x) = x^2, \quad a = 1$
$\Rightarrow p'(x) = 2x$
$\Rightarrow p''(x) = 2$
$= -x^2 \cos x + (2x) \sin x + 2 \cos x + C$

11. Find the following indefinite integrals:

(a) $\displaystyle\int \frac{x^2}{x^3 + 1} \, dx$

(b) $\displaystyle\int (x^2 + 1) \cos 2x \, dx$

ANSWER:

(a) Use substitution! Let $u = x^3 + 1$, then $du = 3x^2 dx$, $\frac{1}{3} du = x^2 dx$

$$\int \frac{x^2}{x^3 + 1} \, dx = \frac{1}{3} \int \frac{1}{u} \, du = \frac{1}{3} \ln |u| + C = \frac{1}{3} \ln |x^3 + 1| + C$$

(b) Using Table III #16, or integrating by parts (twice), we get

$$\int (x^2 + 1) \cos 2x \, dx = \frac{1}{2}(x^2 + 1) \sin 2x + \frac{1}{2} x \cos 2x - \frac{1}{4} \sin 2x + C$$

$$= \frac{1}{2} x^2 \sin 2x + \frac{1}{2} \sin 2x + \frac{1}{2} x \cos 2x - \frac{1}{4} \sin 2x + C$$

$$= \frac{1}{2} x^2 \sin 2x + \frac{1}{2} x \cos 2x + \frac{1}{4} \sin 2x + C$$

12. Find the following indefinite integrals:

(a) $\displaystyle\int \frac{1}{2x + 3} \, dx$

(b) $\displaystyle\int \frac{1}{\sin^3 x} \, dx$

ANSWER:

(a) $w = 2x + 3 \Rightarrow dw = 2x \, dx \Rightarrow x \, dx = \frac{1}{2} dw$

$$\int \frac{1}{2x + 3} \, dx = \frac{1}{2} \int \frac{dw}{w} = \frac{1}{2} \ln |w| + C = \frac{1}{2} \ln |2x + 3| + C$$

(b) $\displaystyle\int \frac{1}{\sin^3 x} \, dx$

Integral Table #19, $m = 3$

$$= -\frac{1}{2} \frac{\cos x}{\sin^2 x} + \frac{1}{2} \int \frac{1}{\sin x} \, dx$$

Integral Table #20

$$= -\frac{1}{2} \frac{\cos x}{\sin^2 x} + \frac{1}{4} \ln \left| \frac{\cos x - 1}{\cos x + 1} \right| + C$$

13. Integrate: (Please give exact answers.)

(a) $\displaystyle\int \frac{1}{\sqrt{3x + 7}} \, dx$

(b) $\displaystyle\int_1^2 x^3 \ln x \, dx$

(c) $\displaystyle\int \frac{2t}{e^{3t}}\, dt$

(d) $\displaystyle\int_{-13}^{13} \frac{(\sin\theta)^7}{\theta^2}\, d\theta$

(e) $\displaystyle\int \frac{\sqrt{u}}{\sqrt{u}+1}\, du$

ANSWER:

(a) Let $w = 3x + 7$, $dw = 3dx$.

$$= \int \frac{1}{\sqrt{w}} \frac{dw}{3}$$

$$= \frac{1}{3}\int w^{-\frac{1}{2}}\, dw = \frac{1}{3}\frac{w^{\frac{1}{2}}}{\frac{1}{2}} + C = \frac{2}{3}\sqrt{3x+7} + C$$

Common mistake: $\displaystyle\int (3x+7)^{-\frac{1}{2}}\, dx = (3x+7)^{\frac{1}{2}}$

$$\int x^3 \ln x\, dx = \int \ln x\, d\left(\frac{x^4}{4}\right) = \frac{x^4}{4}\ln x - \int \frac{x^4}{4} d(\ln x)$$

(b)
$$= \frac{x^4}{4}\ln x - \int \frac{x^4}{4}\cdot\frac{1}{x}\, dx$$

$$= \frac{x^4}{4}\ln x - \frac{1}{4}\cdot\frac{x^4}{4} + C$$

$$\int_1^2 x^3 \ln x\, dx = 4\ln 2 - \frac{15}{16}$$

Common mistake: Miss $\frac{1}{4}$ during copying.

$$\int 2t\, d\left(\frac{e^{-3t}}{-3}\right) = 2t\frac{e^{-3t}}{-3} - \int \frac{e^{-3t}}{-3} d(2t)$$

(c)
$$= -\frac{2}{3}te^{-3t} + \frac{2}{3}\int e^{-3t}\, dt$$

$$= -\frac{2}{3}te^{-3t} - \frac{2}{9}e^{-3t} - C$$

Common mistake:

(1) Take $\dfrac{1}{e^{3t}}$ as $e^{3t}$.

(2) Miss a sign during copying.

(d) $= 0$.

Reason: $\sin(-\theta) = -\sin\theta \Rightarrow \dfrac{[\sin(-\theta)]^7}{(-\theta)^2} = -\dfrac{(\sin\theta)^7}{\theta^2}$

i.e., $\dfrac{(\sin\theta)^7}{\theta^2}$ is an <u>odd</u> function, the graph is symmetric with respect to the origin.

Note also that near zero, the function behaves like $\frac{\theta^7}{\theta^2} = \theta^5$, so it is bounded there. So $\displaystyle\int_{-13}^{0}$ cancels

with $\displaystyle\int_{0}^{13}$.

Common mistake: Do not recognize the symmetry.

(e) Let $w = \sqrt{u}+1$, $dw = \dfrac{1}{2}u^{-\frac{1}{2}}\, du$, $du = 2\sqrt{u}\, dw = 2(w-1)dw$.

$$\int \frac{2(w-1)^2}{w}\,dw = 2\int \frac{w^2-2w+1}{w}\,dw = 2\int \left(w-2+\frac{1}{w}\right)dw$$

$$= 2\left[\frac{w^2}{2}-2w+\ln|w|\right]$$

$$= w^2 - 4w + 2\ln|w| + C$$
$$= (\sqrt{u}+1)^2 - 4(\sqrt{u}+1) + 2\ln|\sqrt{u}+1| + C$$
$$= u - 2\sqrt{u} + 2\ln(\sqrt{u}+1) + C$$

Common mistake: Fail to get $du = 2(w-1)dw$.

14. Find

(a) $\displaystyle\int \sqrt{1-3x}\,dx$

(b) $\displaystyle\int x\ln x\,dx$

ANSWER:

(a) Let $w = 1 - 3x$, $dw = -3dx$. By substitution,

$$\int \sqrt{1-3x}\,dx = -\frac{1}{3}\int \sqrt{w}\,dw$$

$$= -\frac{1}{3}\cdot\frac{2}{3}w^{\frac{3}{2}} + C$$

$$= -\frac{2}{9}(1-3x)^{\frac{3}{2}} + C$$

(b) Let $u = \ln x$, $v' = x$, so $u' = \frac{1}{x}$ and $v = \frac{x^2}{2}$. Integrating by parts gives:

$$\int x\ln x\,dx = \frac{1}{2}\ln x \cdot x^2 - \int \frac{x}{2}\,dx + C$$

$$= \frac{1}{2}x^2\ln x - \frac{x^2}{4} + C$$

15. Find the following antiderivatives:

(a) $\displaystyle\int \frac{4+x}{\sqrt{x}}\,dx$

(b) $\displaystyle\int \frac{1+\sin(2x)}{2}\,dx$

(c) $\displaystyle\int \frac{1}{(1+x)^2}\,dx$

(d) $\displaystyle\int \frac{\ln(1+x)}{1+x}\,dx$

(e) $\displaystyle\int \ln\left(\frac{1}{x}\right)\,dx$

ANSWER:

(a) $\displaystyle\int \frac{4+x}{\sqrt{x}}\,dx = \int \left(\frac{4}{\sqrt{x}}+\sqrt{x}\right)dx = 8\sqrt{x} + \frac{2}{3}x^{\frac{3}{2}} + C$

(b) $\displaystyle\int \frac{1+\sin(2x)}{2}\,dx = \int \left(\frac{1}{2}+\frac{1}{2}\sin(2x)\right)dx = \frac{1}{2}x - \frac{1}{4}\cos(2x) + C$

(c) $\displaystyle\int (1+x)^{-2}\,dx = -\frac{1}{1+x} + C$

(d) We first set $u = 1 + x$, $du = dx$ to get $\displaystyle\int \frac{\ln(1+x)}{1+x}\, dx = \int \frac{\ln u}{u}\, du$. Now set $v = \ln u$, $dv = \frac{1}{u}\, du$ to get

$$\int v\, dv = \frac{v^2}{2} + C = \frac{\left(\ln(1+x)\right)^2}{2} + C$$

(e) $\displaystyle\int \ln\left(\frac{1}{x}\right) dx = \int -\ln x\, dx$. We integrate by parts with $u = -\ln x$, $dv = dx$, to get

$$-\int \ln x\, dx = -x \ln x + \int 1\, dx = -x \ln x + x + C$$

16. Find formulas for the following indefinite integrals (anti-derivatives):

(a) $\displaystyle\int (x+2)(x-2)\, dx$

(b) $\displaystyle\int \frac{1+e^t}{e^t}\, dt$

(c) $\displaystyle\int \frac{1-\ln x}{x}\, dx$

(d) $\displaystyle\int (x-1)e^{-x}\, dx$

ANSWER:

(a) $\displaystyle\int (x+2)(x-2)\, dx = \int (x^2 - 4)\, dx = \frac{x^3}{3} - 4x + C.$

(b) $\displaystyle\int \frac{1+e^t}{e^t}\, dt = \int (e^{-t} + 1)\, dt = -e^{-t} + t + C.$

(c) Set $u = \ln x$, $du = \frac{1}{x} dx$. Substitute to get
$$\int \frac{1-\ln x}{x}\, dx = \int (1-u)\, du = u - \frac{u^2}{2} + C = \ln|x| - \frac{(\ln|x|)^2}{2} + C.$$

(d)
$$\int (x-1)e^{-x}\, dx = \int (xe^{-x} - e^{-x})\, dx.$$

We integrate $\displaystyle\int xe^{-x}\, dx$ by parts with $u = x$, $v' = e^{-x}$ and $u' = 1$, $v = -e^{-x}$.

$$\int xe^{-x}\, dx = -xe^{-x} + \int e^{-x}\, dx = -xe^{-x} - e^{-x} + C.$$

Thus

$$\int (xe^{-x} - e^{-x})\, dx = -xe^{-x} - e^{-x} - \int e^{-x}\, dx$$
$$= -xe^{-x} - e^{-x} + e^{-x} + C$$
$$= -xe^{-x} + C.$$

17. Evaluate the following. Give both an exact, but possibly symbolic, value (e.g., $\frac{3}{4}$, $\sin 3$, $\ln 2$, ...) and a decimal approximation accurate to two decimal places.

(a) $\displaystyle\int_0^{\frac{1}{2}} \frac{1}{1-x^2}\, dx$

(b) $\displaystyle\int_0^4 \frac{4x}{\sqrt{x^2+9}}\, dx$

(c) $\displaystyle\int_1^3 \ln x\, dx$

ANSWER:

(a) We use the table of integrals to solve the integral $\int_0^{\frac{1}{2}} \frac{1}{1-x^2}\,dx$. The table of integrals says:

$$\int \frac{1}{(x-a)(x-b)}\,dx = \frac{1}{a-b}(\ln|x-a| - \ln|x-b| + C)$$

Since $x^2 - 1 = (x-1)(x+1)$, we use $a = 1$ and $b = -1$. Substituting for $a$ and $b$ in the formula, we get:

$$\int_0^{\frac{1}{2}} \frac{1}{1-x^2}\,dx = -\int_0^{\frac{1}{2}} \frac{1}{(x-1)(x+1)}\,dx$$

$$= -\left(\frac{1}{2}\right)\left(\ln|x-1| - \ln|x+1|\right)\Big|_0^{\frac{1}{2}}$$

$$= -\left(\frac{1}{2}\right)\left(\ln\left|\frac{x-1}{x+1}\right|\right)\Big|_0^{\frac{1}{2}}$$

$$= \ln\sqrt{\left|\frac{x+1}{x-1}\right|}\,\Big|_0^{\frac{1}{2}}$$

$$= \ln\sqrt{3} - \ln 1 = \ln\sqrt{3} \approx 0.5943.$$

(b) Set $u = x^2 + 9$, $du = 2x\,dx$. So substituting, $\int_0^4 \frac{4x}{\sqrt{x^2+9}}\,dx = 2\int_{u=9}^{u=25} \frac{du}{\sqrt{u}} = 2 \cdot 2u^{1/2}\Big|_9^{25} = 4(5-3) = 8.$

(c) We integrate $\int_1^3 \ln x\,dx$ by parts with $u = \ln x$, $v' = 1$ and $u' = \frac{1}{x}$, $v = x$. $\int_1^3 \ln x\,dx = x\ln x\Big|_1^3 - \int_1^3 dx = (x\ln x - x)\Big|_1^3 = 3\ln 3 - 3 - 0 + 1 = 3\ln 3 - 2 \approx 1.296.$

18. Integrate:

(a) $\int \frac{x^2+1}{\sqrt{x}}\,dx$

(b) $\int (\sin^3 2\theta + 1)\cos 2\theta\,d\theta$

(c) $\int \frac{3x^2 + \cos x}{x^3 + \sin x}\,dx$

(d) $\int_0^{\frac{\sqrt{3}}{2}} \frac{dx}{\sqrt{1-x^2}}$

(e) $\int_0^{\ln 2} \frac{x}{e^x}\,dx$

ANSWER:

(a) $\int \frac{x^2+1}{\sqrt{x}}\,dx = \int (x^{\frac{3}{2}} + x^{-\frac{1}{2}})\,dx = \frac{2}{5}x^{\frac{5}{2}} + 2x^{\frac{1}{2}} + C$

(b)

$$\int (\sin^3 2\theta + 1)\cos 2\theta\,dt = \int \sin^3 2\theta \cos 2\theta\,d\theta + \int \cos 2\theta\,d\theta$$

In the first integral, let $u = \sin^2 2\theta$, $du = 2\sin 2\theta \cos 2\theta \cdot 2\,d\theta = 4\sin 2\theta \cos 2\theta\,d\theta$. So the first integral can be simplified to:

$$\frac{1}{4}\int u\,du = \frac{1}{4}\frac{u^2}{2} + C = \frac{1}{8}u^2 + C = \frac{1}{8}\sin^4 2\theta + C.$$

The second integral is simply $\frac{1}{2}\sin 2\theta + C$, so the answer is $\frac{1}{8}\sin^4 2\theta + \frac{1}{2}\sin 2\theta + C.$

(c) Substitute $u = x^3 + \sin x$ and $du = (3x^2 + \cos x)dx$. Then

$$\int \frac{3x^2 + \cos x}{x^3 + \sin x}\, dx = \int \frac{du}{u}$$
$$= \ln|u| + C$$
$$= \ln|x^3 + \sin x| + C.$$

(d) From the tables, $\displaystyle\int_0^{\frac{\sqrt{3}}{2}} \frac{dx}{\sqrt{1-x^2}} = \arcsin x \Big|_0^{\frac{\sqrt{3}}{2}} = \arcsin \frac{\sqrt{3}}{2} - \arcsin 0 = \frac{\pi}{3}$

(e)

$$\int_0^{\ln 2} \frac{x}{e^x}\, dx = \int_0^{\ln 2} xe^{-x}\, dx$$

Integrate by parts: set $u = x, v' = e^{-x}$, and $u' = 1, v = -e^{-x}$

$$\int_0^{\ln 2} xe^{-x}\, dx = -xe^{-x}\Big|_0^{\ln 2} + \int_0^{\ln 2} e^{-x}\, dx$$
$$= \left(-xe^{-x} - e^{-x}\right)\Big|_0^{\ln 2}$$
$$= -\ln 2\, e^{-\ln 2} - e^{-\ln 2} - (-1)$$
$$= -\ln 2 \cdot \left(\frac{1}{2}\right) - \frac{1}{2} + 1$$
$$= \frac{1}{2} - \frac{1}{2}\ln 2.$$

19. Evaluate the following integrals symbolically, (i.e., don't use numerical integration programs.)

(a) $\displaystyle\int_{\frac{\pi}{6}}^{\frac{\pi}{2}} \frac{d\theta}{\tan \theta}$.

(b) $\displaystyle\int_{-\pi}^{\pi} e^{2x} \cos 2x\, dx$.

(c) $\displaystyle\int u^{-1} \ln u\, du$.

(d) $\displaystyle\int \frac{x^2}{(1+x^2)}\, dx$.

(Hint: Use integral tables.)

ANSWER:

(a) $\displaystyle\int_{\frac{\pi}{6}}^{\frac{\pi}{2}} \frac{d\theta}{\tan \theta} = \int_{\frac{\pi}{6}}^{\frac{\pi}{2}} \frac{\cos \theta d\theta}{\sin \theta} = \ln|\sin \theta|\Big|_{\frac{\pi}{6}}^{\frac{\pi}{2}} = \ln 2.$

(b) Refering to the table of integrals, we get

$$\int_{-\pi}^{\pi} e^{2x} \cos 2x\, dx = \frac{1}{8} e^{2x}(2\cos 2x + 2\sin 2x)\Big|_{-\pi}^{\pi}$$

$$= \frac{1}{4} e^{2x}(\cos 2x + \sin 2x)\Big|_{-\pi}^{\pi} = \frac{1}{4}(e^{2\pi} - e^{-2\pi}).$$

(c) Substituting $x = \ln u, dx = \frac{1}{u}\, du$ we get

$$\int u^{-1} \ln u\, du = \int x\, dx = \frac{x^2}{2} + C = \frac{(\ln u)^2}{2} + C.$$

(d) $\displaystyle\int \frac{x^2}{1+x^2}\, dx = \int \left(1 - \frac{1}{1+x^2}\right) dx = x - \arctan x + C.$

514

20. Compute the following indefinite integrals:

(a) $\int \sin x(\cos x + 5)^7\, dx$

(b) $\int \dfrac{\ln x\, dx}{x}$

(c) $\int xe^{2x}\, dx$

ANSWER:

(a) Let $u = \cos x + 5$. Then $du = -\sin x\, dx$.

$$\int \sin x(\cos x + 5)^7\, dx = -\int u^7\, du = -\frac{u^8}{8} + C = -\frac{(\cos x + 5)^8}{8} + C.$$

(b) Let $u = \ln x$. Then $du = \dfrac{1}{x}\, dx$.

$$\int \frac{\ln x\, dx}{x} = \int u\, du = \frac{u^2}{2} + C = \frac{(\ln x)^2}{2} + C.$$

(c) Integrating by parts with $u = x$, $v' = e^{2x}$, we get

$$\int xe^{2x}\, dx = \frac{xe^{2x}}{2} - \int \frac{e^{2x}}{2}\, dx = \frac{xe^{2x}}{2} - \frac{e^{2x}}{4} + C.$$

21. TRUE/FALSE questions. For each statement, write whether it is true or false and provide a short explanation or counterexample.

(a) If the left-hand sum, LEFT($n$), for $\int_a^b f(x)\, dx$ is too large for one value of $n$, it will be too large for all values of $n$.

(b) If the average value of $f(x)$ on the interval $2 \le x \le 5$ is between 0 and 1 then $f$ is between 0 and 1 on the interval $2 \le x \le 5$.

(c) $\int_1^2 \sin x^2\, dx > 3$.

(d) If $f' > g'$ for all $a < x < b$ then the left-hand Riemann sum approximation of $\int_a^b f\, dx$ will have larger error than the left-hand Riemann sum for $\int_a^b g\, dx$.

ANSWER:

(a) FALSE. Try, for example, $\int_{-1}^1 |x|\, dx = 1$. LEFT(1) = 2 is too big, but LEFT(2) = 1 + 0 = 1 is exactly right.

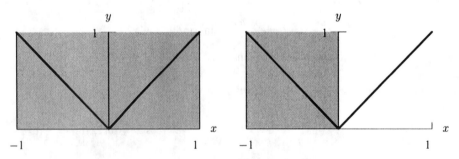

*Figure 7.8.23*: LEFT(1) and LEFT(2) for $f(x) = |x|$

(b) FALSE. Consider $f(x) = x - 3.3$. As can be seen from the figure below, the average value of $f(x)$ over the interval is between 0 and 1, but not all values of $f(x)$ lie between 0 and 1.

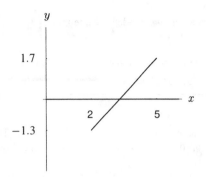

(c)　FALSE. Since $|\sin(x^2)| \leq 1$ for all $x$, $\displaystyle\int_1^2 \sin(x^2)\,dx \leq 1 \cdot (2-1) = 1$.

(d)　FALSE. Let $f(x) = 1$ and $g(x) = 2 - x$ on the interval $0 \leq x \leq 5$. Then $f'(x) = 0$, and $g'(x) = -1$, so $f'(x) > g'(x)$ in this interval. For $f$, LEFT(1) $= 1 \cdot (5 - 0) = 5$, and for $g$, LEFT(1) $= 2 \cdot (5 - 0) = 10$. Evaluating $f$ and $g$ directly, we get $\int_0^5 f(x)\,dx = 5$, and $\int_0^5 g(x)\,dx = -2.5$. So although $f'(x) > g'(x)$, the error in the left-hand Riemann sum is greater for $g$ than for $f$.

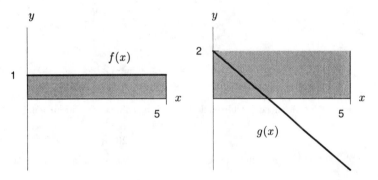

***Figure 7.8.24:*** Graphs of $f(x)$ and $g(x)$; shaded areas show LEFT(1)

# Chapter 8 Exam Questions

1. A rectangular lake is 100 km long and 60 km wide. The depth of the water at any point of the surface is a tenth of the distance from the *nearest* shoreline. How much water does the lake contain (in km$^3$)?

   ANSWER:

   We find the volume by slicing the lake horizontally.

   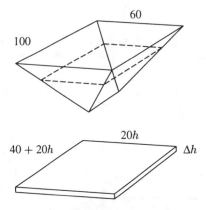

   Note that at height $h$ from the bottom, the volume of a slice of water of thickness $\Delta h$ is approximately

   $$(40 + 20h)(20h)\Delta h.$$

   Since the maximum depth is $h = \frac{30}{10} = 3$ km, summing up all these slices yields

   $$\begin{aligned}
   \text{Volume} &= \int_0^3 (40 + 20h)20h \, dh \\
   &= \int_0^3 400h^2 + 800h \, dh \\
   &= \frac{400}{3}h^3 + 400h^2 \Big|_0^3 \\
   &= 7200 \, \text{km}^3.
   \end{aligned}$$

2. Find the area of the dumbbell shaped region bounded by the curve $y^2 = x^6(1 - x^2)$.

   [Hint 1: Sketch the graphs of $y = x^3\sqrt{1 - x^2}$ and $y = -x^3\sqrt{1 - x^2}$ (using your calculator) and use symmetry to decide what integral to evaluate.

   Hint 2: You may find that the substitution $x = \sin\theta$ is helpful in evaluating your integral, as well as **??** in the table of integrals.]

   ANSWER:

   See Figure 8.1.1. By symmetry, we see that Area $= 4\int_0^1 x^3\sqrt{1 - x^2} \, dx$. Set $x = \sin\theta, dx = \cos\theta \, dt$ and substitute to get $4\int_0^{\frac{\pi}{2}} \sin^3\theta\cos^2\theta \, d\theta$. Now, we write

   $$4\int_0^{\frac{\pi}{2}} \sin^3\theta\cos^2\theta \, d\theta = 4\int_0^{\frac{\pi}{2}} (1 - \cos^2\theta)\sin\theta\cos^2\theta \, d\theta = 4(-\frac{\cos^5\theta}{5} + \frac{\cos^3\theta}{3})\Big|_0^{\frac{\pi}{2}} = \frac{8}{15}.$$

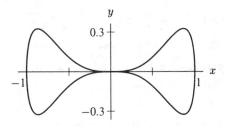

*Figure 8.1.1*

**Focus on Engineering**

3.  It's time for the School of Engineering class picture and you are the photographer! You stand at the origin with your camera and your classmates are strung out along the curve $y = e^{-x}$ from $(0, 1)$ to $(2, e^{-2})$.

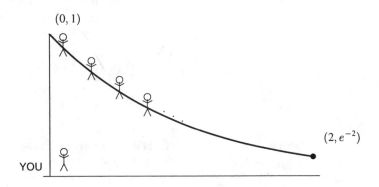

(a)  As a function of $x$, what is your distance to your classmate at a point $(x, y)$ on the curve?

(b)  Write down an integral that gives the average value of the function in (a).

(c)  Use your calculator to evaluate the integral in (b) to one decimal place. Say what you are doing.

(d)  You focus your camera according to your answer in part (c). Who is more in focus, the person at $(0, 1)$ or the person at $(2, e^{-2})$?

(e)  Approximately where on the curve should you tell your best friend to stand so that she will be in focus? (Use your calculator to solve graphically for her $x$-coordinate.)

   ANSWER:

(a)  Distance $= S(x) = \sqrt{x^2 + e^{-2x}}$

(b)  $\overline{S(x)} = \frac{1}{2} \int_0^2 \sqrt{x^2 + e^{-2x}} \, dx$

(c)  LEFT(400) gives 1.1955. RIGHT(400) gives 1.1980. So the true value is 1.197 to one decimal place.

(d)  $S(0) = 1; S(2) = \sqrt{4 + e^{-4}} \approx 2.005$. Thus the person at $(0,1)$ is more in focus.

(e)  Graphing $\sqrt{x^2 + e^{-2x}} - 1.197$, we see that it is 0 at $x \approx 1.16$.

4.  Alice starts at the origin and walks along the graph of $y = \dfrac{x^2}{2}$ at a velocity of 10 units/second.

(a)  Write down the integral which shows how far Alice has travelled when she reaches the point where $x = a$.

(b)  You want to find the $x$-coordinate of the point Alice reaches after travelling for 2 seconds. Find upper and lower estimates, differing by less than 0.2, for this coordinate. Explain your reasoning carefully.

   ANSWER:

(a)  $L(a) = \displaystyle\int_0^a \sqrt{1 + x^2} \, dx$

(b)   We want to find $a$ such that $\int_0^a \sqrt{1+x^2}\,dx = 20$. Since $\sqrt{1+x^2}$ is increasing, the left hand side gives a lower estimate, the right hand side gives the upper estimate for this integral.

With $n = 500$, RHS for $\int_0^{6.0} \sqrt{1+x^2}\,dx = 19.52\ldots$ so $\int_0^{6.0} \sqrt{1+x^2}\,dx < 20$.

With $n = 500$, LHS for $\int_0^{6.1} \sqrt{1+x^2}\,dx = 20.07\ldots$ so $\int_0^{6.1} \sqrt{1+x^2}\,dx > 20$.

Thus $6.0 < a < 6.2$ (more accurate than asked).

5.   A coffee filter is in the shape of a cone, as shown below. When it is filled with water to a height $h$ cm, the rate at which coffee flows out the hole at the bottom is given by

$$\left(\begin{array}{c}\text{Volume of coffee which}\\ \text{flows out per second}\end{array}\right) = \sqrt{h}\ \text{cm}^3/\text{sec}.$$

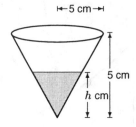

(a)   What is the radius of the surface of the coffee when it is at height of $h$?

(b)   What is the approximate volume of the "slice" of coffee lying between $h$ and $h + \Delta h$?

(c)   Given that when the height is $h$, the coffee is leaving at a rate of $\sqrt{h}$ cm$^3$/sec, approximately how long does it take for the height of the coffee to fall from $h + \Delta h$ to $h$?

(d)   Suppose the coffee filter starts full. Write an integral representing the total amount of time it takes for the coffee filter to empty, and hence find the time for the filter to empty. Give your answer to the nearest second.

ANSWER:

(a)   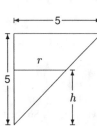   By similar triangles $\dfrac{r}{h} = \dfrac{5}{5}$ so   "Slice" is disc-shaped

$r = h$.

(b)   Volume = Area $\times \Delta h = \pi h^2 \Delta h$

(c)   time $= \dfrac{\text{volume}}{\text{rate}} = \dfrac{\pi h^2 \Delta h}{\sqrt{h}} = \pi h^{\frac{3}{2}} \Delta h$

(d)   $\int_0^5 \pi h^{\frac{3}{2}}\,dh = \dfrac{2\pi}{5}\left[h^{\frac{5}{2}}\right]_0^5 = 70$ seconds

6.   In a recent archaeological expedition, a scroll was discovered containing a description of a plan to build what appears to be the Tower of Babel. According to the manuscript, the tower was supposed to have a circular cross section and "go up to the heavens" (i.e., be infinitely high). A mathematician was consulted to solve some of the questions posed by the archaeologists. The mathematicians plotted half of the silhouette of the tower on a set of coordinate axis with the $y$-axis running through the center and discovered that it was approximated by the curve $y = -100\ \ln\left(\frac{x}{5}\right)$. Please answer the questions posed by the archaeologists:

(a)   Would such a tower have finite volume? Justify your work completely.

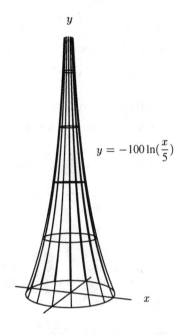

$$y = -100\ln\left(\frac{x}{5}\right)$$

(b)   The manuscript mentions that 4200 cubic "shrims" (Babel's unit of length) of stones were available to build the tower. The base of the tower was to have radius 4 shrims. Did they have enough? Explain.

ANSWER:

(a)   If we slice horizontally, the volume of one disk with radius $x$ and thickness $dy$ is $\pi(x^2)dy$. Now $y = -100\ln\left(\frac{x}{5}\right)$, so $\frac{x}{5} = e^{-\frac{y}{100}}$ and $x = 5e^{-\frac{y}{100}}$. Consequently,

$$\begin{aligned}
\text{Volume} &= \pi\int_0^\infty \left(5e^{-\frac{y}{100}}\right)^2 dy \\
&= \pi\int_0^\infty 25e^{-\frac{y}{50}}\, dy \\
&= -1250\pi e^{-\frac{y}{50}}\Big|_0^\infty \\
&= 1250\pi
\end{aligned}$$

(b)   If we had done the above integral in "shrims", then we would have found the volume of a tower with radius of 5 shrims at the base, since $-100\ln\frac{x}{5}$ passes through the $x$-axis at $x = 5$. Its volume would be $1250\pi < 4200$. Since a tower of base radius 4 shrims would require less than $1250\pi$ cubic shrims, they would have enough stone.

7.   Consider the region bounded by $y = e^x$, the $x$-axis and the lines $x = 0$ and $x = 1$. Find the volume of the solid whose base is the given region and whose cross sections perpendicular to the $x$-axis are isosceles right triangles with hypotenuses lying in the region.

ANSWER:

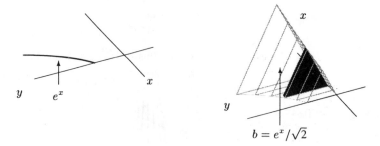

*Figure 8.1.2*                              *Figure 8.1.3*

We slice perpendicular to the $x$-axis. As stated in the problem, the cross-sections obtained thereby are isosceles right triangles with hypotenuse length $y = e^x$. Let $b$ be the length of the base. Then $b^2 + b^2 = e^{2x}$ by the Pythagorean Theorem, which means that $2b^2 = e^{2x}$, whence $b = \dfrac{e^x}{\sqrt{2}}$. Hence, the volume of one triangular section is $\dfrac{lw}{2}\,dx = \dfrac{b^2}{2}\,dx = \dfrac{e^{2x}}{4}\,dx$. Therefore,

$$\begin{aligned}
\text{Volume} &= \int_0^1 \frac{e^{2x}}{4}\,dx \\
&= \left.\frac{e^{2x}}{8}\right|_0^1 = \frac{e^2 - 1}{8} \approx 0.80.
\end{aligned}$$

8. (a) You love the function $y = \frac{2}{3}x^{\frac{3}{2}}$ and you also love the number 4. What is the arc length of this curve from $x = 0$ to $x = 4$?

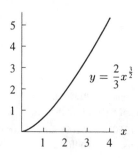

*Figure 8.1.4*

(b) You have a gold chain which is exactly 4 feet long. As a tribute to your favorite function you want to mount your chain in the shape of $y = \frac{2}{3}x^{\frac{3}{2}}$ from $x = 0$ to $x = 4$ on a beautiful rectangular piece of rosewood. If the lower left corner is labeled with the coordinate $(0, 0)$ and the upper right corner is labeled with the coordinate $(4, \frac{16}{3})$ and a unit on the $x$-axis and a unit on the $y$-axis represent the same number of feet, what are the dimensions of the piece of wood in feet?

ANSWER:

(a)

$$\text{Arclength} = \int_0^4 \sqrt{1 + \left(\frac{dy}{dx}\right)^2}\,dx = \int_0^4 \sqrt{1 + (\sqrt{x})^2}\,dx$$

$$= \int_0^4 \sqrt{1+x}\, dx = \frac{2}{3}(1+x)^{\frac{3}{2}}\Big|_0^4$$

$$= \frac{2}{3}(5^{\frac{3}{2}} - 1)$$

$$\approx 6.787$$

(b)   We have 4 feet for $\frac{2}{3}(5\sqrt{5} - 1)$ units. Hence, the dimensions of the wood are

$$\frac{4}{\frac{2}{3}(5\sqrt{5} - 1)} \cdot 4 \approx 2.36 \text{ ft by } \frac{4}{\frac{2}{3}(5\sqrt{5} - 1)}\left(\frac{2}{3}\right) \cdot 4^{\frac{3}{2}} = 3.143 \text{ ft.}$$

9.   Suppose that a new office building is being planned. The architect wants to design a building that is thick at the base and eventually tapers to a small flat roof at the top. The building is to have 10 floors, and each floor is to be 15 feet high. For purposes of air conditioning the building, an estimate of the total volume is needed. You have been hired as a consultant at an exorbitant salary to do this. You have been provided with the following information which shows how much area, in units of 100 square feet, each of the 10 floors will contain:

| Floor # | Ground | 2 | 3 | 4 | 5 | 6 | 7 | 8 | 9 | 10 | Roof |
|---------|--------|----|----|----|----|----|----|----|----|----|------|
| Area    | 25     | 23 | 20 | 18 | 16 | 14 | 12 | 10 | 9  | 8  | 7    |

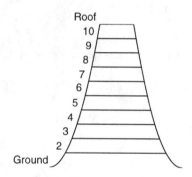

Earn your wage: find an approximate value for the volume of the entire building. Explain what you are doing.

ANSWER:

Since area is a decreasing function of height (floor #), starting from the ground, a left-hand sum gives an overestimate of the volume (area × height) and a right-hand sum gives an underestimate. Therefore,

$$\text{Overestimate} = 15 \cdot (25 + 23 + 20 + 18 + 16 + 14 + 12 + 10 + 9 + 8) \cdot 100$$
$$= 232500 \text{ ft}^3$$

$$\text{Underestimate} = 15 \cdot (23 + 20 + 18 + 16 + 14 + 12 + 10 + 9 + 8 + 7) \cdot 100$$
$$= 205500 \text{ ft}^3$$

An approximate value for the volume of the entire building is given by the average of the overestimate and the underestimate, $\frac{232500 + 205500}{2} = 219000 \text{ ft}^3$.

10.   The circle $x^2 + y^2 = a^2$ is rotated around the $y$-axis to form a solid sphere of radius $a$. A plane perpendicular to the $y$-axis at $y = a/2$ cuts off a spherical cap from the sphere. What fraction of the total voume of the sphere is contained in the cap?

ANSWER:

A cross-section of the sphere is shown in Figure 8.1.5.

522

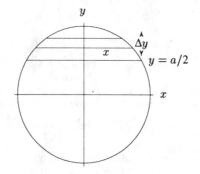

*Figure 8.1.5*

As can be seen from Figure 8.1.5,

$$\text{Volume of cap} = \int_{a/2}^{a} \pi x^2 \, dy$$

$$= \int_{a/2}^{a} \pi(a^2 - y^2) \, dy$$

$$= \pi \left[ a^2 y - \frac{y^3}{3} \right] \Big|_{a/2}^{a}$$

$$= \frac{5\pi a^3}{24},$$

whereas the volume of the entire sphere is given by the formula

$$\text{Volume of sphere} = \frac{4}{3}\pi a^3.$$

So we have

$$\frac{\text{Volume of cap}}{\text{Total volume}} = \frac{5\pi a^3/24}{4\pi a^3/3} = \frac{5}{32}.$$

11.  (a)  Set up a Riemann sum approximating the volume of the torus (donut) obtained by rotating the circle $(x-3)^2 + y^2 = 1$ about the $y$-axis.

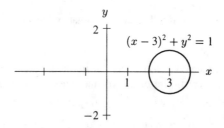

(b)  Write an integral representing the volume of the torus. (Do not evaluate the integral.)
ANSWER:

(a)  Consider a horizontal slice at height $y$ with thickness $\Delta y$, as shown in Figure 8.1.6.

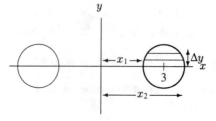

*Figure 8.1.6*

This slice will have volume of

$$\Delta V \approx \pi(x_2^2 - x_1^2)\Delta y$$
$$= \pi\left((3 + \sqrt{1 - y^2})^2 - (3 - \sqrt{1 - y^2})^2\right)\Delta y.$$

So the entire volume will be the sum of all such slices,

$$\text{Volume} \approx \sum \pi\left((3 + \sqrt{1 - y^2})^2 - (3 - \sqrt{1 - y^2})^2\right)\Delta y.$$

(b)  In the limit as the number of slices goes to infinity, we have

$$\text{Volume} = \int_{-1}^{1}\left((3 + \sqrt{1 - y^2})^2 - (3 - \sqrt{1 - y^2})^2\right)dy.$$

## Problems and Solutions for Section 8.2

1.  When an oil well burns, sediment is carried up into the air by the flames and is eventually deposited on the ground. Less sediment is deposited further away from the oil well. Experimental evidence indicates that the density (in tons/square mile) at a distance $r$ from the burning oil well is given by

$$\frac{7}{1 + r^2}.$$

(a)  Find a Riemann sum which approximates the total amount of sediment which is deposited within 100 miles of the well. Explain your work.

(b)  Find and evaluate an integral which represents this total deposit.

ANSWER:

(a)  The area where sediment is deposited is a disk with radius 100. The density of sediment deposited is a function of the distance from the burning oil well, so we can cut the disk into rings of radius $r$ from the center with width $\Delta r$. For narrow enough rings, the density is nearly constant. Thus, the sediment in each ring equals the area of the ring, which is about $2\pi r\Delta r$, multiplied by its density (i.e. for a ring with radius $r$ we get $\frac{7}{1+r^2} \cdot 2\pi r\Delta r$). We can add up the areas of these rings multiplied by their densities to find the total amount of sediment deposited. The Riemann sum we want is:

$$\sum \frac{14\pi r\Delta r}{1 + r^2}.$$

(b)  The integral is $\int_0^{100} \frac{14\pi r}{1 + r^2}\, dr$. Set $u = 1 + r^2, du = 2r dr$ and substitute to get

$$\int_0^{100} \frac{14\pi r}{1 + r^2}\, dr = \int_1^{10001} \frac{7\pi du}{u}$$
$$= 7\pi \ln|u|\Big|_1^{10001}$$
$$= 7\pi \ln(10001) \approx 202.5 \text{ tons.}$$

2.  A straight road goes through the center of a circular city of radius 5 km. The density of the population at a distance $r$ (in km) from the road is well approximated by

$$D(r) = 20 - 4r$$

(in thousand people per km$^2$). Find the total population of the city.

ANSWER:

A strip of the city, of width $\Delta r$, that lies parallel to the road at distance $r$ from it will have length $\sqrt{25 - r^2}$ and hence area $\sqrt{25 - r^2}\Delta r$. The population in the strip is thus $(20 - 4r)\sqrt{25 - r^2}\Delta r$. The integral representing the population of the city is thus:

$$\text{Population} = 2 \int_0^5 (20 - 4r)\sqrt{25 - r^2}\, dr \approx 226{,}000 \text{ people.}$$

3. The globular cluster M13 is a spherical distribution of stars which orbits our galaxy. Suppose that the density of stars in the cluster is purely a function of distance $r$ from the center of the cluster and is given as

$$\rho(r) = \left(1 + \left(\frac{r}{100}\right)^3\right)^{-5} \frac{\text{stars}}{(\text{ly})^3}$$

where $r$ is measured in light-years, and $0 \le r \le 100 ly$. (One light-year is the distance light travels in one year; "light-year" is abbreviated as "ly".)

(a) Set up a Riemann sum which approximates the total number of stars in M13.

(b) Set up an integral whose value is the exact number of stars in M13.

(c) Evaluate the integral in part (b) to compute the total number of stars in M13. If you evaluate the integral numerically (e.g., on your calculator), you will get full credit for part (c) only if you:

(i) Give a number which is within 10,000 stars of the true value of the integral.

(ii) Give justification for your answer being accurate to within 10,000 stars.

ANSWER:

(a) To get full credit (12 points), you had to write:

$$\sum_{1 \le n \le N} \left(4\pi \cdot r_n^2 \cdot \left(1 + \left(\frac{r_n}{100}\right)^3\right)^{-5}\right) \cdot \Delta r$$

where $\Delta r = \dfrac{100}{N}$, and where $r_n = n \cdot \dfrac{100}{N}$. By the way, this equation is derived by observing that the number of stars in a spherical shell at radius $r$ and of thickness $\Delta r$ is approximately equal to:

$$(\text{Volume of shell}) \times \left(1 + \left(\frac{r}{100}\right)^3\right)^{-5},$$

where the volume of the shell is approximately Area$\times \Delta r$, where the Area $= 4 \cdot \pi \cdot r^2$.

(b) For full credit (7 points), you had to write:

$$\int_0^{100} 4 \cdot \pi \cdot r^2 \cdot \left(1 + \left(\frac{r}{100}\right)^3\right)^{-5} \cdot dr.$$

(c) Full credit was (6 points). The integral could be computed with the substitution $u = \left(\dfrac{r}{100}\right)^3$.

Then, $du = 3dr \cdot \dfrac{r^2}{(100)^3}$. Thus, the integral above is equal to

$$\left(4 \cdot \frac{\pi}{3}\right) \cdot (100)^3 \cdot \int_0^1 (1 + u)^{-5} \cdot du.$$

This last integral can be done using the fundamental theorem of calculus with the observation that $(1 + u)^{-5} = \dfrac{d}{du}\left(-\dfrac{1}{4} \cdot (1 + u)^{-4}\right)$. Thus, the final answer is

$$\left(4 \cdot \frac{\pi}{3}\right) \cdot \frac{(100)^3}{4} \cdot \left(1 - \frac{1}{16}\right) = 10^6 \cdot \frac{\pi}{3} \cdot \frac{15}{16} \approx 981{,}748.$$

Many people tried to do this problem numerically. Only two people gave a believable justification for their answer being within 10,000 of the correct value. The integrand is not always convex, nor concave nor increasing nor decreasing. You must split the integral into two or more pieces which are solely increasing or solely decreasing (or, solely concave or solely convex). Then, you can use left and right sums (or midpoint and trapezoid sums) to estimate the contribution from each piece.

4. A cylindrically-shaped mug with a 3 cm radius and a 10 cm height is filled with tea. You have added some sugar to the tea, which tends to settle to the bottom of the mug. It turns out that the density $\rho$ of sugar (in gm/cm$^3$) in the tea, as a function of the height, $h$, in cm, above the bottom of the mug, is given by the formula $\rho(h) = 0.01(10 - h)$.

10 cm

(a) Write a Riemann sum that approximates the total mass of sugar (in grams) in the mug of tea. Show your work clearly.

(b) Turn the Riemann sum into the integral that gives the exact amount of sugar in the mug, and evaluate the integral.

ANSWER:

(a) Slice horizontally.
Volume of slice at height $h$ is $\pi(r^2)\Delta h$
Sugar in slice $= \pi(3^2)\Delta h(0.01(10 - h))$
Total sugar $= \displaystyle\sum_{\text{all slices}} 9\pi(0.01)(10 - h)\Delta h$

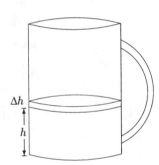

(b) Total sugar $= \displaystyle\int_0^{10} 0.09\pi(10 - h)dh$

$= 0.09\pi\left[10h - \dfrac{h^2}{2}\right]_0^{10}$

$= 0.09\pi(50)$

$= 4.5\pi$ gm

5. After Mt. St. Helens erupted in 1980, it was found that ash was spread in decreasing density as a function of distance $r$ from the center of the crater. Say that the density $\rho$ of ash at a distance $r$ (meters) from the center of the crater is given as follows:

$$\rho(r) = \frac{2000}{1 + r^2} \quad \text{kg/m}^2$$

(a) Write a Riemann sum that approximates the total mass of ash deposited within a 1000-meter radius of the center of the crater.

(b) Turn your Riemann sum from part (a) into a definite integral and evaluate that integral to find the exact value of the total mass of ash within 1000 meters of the center of the crater.

ANSWER:

(a) Partition $0 \le r \le 1000$ into rings of width $\Delta r = \dfrac{1000}{N}$. The mass of ash in the $i$-th ring is

$$m_i = \underbrace{A_i}_{\text{Area}} \ \underbrace{\rho_i}_{\text{Density}} = (2\pi r_i \Delta r)\frac{2000}{1 + r_i^2}.$$

$$\text{Total mass} = \sum_{i=1}^{N} \frac{4000\pi r_i}{1 + r_i^2}\Delta r$$

(b) $$\int_0^{1000} \frac{4000\pi r}{1 + r^2}\,dr = 2000\pi \int_1^{1,000,001} \frac{dw}{w} = \left[2000\pi \ln w\right]_1^{1,000,001} \approx 86,805 \text{ kg}$$

6. A thin strip of nutrients 20 cm long is placed in a circular petri dish of radius 10 cm, as shown. The population density of bacteria in the disk after 3 hours is given by $\frac{80}{D+4}$ bacteria/cm$^2$ where $D$ is the distance (in cm) to the nutrient strip.

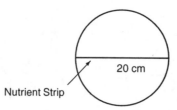

Nutrient Strip

20 cm

(a) Write a general Riemann sum that approximates the number of bacteria in the dish 3 hours after the nutrient strip is introduced. You must explain your reasoning carefully and clearly. Any variables you use must be clearly identified in words.

(b) Write an integral that gives the number of bacteria in the petri dish 3 hours after the nutrient strip has been introduced. You need not evaluate.

ANSWER:

(a) Partition $[0, 10]$ into $n$ equal pieces each of width $\Delta D$. Let $D_i$ be in the $i$-th interval.

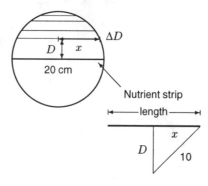

Use Pythagorean Theorem:
$x^2 + D^2 = 100$
$x = \sqrt{100 - D^2}$
or put axes through the center of the circle.
$x^2 + y^2 = 100$
$|y|$ corresponds to $D$,
$2|x|$ corresponds to length.

$$\begin{pmatrix} \text{\# of bacteria} \\ \text{in a strip} \end{pmatrix} \approx (\text{density})(\text{area})$$

$$= \frac{80}{D_i + 4}\frac{\text{bact}}{(\text{cm})^2}\,2x_i\Delta D(\text{cm})^2$$

$$= \frac{80}{D_i + 4}2\sqrt{100 - D_i^2}\Delta D$$

$$\text{Total \# of bacteria} \approx \underbrace{2}_{\substack{\text{for the other 1/2} \\ \text{of the petri dish}}} \sum_{i=1}^{n} \frac{80}{D_i + 4} 2\sqrt{100 - D_i^2} \Delta D$$

Common errors:

(1) The area of a strip is NOT $2\pi r$.

(2) $D$ is the distance from a line–so don't cut into concentric circles.

(3) A general Riemann sum should not be a sum from 1 to 10 or 0 to 9 or 1 to 3.

(4) Many people introduced new variables; didn't say what they were, and then lost track of them.

(b)

$$\lim_{n \to \infty} 2 \sum_{i=1}^{n} \frac{80}{D_i + 4} 2\sqrt{100 - D_i^2} \Delta D = 2 \int_0^{10} \frac{80}{D + 4} 2\sqrt{100 - D^2} \, dD = 320 \int_0^{10} \frac{\sqrt{100 - D^2}}{D + 4} \, dD$$

Common error: You don't want to integrate from $0 \to 20$ since $D$ can only be as big as 10.

An odd error: Some folks integrated from 0 to 3. I don't know why.

The integral should involve the variable $D$ and no other variable.

7. The density of cars (in cars per mile) down a 20-mile stretch of the Massachusetts Turnpike starting at a toll plaza is given by

$$\rho(x) = 500 + 100 \sin(\pi x)$$

where $x$ is the distance in miles from the toll plaza and $0 \le x \le 20$.

(a) Write a Riemann sum which estimates the total number of cars down the 20-mile stretch. Explain your reasoning.

(b) Convert this sum to an integral and evaluate it.

ANSWER:

(a) Divide the 20-mile stretch into $n$ pieces of length $\frac{20}{n} = \Delta x$. An estimate of the number of cars in any segment is simply $\rho(x_i)\Delta x$, where $x_i$ is a point in the $i^{\text{th}}$ segment. The total number of cars will therefore be approximately

$$\sum_{i=0}^{n-1} \rho(x_i)\Delta x.$$

(b) Letting $n$ go to $\infty$, we get the integral

$$\int_0^{20} \rho(x) \, dx = \int_0^{20} (500 + 100\sin(\pi x)) \, dx$$

$$= 500x - \frac{100}{\pi}\cos(\pi x)\Big|_0^{20}$$

$$= 10000 - \frac{100}{\pi}\cos(20\pi) + \frac{100}{\pi}$$

$$= 10000$$

8. A chlorine solution is poured over the surface of a rectangular swimming pool that is 25 meters long, 10 meters wide and 2 meters deep everywhere. Before the circulating pumps in the pool are turned on, it is discovered that the density of the chlorine solution at a height $h$ meters above the bottom of the pool is given by $\rho(h) = 100h$ gm/m$^3$. In other words, the chlorine solution has distributed itself so that its density increases linearly from the bottom of the pool.

(a) Write a Riemann sum that approximates the total mass of chlorine solution in the pool.

(b) Turn the Riemann sum in part (a) into a definite integral that gives the exact total mass of chlorine solution in the pool, and evaluate the integral.

ANSWER:

(a) Slice the pool into $n$ thin horizontal slices.

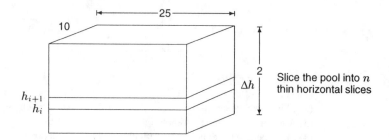

Slice the pool into $n$ thin horizontal slices

Find the mass over the $i$-th slice (shaded above). We will assume that density is approximately constant over a very thin slice. So, over the $i$th slice, density $\approx \rho(h_i) = 100h_i$ gm/cm$^3$. mass=density$\times$volume. The volume of the $i$-th slice is $\ell \cdot w \cdot h = 25 \cdot 10 \cdot \Delta h = 250\Delta h$. So, the mass of the $i$-th slice $= (100h_i)(250\Delta h) = 25,000h_i\Delta h$.

To find total mass, we sum up the masses of all $n$ slices:

$$\text{Mass} = \sum_{i=0}^{n-1} 25,000h_i\Delta h$$

Alternatively, if we had let $h_i$ represent the <u>top</u> height of our slice, then the bottom height would be $h_{i-1}$, and our sum would be: $\sum_{i=1}^{n} 25,000h_i\Delta h$. (Either answer is fine.)

(b)  As the number of slices approaches $\infty$, or $\Delta h \to 0$, we get:

$$\text{Mass} = \lim_{n\to\infty}\left(\sum_{i=0}^{n-1} 25,000h_i\Delta h\right) = \int_0^2 25,000h\,dh$$

Evaluate:

$$= 12,500h^2\Big|_0^2 = 50,000 \text{ g or } 50 \text{ kg}$$

9.  Circle City is circular with a radius of four miles. Right in the center is a circular park with diameter one mile. No one lives in the park. Elsewhere the population density is $4000(5-r)$ people per square mile, where $r$ is the distance from the center in miles.

(a)  What is the total population of Circle City? Explain how you get your answer.
(b)  What is the average density of population of the whole city?

ANSWER:

(a)  Consider concentric slices of the city of width $\Delta r$. A slice at distance $r$ from the center has approximate area $2\pi r\Delta r$. Assuming that the population is constant on each slice, the population of a slice at distance $r$ from the center is about

$$\text{Density} \cdot \text{Area} = 4000(5-r) \cdot 2\pi r\Delta r.$$

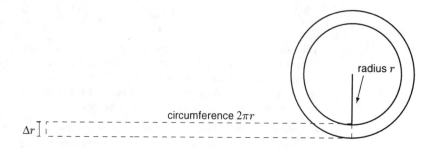

radius $r$

circumference $2\pi r$

$\Delta r$

So the total population is about

$$\sum 4000(5-r) \cdot 2\pi r\Delta r,$$

where $r$ runs between 1 and 4. As $\Delta r \to 0$, this Riemann sum becomes the integral

$$\int_1^4 4000(5-r)2\pi r \, dr = \int_1^4 (40000\pi r - 8000\pi r^2) \, dr$$

$$= 20000\pi r^2 - \frac{8000\pi r^3}{3}\Big|_1^4$$

$$= 320000\pi - \frac{512000\pi}{3} - 20000\pi + \frac{8000\pi}{3}$$

$$= 132000\pi$$

$$\approx 415000.$$

(b)   Average density of population $= \dfrac{\text{total population}}{\text{area of city}} = \dfrac{132000\pi}{\pi(4^2-1)} = 8800.$

10.   A 5-gram drop of thick red paint is added to a large can of white paint. A red disk forms and spreads outward, growing lighter at the edges. Since the amount of red paint stays constant through time, the density of the red paint in the disk must vary with time. Suppose that its density $p$ in gm/cm$^2$ is of the form

$$p = k(t)f(r)$$

for some functions $k(t)$ of time and $f(r)$ of the distance to the center of the disk.

(a)   Let $R(t)$ be the radius of the disk at time $t$. Write an integral that expresses the fact that there are 5 grams of red paint in the disk. Explain.
(Hint: Divide the disk into thin concentric rings and ask yourself how much paint there is in each ring.)

(b)   For fixed $r$ write down an integral for the average density of red paint at a distance $r$ from the center of the disk from 0 to $T$ seconds.

ANSWER:

(a)   $5 = k(t) \displaystyle\int_0^{R(t)} f(r)2\pi r \, dr$, since each ring has area $2\pi r \, dr$.

(b)

$$\text{average density} = \frac{1}{T}\int_0^T f(r)k(t) \, dt = \frac{f(r)}{T}\int_0^T k(t) \, dt.$$

We can factor out $f(r)$ from the integral because $f(r)$ doesn't depend on $t$.

11.   A flat metal plate is in the shape determined by the area under the graph of $f(x) = \dfrac{1}{1+x}$ between $x = 0$ and $x = 5$. The density of the plate $x$ units from the $y$-axis is given by $x^2$ grams/cm$^2$.

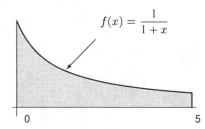

(a)   Write down a Riemann sum with 5 terms which approximates the total mass. Is your approximation an underestimate or an overestimate? Explain.

(b)   Write down a definite integral which gives the exact value of the total mass of the plate.

(c)   Evaluate the integral you found in part (b).

ANSWER:

(a)   The height at distance $x$ from the $y$-axis is $1/(1+x)$ cm, and the density is $x^2$ gm/cm$^2$, so the plate has "linear density" $x^2/(1+x)$ gm/cm at position $x$.

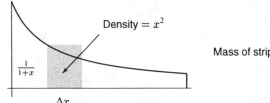

Mass of strip of width $\Delta x \approx \dfrac{x^2 \Delta x}{1+x}$

We can suppose, as an approximation, that this density is constant on each centimeter of the plate; so the total mass is approximately

$$\sum_{i=0}^{4} \frac{x_i^2}{1+x_i}(1) = 0 + 1/2 + 4/3 + 9/4 + 16/5 = 437/60 \approx 7.2833 \text{ gm.}$$

Since we have used LEFT(5) on $\dfrac{x^2}{1+x}$, which is an *increasing* function for $x > 0$, our approximation is an *underestimate*.

(b)  $M = \displaystyle\int_0^5 \frac{x^2}{1+x}\,dx$

(c)  Divide the denominator into the numerator. Since

$$\frac{x^2}{1+x} = \frac{(x^2-1)+1}{x+1} = x - 1 + \frac{1}{1+x},$$

we find that

$$\int_0^5 \frac{x^2}{1+x}\,dx = \left(\frac{x^2}{2} - x + \ln(1+x)\right)\Bigg|_0^5 = \frac{15}{2} + \ln 6 \approx 9.292 \text{ gm.}$$

12.  An object is in the shape drawn below; its boundary is obtained by rotating the parabola $y = 2x^2$ (for $0 \le x \le 1$) around the $y$ axis. (Units are in centimeters.) Suppose that the density of this object varies with height according to the rule $\rho(y) = 8 \cdot (2 - y)$ grams/cm$^3$.

(a)  Set up a Riemann sum which computes (approximately) the weight in grams of this object.

(b)  Compute the exact weight in grams of this object.

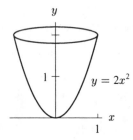

ANSWER:

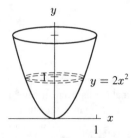

(a)  $\displaystyle\sum_{y=0}^{2} \pi \cdot \frac{y}{2} \cdot 8(2-y)\Delta y$

$$\int_0^2 \pi(8y - 4y^2)dy = \pi\left(4y^2 - \frac{4}{3}y^3\right)\Bigg|_0^2$$

(b)
$$= \pi\left(16 - \frac{4}{3} \cdot 8\right)$$
$$= \frac{16}{3}\pi$$

13. The density of a compressible liquid is $40(5 - h)$ kg/m$^3$ at a height of $h$ meters above the bottom.

   (a) The liquid is put in the container shown below, whose cross sections are isosceles triangles. It has straight sides, and looks like a triangular prism. How many kg will it hold when placed as shown in Figure 8.2.7, resting on the triangular side?

   (b) How many kg will it hold if it is placed (with some support, of course) as shown in Figure 8.2.8?

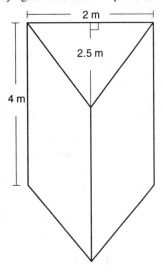

**Figure 8.2.7**: Container on End          **Figure 8.2.8**: Container on Side

ANSWER:

(a) The volume of a single horizontal slice is Area $\times \Delta h = \frac{1}{2}(2)(2.5)\Delta h$. The mass of such a slice is simply $40(5 - h)(2.5)\Delta h$ kg. Hence

$$\text{The total mass} = \int_0^4 (2.5)(40)(5 - h)\, dh$$
$$= \int_0^4 (500 - 100h)\, dh$$
$$= 500h - 50h^2\Big|_0^4 = 2000 - 800$$
$$= 1200 \text{ kg}$$

(b) The volume of a single hrizontal slice at height $h$ is $4 \cdot \dfrac{2}{2.5} \cdot h \cdot \Delta h$. The mass of such a slice will be $128(5 - h)\Delta h$. Hence,

$$\text{The total mass} = \int_0^{2.5} (128(5 - h)h\, dh$$
$$= \int_0^{2.5} (640h - 128h^2)\, dh$$
$$= \left(320h^2 - \frac{128}{3}h^3\right)\Bigg|_0^{2.5}$$
$$= 2000 - \frac{2000}{3}$$

$$\approx 1333 \text{kg}$$

## *Problems and Solutions for Section 8.3*

1. The Great Cone of Haverford College is a monument built by freshmen during a customs week long, long ago. It is 100 ft. high and its base has a diameter of 100 ft. It has been built from bricks (purportedly made of straw) which weigh 2 lbs/ft³. Use a definite integral to approximate the amount of work required to build the Cone.

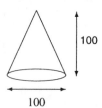

100

100

ANSWER:

Work = Force × Distance, so the amount of work necessary to raise a volume of brick to height $x$ above the ground is $2x$ foot-pounds per cubic foot. We now think of the cone as being made of a series of thin horizontal layers, each of height $\Delta x$. Such a layer, at height $x$, would have radius $r(x) = 50 - x/2$; its area would therefore be $\pi r(x)^2$, and its volume approximately $\pi r(x)^2 \Delta x$, since $\Delta x$ is small. Raising a layer of radius $r(x)$ to height $x$ would thus take $2x\pi r(x)^2 \Delta x$ foot-pounds; so if we have $n$ such layers, we can construct a Riemann sum approximation of the total work done as follows:

$$W \approx \sum_{i=0}^{n-1} 2\pi x_i r(x_i)^2 \Delta x = \sum_{i=0}^{n-1} 2\pi x_i \left(50 - \frac{x_i}{2}\right)^2 \Delta x \quad \text{foot-pounds}$$

The corresponding definite integral is

$$\int_0^{100} 2x\pi \left(50 - \frac{x}{2}\right)^2 dx = 2500\pi x^2 - \frac{100}{3}\pi x^3 + \frac{\pi}{8}x^4 \Big|_0^{100}$$

$$= 12500000\frac{\pi}{3}$$

$$\approx 1.3 \times 10^7 \quad \text{foot-pounds.}$$

2. The force of gravitational attraction between a thin rod of mass $M$ and length $L$ and a particle of mass $m$ lying on the same line as the rod at a distance of $A$ from one of the ends is

$$\frac{GmM}{A(L+A)}.$$

Use this result to set up an integral for the total force due to gravity between two thin rods, both of mass $M$ and length $L$, lying along the same line and separated by a distance $A$. You need not evaluate the integral. Explain what you are doing.

[Hint: Divide one of the rods into small pieces, each of length $dx$ and mass $\frac{M}{L} dx$. Apply the formula above to each of the pieces, then form a Riemann sum. You know the rest...]

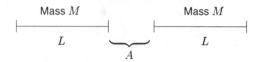

Mass $M$            Mass $M$

$L$            $L$

$A$

ANSWER:

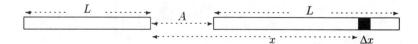

$L$            $A$            $L$

$x$            $\Delta x$

Consider a small chunk of the right-hand rod, of length $\Delta x$ and at distance $x$ from the right end of the left rod; it has mass $\dfrac{M}{L}\Delta x$. By the formula given, the gravitational attraction between the left rod and this piece is approximately $\dfrac{GM^2\Delta x}{Lx(L+x)}$. We can therefore approximate the gravitational attraction between the two rods by adding up the contributions from each of the $n$ pieces of the right rod:

$$F \approx \sum_{i=0}^{n-1} \frac{GM^2\Delta x}{Lx_i(L+x_i)}, \qquad \text{where } \Delta x = \frac{L}{n}.$$

The corresponding definite integral is then:

$$F = \int_A^{A+L} \frac{GM^2\,dx}{Lx(L+x)}.$$

## Problems and Solutions for Section 8.4

1. A study of the costs to produce airplanes in World War II led to the theory of "learning curves," the idea of which is that the marginal cost per plane decreases over the duration of a production run. In other words, with experience, staff on an assembly line can produce planes with greater efficiency. The 90% learning curve describes a typical situation where the marginal cost, $MC$, to produce the $x^{th}$ plane is given by

$$MC(x) = M_0 x^{\log_2 0.9},$$

where $M_0 =$ marginal cost to produce the first plane.

[Note: You may use the fact that $\log_2 x = \dfrac{\ln x}{\ln 2}$.]

(a) If a plant produces planes with a 90% learning curve on production costs, and the marginal cost for the first plane is $500,000, then what is the marginal cost to produce the second plane? The fourth plane?

(b) Recall that marginal cost is related to total cost as follows:

$$MC(x) = C'(x),$$

where $C(x) =$ total cost to produce $x$ units. Given this, and the formula for $MC(x)$ with $M_0 = \$500,000$, find a formula for $C(x)$. What, physically, is the meaning of the constant in you formula for $C(x)$?

(c) If the constant for $C(x)$ is $20 million, and $M_0 = \$500$ thousand, then what, approximately, is $C(50)$?

ANSWER:

(a) $M_0 = 0.5$ (million dollars). So,

$MC(2) = (0.5)2^{\log_2 0.9} \approx (0.5)2^{-0.152} \approx 0.450$ (million dollars).
$MC(4) = (0.5)4^{\log_2 0.9} \approx (0.5)2^{2(-0.152)} \approx 0.405$ (million dollars).

(b)

$$C(x) = \int MC(x)\,dx$$

$$= \int (0.5)x^{\log_2 0.9}\,dx$$

$$= \frac{0.5}{1+\log_2 0.9}x^{1+\log_2 0.9} + K$$

$$\approx 0.590x^{0.848} + K.$$

$K$ is the cost if no planes are produced; it represents the costs of setting up the plant for production.

(c)   Given $K = 20$ million, we have

$$C(50) \approx (0.590)50^{0.848} + 20 \approx 36.277 \ (\text{millions}),$$

so the cost is approximately 36,277,000 dollars.

2.   Rank in order of increasing present value, assuming 7% interest compounded continuously. No work need be shown.

(a)   $1000, paid today.
(b)   $1050, paid six months from now.
(c)   $1085, paid a year from now.
(d)   $1050, paid continuously over the next year.

   ANSWER:

   For (a), the present value is just $1000. The present value of $1050 paid six months from now is $1050e^{(-0.07)(0.5)} = \$1013.89$. For $1085 paid in a year, the present value is $1085e^{-0.07} = \$1011.65$.

   The present value of (d) is $\int_0^1 1050e^{-0.07t} \, dt = \$1014.09$. Thus, (a) < (c) < (b) < (d).

3.   On each of January 1, 1991 and January 1, 1992, a person deposits 1000 dollars in a savings bank.

(a)   On the last day of each year, the bank deposits interest in the account at a rate of 8%, compounded annually. Write down a sum that gives the size of the bank account after the second interest deposit (at the end of 1992). Do not evaluate the sum.
(b)   Write down a sum that gives the size of the bank account at the end of 1992 if the interest is compounded 4 times per year. Do not evaluate the sum.
(c)   Write down a sum and/or integral for the size of the bank account at the end of 1992 if the interest is compounded continuously. Do not evaluate your expression.

   ANSWER:

(a)   $[1000 + (1000(1 + 0.08))](1 + 0.08)$
(b)   $\left[1000 + \left(1000\left(1 + \frac{0.08}{4}\right)^4\right)\right]\left(1 + \frac{0.08}{4}\right)^4$
(c)   $[1000 + 1000e^{0.08}]e^{0.08}$

<u>Remarks</u>

- The answer should be about 2000.
- No integral in (c): this is not an income stream.

4.   By the year 1996 you will have made your first million dollars. You invest it in a new company on January 1, 1997. The new company starts to earn a profit six months later. Thus, starting July 1, 1997, you receive income from the company in a continuous stream at a constant rate of $\frac{1}{2}$ million dollars per year.

   Your bank offers interest at a nominal rate of 8% per year, compounded continuously.

(a)   When will you have received an income of $1 million from the company? (Do <u>not</u> take into account the bank's interest; this question is simply asking when the total income you have received will reach $1 million.) Give an exact date as an answer.
(b)   Consider your answer to (a): Is your investment just paid off at that time? If not, is your investment paid off at a later date or is it paid off at an earlier date? Explain your answer.
   Suppose $T$ is measured in years from January 1, 1997.
(c)   What is the future value of your original investment of $1 million at time $T$?
(d)   What is the future value at time $T$ of the income that you have received by that time?
(e)   After how many years, $T$, will your investment have paid off? During what month of what year will this happen?

   ANSWER:

(a)   July 1, 1999.
(b)   No. The present value of the earned $1 million is less than $1 million, so it will pay off later.
(c)   $B = 10^6 e^{0.08T}$

(d)   Future value at $T = \int_{\frac{1}{2}}^{T} \dfrac{10^6}{2} e^{0.08(T-t)} dt = 6,004,934 e^{0.08T} - 6,250,000.$

(e)   It will be paid off when future values equal $10^6 e^{0.08T} = 6,004,934 e^{0.08T} - 6,250,000.$

$T = \dfrac{1}{0.08} \ln \left( \dfrac{6,250,000}{5,004,934} \right) \approx 2.78$ years.

Since $0.78$ years $= 9.36$ months, this is October 1999.

5.   Somebody offers to pay you money in one of the following ways:

- Two \$54 payments, one six months from now and one twelve months from now.
- Payment in a continuous cash flow over the next year at a constant rate of \$107 per year.

These payments are to be deposited into a bank account that earns 10% interest compounded continuously. You want to determine which plan is preferable, i.e., which plan has a larger present value.

(a)   Find the present value of payment plan (i).

(b)   Write a Riemann sum that approximates the present value of the second payment plan. Show all your work clearly.

(c)   Turn your Riemann sum in part (b) into a definite integral that gives the exact present value of payment plan (ii), and evaluate the integral. Which payment plan has the larger present value?

ANSWER:

(a)   $P = 54 e^{-0.1(0.5)} + 54 e^{-0.1(1)} = \$100.23$

$t = 0.5$ year is 6 months from now. $t = 1$ year is the payment 1 year from now.

(b)

Amount of money deposited is ($107\Delta t$)

Portion $0 \leq t \leq 1$ year into $N$ subintervals of width $\Delta t = \dfrac{1}{N}$. On each subinterval, you are paid ($107\Delta t$) dollars. On the $i$-th subinterval, as pictured above, the present value of the payment will be approximately $(107\Delta t) e^{-0.1 t_i}$. The total present value of the payments is therefore approximated by the Riemann sum

$$\sum_{i=1}^{N} 107 e^{-0.1 t_i} \Delta t$$

(c)   $P = \displaystyle\int_{0}^{1} 107 e^{-0.1t} dt$

$= -1070 e^{-0.1t} \Big|_{0}^{1}$

$= -1070 (e^{-0.1} - 1)$

$= \$101.82$

The second payment plan is better because it has the larger present value.

6.   You have a bank account that earns 8% nominal annual interest compounded continuously, and you want to have \$80,000 in the bank account in five years so that you can buy a brand new Porsche.

(a)   How much money would you have to deposit in one lump sum today so that the account balance would be \$80,000 in five years?

(b)   If you instead deposit money in the account at a constant continuous rate of $K$ dollars per year, then write a Riemann sum in terms of $K$ that approximates the balance of the account after five years.

(c)   Turn the Riemann sum from part (b) into a definite integral that gives the exact balance after five years. Evaluate the integral in terms of the constant $K$.

(d)   At what constant continuous rate $K$ dollars per year would you have to deposit money so that the balance of the account would be \$80,000 after five years?

ANSWER:

(a) There are two ways of looking at this. You can either find the necessary size of a deposit $P$ dollars so that the future value $F$ of the deposit in five years is $80,000; or you can realize that this is equivalent to finding the *present value* of $80,000:

$$P = Fe^{-it} = (\$80,000)e^{-0.08(5)} = \$53,625.60$$

(b) Partition the time interval $0 \le t \le 5$ into $N$ subintervals of width $\Delta t = \dfrac{5}{N}$. The amount of money deposited during the $i$-th time subinterval at time $t_i$ is $K\Delta t$ dollars, and the future value of this amount of money is $Ke^{0.08(5-t_i)}\Delta t$ dollars. Therefore, the total bank balance after five years will be approximated by $\displaystyle\sum_{i=1}^{N} Ke^{0.08(5-t_i)}\Delta t$

(c) $w = 0.08(5-t) \Rightarrow dw = -0.08dt \Rightarrow dt = -12.5dw$

$$F = \int_0^5 Ke^{0.08(5-t)}dt = -12.5K \int_{0.4}^0 e^w dw = -12.5K\left[e^w\right]_{0.4}^0 = 12.5K(e^{0.4}-1)$$

(d) $12.5K(e^{0.4}-1) = 80,000 \Rightarrow K = \dfrac{80,000}{12.5(e^{0.4}-1)} = \$13,012.77$ per year

As an aside, notice that the total amount of money deposited would be $5K = 65,063.83$, which is larger than the lump sum deposit in part (a). This is to be expected, since the money will be in the bank for less time overall.

7. It is estimated that in fifteen years, it will cost $200,000 to send a child to a four-year college.

(a) Find the present value of a college education that will cost $200,000 in fifteen years, assuming you could get 6% nominal annual interest on your money compounded continuously. Based on the current cost of a four-year college education, does the estimated $200,000 in fifteen years sound high? Say you want to set up an account at a bank that offers 6% nominal annual interest compounded continuously, so that fifteen years from today, the account has $200,000 in it for your child's college education. In parts (b) through (d) you will determine at what constant continuous rate $K$ dollars per year you would need to deposit money.

(b) Set up a differential equation for the rate of change of your bank balance, where $B = f(t)$ is your bank balance at time $t$.

(c) Solve this differential equation for an initial balance of zero.

(d) Use your solution to part (c) to find $K$.

ANSWER:

(a) $\dfrac{200,000}{e^{.06(15)}} = \$81,313.93$. This is $\sim$ $20,000 per year (present value) which is about the current cost.

(b) $\dfrac{dB}{dt} = 0.06B + K$

(c) $\dfrac{dB}{dt} = 0.06\left(B + \dfrac{K}{0.06}\right)$, so $\displaystyle\int \dfrac{dB}{B + \frac{K}{0.06}} = \int 0.06dt$. $\ln\left|B + \dfrac{K}{0.06}\right| = 0.06t + C$, so

$B + \dfrac{K}{0.06} = Ae^{0.06t}$. When $t=0$, $B=0$ so $A = \dfrac{K}{0.06}$ $B = \dfrac{K}{0.06}(e^{0.06t}-1)$

(d) We want to find $K$ so that $B = 200,000$ when $t = 15$.

$200,000 = \dfrac{K}{0.06}(e^{.06(15)}-1)$ and $K = \$8221.41$ dollars per year.

8. An insurance salesman offers you a life insurance policy with the following terms. You are to make payments at a rate of $1000 per year until age 70. If you pass away at any time, the policy will pay $150,000. Consider the payments to be made at a constant continuous rate of $1000 per year.
You are 30 years old, and you have a bank account that you know will offer you 5% nominal annual interest compounded continuously for an indefinite amount of time.

(a) Let's say you're feeling unlucky, and you think that you will die at age 70 (40 years from the time you start making payments for this insurance policy). If you had deposited your payments in the bank account, then what would be your balance at the time of your death?

(b)   Based on your answer to part (a), if you die at age 70, are you better off depositing your money in the bank or buying the insurance policy?

(c)   If you were to stop making payments in the bank account after 40 years, when you turn age 70, just as you would stop making payments on the life insurance policy, then you would simply earn interest on the bank balance that you calculated in part (a) until you died. How many years after age 70 would it be until that balance was $150,000?

(d)   Based on your answer to part (c), if you thought you would live until age 80, are you better off depositing your money in the bank or buying the insurance policy?

ANSWER:

(a)   $FV = \int_0^{40} 1000e^{0.05(40-t)}\,dt$. Let $w = 0.05(40 - t) \Rightarrow dw = (-20)^{-1}dt$.

$$= 1000 \int_2^0 e^w(-20dw) = -20,000e^w \Big|_2^0 = 20,000(e^2 - 1) = \$127,781.12$$

(b)   You are better off buying the insurance policy because the future value of your payments is less than the $150,000 future value of the insurance policy.

(c)   Find $T$ such that the present value of $150,000 is $127,781.12:

$$127,781.12 = 150,000e^{-0.05T} \Rightarrow T = -20\ln\left(\frac{127,781.12}{150,000}\right) = 3.21 \text{ years}$$

(d)   The result in part (c) means that if you live more than 3.21 years past the age of 70, you would have been better off depositing your money for 40 years in the bank account. This is because at age 73.21, the bank balance reaches $150,000, and obviously after that point, the bank balance exceeds the $150,000 that your beneficiaries could collect from the insurance policy.

9.   You have $100,000 that you want to invest. Some "business men" are willing to sell you a machine for your $100,000 that prints money. You figure that every day you can print $300 with the machine, and you would deposit the $300 each day in a "special" bank account at BCCI. Your friends at BCCI will only be able to offer you 5% nominal annual interest, compounded continuously, due to the "sensitive nature" of the transaction. It would be your intention to print money each day for one year.

(a)   Write a sum that gives the exact value of your bank balance after one year. Do not attempt to evaluate the sum.

(b)   If you were depositing the money that you printed in a continuous stream at a constant rate of $300 per day into the same bank account, then what definite integral would give your balance after one year? Evaluate the definite integral. (This result is very close to the numerical value of the sum you wrote in part (a).)

(c)   If you had just taken the original $100,000 and placed it in a regular bank account that compounds interest annually, then what interest rate would you have had to earn in order for this option to be more profitable than the money machine (legal concerns aside)?

ANSWER:

(a)   Each daily deposit earns at a daily interest rate of $\dfrac{0.05}{365}$ for a period of $365 - t$ days. So at the end of the year, a deposit of $300 made at time $t$ has increased to $300e^{\frac{0.05}{365}[365-t]}$. The sum for the entire year is

$$\text{Balance} = \sum_{i=1}^{365} \underbrace{300}_{\text{units=\$/day}} e^{\frac{0.05}{365}[365-t_i]}\Delta t \,(\Delta t = 1 \text{ day})$$

This sum evaluated turns out to be $112,276.01.

$$\text{Balance} = \int_0^{365} 300 e^{\frac{0.05}{365}[365-t]} dt$$

(b)
$$= 300 \left(-\frac{365}{0.05}\right) e^{\frac{0.05}{365}[365-t]} \Big|_0^{365}$$

$$= 300 \left(-\frac{365}{0.05}\right) [e^0 - e^{0.05}] = \$112,283.70$$

(c)    For $100,000 to become greater than the amount earned from the money machine (part (b)), then the annual (compounded once) interest rate, $r$, is needed such that:

$112,283.70 = 100,000(1+r)$

$1.1228370 = 1 + r$

$.1228370 = r \Rightarrow 12.28\%$

10.    The *capital value* of an asset such as a machine is sometimes defined as the present value of all future net earnings of the asset. The actual lifetime of the asset may not be known, and since some assets last indefinitely, the capital value of the asset may be written in the form

$$\int_0^\infty K(t)e^{-rt}\, dt,$$

where $K(t)$ is the annual rate of earnings produced by the asset at time $t$, and $r$ is the annual interest rate, compounded continuously. Find the capital value of an asset that generates income at a rate of $500 per year, with an interest rate of 10%.

ANSWER:

$K(t)$ is constant, $500/yr and $r = 0.1$. So

$$\text{capital value} = \int_0^\infty 500 e^{-0.1t}\, dt$$

$$= 500 \cdot \left(-\frac{1}{0.1} e^{-0.1t}\right)\Big|_0^\infty$$

$$= \frac{500}{0.1}$$

$$= \$5000$$

## Review Problems and Solutions for Chapter 8

1.    The price of crude oil in the recent past was well approximated by $P(t) = 40 - (t-4)^2$, where $P(t)$ is measured in $US/barrel, and time $t$ is measured in months, with $t = 0$ on July 1, 1990. In the same time period, Saudi Arabia produced oil at a rate well approximated by $R(t) = 160 + 30\arctan(t-3)$ (measured in million barrels per month). Assume that the oil is sold continuously two months after its production. How much did Saudi Arabia get for the oil it produced in the second half of 1990?

ANSWER:

If $P(t) = 40 - (t-4)^2$ is the price per barrel at time $t$, and $R(t) = 160 + 30\arctan(t-3)$ is the number of barrels produced in millions of barrels/month, then $P(t)R(t-2)$ is the rate at which money is made in millions of dollars/month, since oil is not sold until 2 months after its production. The total amount of money made, in millions of dollars, is given by

$$\int_0^6 (40 - (t-4)^2)(160 + 30\arctan(t-5))\, dt \approx 29608.$$

So $29.6 billion is made in the second half of 1990.

*Problems and Solutions for Focus on Modeling: Distribution Functions* ━━━━━

1.  A lightbulb company is interested in the lifespan of their lightbulbs. They have 10,000 lightbulbs burning and have collected the following information.
    After 2 months, 98% of the bulbs were still working.
    After 8 months, 80% of the bulbs were still working.
    We summarize all the data collected below: (Read carefully: the data was not collected at regular intervals.)

    percentage per month

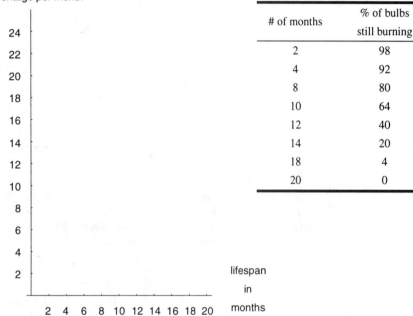

| # of months | % of bulbs still burning |
|:---:|:---:|
| 2 | 98 |
| 4 | 92 |
| 8 | 80 |
| 10 | 64 |
| 12 | 40 |
| 14 | 20 |
| 18 | 4 |
| 20 | 0 |

    (a)  How many bulbs out of the original 10,000 burned out during the first 4 months?
    (b)  Use the axes above to draw a histogram for the lifespan of a bulb reflecting all the information in the table. (Do not smooth out the graph.)
    (c)  Approximate the average lifespan of a lightbulb. Explain your reasoning clearly.

    ANSWER:

    (a)  After four months, 92% of the original 10,000 lightbulbs were still burning. This means that 8%, or $10,000 \cdot 0.08 = 800$ lightbulbs, had burned out already.
    (b)  Since 2% of the bulbs die out within the first two months, we assume that 1% of the bulbs die out per month during this period. Between 2 and 4 months, 6% of the bulbs die out, or 3% per month. Between 4 and 8 months, 12% die out, or 3% a month. Between 8 and 10 months, $\frac{80-64}{2} = 8\%$ a month die out. Between 10 and 12 months, $\frac{24}{2} = 12\%$ a month die out. Between 12 and 14 months, $\frac{20}{2} = 10\%$ a month die out. Between 14 and 18 months, $\frac{16}{4} = 4\%$ a month die out, and between 18 and 20 months, $\frac{4}{2} = 2\%$ a month die out.

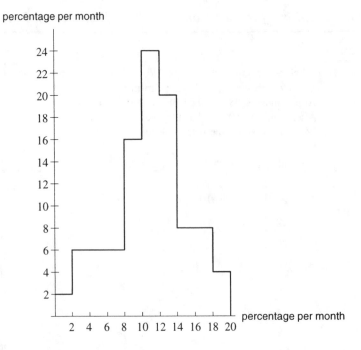

percentage per month

(c)    Since 1% of the bulbs die per month over the first two months, 2% of the bulbs have an average lifespan of 1 month. Between 2 and 8 months, 3% die out per month, so 18% have an average lifespan of 5 months. Between 8 and 10 months, 8% die out per month, so 16% have an average lifespan of 9 months, and so on. Thus:

$$\text{Average Lifespan} \approx 1(2\%) + 5(18\%) + 9(16\%) +$$
$$11(24\%) + 13(20\%) + 16(16\%) + 19(4\%)$$
$$= 10.92 \text{ months}.$$

2.    The probability density function $f(x)$ shown below describes the chances that a computer circuit board will cost a manufacturer more than a certain number of dollars to produce. In this case, the cost of the circuit board, $x$, is measured in thousands of dollars.

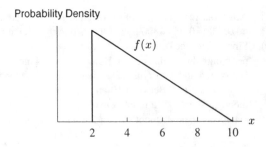

(a)    What is the probability that the circuit board will cost more than $10 thousand to produce? What is the probability that the circuit board will cost less than $2 thousand to produce? What is the probability that the circuit board will cost between $2 thousand and $10 thousand to produce? Is it more likely that the circuit board will cost more or less than $6 thousand?

(b)    Show on the graph below, and describe in words, the geometrical interpretation of the probability that the circuit card will cost between $2 thousand and some amount $b thousand. (Assume that $b$ is between 2 and 10.)

Probability Density

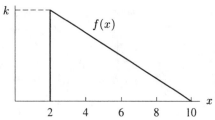

(c) Write a definite integral in terms of $f(x)$ that gives the probability that the circuit card will cost between \$2 thousand and some amount \$$b$ thousand. Do not attempt to evaluate the integral.

(d) Given your answers above, find the value of $k$, the height of the triangle that describes the probability density function.

ANSWER:

(a) Probability more than \$10 thousand=probability less than \$2 thousand= 0.
Probability between \$2 and \$10 thousand= 1.
More likely less than \$6 thousand.

(b) Probability between \$2 and \$$b$ thousand=Area under $f(x)$ between \$2 and \$$b$ thousand.

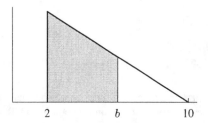

(c) $= \displaystyle\int_{2}^{b} f(x)dx$

(d) Area of $\Delta = 1$, so $\dfrac{1}{2} \cdot 8k = 1k = \dfrac{1}{4}$

## *Problems and Solutions for Focus on Modeling: More on Distribution Functions*

1. Suppose that the distribution of family sizes in the city of Boston in the year 1956 was given by:

| Size: | 2 | 3 | 4 | 5 | 6 | $\geq 7$ |
|---|---|---|---|---|---|---|
| # of Families: | 13 921 | 9770 | 8955 | 5251 | 2520 | 2426 |

Represent this data on a histogram as a density distribution function.

ANSWER:

The total number of families in Boston, according to this data, was: $13,921 + 9770 + 8955 + 5251 + 2520 + 2426 = 42843$.

The percentage of families by sizes are therefore:

| Size: | 2 | 3 | 4 | 5 | 6 | $\leq 7$ |
|---|---|---|---|---|---|---|
| %: | 32.5 | 23 | 21 | 12 | 6 | 5.5 |

and gives the following histogram:

542

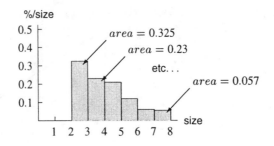

We assumed that there are no families with size $\geq 8$. If the biggest family had $F$ individuals, then the "tail" from 7 to $F$ must have area $= 0.055$.

2. Using the data in Problem 1, find the mean of family sizes in the city of Boston in the year 1956. Assume that all of the families with 7 or more members had precisely 7 members. (You do not need to have answered Problem 1 in order to answer this question.)

   ANSWER:

   Let

   $N_i$ = # of families with $i$ people

   $N$ = total # of families

   $P_i = \dfrac{N_i}{N}$

   $\Rightarrow$ mean $= \displaystyle\sum_{i=1}^{7} i \cdot P_i \approx 3.53$ people

3. (a) Let $p(t)$ be a probability density which is defined for $0 \leq t \leq 1$. Which of the following could be the cumulative distribution function for $p$? (Remember that the cumulative distribution function at time $t$ is the integral of $p$ from 0 to $t$.)

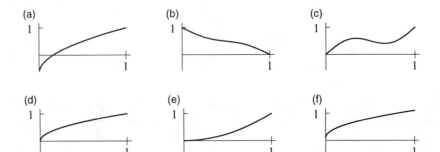

   (b) Draw a probability density function whose mean is <u>substantially</u> smaller than its median. (Make the difference unambiguous to get full credit.)

   ANSWER:

   (a) Diagrams (d) and (e). In (a), the function is negative, in (f) it exceeds 1, and in (b) and (c) the function decreases.

   (b) Here are some possible examples:

4. A professor gives the same 100-point final exam year after year and discovers that this students' scores tend to follow the triangular probability density function $f(x)$ pictured below:

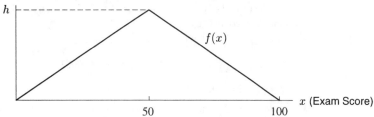

Probability Density

(All persons, places, and events in this story are fictitious. Any similarity to real persons or situations are purely coincidental.)

(a) TRUE or FALSE: The median, mean, and mode all describe the same point on this probability density function.

(b) What is the probability that a student's score will lie in the range $0 \leq x \leq 100$? Use this fact to find the value of the height $h$ of the triangular probability density function.

(c) Find the equation of the probability density function $f(x)$ in the range $0 \leq x \leq 50$.

(d) What fraction of the students would you expect to score below 25 points on the exam? What fraction of the students would you expect to score below 75 points on the exam?

ANSWER:

(a) TRUE

(b) Prob$(0 \leq x \leq 100) = 1$

$$\text{Prob}(0 \leq x \leq 100) = \frac{1}{2} \underbrace{(100 - 0)}_{\text{Base}} h = 50h = 1 \Rightarrow h = \frac{1}{50} = 0.02$$

(c) Slope$= \dfrac{\Delta y}{\Delta x} = \dfrac{h}{50 - 0} = \dfrac{\frac{1}{50}}{50} = \dfrac{1}{2500}$

$f(x) = y - mx$ (line through origin)

$$f(x) = \frac{1}{2500} x$$

(d) Prob$(0 \leq x < 25) = \text{Prob}(75 < x \leq 100)$    (since $f(x)$ symmetrical)

$$= \int_0^{25} f(x)\,dx = \int_0^{25} \frac{1}{2500} x\,dx = \left[\frac{x^2}{5000}\right]_0^{25} = 0.125 = \frac{1}{8}$$

The fraction of students that would be expected to score below 75 is 7/8.

5. The distribution of people's ages in the United States is essentially constant, or uniform, from age 0 to age 60, and from there it decreases linearly until age 100. This distribution $p(x)$ is shown below, where $x$ is age in years, and $p$ measures probability density. Such a probability distribution is called *trapezoidal*.

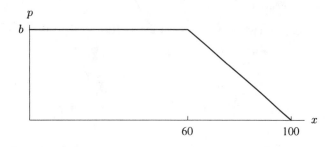

(a) According to this simplified model of the distribution of people's ages in the United States, what fraction of the population is older than 100? What fraction is between 0 and 100 years old?

(b) In terms of the length of the base, $b$, of the trapezoidal distribution (notice that the base of the trapezoid lies along the $p$-axis), find the fraction of the population that is between 0 and 60 years old.

(c) In terms of $b$, find the fraction of the population that is between 60 and 100 years old.

(d) Use the results of parts (a), (b), and (c) to find the value of $b$.

(e) Find the median age of the United States population.

ANSWER:

(a) 0% are older than 100, 100% are between 0 and 100.

(b) $\displaystyle\int_0^{60} p(x)dx = $ area of rectangle $= 60b$

(c) $\displaystyle\int_{60}^{100} p(x)dx = $ area of triangle from 60 to 100 $= \frac{1}{2} \cdot 40 \cdot b = 20b$

(d) Total area under the probability distribution $p(x) = 100\% = 1$. So $60b + 20b = 1 \Rightarrow 80b = 1 \Rightarrow$
$b = \dfrac{1}{80}$

(e)

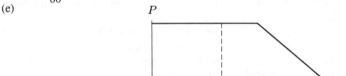

Let $a = $ median age. This value $a$ should be in the middle, i.e., half the population should be older and half younger. Thus, the area under $p(x)$ to the <u>left</u> of $a$ should equal the area under $p(x)$ to the <u>right</u> of $a$. Or, the area under $p(x)$ to the left of $a$ should be $\frac{1}{2}$ the total, or $\frac{1}{2} \cdot 1 = \frac{1}{2}$.

$$\int_0^a p(x)dx = \text{area of rectangle} = ab = a \cdot \frac{1}{80} = \frac{1}{2} \Rightarrow a = 40 \text{ years}$$

6. In a hydrogen atom in the unexcited state, the probability of finding the sole electron within $x$ meters of the nucleus is given by

$$F(x) = \frac{4}{(a_0)^3} \int_0^x r^2 e^{\frac{-2r}{a_0}} \, dr, \qquad x \geq 0,$$

where $a_0 \approx 5.29 \times 10^{-11}$ meters.

(a) $F(x)$, as given above, is a cumulative probability distribution function. What is its corresponding probability density function $f(x)$? Sketch a graph of $y = f(x)$. What happens to $f(x)$ as $x \to \infty$ and what is $f(0)$?
[Hint: Find $f'(x)$ to locate any local maxima or minima.]

(b) Carry out the integration given in the definition of $F(x)$ to find a more likable formula for $F(x)$. Simplify your formula. (Remember to evaluate the integral between 0 and $x$.)

(c) What is the probability that the electron will be found within a sphere of radius $a_0$?

(d) What is the probability that the electron will be found within $\frac{3}{2}a_0$ meters of the nucleus?

ANSWER:

(a) The probablity density function is $f(x) = F'(x) = \dfrac{4}{a_0^3}x^2 e^{-\frac{2x}{a_0}}$. It's easy to see that $f(0) = 0$.
As $x \to \infty$, $f(x) \to 0$

$$f'(x) = \frac{4}{a_0^3}\left(2xe^{-\frac{2x}{a_0}} - \frac{2}{a_0}x^2 e^{-\frac{2x}{a_0}}\right)$$
$$= \frac{8x}{a_0^3}e^{-\frac{2x}{a_0}}\left(1 - \frac{x}{a_0}\right).$$

Therefore $f'(x) = 0$ for $x = 0$ and $x = a_0$. Additionally, $f(x) \geq 0$ for all $x$. Since $f(0) = 0$ and $f(x) \to 0$ as $x \to \infty$, we deduce that $x = a$ is a maximum (both local and global) and $x = 0$ is a minimum (both local and global).

(b)

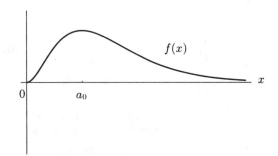

(c)

$$F(x) = \frac{4}{a_0^3} \int_0^x r^2 e^{-\frac{2r}{a_0}} \, dr$$

$$= \frac{4}{a_0^3} \left( -\frac{a_0}{2} r^2 e^{-\frac{2r}{a_0}} \Big|_0^x + \int_0^x a_0 r e^{\frac{-2r}{a_0}} \, dr \right)$$

$$= \frac{4}{a_0^3} \left( -\frac{a_0}{2} x^2 e^{-\frac{2x}{a_0}} + a_0 r \left( -\frac{a_0}{2} \right) e^{-\frac{2r}{a_0}} \Big|_0^x + \frac{1}{2} \int_0^x a_0^2 e^{\frac{-2r}{a_0}} \, dr \right)$$

$$= \frac{4}{a_0^3} \left( -\frac{1}{2} a_0 e^{\frac{-2x}{a_0}} x^2 - \frac{1}{2} a_0^2 e^{\frac{-2x}{a_0}} x - \frac{1}{4} a_0^3 e^{\frac{-2x}{a_0}} + \frac{1}{4} a_0^3 \right)$$

$$= e^{\frac{-2x}{a_0}} \left( -\frac{2x^2}{a_0^2} - \frac{2x}{a_0} - 1 \right) + 1.$$

(d)  Probability of finding an electron in a shell of radius $a_0$ is

$$F(a_0) = e^{-\frac{2a_0}{a_0}} \left( -\frac{2a_0^2}{a_0^2} - \frac{2a_0}{a_0} - 1 \right) + 1$$

$$= 1 - \frac{5}{e^2}.$$

(e)  Probability of finding an electron in a shell of radius $\frac{3}{2} a_0$ is

$$F\left( \frac{3}{2} a_0 \right) = e^{-\frac{3a_0}{a_0}} \left( -\frac{2(\frac{9}{4} a_0^2)}{a_0^2} - \frac{3a_0}{a_0} - 1 \right) + 1$$

$$= 1 - \frac{17}{2e^3}.$$

7.  In March 1995 the space shuttle carried an experiment designed by a Harvard student who studies the growth of crystals. Suppose the *probability density* function of the length, $x$ cm, of a crystal grown in space is modeled by

$$p(x) = xe^{-x} \quad \text{for } x \geq 0.$$

The *cumulative distribution* function giving the probability that a crystal has length $\leq 2$ cm is represented by $P(t)$.

(a)  Which of the quantities (i) - (x) below best approximates the probability that a crystal has length between 2 cm and 2.01 cm?

(b)  Which of the quantities (i) - (x) represents precisely the probability that a crystal has length less than 2.01 cm?

Possible answers for parts (a) and (b):

(i)  $p(2)$　　　　　　　　　　　　　　(vi)  $P(2)$

(ii)  $p(2.01) - p(2)$　　　　　　　　　(vii)  $P(2.01)$

(iii)  $p(2)(0.01)$           (viii)  $P(2)(0.01)$

(iv)  $\dfrac{p(2)}{0.01}$           (ix)  $\dfrac{P(2)}{0.01}$

(v)  $\dfrac{p(2.01) - p(2)}{0.01}$           (x)  $\dfrac{P(2.02) - P(2)}{0.01}$

(c)  Find a formula for the cumulative distribution function $P(t)$ for $t \geq 0$.

(d)  What is the median crystal length that this model predicts? Give your answer to two decimal places.

(e)  Set up an integral giving the mean crystal length predicted by this model.

(f)  Calculate the mean crystal length. Give an exact answer.

ANSWER:

(a)  Choice (iii) since

$$\begin{pmatrix} \text{Probability that crystal has} \\ \text{length between 2 and 2.01 cm} \end{pmatrix} = \begin{pmatrix} \text{Area under } p(x) \\ \text{between 2 and 2.01} \end{pmatrix} \approx p(2) \cdot (0.01).$$

(b)  Choice (vii) since by the definition of $P(t)$, $P(2.01)$ is the probability that crystal has length up to 2.01.

(c)  By definition,

$$P(t) = \int_{-\infty}^{t} p(x)dx.$$

Here the lower limit can be replaced by 0 since crystals cannot have negative length, and $p(x) = xe^{-x}$ for $x \geq 0$, so

$$P(t) = \int_{0}^{t} xe^{-x}dx$$
$$= -te^{-t} - e^{-t} + 1, \quad \text{through integration by parts}$$
$$= 1 - \frac{t+1}{e^t}.$$

(d)  The median $T$ is the value of length such that

$$\int_{0}^{T} p(x)dx = \frac{1}{2}$$
$$P(t) = \frac{1}{2}$$
$$-Te^{-T} - e^{-T} + 1 = \frac{1}{2}$$
$$e^{-T}(T+1) = \frac{1}{2}$$
$$e^{-T}(T+1) - \frac{1}{2} = 0.$$

Using the calculator to graph this equation and tracing, we get that $T \approx 1.68$.

(e)  By definition,

$$\text{Mean} = \int_{-\infty}^{\infty} xp(x)dx = \int_{0}^{\infty} x(xe^{-x})dx.$$

(f)  Evaluating the integral from part (e),

$$\text{Mean} = \lim_{b \to \infty} \int_{0}^{b} x(xe^{-x})dx$$
$$= \lim_{b \to \infty} \left[ \left(-x^2e^{-x} - 2xe^{-x} - 2e^{-x}\right) \Big|_{0}^{b} \right], \quad \text{from tables}$$
$$= \lim \left[ \left(-b^2e^{-b} - 2be^{-b} - 2e^{-b}\right) - (0 - 0 - 2) \right]$$
$$= 2.$$

# Chapter 9 Exam Questions

1. Construct the Taylor polynomial approximation of degree 3 to the function $f(x) = \arctan x$ about the point $x = 0$. Use it to approximate the value $f(0.25)$. How does the approximation compare to the actual value?

   ANSWER:

$$f(x) = \arctan x \quad f(0) = 0$$
$$f'(x) = \frac{1}{1 + x^2} \quad f'(0) = 1$$
$$f''(x) = \frac{-2x}{(1 + x^2)^2} \quad f''(0) = 0$$
$$f'''(x) = \frac{-2(1 + x^2)^2 + (2x)2(1 + x^2)(2x)}{(1 + x^2)^4} = \frac{6x^2 - 2}{(1 + x^2)^3} \quad f'''(0) = -2$$

The third-degree Taylor polynomial approximation for $\arctan x$ around 0 is

$$\arctan x \approx P_3(x) = f(0) + \frac{f'(0)}{1!}x + \frac{f''(0)}{2!}x^2 + \frac{f'''(0)}{3!}x^3 = x - \frac{1}{3}x^3,$$

so $f(.25) \approx .25 - (.25)^3/3 = 0.24479$. The actual value of $f(0.25)$ is $\approx 0.24498$, so the Taylor approximation is accurate to three decimals.

2. (a) Estimate the value of $\int_0^1 e^{-x^2}\, dx$ using both left- and right-hand Riemann sums with $n = 5$ subdivisions.
   (b) Approximate the function $f(x) = e^{-x^2}$ with a Taylor polynomial of degree 6.
   (c) Estimate the integral in (a) by integrating the Taylor polynomial approximation from (b).
   (d) Indicate briefly how you could improve the results in both cases.

   ANSWER:

   (a) With $n = 5$ subdivisions, and $\Delta x = 1/n = 1/5$,

$$\text{LEFT}(5) = \sum_{i=0}^{4} \frac{1}{5}e^{-x_i^2} = \frac{1}{5}\left(1 + e^{-\frac{1}{25}} + e^{-\frac{4}{25}} + e^{-\frac{9}{25}} + e^{-\frac{16}{25}}\right) \approx 0.80758$$

$$\text{RIGHT}(5) = \sum_{i=1}^{5} \frac{1}{5}e^{-x_i^2} = \frac{1}{5}\left(e^{-\frac{1}{25}} + e^{-\frac{4}{25}} + e^{-\frac{9}{25}} + e^{-\frac{16}{25}} + e^{-1}\right) \approx 0.68116$$

   Because $e^{-x^2}$ is monotone decreasing between 0 and 1, the true value of $\int_0^1 e^{-x^2}\, dx$ is less than the left-hand sum, and greater than the right-hand sum.

   (b) The Taylor polynomial around 0, to degree 3, for $e^x$ is:

$$e^x \approx P_3(x) = 1 + \frac{1}{1!}x + \frac{1}{2!}x^2 + \frac{1}{3!}x^3.$$

   Substitute $-x^2$ for $x$ into the above expression to obtain:

$$e^{-x^2} \approx 1 - \frac{1}{1!}x^2 + \frac{1}{2!}x^4 - \frac{1}{3!}x^6.$$

(c)   Integrating the polynomial above from 0 to 1 gives:

$$\int_0^1 e^{-x^2}\, dx \approx \left. \left( x - \frac{1}{3}x^3 + \frac{1}{10}x^5 - \frac{1}{42}x^7 \right) \right|_0^1 \approx 0.74286.$$

(d)   We could improve the estimate in part (a) by using more subdivisions, or by using a more sophisticated scheme, such as Simpson's rule, for estimating the integral. We could improve the estimate in part (b) by using a higher-degree Taylor polynomial.

3.   The graph of $y = f(x)$ is given below.

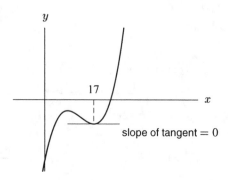

Suppose we approximate $f(x)$ near $x = 17$ by the second degree Taylor polynomial centered about 17,

$$a + b(x - 17) + c(x - 17)^2.$$

Determine the sign of $a$, $b$, and $c$ and circle the correct answer.

(a)   $a$ is          positive          negative          zero
       Reasoning:
(b)   $b$ is          positive          negative          zero
       Reasoning:
(c)   $c$ is          positive          negative          zero
       Reasoning:

ANSWER:

(a)   negative
       "$a$" is a constant, equal to $f(17)$, <u>not</u> $f(0)$, which is negative according to the graph.
(b)   zero
       "$b$" corresponds to $f'(17)$, which is 0.
(c)   positive
       "$c$" corresponds to $f''(17)$, which is $> 0$ since $f(x)$ is concave up at $x = 17$.

4.   Write down the fourth degree Taylor polynomial for $\cos(3x^2)$ about $x = 0$.
       ANSWER:

       The Taylor expansion for $\cos t$ about $x = 0$ is

$$\cos t = 1 - \frac{t^2}{2!} + \dots.$$

Substituting $3x^2$ for $t$ gives

$$\cos(3x^2) = 1 - \frac{(3x^2)^2}{2!} + \dots$$
$$= 1 - \frac{9}{2}x^4 + \dots.$$

5. Suppose a function satisfies $f(2) = 4$, $f'(2) = 3$, $f''(2) = -5$, $f'''(2) = 12$. Write down the third degree Taylor polynomial for $f$ about $x = 2$.

ANSWER:

In general,

$$f(x) \approx f(a) + f'(a)(x-1) + \frac{f''(a)(x-a)^2}{2!} + \dots + \frac{f^{(n)}(a)(x-a)^n}{n!}.$$

Here, $a = 2$. Making this substitution gives

$$f(x) \approx P_3(x) = 4 + 3(x-2) - \frac{5}{2}(x-2)^2 + \frac{12}{6}(x-2)^3$$

$$= 4 + 3(x-2) - \frac{5}{2}(x-2)^2 + 2(x-2)^3.$$

6. The function $g$ has the Taylor approximation

$$g(x) \approx c_0 + c_1(x-a) + c_2(x-a)^2,$$

and the graph given below:

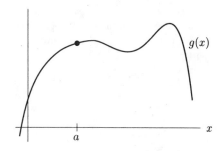

What can you say about the signs of $c_0$, $c_1$, and $c_2$? (Circle your answers; no reasons need be given.)

(a)   $c_0$ is negative          zero          positive
(b)   $c_1$ is negative          zero          positive
(c)   $c_2$ is negative                        positive

ANSWER:

From the picture, we see that $g(a) > 0$, $g'(a) > 0$, and $g''(a) < 0$. Since

$$g(x) \approx g(a) + g'(a)(x-a) + \frac{g''(a)}{2!}(x-a)^2,$$

we can differentiate to get $c_0 = g(a)$, $c_1 = g'(a)$, and $c_2 = g''(a)$. So in fact $c_0$ is positive, $c_1$ is positive, and $c_2$ is negative.

## Problems and Solutions for Section 9.2

1. (a)   Show that $\int_1^\infty \frac{1}{x}\, dx$ does not converge.

   (b)   Use part (a) to show that the harmonic series

$$1 + \frac{1}{2} + \frac{1}{3} + \frac{1}{4} + \frac{1}{5} + \frac{1}{6} + \cdots$$

   does not converge. (Hint: Consider a left hand sum of $f(x) = \frac{1}{x}$ with $\Delta x = 1$.)

   ANSWER:

   (a)   $\int_1^\infty \frac{1}{x}\, dx = \lim_{b \to \infty} \ln x \Big|_1^b = \lim_{b \to \infty} \ln b$. As $b \to \infty$, $\ln b \to \infty$, so $\int_1^\infty \frac{1}{x}\, dx$ diverges.

(b)   Since $\dfrac{1}{x}$ is a decreasing function for $x \geq 1$, any left-hand sum over the interval $[1, \infty)$ is greater than $\displaystyle\int_1^\infty \dfrac{1}{x}\,dx$, which diverges. Consider a left-hand sum with $\Delta x = 1$.

$$\text{left-hand sum} = 1 \cdot 1 + 1 \cdot \frac{1}{2} + 1 \cdot \frac{1}{3} + \cdots$$

$$= 1 + \frac{1}{2} + \frac{1}{3} + \cdots.$$

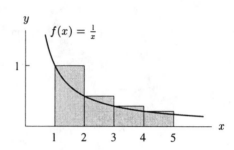

Thus the harmonic series does not converge.

2.   (a)   Find the Taylor polynomial of degree 3 around $x = 0$ for the function

$$f(x) = \sqrt{1 - x}.$$

(b)   Use your answer to part (a) to give approximate values to $\sqrt{\frac{1}{2}}$ and $\sqrt{0.9}$.

(c)   Which approximation in part (b) is more accurate? Explain why.

ANSWER:

(a)

$$
\begin{array}{ll}
f(x) = \sqrt{1 - x} & f(0) = 1 \\[2mm]
f'(x) = -\dfrac{1}{2}(1 - x)^{-\frac{1}{2}} & f'(0) = -\dfrac{1}{2}(1 - 0)^{-\frac{1}{2}} = -\dfrac{1}{2} \\[2mm]
f''(x) = -\dfrac{1}{4}(1 - x)^{-\frac{3}{2}} & f''(0) = -\dfrac{1}{4}(1 - 0)^{-\frac{3}{2}} = -\dfrac{1}{4} \\[2mm]
f'(x) = -\dfrac{3}{8}(1 - x)^{-\frac{5}{2}} & f'''(0) = -\dfrac{3}{8}(1 - 0)^{-\frac{5}{2}} = -\dfrac{3}{8}
\end{array}
$$

So   $P_3(x) = f(0) + \dfrac{f'(0)}{1}x + \dfrac{f''(0)}{2!}x^2 + \dfrac{f'''(0)}{3!}x^3$

$$= 1 - \frac{1}{2}x - \frac{1}{8}x^2 - \frac{1}{16}x^3.$$

(b)   Use $P_3(x)$ obtained above with $x = \dfrac{1}{2}$:

$$\sqrt{1 - \frac{1}{2}} = \sqrt{\frac{1}{2}} \approx 1 - \frac{1}{2}\left(\frac{1}{2}\right) - \frac{1}{8}\left(\frac{1}{2}\right)^2 - \frac{1}{16}\left(\frac{1}{2}\right)^3 \approx 0.7109.$$

Use $P_3(x)$ obtained above with $x = 0.1$:

$$\sqrt{1 - 0.1} = \sqrt{0.9} \approx 1 - \frac{1}{2}(0.1) - \frac{1}{8}(0.1)^2 - \frac{1}{16}(0.1)^3 \approx 0.9487$$

(c)   We expect the approximation to be more accurate for $\sqrt{0.9}$ because 0.1 is significantly closer to 0 than 0.5 is. The actual value for $\sqrt{0.9}$ is $\approx 0.9487$, while the actual value for $\sqrt{0.5}$ is $\approx 0.7071$, so our expectations are correct.

## Problems and Solutions for Section 9.3

1.   (a)   Use the formula for the Taylor polynomial approximation to the function $g(x) = e^x$ about $x_0 = 0$ to construct a polynomial approximation of degree 6 to $f(x) = e^{x^2}$.

(b)  Use the approximation you constructed in (a) to estimate the value of $e^{(0.2)^2}$.

(c)  What is the error in this approximation?

ANSWER:

(a)  The third degree Taylor polynomial about $x = 0$ for $e^x$ is $P_3(x) = 1 + x + \frac{x^2}{2!} + \frac{x^3}{3!}$. Replace $x$ by $x^2$:

$$e^{x^2} \approx 1 + x^2 + \frac{x^4}{2!} + \frac{x^6}{3!}.$$

(b)  Substitute $x = 0.2$:

$$e^{(0.2)^2} \approx 1 + (0.2)^2 + \frac{(0.2)^4}{2!} + \frac{(0.2)^6}{3!}$$

$$= 1.040810666\ldots$$

(c)  The true value of $e^{(0.2)^2}$ is $1.040810774\ldots$ The error is thus less than $1.1 \times 10^{-7}$.

2.  Answer the following questions about Taylor series. If you are asked to find a Taylor series, you may start with a series that you already know and modify it or you may derive the series "from scratch." Also, if you are asked to find a Taylor series, either give the answer in summation notation, or give at least the first four non-zero terms so that the pattern is apparent.

(a)  Consider the function $f(x) = 1 - \cos x$.

(i)  Find the Maclaurin series for $f(x)$.

(ii)  Based on the Maclaurin series for $1 - \cos x$, what do you conclude about the value of the following limit:

$$\lim_{x \to 0} \frac{1 - \cos x}{x^2}$$

(b)  As you know, the function $f(x) = e^{\frac{-x}{2}}$ gives the form of the normal probability density function (or bell-shaped curve).

(i)  Find the Maclaurin series for $f(x)$.

(ii)  Find the Maclaurin series for the indefinite integral of $f(x)$ by integrating term-by-term the Maclaurin series you obtained above for $f(x)$.

ANSWER:

(a)  (i)  $\cos x = 1 - \frac{x^2}{2!} + \frac{x^4}{4!} - \frac{x^6}{6!} + \frac{x^8}{8!} - \cdots$

$$1 - \cos x = \frac{x^2}{2!} - \frac{x^4}{4!} + \frac{x^6}{6!} - \frac{x^8}{8!} + \cdots$$

$$\Rightarrow \quad = \sum_{i=1}^{\infty} \frac{(-1)^{i+1} x^{2i}}{(2i)!}$$

$$\lim_{x \to 0} \frac{1 - \cos x}{x^2} = \lim_{x \to 0} \left[ \frac{\frac{x^2}{2!} - \frac{x^4}{4!} + \frac{x^6}{6!} - \frac{x^8}{8!} + \cdots}{x^2} \right]$$

(ii)

$$= \lim_{x \to 0} \left[ \frac{1}{2} - \underbrace{\frac{x^2}{4!} + \frac{x^4}{6!} - \frac{x^8}{8!}}_{\substack{\text{All terms that have a} \\ \text{power of } x \to 0}} + \cdots \right] = \frac{1}{2}$$

(b)  (i)  $e^y = 1 + y + \frac{y^2}{2!} + \frac{y^3}{3!} + \cdots$  Let $y = -\frac{x^2}{2}$.

$$e^{-\frac{x^2}{2}} = 1 - \frac{x^2}{2} + \frac{x^4}{2^2(2!)} - \frac{x^6}{2^3(3!)} + \cdots = \sum_{i=0}^{\infty} \frac{(-1)^i x^{2i}}{2^i(i!)}$$

(ii) $\displaystyle\int e^{-\frac{x^2}{2}}\,dx = \int\left[1 - \frac{x^2}{2} + \frac{x^4}{2^2(2!)} - \frac{x^6}{2^3(3!)} + \ldots\right]dx$

$\displaystyle = x - \frac{x^3}{3(2)} + \frac{x^5}{5(2^2)(2!)} - \frac{x^7}{7(2^3)3!} + \ldots + C$

$\displaystyle = \sum_{i=0}^{\infty} \frac{(-1)^i x^{2i+1}}{(2i+1)2^i(i!)} + C$

3. There is no closed-form antiderivative to the function $f(x) = \sin(x^2)$, but a numerical approximation to the following definite integral is desired: $\displaystyle\int_0^1 \sin(x^2)\,dx$.

(a) Find the Taylor series centered at $a = 0$ (i.e., the Maclaurin series) for $f(x) = \sin(x^2)$. Either express the series in summation notation, or show enough terms so that the pattern is apparent (at least three non-zero terms).

(b) Find the Maclaurin series for an antiderivative $F(x)$ of the function $f(x) = \sin(x^2)$. Do this by integrating the Maclaurin series from part (a) term-by-term. Again, either express your answer in summation notation, or show enough terms so that the pattern is apparent.

(c) Using the series from part (b) for $F(x) = \displaystyle\int \sin(x^2)\,dx$ and the fundamental theorem of calculus, estimate the value of the following definite integral correct to three decimal places, i.e., correct to the thousandths place: $\displaystyle\int_0^1 \sin(x^2)\,dx$. In doing this, be sure to demonstrate how you know you have three decimal places of accuracy.

ANSWER:

(a) Use the series for $\sin x$, except plug in $x^2$ for $x$: $\displaystyle\sin x \approx x - \frac{x^3}{3!} + \frac{x^5}{5!} - \ldots = \sum_{i=0}^{\infty} \frac{(-1)^i x^{2i+1}}{(2i+1)!}$

So $\displaystyle\sin(x^2) \approx x^2 - \frac{x^6}{3!} + \frac{x^{10}}{5!} - \ldots = \sum_{i=0}^{\infty} \frac{(-1)^i (x^2)^{2i+1}}{(2i+1)!} = \sum_{i=0}^{\infty} \frac{(-1)^i x^{4i+2}}{(2i+1)!}$

(b)

$\displaystyle\int \sin(x^2)\,dx \approx \int\left(x^2 - \frac{x^6}{3!} + \frac{x^{10}}{5!} - \ldots\right)dx = \frac{x^3}{3} - \frac{x^7}{7\cdots 3!} + \frac{x^{11}}{11\cdots 5!} = \ldots$

$\displaystyle = \sum_{i=0}^{\infty} \frac{(-1)^i x^{4i+3}}{(4i+a)\cdot[(2i+1)!]}$

(c) Approximate $F(x) = \displaystyle\int \sin x^2\,dx \approx P_7(x) = \frac{x^3}{3} - \frac{x^7}{7\cdot 3!}$. Then

$\displaystyle\int_0^1 \sin(x^2)\,dx = F(1) - F(0) \approx P_7(1) - P_7(0) = \frac{13}{42} \approx 0.30952$

round off to 3 decimal places $=0.310$.

Now approximate $f(x) \approx P_{11}(x) = \frac{x^3}{3} - \frac{x^7}{7\cdot 3!} + \frac{x^{11}}{11\cdot 5!}$. Then

$\displaystyle\int_0^1 \sin(x^2)\,dx = F(1) - F(0) \approx P_{11}(1) - P_{11}(0) = \frac{1}{3} - \frac{1}{42} + \frac{1}{1320}$

$\displaystyle = \frac{13}{42} + \frac{1}{1320} = \frac{2860}{9240} + \frac{7}{9240} = \frac{2867}{9240} \approx 0.310281.$

These approximations agree to the first 3 decimal places, so our answer is $0.310$.
(The exact answer to 10 decimal places is 0.3102683017.)

4. (a) Find the Taylor expansion for $f(x) = -\ln(1 - 2x)$ by substituting into the series for $\ln(1 + x)$.

(b)   Plot both $f(x)$ and its Taylor polynomials of various degrees and use the graphs to guess what the interval of convergence is.

[Hint: Begin with the 3rd degree approximation. It's a good idea to use approximations as high as 10th degree!]

ANSWER:

(a)   We know that $\ln(1 + x) = x - \dfrac{x^2}{2} + \dfrac{x^3}{3} - \dfrac{x^4}{4} + \cdots$. So

$$-\ln(1 - 2x) = -\left(-2x - 2x^2 - \frac{8}{3}x^3 - 4x^4 + \cdots\right)$$

$$= 2x + 2x^2 + \frac{8}{3}x^3 + 4x^4 + \cdots.$$

(b)   We examine the behavior of $P_n(x)$ as $n$ gets bigger:

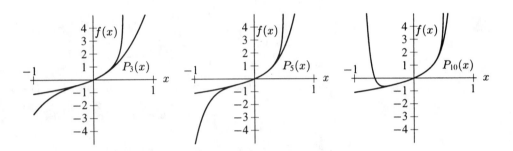

As $n$ gets large, the $P_n(x)$ seem to converge on the interval $[-\frac{1}{2}, \frac{1}{2}]$. In fact, it can be shown algebraically that $P_n(x)$ converges to $-\ln(1 - 2x)$ as $n \to \infty$ for $-\dfrac{1}{2} \le x < \dfrac{1}{2}$.

5.   (a)   Write down the Taylor series for $\cos x$ at $x = 0$.
     (b)   Use part (a) to write down the Taylor series for $\cos(\sqrt{x})$ at $x = 0$.
     (c)   To what number does the series

$$1 - \frac{2}{2!} + \frac{4}{4!} - \frac{8}{6!} + \frac{16}{8!} - \cdots$$

converge?

ANSWER:

(a)   Let $f(x) = \cos x$. Then

$$\begin{aligned}
f(0) &= \cos 0 &&= 1 \\
f'(0) &= -\sin 0 &&= 0 \\
f''(0) &= -\cos 0 &&= -1 \\
f'''(0) &= \sin 0 &&= 0 \\
f^{(4)}(0) &= \cos 0 &&= 1 \\
\vdots && \vdots && \vdots
\end{aligned}$$

Therefore, $\cos x = 1 - \dfrac{x^2}{2!} + \dfrac{x^4}{4!} - \dfrac{x^6}{6!} + \cdots$.

(b)   Replacing $x$ by $\sqrt{x}$ in the series, we get

$$\cos(\sqrt{x}) = 1 - \frac{x}{2!} + \frac{x^2}{4!} - \frac{x^3}{6!} + \cdots.$$

(c)   Note that $\cos(\sqrt{2}) = 1 - \dfrac{2}{2!} + \dfrac{4}{4!} - \dfrac{8}{6!} + \cdots$, so the series converges to $\cos\sqrt{2} \approx 0.1559\ldots$

6.  (a) Write the Taylor series about 0 for $\dfrac{1}{1-x}$.

    (b) Use the derivative of the series you found in part (a) to help you calculate the Taylor series about 0 for $\dfrac{x}{(1-x)^2}$.

    (c) Use your answer to part (b) to calculate the exact value of

    $$\frac{1}{2} + \frac{2}{4} + \frac{3}{8} + \frac{4}{16} + \frac{5}{32} + \frac{6}{64} + \dots.$$

    ANSWER:

    (a) The Taylor series for $1/(1-x)$ about $x = 0$ is

    $$\frac{1}{1-x} = 1 + x + x^2 + x^3 + \dots.$$

    (b) We differentiate the equation in (a) as follows:

    $$\frac{d}{dx}\left(\frac{1}{1-x}\right) = \frac{d}{dx}(1 + x + x^2 + x^3 + \dots)$$
    $$\frac{1}{(1-x)^2} = 1 + 2x + 3x^2 + 4x^3 + \dots.$$

    We can then multiply both sides by $x$ to get the Taylor series for $x/(1-x)^2$:

    $$\frac{x}{(1-x)^2} = x + 2x^2 + 3x^3 + 4x^4 + \dots.$$

    (c) Substituting $x = 1/2$ into the equation in part (b) gives

    $$\frac{\frac{1}{2}}{(1-\frac{1}{2})^2} = \frac{1}{2} + 2\left(\frac{1}{2}\right)^2 + 3\left(\frac{1}{2}\right)^3 + 4\left(\frac{1}{2}\right)^4 + \dots$$
    $$2 = \frac{1}{2} + \frac{2}{4} + \frac{3}{8} + \frac{4}{16} + \frac{5}{32}.$$

7.  According to the theory of relativity, the energy, $E$, of a body of mass $m$ is given as a function of its speed, $v$, by

    $$E = mc^2\left(\frac{1}{\sqrt{1 - v^2/c^2}} - 1\right)$$

    where $c$ is a constant, the speed of light.

    (a) Assuming $v < c$, expand $E$ as a series in $v/c$, as far as the second nonzero term.

    (b) Explain why the series shows you that if $v/c$ is very small, $E$ can be well approximated as follows:

    $$E \approx \frac{1}{2}mv^2.$$

    (c) Part (a) approximates $E$ using two terms; part (b) uses one term. You will now compare the accuracy of the two approximations. If $v = 0.1c$, by what percentage do the approximations in parts (a) and (b) differ?

    ANSWER:

    (a) The expansion of $E$ is given by

    $$E = mc^2\left[\left(1 - \frac{v^2}{c^2}\right)^{-1/2} - 1\right]$$
    $$= mc^2\left[1 + \frac{1}{2}\frac{v^2}{c^2} + \frac{(-1/2)(-3/2)}{2!}\left(\frac{-v^2}{c^2}\right)^2 \dots - 1\right]$$
    $$= mc^2\left[\frac{1}{2}\frac{v^2}{c^2} + \frac{3}{8}\frac{v^4}{c^4}\dots\right].$$

(b)  When $v/c$ is very small, we can ignore all but the first term, so

$$E \approx mc^2 \cdot \frac{1}{2}\frac{v^2}{c^2} = \frac{1}{2}mv^2.$$

(c)  Approximating $E$ using two terms gives

$$E = mc^2 \cdot \frac{1}{2}\frac{v^2}{c^2}\left[1 + \frac{3}{4}\frac{v^2}{c^2} + \ldots\right] = \frac{1}{2}mv^2\left[1 + \frac{3}{4}\frac{v^2}{c^2}\right]$$

So if $v/c = 0.1$, the two approximations differ by $(3/4)(0.1)^2 = 0.0075 = 0.75\%$.

## Problems and Solutions for Section 9.4

1.  A radioactive isotope is released into the air as an industrial by-product. This isotope is not very stable due to radioactive decay. Two-thirds of the original radioactive material loses its radioactivity after each month. If 10 grams of this isotope are released into the atmosphere at the end of the first and every subsequent month, then

    (a)  how much radioactive material is in the atmosphere at the end of the twelfth month? If the answer involves a sum, write it in closed form.

    (b)  In the long run, i.e., if the situation goes on *ad infinitum*, what will be the amount of this radioactive isotope in the atmosphere at the end of each month?

    ANSWER:

(a)

| Month #$n$ | Amount in atmosphere at end of month |
|---|---|
| 1 | 10 |
| 2 | $\frac{1}{3}(10)$ from previous month $+$ $10$ newly released |
| 3 | $\frac{1}{3}\left(\frac{1}{3}10 + 10\right) + 10 = \left(\frac{1}{3}\right)^2 \cdot 10 + \left(\frac{1}{3}\right)10 + 10$ |
| $\vdots$ | $\vdots$ |
| $n$ | $10 + \left(\frac{1}{3}\right)10 + \left(\frac{1}{3}\right)^2 10 + \left(\frac{1}{3}\right)^3 + \ldots + \left(\frac{1}{3}\right)^{n-1}10$ |

So after 12 months:
$$S_{12} = 10 + \frac{1}{3}10 + \left(\frac{1}{3}\right)^2 10 + \ldots + \left(\frac{1}{3}\right)^{11}\cdot 10$$

$$\frac{1}{3}S_{12} = \frac{1}{3}10 - \left(\frac{1}{3}\right)^2 10 + \ldots + \left(\frac{1}{3}\right)^{11}\cdot 10 + \left(\frac{1}{3}\right)^{12}\cdot 10$$

$$S_{12} - \frac{1}{3}S_{12} = 10 - \left(\frac{1}{3}\right)^{12}\cdot 10 \Rightarrow S_{12} = \frac{10 - \left(\frac{1}{3}\right)^{12}\cdot 10}{1 - \frac{1}{3}}$$

(b)  In the long run, i.e., as $u \to \infty$, we need the sum of the infinite geometric series. Here $a = 10, r = \frac{1}{3}$ so the series converges to $\frac{a}{1-r} = \frac{10}{1 - \frac{1}{3}} = 15.$

2.  (a)  Find the exact value of the following:

$$\frac{3}{7} + \left(\frac{3}{7}\right)^2 + \ldots + \left(\frac{3}{7}\right)^{100}$$

(b)    Find the exact value of the infinite product

$$e^{1/2} \cdot e^{1/4} \cdot e^{1/8} \cdot e^{1/16} \cdot \ldots \cdot e^{1/2n} \cdot \ldots$$

ANSWER:

(a)    We can rearrange the given sum to apply the formula for a geometric series:

$$\frac{3}{7} + \ldots + \left(\frac{3}{7}\right)^{100} = \frac{3}{7}\left(1 + \frac{3}{7} + \ldots + \left(\frac{3}{7}\right)^{99}\right)$$
$$= \frac{3}{7}\left(\frac{1 - \left(\frac{3}{7}\right)^{100}}{1 - \frac{3}{7}}\right)$$
$$= \frac{3}{4}\left(1 - \left(\frac{3}{7}\right)^{100}\right).$$

(b)    We can write the given product as follows:

$$e^{1/2} \cdot e^{1/4} \cdot e^{1/8} \cdot \ldots = e^{1/2+1/4+1/8+\ldots+1/2^n+\ldots}$$
$$= e^1, \quad \text{since } \tfrac{1}{2} + \tfrac{1}{4} + \tfrac{1}{8} + \ldots = 1$$
$$= e.$$

3.    Suppose the government spends \$1 million on highways. Some of this money is earned by the highway workers who in turn spend \$500,000 on food, travel, and entertainment. This causes \$250,000 to be spent by the workers in the food, travel, and entertainment industries. This \$250,000 causes another \$125,000 to be spent; the \$125,000 causes another \$62,500 to be spent, and so on. (Notice that each expenditure is half the previous one.) Assuming that this process continues forever, what is the total spending generated by the original \$1 million expenditure? (Include the original \$1 million in your total.)

ANSWER:

Total spending (in millions of dollars) is given by

$$\text{Total spending} = 1 + \frac{1}{2} + \frac{1}{4} + \frac{1}{8} + \ldots$$

This is a convenient geometric series with $a = 1$, $x = \frac{1}{2}$, so its sum will be given by

$$S = \frac{a}{1-x} = \frac{1}{1-\frac{1}{2}} = 2 \text{ million dollars.}$$

## Problems and Solutions for Focus on Theory: Convergence Theorems

1.    TRUE/FALSE questions. For each statement, write whether it is true or false and provide a short explanation or counterexample.

(a)    If $\sum a_k$ is the sum of a series of numbers, and $\lim_{k\to\infty} a_k = 0$, then the series converges.
(b)    If a power series $\sum a_k x^k$ converges at $x = 1$ and $x = 2$ then it converges at $x = -1$.

ANSWER:

(a)    FALSE. $\lim_{k\to\infty} \frac{1}{k} = 0$, but $\sum_{k=1}^{\infty} \frac{1}{k}$, is equal to $1 + \frac{1}{2} + \frac{1}{3} + \frac{1}{4} + \cdots$, which diverges.

(b)    TRUE. Since the series is centered at $x = 0$, its interval of convergence is centered at $x = 0$. Hence it will converge for at least all $x$ with $|x| < 2$, in particular $x = -1$.

*Problems and Solutions for Focus on Theory: The Error in Taylor Approximations* ━━━

1. (a) Find the 12-th degree Taylor polynomial for $x \sin(x^2)$ centered at $x = 0$.
   (b) Suppose you use the first two non-zero terms of the series to approximate $x \sin(x^2)$ for $0 < x < 1$.
      (i) Is your approximation too big or too small? Explain.
      (ii) Is the magnitude of the error always less than 0.1667?   Yes   No
      (iii) Is the magnitude of the error always less than 0.0084?   Yes   No
   (c) Suppose you use the first two non-zero terms of the series to approximate $x \sin(x^2)$ for $-1 < x < 0$. Is your approximation too big or too small?
   ANSWER:

   (a) We know: $\sin u = u - \dfrac{u^3}{3!} + \dfrac{u^5}{5!} - \cdots$
   so
   $$\sin(x^2) = x^2 - \frac{(x^2)^3}{3!} + \frac{(x^2)^5}{5!} \cdots$$

   $$= x^2 - \frac{x^6}{3!} + \frac{x^{10}}{5!} \cdots$$
   so
   $$x \sin(x^2) = x \left( x^2 - \frac{x^6}{3!} + \frac{x^{10}}{5!} \cdots \right)$$
   $$= x^3 - \frac{x^7}{3!} + \frac{x^{11}}{5!} - \cdots$$

   N.B. The next nonzero term contains $x^{15}$ so the degree would be too high.
   N.B. Degree of poly $=$ highest power of variable, so you do <u>not</u> need 12 terms in expansion.

   (b) (i) The series above is alternating, terms are decreasing monotonically so the sign of the error $=$ sign of first term omitted. So for $x$ positive (e.g., $x \in (0, 1)$), the sign of error is the same as sign of $\dfrac{x^{11}}{5!}$, i.e., positive, so approximation is too small.
      (ii) The error is always less than $\dfrac{x^{11}}{5!}$ in size. The error is largest for $x \approx 1$ so error $\le \dfrac{1}{5!}$. Hence yes and
      (iii) yes.

   (c) Again, the sign of error $=$ the sign of first term omitted, i.e., $\dfrac{x^{11}}{5!}$. For $x \in (-1, 0)$, $\dfrac{x^{11}}{5!}$ is <u>negative</u> so the approximation is an overestimate.

2. The function $h(x)$ is a continuous differentiable function whose graph is drawn below. The accompanying table provides some information about $h(x)$ and its derivatives.

| $x$ | $h(x)$ | $h'(x)$ | $h''(x)$ | $h'''(x)$ |
|---|---|---|---|---|
| 0 | 2 | 1 | 0.50 | 0.25 |
| 1 | 3.29 | 1.64 | 0.82 | 0.41 |
| 2 | 5.43 | 2.71 | 1.35 | 0.67 |
| 3 | 8.96 | 4.48 | 2.24 | 1.12 |

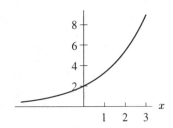

   (a) Which of the following is closest to $h(2.1)$?
      (i)  $2 + 2.1 + \dfrac{0.5}{.2}(2.1)^2 + \dfrac{0.25}{6}(2.1)^3$
      (ii) $2 + 2.1 + 0.5(2.1)^2 + 0.25(2.1)^3$

(iii) $2 + 2.1 + \dfrac{0.5}{2}(2.1)^2$

(iv) $5.43 + 2.71(2.1) + \dfrac{1.35}{2}(2.1)^2 + \dfrac{0.67}{6}(2.1)^3$

(v) $5.43 + 2.71(0.1) + \dfrac{1.35}{2}(0.1)^2 + \dfrac{0.67}{6}(0.1)^3$

(vi) $5.43 + 2.71(2.1) + 1.35(2.1)^2 + .67(2.1)^3$

(vii) $3.29 + 1.64(1.1) + \dfrac{0.82}{2}(1.1)^2 + \dfrac{0.41}{6}(1.1)^3$

(b)   $h(x)$, $h'(x)$, $h''(x)$ and $h'''(x)$ are all increasing functions. Suppose we use a tangent line approximation at zero to approximate $h(0.2)$. Find a good <u>upper</u> bound for the error.

ANSWER:

(a)   (v)

We want to approximate $f(2.1)$. Center our Taylor polynomial about a nearby point at which we know $h$ and its derivatives:

$$h(x) \approx h(2) + h'(2)(x-2) + \frac{h''(1)}{2}(x-2)^2 + \frac{h'''(2)}{6}(x-2)^3 \text{ for } x \text{ near } 2.$$

$$h(2.1) \approx 5.43 + (2.71)(2.1-2) + \frac{1.35}{2}(2.1-2)^2 + \frac{67}{6}(2.1-2)^3$$

<u>Common errors</u>:

(iv) Look at the <u>size</u> of this answer: it's much larger than $h(3)$!

(i) It's much better to center your polynomial closer to the $x$- value in question.

(b)   The tangent line approximation is a <u>linear</u> approximation: degree 1.

$$\text{Error} = E_1(.2) \leq \left| \frac{h''(c)}{2!}(.2)^2 \right| \text{ for some } c \in [0, .2]$$

$$\text{Error} \leq \left| \frac{h''(c).04}{2} \right| = h''(c)(.02) < .82(.02) \text{ Choose } .82 \underline{\text{NOT}} .5. \ .5 \leq h''(c) \text{ and we want}$$

something $\geq h''(c)$. $h''(x)$ is increasing.

$$\text{Error} < .0164$$

since $\begin{cases} |E_n(b)| \leq \dfrac{f^{(n+1)}(c)}{(n+1)!}(b-a)^{n+1} & \text{for some } c \text{ between } a \text{ and } b \\[2mm] b = .2 \\ a = \text{center} = 0 \\ n = \text{degree of poly.} = 1 \end{cases}$

Note: The error is definitely positive–the tangent line lies below the curve for $x > 0$ (since the curve is concave up).

<u>Common errors</u>:

1) A tangent <u>line</u> is linear, i.e., degree <u>1</u>.

2) |Error| is not automatically less than the size of the first unused term. This is true if a series has terms which are alternating in sign, decreasing in magnitude, and going to zero. Otherwise, often |Error| is about the same size as the first unused term–but <u>not always</u>–and <u>not necessarily less than</u> that term.

3) Finding a lower bound for $h''(c)$ instead of an upper bound.

# Chapter 10 Exam Questions

*Problems and Solutions for Section 10.1*

1.  Suppose that the function $P(t)$ satisfies the differential equation

    $$P'(t) = P(t)(4 - P(t))$$

    with the initial condition $P(0) = 1$. Even without knowing an explicit formula for $P(t)$ we can find many of its properties. For example, note first that

    $$P'(0) = P(0)(4 - P(0)) = 1(4 - 1) = 3.$$

    (a)  Find $P''(t)$ in terms of $P(t)$. Find $P''(0)$.
    (b)  Which of the following is a possible graph for $P(t)$ for small $t > 0$? Explain.

    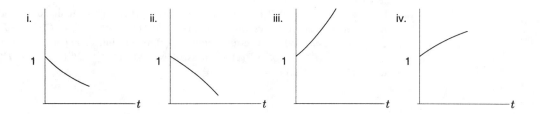

    (c)  Since $P(0) = 1$, the function $P(t)$ starts out less than 4. If it reaches 4, that is, if there is a first time $t_0$ where $P(t_0) = 4$ then

    $$P'(t_0) = P(t_0)(r - P(t_0)) = 0.$$

    So near $t_0$ the graph of $P$ would look like either of the graphs below:

    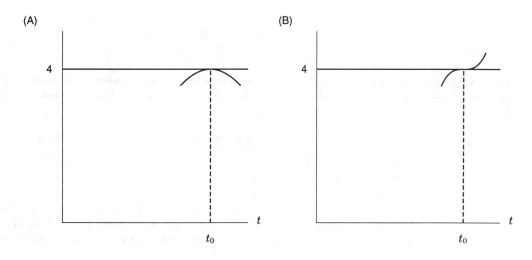

    Is either of these consistent with $P(t)$ satisfying the equation $P'(t) = P(t)(4 - P(t))$? Explain.
    (d)  Sketch the complete graph of the function $P(t)$, $t > 0$. Explain any critical points, inflection points, concavity, and the behavior of $P(t)$ as $t \to \infty$.

ANSWER:

(a)

$$P''(t) = \frac{d}{dt}(P'(t)) = \frac{d}{dt}\left(P(t)(4 - P(t))\right)$$

$$= \left(\frac{d}{dt}P(t)\right)(4 - P(t)) + P(t)\frac{d}{dt}(4 - P(t))$$

$$= 4P'(t) - P'(t)P(t) - P(t)P'(t)$$

$$= P'(t)(4 - 2P(t))$$

$$= P(t)(4 - P(t))(4 - 2P(t))$$

$$P''(0) = P(0)(4 - P(0))(4 - 2P(0))$$

$$= 6$$

(b) We know that $P''(0) = 6$, $P'(0) = 3$. Since $P'(0) > 0$, i. and ii. are out. Since $P''(0) > 0$, iv. is out (it is concave down), so the correct answer is iii.

(c) Neither of the two graphs is consistent. In the first graph, when $t > t_0$, $P(t) < 4$, so $P'(t) = P(t)(4 - P(t)) > 0$, which contradicts the fact that $P(t)$ is decreasing when $t > t_0$.

In the second graph, when $t > t_0$, $P(t) > 4$, so $P'(t) = P(t)(4 - P(t)) < 0$. This contradicts the fact that $P(t)$ is increasing when $t > t_0$. We can also conclude that $P(t)$ can never reach 4.

(d) From (c), we know that $P(t)$ never reaches 4. An argument similar to that of (c) shows that $P(t)$ never reaches 0 as t decreases. So $0 < P(t) < 4$, and therefore $P'(t) = P(t)(4 - P(t)) > 0$; i.e. $P(t)$ is increasing and has no critical points. $P(t)$ has one inflection point, $t_1$, where $P(t_1) = 2$. When $t > t_1$, $P''(t) < 0$, so $P(t)$ is concave down. When $t < t_1$, $P''(t) > 0$, so $P(t)$ is concave up. Finally, $\lim_{t \to \infty} P(t) = 4$.

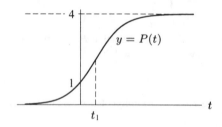

## Problems and Solutions for Section 10.2

1. Note that the point $(0, 2)$ is on the graph of each of the following three equations:

(a) $y^2 - 2\cos x = 2$
(b) $x \sin y + y = 2$
(c) $\ln|y/(1 - y)| = 0.71x + \ln 2$

Following are slope fields for two of the three equations. Identify which two equations have these slope fields. Label each graph with the letter $a$, $b$, or $c$. and explain why you made each choice. On each graph, draw the curve described by the appropriate equation ($a$, $b$, or $c$) that goes through the point $(0, 2)$.

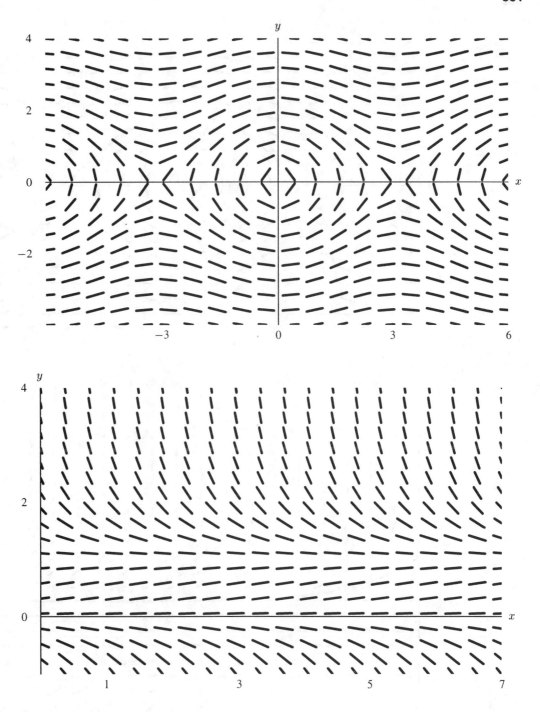

ANSWER:

The first slope field seems to repeat every $\pi$ units in the $x$-direction, so it corresponds to the slope field given by equation (a).

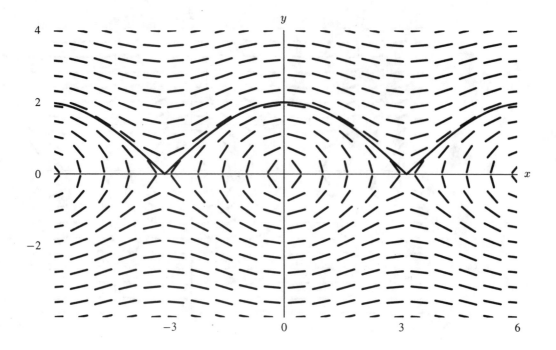

The second slope field does not depend on $x$, so it must correspond to equation (c).

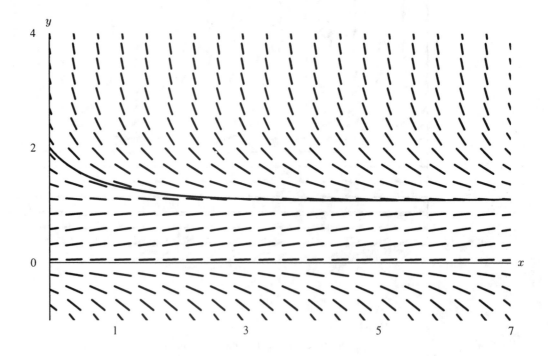

2. The slope field for the differential equation $\dfrac{dy}{dx} = x - y$ is shown below.

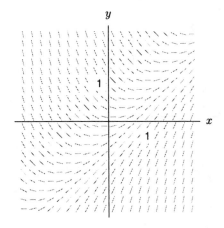

On the slope field, sketch the solution curve to the differential equation starting at $x = 0$, $y = 1$ and ending at $x = 1$. From your sketch, approximate the value of $y$ when $x = 1$.

ANSWER:

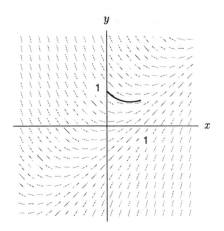

The sketch (shown above) looks like this:

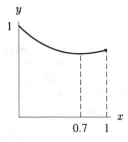

Notice the solution curve starts increasing at about $x = 0.7$. At $x = 1$, it looks like $y \approx 0.75$.

3.  Match the four direction fields (slope fields) with four of the differential equations. (One equation does not match!) No reasons are required.

(a)

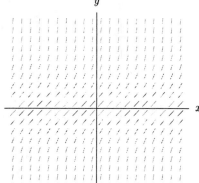

(b)

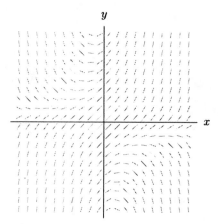

(c)

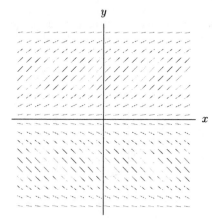

(d)

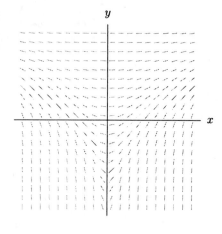

(i) $y' = xy + 1$ corresponds to graph ____

(ii) $y' = \sin x$ corresponds to graph ____

(iii) $y' = xe^{-y}$ corresponds to graph ____

(iv) $y' = y^2 + 1$ corresponds to graph ____

(v) $y' = \sin y$ corresponds to graph ____

ANSWER:

(i) $y' = xy + 1$ corresponds to graph (b)

(ii) $y' = \sin x$ corresponds to none of the graphs

(iii) $y' = xe^{-y}$ corresponds to graph (d)

(iv) $y' = y^2 + 1$ corresponds to graph (a)

(v) $y' = \sin y$ corresponds to graph (c)

4. Match the slope fields to the equations. Explain.

[Note: One slope field will not have a corresponding equation.]

$$(\text{I}) \frac{dy}{dx} = (x - y)^2 \qquad (\text{II}) \frac{dy}{dx} = (x + y)^2 \qquad (\text{III}) \frac{dy}{dx} = x^2 - y^2$$

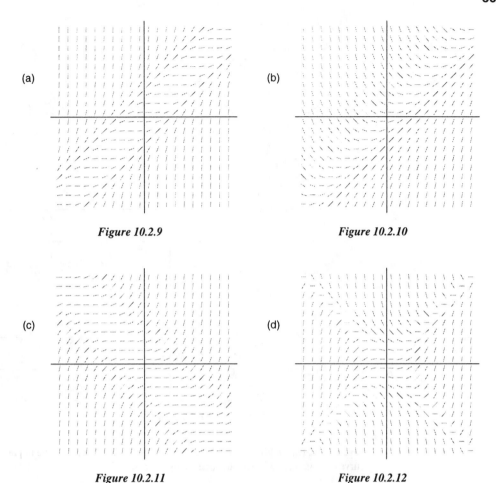

(a)

*Figure 10.2.9*

(b)

*Figure 10.2.10*

(c)

*Figure 10.2.11*

(d)

*Figure 10.2.12*

ANSWER:

(I) corresponds to (a).

Since $(x - y)^2 \geq 0$, the equation in (I) doesn't produce the slope field in (b) or in (d). Note that $(x - y)^2 = 0$ when $y = x$, i.e., along the line $y = x$, $\frac{dy}{dx} = 0$. This fits with (a).

(II) corresponds to (c).

Again, we can exclude (b) and (d) as $\frac{dy}{dx} = (x + y)^2 \geq 0$ for all $x$ and $y$, so the slope must be positive everywhere. Since $\frac{dy}{dx} = (x + y)^2 = 0$ if and only if $y = -x$, we should find little horizontal line segments along the line $y = -x$ on the slope field. This occurs in (c), but not in (a), so (c) must be the answer.

(III) corresponds to (d).

We can exclude (a) and (c) because $\frac{dy}{dx}$ is negative at some points. Notice that $\frac{dy}{dx} = x^2 - y^2 = (x - y)(x + y)$, so $\frac{dy}{dx} = 0$ where $y = x$ or $y = -x$. The corresponding slope field should thus have horizontal line segments on the lines $y = x$ and $y = -x$. This is the case only in (d).

5. This problem concerns the differential equation

$$\frac{dy}{dx} = x - \frac{1}{2}y.$$

(a) Show that $y = 2x - 4$ is the unique solution of the equation that is a straight line. (Write $y = ax + b$ and show that $a$ must equal 2 and $b$ must equal $-4$.)

(b) Give a reasonable sketch of the direction field for the equation. Take account of your answer to part (a). (If you use the slope field program, try $-4 \leq x < 4$, $-4 \leq y \leq 4$ with $x$ scale and $y$ scale both 1.)

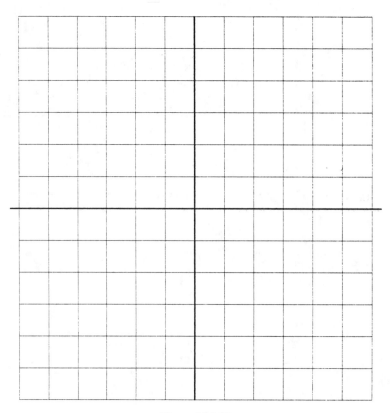

*Figure 10.2.13*

(c)   Take a point $(x_0, y_0)$ in the first quadrant which does not lie on the line in part (a). Can a solution curve through $(x_0, y_0)$ cross the line? Why or why not?

(d)   Show that

$$y = 2x - 4 + Ce^{-\frac{x}{2}}$$

is a solution for *any* constant C.

(e)   Find the solution passing through the point $(0, -2)$ and describe its qualitative behavior as $x \to \pm\infty$.

ANSWER:

(a)   Suppose we substitute $y = ax + b$ into the right hand side of the equation to get $x - \frac{1}{2}(ax + b) = (1 - \frac{a}{2})x - \frac{b}{2}$. But we know that the left-hand side of the equations, $\frac{dy}{dx}$, must be a constant, namely $a$. This implies that the factor multiplying $x$ in the right-hand side is zero, so $a = 2$. Then we are left with $a = -\frac{b}{2}$, so $b = -4$. Hence $y = 2x - 4$ is the sole linear solution.

(b)

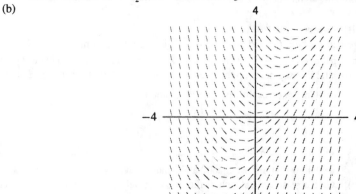

(c) No. To find a solution curve for the differential equation, we only need to know one point it passes through (and then we can solve for the constants in this first order equation). If some two curves cross, then the point of intersection must define two different solution curves which is clearly not possible, so each point will yield one solution curve.

(d) For $y = 2x - 4 + Ce^{-\frac{x}{2}}$, $\frac{dy}{dx} = 2 - \frac{1}{2}Ce^{-\frac{x}{2}}$. On the other hand, $x - \frac{1}{2}y = x - (x - 2 + \frac{1}{2}Ce^{-\frac{x}{2}}) = 2 - \frac{1}{2}Ce^{-\frac{x}{2}}$. Therefore, $y = 2x - 4 + Ce^{-\frac{x}{2}}$ is a solution of $\frac{dy}{dx} = x - \frac{1}{2}y$.

(e) For $x = 0$, $y = -2$, we have $-2 = -4 + C$; $C = 2$. So $y = 2x - 4 + 2e^{-\frac{x}{2}}$.
As $x \to \infty$, $y \to 2x - 4$. As $x \to -\infty$, $y \to \infty$ since $e^{-\frac{x}{2}} \to \infty$.

## Problems and Solutions for Section 10.3

1. Consider the differential equation

$$\frac{dy}{dx} = x^2 + y.$$

(a) Use Euler's method with two steps to approximate the value of $y$ when $x = 2$ on the solution curve that passes through $(1,3)$. Explain clearly what you are doing on a sketch. Your sketch should show the coordinates of all the points you have found.

(b) Are your approximate values of $y$ an under- or over-estimate? Explain how you know.

ANSWER:

(a) (Use $\Delta x = 0.5$.)

| $x$ | $y$ | slope | $\Delta y$ |
|-----|-----|-------|-----|
| 1 | 3 | 4 | 2 |
| 1.5 | 5 | 7.25 | 3.625 |
| 2 | 8.625 | | |

$y = 8.625$

(b) From the slope field, we see that the curve is concave up, so we have an underestimate.
Alternatively, $y'' = \dfrac{d}{dx}(y') = \dfrac{d}{dx}(x^2 + y) = 2x + y' = 2x + x^2 + y > 0$.

2. The slope field for the differential equation $\dfrac{dy}{dx} = -\dfrac{x}{y}$ is shown below.

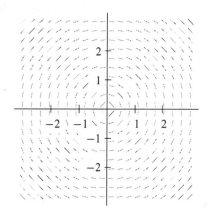

(a) Starting from the point $x = 0$, $y = 2$, use Euler's method with $N = 3$ subdivisions to approximate the value of $y$ when $x = 1$.

(b) Sketch on the slope field where each step of Euler's method takes you. Based on your sketch, would you say Euler's method provides an underestimate or an overestimate of the true solution?

(c) Show that the equation $x^2 + y^2 = C$, where $C$ is a constant, satisfies the differential equation, and find the value of $C$ for the solution passing through the starting point $x = 0$, $y = 2$.

ANSWER:

(a) $\Delta x = \dfrac{1}{N} = \dfrac{1}{3}$

At $(0, 2)$, $\dfrac{dy}{dx} = -\dfrac{0}{2} = 0$. Therefore, $y_1 = y_0 + \dfrac{dy}{dx}\Delta x = 2 + 0\left(\dfrac{1}{3}\right) = 2$.

At $\left(\dfrac{1}{3}, 2\right)$, $\dfrac{dy}{dx} = -\dfrac{\frac{1}{3}}{2} = -\dfrac{1}{6}$. Therefore, $y_2 = y_1 + \dfrac{dy}{dx}\Delta x = 2 - \dfrac{1}{6}\left(\dfrac{1}{3}\right) = \dfrac{35}{18} \approx 1.944$.

At $\left(\dfrac{2}{3}, \dfrac{35}{18}\right)$, $\dfrac{dy}{dx} = -\dfrac{\frac{2}{3}}{\frac{35}{18}} = -\dfrac{12}{35}$. Therefore, $y_3 = y_2 + \dfrac{dy}{dx}\Delta x = \dfrac{35}{18} - \dfrac{12}{35}\left(\dfrac{1}{3}\right) = \dfrac{1153}{630} \approx 1.8302$.

Since $y(1) \approx y_3$, $y(1) \approx 1.8302$.

(b) See the slope field below. The solution curve starting at $(0, 2)$ is concave down for $0 \le x \le 1$. Therefore, Euler's method produces an <u>overestimate</u> of the solution, which should also be apparent from the sketch on the slope field.

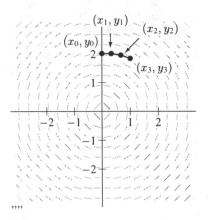

(c) $y = \sqrt{C - x^2} \Rightarrow \dfrac{dy}{dx} = \dfrac{-2x}{2\sqrt{C - x^2}} = -\dfrac{x}{\sqrt{C - x^2}} = -\dfrac{x}{y}$

Therefore, the equation $x^2 + y^2 = C$ satisfies the differential equation. Since the particular solution of interest passes through $(0, 2)$, plug that point into the equation to find $C = 4$.

As an aside, notice this means that the true solution to the differential equation passing through $(0, 2)$ is the circle $x^2 + y^2 = 4$. Thus, the true value of $y$ when $x = 1$ is $y = \sqrt{4 - 1^2} = \sqrt{3} = 1.7321$. The result from part (b) that Euler's method provides an overestimate of the solution is, therefore, correct.

3. In a number of applications, differential equations of the following form appear:

$$\frac{dy}{dt} = k(A - y)$$

For a particular problem, let's say $k = 0.5$, and $A = 2$. You are given that $y = 1$ when $t = 0$, and you are interesting in finding the value of $y$ when $t = 1$.

(a) The slope field for the differential equation is shown below. Sketch the solution to the differential equation starting from $y = 1, t = 0$.

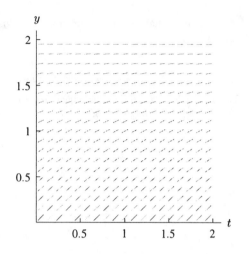

(b) From your sketch in part (a), estimate the value of $y$ when $t = 1$. What happens to $y$ as $t \to \infty$?

(c) Use Euler's method with $N = 3$ subdivisions of the interval $0 \le t \le 1$ to find an approximation of $y$ when $t = 1$, if you start from $y = 1$ at $t = 0$.

(d) Sketch on the slope field where each Euler's method step takes you. Is the Euler method approximation of $y(1)$ an overestimate or an underestimate, and why?

ANSWER:

(a)

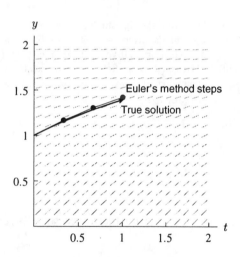

(b) The solution $y(1)$ looks to be approximately 1.4.

As $t \to \infty$, $y \to 2$.

(c) $\Delta t = \dfrac{1}{3}$. $y_0 = 1$. $y_0' = 0.5(2 - 1) = 0.5$

$$y_1 = y_0 + y_0'\Delta t = 1 + 0.5\left(\frac{1}{3}\right) = 1.16 \qquad y_1' = 0.5(2 - 1.16) = 0.416$$

$$y_2 = y_1 + y_1'\Delta t = 1.16 + 0.416\left(\frac{1}{3}\right) = 1.305 \qquad y_2' = 0.5(2 - 1.305) = 0.3472$$

$$y(1) \approx y_3 = y_2 + y_2'\Delta t = 1.305 + 0.3472\left(\frac{1}{3}\right) = 1.42\ldots$$

The Euler's method estimate is $y(1) \approx 1.42$.

(d) See the slope field above. From the sketch of the solution in part (a), $y$ appears to be concave down, which means that Euler's method yields an overestimate.

The true solution to the differential equation with initial condition $y = 1$ when $t = 0$ is $y(t) = 2 - e^{-0.5t}$. Thus, the exact solution for part (c) is $y(1) = 2 - e^{-0.5} = 1.39346934\ldots$.

4.  As we shall see in the study of population growth with limited resources, differential equations such as the following appear:

$$\frac{dy}{dx} = y(2 - y)$$

Given that when $x = 0, y = 3$, you will find the value of $y$ when $x = 1$.

(a)  The slope field for the differential equation is shown below. Sketch the solution to the differential equation passing through $(0, 3)$.

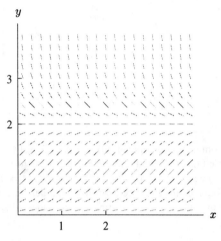

(b)  From your sketch, estimate the value of $y$ when $x = 1$. Also, what happens to $y$ as $x \rightarrow \infty$?

(c)  Use Euler's method with $N = 4$ subdivisions of the interval $0 \leq x \leq 1$ to find an approximation of $y$ when $x = 1$, if you start from the point $(0, 3)$.

(d)  Sketch on the slope field where the Euler's method steps take you. In particular, is the Euler method approximation of $y(1)$ an overestimate or an underestimate, and why?

ANSWER:

(a)

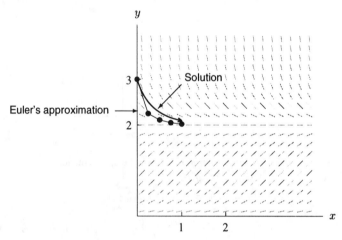

(b)  $y(1) \approx 2.2$
As $x \rightarrow \infty$, $y \rightarrow 2$ asymptotically.

(c)

| $x$ | $y$ | $\Delta y = \dfrac{dy}{dx}\Delta x = y(2-y)(0.25)$ |
|-----|-----|-----------------------------------------------------|
| 0 | 3 | $3(2 - 3)(0.25) = -0.75$ |
| 0.25 | 2.25 | $2.25(2 - 2.25)(0.25) = -0.14$ |
| 0.5 | 2.11 | $2.11(2 - 2.11)(0.25) = -0.06$ |
| 0.75 | 2.05 | $2.05(2 - 2.05)(0.25) = -0.03$ |
| 1.0 | 2.02 | |

$y(1) \approx 2.02$ by Euler's method, $N = 4$

True Answer: $y(1) = \dfrac{2}{1 - \frac{1}{3}e^{-2}} = 2.09$

(d)   Since the graph of $y(x)$ appears to be concave <u>up</u> over the interval, the Euler approximation is an <u>underestimate</u>.

5.   For the differential equation represented by the slope field below, sketch the solution curve with $y(0) = 0$.

(a)

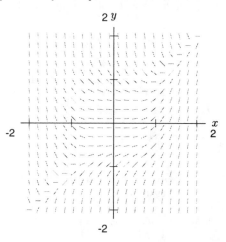

(b)   On the same slope field, use $\Delta x = 0.5$ to sketch, as accurately as you can, two steps of Euler's approximation to this solution curve. (End at $x = 1$.)

ANSWER:

(a)

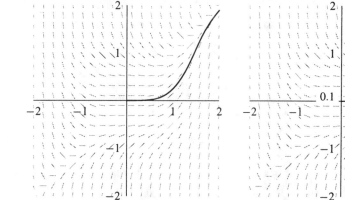

***Figure 10.3.14:*** Solution curve using slope field (for part (a))          ***Figure 10.3.15:*** Euler's method with 2 divisions (for part (b))

(b)   Using Euler's method with 2 divisions, we get $y(0.5) = 0.5(0) = 0$. And $y(1) = 0 + 0.5 \left( \left. \dfrac{dy}{dx} \right|_{(0,0.5)} \right)$. The slope field at $(0.5, 0)$ is not very steep—it looks like it is approximately 0.2. So $y(1) \approx 0.5(0.2) = 0.1$. Since the solution curve is concave up, the Euler's method approximation must lie below it.

6.   Consider the solution with $y(0) = 0$ to the differential equation

$$\frac{dy}{dx} = \frac{4}{1 + x^2}$$

(a)   What is the exact value of $y(1)$?

(b)   If you use Euler's method with 1 million steps to approximate your answer to part (a), will your approximation be an over- or underestimate? Give a reason for your answer.

(c)   Use Euler's method with 2 steps to approximate your answer to part (a).

ANSWER:

(a)   Solving explicitly for $y$ gives $y = 4\arctan x + C$. Since $y = 0$ when $x = 0$, we have $C = 0$ so $y = 4\arctan x$. Thus $y(1) = 4\arctan 1 = 4(\pi/4) = \pi$. So $y(1) = \pi$.

(b)   A graph of $y$ is shown in Figure 10.3.16.

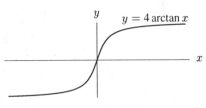

**Figure 10.3.16**

As we can see from the graph, the solution curve $y$ is concave down, so Euler's method gives an overestimate.

(c)   Take $\Delta x = 0.5$. Then $y(0.5) \approx y(0) + y'(0) \cdot \Delta x = 0 + 0.5(4) = 2$. Similarly, $y(1) \approx y(0.5) + y'(0.5) \cdot \Delta x \approx 2 + 0.5[4/(1 + 0.5)^2] = 2 + 0.5(3.2) = 3.6$. So $y(1) \approx 3.6$.

## Problems and Solutions for Section 10.4

1.   Consider the differential equation

$$\frac{dQ}{dt} = 300 - 0.3Q.$$

(a)   Solve the differential equation subject to $Q(0) = 500$.

(b)   Solve the differential equation subject to $Q(0) = 1500$.

(c)   Sketch both solutions on the axes below. Give the coordinates of any intercepts and the equations of any asymptotes.

ANSWER:

(a)   $\dfrac{dQ}{300 - 0.3Q} = dt \Rightarrow Q(t) = ce^{-0.3t} + 1000$
       Using $Q(0) = 500$, we get $c = -500$.
       $Q(t) = -500e^{-0.3t} + 1000$

(b)   $Q(t) = 500e^{-.03t} + 1000$

(c)   

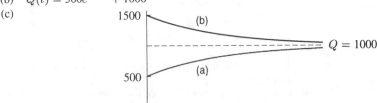

2.   Solve the following differential equations with the given initial conditions:

(a)   $\dfrac{dy}{dx} = \dfrac{x}{y}$   $y = 0$ when $x = 1$

(b)   $\dfrac{dy}{dt} = y^2 + 1$   $y = 1$ when $t = 0$

ANSWER:

(a) $\displaystyle \int y\,dy = \int x\,dx$

$\dfrac{y^2}{2} = \dfrac{x^2}{2} + C$

$0 = \dfrac{1}{2} + C$

so $C = -\dfrac{1}{2}$

$y^2 = x^2 - 1$

(b) $\displaystyle \int \dfrac{dy}{y^2+1} = \int dt$

$\arctan y = t + C$

$\arctan 1 = 0 + C$

so $C = \arctan 1 = \dfrac{\pi}{4}$

$\arctan y = t + \dfrac{\pi}{4}$

$y = \tan\left(t + \dfrac{\pi}{4}\right)$

3. Find the solutions to the following differential equations with the given initial conditions. Solve for $y$ as a function of $x$, and solve for all constants.

(a) $\dfrac{dy}{dx} = \dfrac{1}{\sqrt{xy}}$   $y = 4$ when $x = 0$

(b) $\dfrac{dy}{dx} = \sqrt{4 - y^2}$   $y = 1$ when $x = \dfrac{\pi}{6}$

ANSWER:

(a) $\dfrac{dy}{dx} = \dfrac{1}{\sqrt{xy}} \Rightarrow \sqrt{y}\,dy = \dfrac{1}{\sqrt{x}}\,dx \Rightarrow \displaystyle\int \sqrt{y}\,dy = \int \dfrac{1}{\sqrt{x}}\,dx \Rightarrow \dfrac{2}{3}y^{\frac{3}{2}} = 2\sqrt{x} + C$

Let $x = 0$, $y = 4$ to find $C$: $\dfrac{2}{3}(4)^{\frac{3}{2}} = 2\sqrt{0} + C \Rightarrow C = \dfrac{16}{3}$

$\dfrac{2}{3}y^{\frac{3}{2}} = 2\sqrt{x} + \dfrac{16}{3} \Rightarrow y^{\frac{3}{2}} = 3\sqrt{x} + 8 \Rightarrow y = (3\sqrt{x} + 8)^{\frac{2}{3}}$

(b) $\dfrac{dy}{dx} = \sqrt{4 - y^2} \Rightarrow \dfrac{dy}{\sqrt{4 - y^2}} = dx \Rightarrow \displaystyle\int \dfrac{dy}{\sqrt{4 - y^2}} = \int dx \Rightarrow \arcsin\dfrac{y}{2} = x + C$

Let $x = \dfrac{\pi}{6}$, $y = 1$ to find $C$: $\arcsin\dfrac{1}{2} = \dfrac{\pi}{6} + C \Rightarrow \dfrac{\pi}{6} = \dfrac{\pi}{6} + C \Rightarrow C = 0$

$\arcsin\dfrac{y}{2} = x$

$\dfrac{y}{2} = \sin x$

$y = 2\sin x$

4. Find the solution to the differential equation $y' = \dfrac{5}{1+y}$, satisfying $y(0) = 2$.

ANSWER:

$y' = \dfrac{5}{1+y}$ is the same as $\dfrac{dy}{dx} = \dfrac{5}{1+y}$, so

$$\int (1+y)\,dy = \int 5\,dx,$$

which gives $y + \dfrac{y^2}{2} = 5x + C$. But $y(0) = 2$, so $C = 4$ and

$$y + \dfrac{y^2}{2} = 5x + 4.$$

5. Find the solutions to the following differential equations with the given initial conditions. Solve for $y$ as a function of $x$, and solve for all constants.

(a) $\dfrac{dy}{dx} = xy$   $y = 5$ when $x = 0$

(b) $\dfrac{dy}{dx} = x \sec y \quad y = \dfrac{\pi}{6}$ when $x = 1$

ANSWER:

(a) $\dfrac{dy}{dx} = xy \qquad$ initial condition: $(0, 5)$

$$\Rightarrow \frac{dy}{y} = x\,dx \Rightarrow \int \frac{dy}{y} = \int x\,dx \Rightarrow \ln|y| = \frac{x^2}{2} + C_1$$

$$\Rightarrow e^{\ln|y|} = e^{\frac{x^2}{2}+C_1} \Rightarrow y = e^{\frac{x^2}{2}} \cdot e^{C_1} \Rightarrow y = C_2 e^{\frac{x^2}{2}}$$

Plug in $(0,5)$: $5 = C_2 e^0 \Rightarrow C_2 = 5 \Rightarrow y = 5e^{\frac{x^2}{2}}$

(b) $\dfrac{dy}{dx} = x \sec y \qquad$ initial condition $\left(1, \dfrac{\pi}{6}\right)$

$$\Rightarrow \frac{dy}{\sec y} = x\,dx \Rightarrow \int \cos y\,dy = \int x\,dx \Rightarrow \sin y = \frac{x^2}{2} + C_1$$

Plug in $\left(1, \dfrac{\pi}{6}\right)$: $\sin\dfrac{\pi}{6} = \dfrac{1}{2} + C_1 \Rightarrow \dfrac{1}{2} = \dfrac{1}{2} + C_1 \Rightarrow C_1 = 0$

$$\Rightarrow \sin y = \frac{x^2}{2} \Rightarrow y = \sin^{-1}\left(\frac{x^2}{2}\right) \quad \text{or} \quad y = \arcsin\left(\frac{x^2}{2}\right)$$

6. Solve $\dfrac{dN}{dt} = 4 - 0.2N$, with $N(0) = 0$, and sketch the solution for $t \geq 0$. Label any intercepts or asymptotes clearly.

ANSWER:

$$\frac{dN}{dt} = 4 - 0.2N$$

$$\int \frac{dN}{4 - 0.2N} = \int dt$$

$$\frac{1}{-0.2}\int \frac{dN}{(N-20)} = \int dt$$

$$\ln|N - 20| = -0.2t + C$$

$$N - 20 = C'e^{-0.2t}$$

but $N(0) = 0$, so $C' = -20$:

$$N = 20 - 20e^{-0.2t}$$

$$= 20(1 - e^{-0.2t})$$

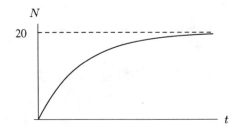

7. This problem concerns the differential equation

$$\frac{dy}{dx} = \frac{2x}{y}$$

Note: You can do part (d) without parts (a)–(c).

(a) Sketch the slope field for the differential equation at the 14 points in the first and second quadrants $-2 \leq x \leq 2, 0 \leq y \leq 2$ ($x$ and $y$ are integers—don't include $(0,0)$).

(b) Sketch in a solution curve passing through $(1, 2)$. Do you expect it to show any symmetry? Explain.

(c) Without plotting any more slopes in the third and fourth quadrants, describe what the slope field must look like there, in terms of the slope field in the first and the second quadrants.

(d) Find an equation for the solution to the differential equation $\frac{dy}{dx} = \frac{2x}{y}$ passing through $(1, 2)$. Is it consistent with your answer to part (b)?

ANSWER:

(a)

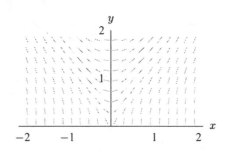

(b)

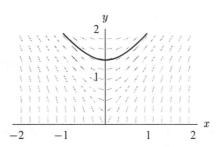

The curve is symmetric with respect to the $y$-axis because the slope at $(x, y)$, which is $\dfrac{2x}{y}$, is exactly the opposite of the slope at $(-x, y)$, which is $-\dfrac{2x}{y}$.

(c) The slope field in the third and fourth quadrants can be obtained by reflecting the slope field in the first and second quadrants with respect to the $x$-axis.

(d)

$$\frac{dy}{dx} = \frac{2x}{y}$$

$$\int y\, dy = \int 2x\, dx$$

$$y^2 = 2x^2 + C.$$

Since the curve passes through $(1, 2)$, $2^2 = 2 + C$, and so $C = 2$. Hence the equation of the curve is $y^2 = 2x^2 + 2$. This curve is indeed symmetric with respect to the $y$-axis, and so our answer is consistent with part (b).

8. Find a formula for the solution to each of the following differential equations.

(a)
$$\frac{dy}{dx} = \frac{\cos^2 y}{x} \quad \text{with} \quad y(1) = \frac{\pi}{4}$$

(b)
$$xy' - (2 + x)y = 0 \quad \text{with} \quad y(1) = 1, \quad y(x) \geq 0 \text{ for all } x$$

ANSWER:

(a) By manipulating the differential equation, we have

$$\frac{dy}{dx} = \frac{\cos^2 y}{x}$$

$$\frac{dy}{\cos^2 y} = \frac{dx}{x}$$

$$\int \sec^2 y \, dy = \int \frac{1}{x} dx$$

$$\tan y = \ln|x| + C$$

$$y = \tan^{-1}\left(\ln|x| + C\right).$$

Since $y(1) = \tan^{-1}(C) = \frac{\pi}{4}$, we get that $C = 1$, so

$$y(x) = \tan^{-1}\left(\ln|x| + 1\right).$$

(b) By manipulating the differential equation, we have

$$y' = \left(\frac{2+x}{x}\right) y$$

$$\frac{dy}{dx} = \left(\frac{2+x}{x}\right) y$$

$$\frac{dy}{y} = \left(\frac{2+x}{x}\right) dx$$

$$\int \frac{dy}{y} = \int \left(\frac{2}{x} + 1\right) dx$$

$$\ln|y| = 2\ln|x| + x + C.$$

Since $y(x) \geq 0$ for all $x$, $|y| = y$ so we can write $\ln y = 2\ln|x| + x + C$ or

$$y = e^c \cdot e^{2\ln|x|+x} = e^c \cdot e^{\ln|x|^2} \cdot e^x$$

$$= Ax^2 e^x, \quad \text{if we let } e^c = A.$$

Using $y(1) = 1$ we get $y(1) = A \cdot 1 \cdot e^1 = 1$, or $A = \frac{1}{e}$, so

$$y(x) = \frac{1}{e} \cdot x^2 e^x = x^2 e^{x-1}.$$

9. Solve the following differential equations. Show your work.

(a) $\dfrac{dP}{dt} + 0.1P = 50$

(b) $\dfrac{dy}{dt} = \dfrac{\sin t}{y^2}$

(c) $\dfrac{dy}{dx} = e^{y-x}$   with $y(\ln 2) = -\ln 2$

ANSWER:

(a) We manipulate the differential equation as follows:

$$\frac{dP}{dt} = -0.1(P - 500)$$

$$\frac{dP}{P - 500} = -0.1 dt$$

$$\int \frac{dP}{P - 500} = \int -0.1 dt$$

$$\ln|P - 500| = -0.1t + C$$

$$P = 500 + Ae^{-0.1t}.$$

(b) We manipulate the differential equation as follows:

$$y^2 dy = \sin t \, dt$$

$$\int y^2 dy = \int \sin t \, dt$$

$$\frac{y^3}{3} = -\cos t + C$$

$$y = \sqrt[3]{A - 3\cos t}.$$

(c) We manipulate the differential equation as follows:

$$\frac{dy}{dx} = \frac{e^y}{e^x}$$

$$e^{-y}\,dy = e^{-x}\,dx$$

$$\int e^{-y}\,dy = \int e^{-x}\,dx$$

$$-e^{-y} = -e^{-x} + C$$

$$e^{\ln 2} = -e^{-\ln 2} + C, \quad \text{since when } x = \ln 2, y = -\ln 2$$

$$-2 = -\frac{1}{2} + C, \quad \text{so } C = -\frac{3}{2}$$

$$e^{-y} = e^{-x} + \frac{3}{2}$$

$$y = -\ln\left(e^{-x} + \frac{3}{2}\right).$$

10. Find the general solution to each of the following differential equations:

(a) $\dfrac{dy}{dt} = a - by$

(b) $\dfrac{dH}{dt} = -3H + tH$

ANSWER:

(a) We can manipulate the differential equation as follows:

$$\frac{dy}{dt} = -b\left(y - \frac{a}{b}\right)$$

$$\frac{dy}{y - \frac{a}{b}} = -b\,dt$$

$$\int \frac{dy}{y - \frac{a}{b}} = \int -b\,dt$$

$$\ln\left|y - \frac{a}{b}\right| = -bt + K$$

$$y - \frac{a}{b} = Ce^{-bt}$$

$$y = \frac{a}{b} + Ce^{-bt}.$$

(b) Similarly,

$$\frac{dH}{dt} = (t - 3)H$$

$$\frac{dH}{H} = (t - 3)dt$$

$$\int \frac{dH}{H} = \int (t - 3)dt$$

$$\ln|H| = \frac{t^2}{2} - 3t + K$$

$$H = Ce^{t^2/2 - 3t}.$$

11. (a) Find a formula for the solution to the differential equation

$$\frac{dy}{dx} = y\cos x \quad y(0) = 4.$$

(b) Find the exact minimum and maximum values of the function $y(x)$ you found in part (a).

ANSWER:

(a)  Separating variables gives

$$\frac{dy}{dx} = y \cos x$$

$$\frac{dy}{y} = \cos x \, dx$$

$$\int \frac{dy}{dy} = \int \cos x \, dx$$

$$\ln |y| = \sin x + C$$

$$|y| = e^C e^{\sin x}$$

$$y = \pm e^C e^{\sin x}$$

$$y = A e^{\sin x}$$

Since $y(0) = A = 4$, we get $y = 4e^{\sin x}$.

(b)  Since $e^t$ is an *increasing function*, it will reach its minimum at the minimal value of its input and it will reach its maximum at the maximal value of its input. So the minimum is reached when $\sin x = -1$ and hence

$$\text{Min} = 4e^{-1} = \frac{4}{e}.$$

Similarly, the maximum is reached when $\sin x = 1$ and so

$$\text{Max} = 4e.$$

12. Find the general solution to each of the following differential equations.

(a)  $\dfrac{d^2 y}{dx^2} = x^2 - 3x + 2$

(b)  $\dfrac{d^2 y}{dx^2} = \cos x$

ANSWER:

(a)

$$\frac{dy}{dx} = \frac{1}{3}x^3 - \frac{3}{2}x^2 + 2x + c_1$$

$$y = \frac{1}{12}x^4 - \frac{1}{2}x^3 + x^2 + c_1 x + c_2.$$

(b)

$$\frac{dy}{dx} = \sin x + c_1$$

$$y = -\cos x + c_1 x + c_2.$$

## *Problems and Solutions for Section 10.5*

1. Consider the Hakosalo residence in Oulu, Finland. Assume that heat is lost from the house only through windows and the rate of change of temperature in °F/h is proportional to the difference in temperature between the outside and the inside. The constant of proportionality is $\frac{1}{29}$. Assume that it is $10°\text{F}$ outside constantly. On a Thursday at noon the temperature inside the house was $65°\text{F}$ and the heat was turned off until 5 pm.

   (a)  Write a differential equation which reflects the rate of change of the temperature in the house between noon and 5 pm.

   (b)  Find the temperature in the house at 5 pm. (You may do this analytically or using your calculator to get a rough estimate.)

(c)  At 5 pm the heat is turned on. The heater generates an amount of energy that would raise the inside temperature by $2°$F per hour if there were no heat loss. Write a differential equation that reflects what happens to the inside temperature after the heat is turned on.

(d)  If the heat is left on indefinitely, what temperature will the inside of the house approach?

ANSWER:

(a)  If $y(t)$ = temperature at time $t$ when $t$ is measured in hours since the heat was turned off, then
$$\frac{dy}{dt} = -\frac{1}{29}(y - 10), \qquad 0 \le t \le 5$$

(b)  Separate variables to get

$$\int \frac{dy}{y - 10} = -\frac{1}{29}\int dt$$

$$\ln|y - 10| = -\frac{1}{29}t + C$$

$$y - 10 = C'e^{-\frac{1}{29}t}$$

$$y = C'e^{-\frac{1}{29}t} + 10$$

If the heat is turned off at noon, when $t = 0, y = 65$. Then we have $65 = C' + 10, C' = 55$, so $y = 55e^{-\frac{1}{29}t} + 10$. Therefore, at 5 p.m, the temperature is

$$y = 55e^{-\frac{5}{29}} + 10 \approx 56.29°\text{F}.$$

(c)  $\frac{dy}{dt} = 2 - \frac{1}{29}(y - 10) = -\frac{1}{29}y + \frac{68}{29}, t > 5.$

(d)  We are looking for an equilibrium solution, i.e. where $\frac{dy}{dt} = 0$. This occurs when $y = 68$. It is a stable equilibrium, since for $y > 68, \frac{dy}{dt} < 0$, and for $y < 68, \frac{dy}{dt} > 0$. In the long run $68°$ F must be the temperature of the house.

2.  Suppose there is a new kind of savings certificate that starts out paying 3% annual interest and increases the interest rate by 1% each additional year that the money is left on deposit. (Assume that interest is compounded continuously and that the interest rate increases continuously.)

(a)  Write a differential equation for $\frac{dB}{dt}$, where $B(t)$ is the balance at time $t$.

(b)  Solve the equation that you found in part (a), assuming an initial deposit of $1000.

(c)  When $t = 7$ years, the interest rate will have risen to 10%. Would it have been better to have invested $1000 at a *fixed* interest rate of 5% for 7 years than to use the variable rate savings certificate described in part (a)? Explain your answer.

ANSWER:

(a)  $\frac{dB}{dt} = B(0.03 + 0.01t)$

(b)  $\int \frac{dB}{B} = \int (0.03 + 0.01t)\, dt$ which gives $\ln|B| = 0.03t + 0.005t^2 + C$, so $B = B_0 e^{0.03t + 0.005t^2}$. Since $B_0 = \$1000$, we have $B = 1000e^{0.03t + 0.005t^2}$.

(c)  With the rate increasing 0.01 every year, we would have $1000e^{0.21 + 0.245} = 1000e^{0.455}$ dollars at the end of 7 years. With a constant rate of 0.5, we would have $1000e^{0.05 \cdot 7} = 1000e^{0.35}$ dollars at the end of 7 years which is smaller.

3.  The population of aphids on a rose plant increases at a rate proportional to the number present. In 3 days the population grew from 800 to 1400.

(a)  Write down a differential equation for the population of aphids at time $t$ in days, where $t = 0$ is the day when there were 800 aphids.

(b)  How long does it take for the population to get 10 times as large?

(c)  What was the population on the day before there were 800?

ANSWER:

(a)  If $P(t)$ is the aphid population at time $t$, then we know that

$$\frac{dP}{dt} = kP$$

$$\int \frac{dP}{P} = \int k\,dt$$
$$\ln |P| = kt + C$$
$$P = e^{kt+C}$$
$$= P_0 e^{kt}$$

Since there are 800 aphids at time $t = 0$, we have $P = 800e^{kt}$.
At $t = 3$, $P = 1400$, so

$$1400 = 800e^{3k}$$
$$\ln \frac{7}{4} = 3k$$
$$k = \frac{1}{3} \ln \frac{7}{4}$$
$$\text{So,} \quad P = 800e^{\left(\frac{1}{3} \ln \frac{7}{4}\right)t}$$

(b) For $P$ to become 10 times as large,

$$8000 = 800e^{\left(\frac{1}{3} \ln \frac{7}{4}\right)t}$$
$$\ln 10 = \left(\frac{1}{3} \ln \frac{7}{4}\right) t$$
$$t = \frac{3 \ln 10}{\ln \frac{7}{4}} \approx 12.34 \text{ days.}$$

(c) On the day before there were 800 aphids, $t = -1$, so

$$P = 800e^{-\frac{1}{3} \ln \frac{7}{4}}$$
$$= 800 \left(\frac{7}{4}\right)^{-\frac{1}{3}}$$
$$\approx 664 \text{ aphids.}$$

4. Newton's Law of Cooling states that the rate of change of temperature of an object is proportional to the difference between the temperature of the object and the temperature of the surrounding air.

   A detective discovers a corpse in an abandoned building, and finds its temperature to be $27°\text{C}$. An hour later its temperature is $21°\text{C}$. Assume that the air temperature is $8°\text{C}$, that normal body temperature is $37°\text{C}$, and that Newton's Law of Cooling applies to the corpse.

   (a) Write a differential equation satisfied by the temperature, $H$, of the corpse at time $t$. Measure $t$ from the moment the corpse is discovered.
   (b) Solve the differential equation.
   (c) How long has the corpse been dead at the moment it is discovered?

   ANSWER:

   (a) $\dfrac{dH}{dt} = k(H - 8)$ where $k$ will be negative.

   (b) $\dfrac{dH}{H-8} = k\,dt \Rightarrow H = Ce^{kt} + 8$
   Since $H(0) = 27$, $27 = Ce^{\circ} + 8$, so $C = 19$.
   Since $H(1) = 21$, $21 = 19e^{k(1)} + 8$ so $k = \ln\left(\frac{13}{19}\right) \approx -0.379$.
   so $H = 19e^{-.379t} + 8$.

   (c) We want $H(T) = 37$, so
   $$T = -\frac{\ln\left(\frac{29}{19}\right)}{.379} \approx 1.1 \text{ hours or 1 hour 7 minutes before the body was found.}$$

5. Cesium 137 ($\text{Cs}^{137}$) is a short–lived radioactive isotope. It decays at a rate proportional to the amount of itself present and has a half-life of 30 years (i.e., the amount of $\text{Cs}^{137}$ remaining $t$ years after $A_0$ millicuries of the radioactive isotope is released is given by $A_0 e^{-\left(\frac{\ln 2}{30}\right)t}$. We will abbreviate millicuries by mCi).

As a result of its operations, a nuclear power plant releases $Cs^{137}$ at a rate of 0.1 mCi per year. The plant began its operations in 1980, which we will designate as $t = 0$. Assume there is no other source of this particular isotope.

(a) Write an integral which gives the total amount of $Cs^{137}$ $T$ years after. (Note: The rest of the problem does not depend on correctly answering part (a).)

(b) Write a differential equation whose solution is $R(t)$, the amount (in mCi) of $Cs^{137}$ in $t$ years. (We are assuming $R(0) = 0$).

(c) After 20 years, approximately how much $Cs^{137}$ will there be?

(d) In the long run, how much $Cs^{137}$ will there be?

(e) Since $Cs^{137}$ poses a great health risk, the government says that the maximum amount of $Cs^{137}$ acceptable in the surrounding environment is 1 mCi (spread over the surroundings). What is the maximum rate at which the station can release the isotope and still be in compliance with the regulations?

ANSWER:

(a) $\displaystyle\int_0^T 0.1 e^{(-\frac{\ln 2}{30})t}\, dt.$

(b) $\frac{dR}{dt} = 0.1 - \frac{\ln 2}{30} R$

(c) Solving the equation in (b), we get:

$$\frac{dR}{0.1 - \frac{\ln 2}{30}R} = dt;$$

$$-\frac{30}{\ln 2} \ln \left| 0.1 - \frac{\ln 2}{30}R \right| = t + C;$$

$$R = -\frac{30}{\ln 2}(e^{-\frac{\ln 2}{30}t + D} - 0.1);$$

$$R = \frac{30}{\ln 2}(0.1 - ke^{-\frac{\ln 2}{30}t}).$$

Now, $R(0) = 0$, so $k = 0.1$, and we have $R = \frac{3}{\ln 2}(1 - e^{-\frac{\ln 2}{30}t})$.

Hence $R(20) = \frac{3}{\ln 2}(1 - e^{-\frac{2\ln 2}{3}}) \approx 1.60$ mCi.

(d) From (c), $R = \frac{3}{\ln 2}(1 - e^{-\frac{\ln 2}{30}t})$. As $t \to \infty$, $e^{-\frac{\ln 2}{30}t} \to 0$, so $R \to \frac{3}{\ln 2} \approx 4.33$mCi.

(e) Take Rate $= r$, then $R = \frac{30}{\ln 2}(r - re^{-\frac{\ln 2}{30}t})$. As $t \to \infty$, $e^{-\frac{\ln 2}{30}t} \to 0$, so $R \to \frac{30}{\ln 2}r$. We set $1 = \frac{30}{\ln 2}r$, then $r = \frac{\ln 2}{30} \approx .023$ mCi/yr.

6. A bank account earns interest at a rate of 2% per year, compounded continuously. Money is deposited into the account in a continuous cash flow at a rate of $500 per year.

(a) Write a differential equation describing the rate at which the balance $B(t)$ is changing. ($t$ is time in years.)

(b) Solve the differential equation given an initial balance of $1000.

(c) Find the amount of money in the bank account after 10 years, assuming an initial balance of $1000.

ANSWER:

(a) The balance increases at a rate of $500 per year from the cash flow and by $2\% \cdot B$ per year from interest, so we have

$$\frac{dB}{dt} = 0.02B + 500.$$

(b) We can manipulate the differential equation as follows:

$$\frac{dB}{dt} = 0.02(B + 25{,}000)$$

$$\frac{dB}{B + 25{,}000} = 0.02dt$$

$$\int \frac{dB}{B + 25{,}000} = \int 0.02dt$$

$$\ln |B + 25{,}000| = 0.02t + C$$

$$B + 25{,}000 = Ae^{0.02t}.$$

When $t = 0$, we have $B = 1000$, so $A = 26,000$, giving

$$B = 26000e^{0.02t} - 25000.$$

(c)   Substituting $t = 10$ in the above equation gives $B = 26000e^{0.02(10)} - 25000 = \$6756.47$.

## Problems and Solutions for Section 10.6

1.   A diligent student has a slow leak in her bike tire, but has been too busy studying for exams to fix it. Assume that the pressure in the tire decreases at a rate proportional to the difference between the atmospheric pressure (15 lbs.) and the tire pressure. Monday at 6:00 pm she pumped up the pressure to 85 lbs. By 6:00 pm Tuesday it was down to 75 lbs. How much longer can she wait to pump up the tire if she wants to keep the pressure at a minimum of 40 lbs.? (You may keep your answer in number of days from Monday at 6:00 pm if you like.)

ANSWER:

Counting in days from Monday at 6pm, we have

$$-\frac{dP}{dt} = k(15 - P), \text{ where } P \text{ is pressure and } k \text{ is constant;}$$

$$\int \frac{1}{P - 15} \, dP = \int k \, dt;$$

$$\ln|P - 15| = kt + C;$$

$$P = 15 + e^{kt+C}.$$

When $t = 0, P = 85$. When $t = 1, P = 75$. Therefore, $85 = 15 + e^C$ and $C = \ln 70$. Now, $75 = 15 + e^k(70)$, and so $k = \ln \frac{6}{7} \approx -0.154$.

To find when $P = 40$, solve $40 = 15 + \left(\frac{6}{7}\right)^t \cdot 70$, yielding $\left(\frac{6}{7}\right)^t = \frac{5}{14}$ and $t = \frac{\ln \frac{5}{14}}{\ln \frac{6}{7}} \approx 6.68$ days.

2.   In trying to model the response to a stimulus, psychologists use the Weber Fechner Law. This law states that the rate of change of a response, $r$, with respect to a stimulus, $s$, is inversely proportional to the stimulus.

(a)   Model this law as a differential equation.

(b)   Solve this differential equation with the initial condition that $r(s_0) = r_0$ for some initial stimulus, $s_0$.

ANSWER:

(a)   Let $k$ be a positive constant. Then, the Weber Fechner Law states that

$$\frac{dr}{ds} = \frac{k}{s}.$$

(b)   To solve this equation, separate variables to obtain

$$dr = k \cdot \frac{ds}{s}$$

and integrate

$$\int dr = k \int \frac{ds}{s}$$

$$r = k \ln|s| + C.$$

Plugging in the initial condition gives $C = r_0 - k \ln|s_0|$. This means the solution is

$$r = k \ln|s| + r_0 - k \ln|s_0|$$

$$= r_0 + k \ln\left|\frac{s}{s_0}\right|.$$

3.  The differential equation describing the motion of a 60-kg woman who has jumped into a swimming pool is given as follows:

$$a = \frac{dv}{dt} = g - \frac{k}{m}v$$

In this equation, $a = \dfrac{dv}{dt}$ on the left hand side is the woman's downward acceleration, $v$ is the woman's downward velocity, $g = 9.8$ m/sec$^2$ is the acceleration due to gravity, and $k = 1960$ kg/sec is the woman's ballistic coefficient in water. This equation assumes that the woman does not attempt to swim to the surface and just allows herself to continue sinking.

(a)  In words, what does each term on the right hand side of the differential equation tell you?
(b)  What is the woman's terminal velocity in the water?
(c)  The woman enters the water with an initial downward velocity of 10 m/sec. Sketch a graph of her downward velocity as a function of time. (You do not need to solve the differential equation to do this.) Explain in words the motion of the woman.

ANSWER:

(a)  $\dfrac{dv}{dt} = \underbrace{g}_{\substack{\text{Velocity increase due to} \\ \text{pull of gravity}}} - \underbrace{\dfrac{k}{m}v}_{\substack{\text{Velocity decrease due to} \\ \text{drag of water}}}$

(b)  $\dfrac{dv}{dt} = 0 \Rightarrow g - \dfrac{k}{m}v = 0 \Rightarrow V_t = \dfrac{mg}{k}$

$$V_t = \frac{(9.8 \text{ m/sec}^2)(60 \text{ kg})}{1960 \text{ kg/sec}} = 0.3 \text{ m/sec}$$

(c)  Downward Velocity (m/sec)

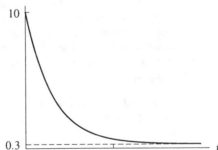

The velocity of the woman decreases exponentially from the moment she enters the water, leveling off to 0.3 m/s.

4.  There is a theory that says the rate at which information spreads by word of mouth is proportional to the product of the number of people who have heard the information and the number who have not. Suppose the total population is N.

(a)  If $p = f(t)$ is the number of people who have the information, how many people do not have the information?
(b)  Write a differential equation that describes the rate, $\dfrac{dp}{dt}$, at which the information spreads by word of mouth.
(c)  Why does this theory make sense?
(d)  Sketch the graph of $p = f(t)$ as a function of time.

ANSWER:

(a)  $N - p$ people do not have information.
(b)  $\dfrac{dp}{dt} = kp(N - p)$.
(c)  This theory makes sense for several reasons. The first is that we would expect the number of people who have the information to grow exponentially when $p$ is small. That is, if $p$ is small, then chances are that each person they come into contact with will not know the information. From the

equation, we can see that $\frac{dp}{dt} = k(pN - p^2)$, so that when $p$ is small, the term $p^2$ on the right-hand side will be small compared to the larger term $pN$. We also expect that at the very beginning and at the very end of the information spreading process, the rate of change of $p$ will be zero. At the very beginning, information spreads slowly because very few people have it. At the end, it spreads slowly because there are few people left to hear it. Notice in the equation that when $p = 0$ or $N$ (the beginning and end of the process), $\frac{dp}{dt} = 0$ as we suspected.

(d)

where $P_0$ is the number of people who have the information initially.

5.  When a bacterial cell is suspended in a fluid, the concentration of a certain drug within the cell will change toward its concentration in the surrounding fluid at a rate proportional to the difference between the two concentrations.

   (a)  Write the differential equation that expresses this relation. (Be sure to define the meaning of the literal quantities involved.)

   (b)  Assume that the concentration in the surrounding fluid is held constant. What is the general solution of the equation in (a)? (This solution will necessarily contain some unknown constants.)

   (c)  Suppose that a patient's blood is infected with these bacteria, which initially contain none of the drug. The patient is given enough of the drug to bring (and hold) its concentration in his blood to 0.0001. After two hours, the concentration within the bacterial cells is found to be 0.00004. Use this to evaluate the unknown constants in (b).

   (d)  How long will it be before the concentration within the bacteria reaches 0.00008?

   ANSWER:

   (a)  Let $k$ equal the concentration of the drug in the cell, $s$ represent the concentration of the drug in the fluid, and $A$ be the constant of proportionality. Then, $\frac{dk}{dt} = (s - k) \cdot A$.

   (b)  If we let $s$ be constant,

$$\int \frac{dk}{s - k} = \int A \, dt \text{ so}$$
$$-\ln(s - k) = At + B$$
$$\text{and } s - k = e^{-At-B}, \text{ so,}$$
$$k = s - e^{-At-B}$$

   Rewrite this as

$$k = s - e^{-B}e^{-At} = s - De^{-At},$$

   where $D = e^{-B}$.

   (c)  Since $k(0) = 0$, $D = s$. We are given $s = 0.0001$, so $k = 0.0001 - 0.0001e^{-At}$. $k(2) = 0.00004$ implies $0.00004 = 0.0001 - 0.0001e^{-2A}$. Solving for $A$, $0.6 = e^{-2A}$ and $A = -\frac{1}{2}\ln(0.6) \approx 0.255$

   (d)  Set $0.00008 = 0.0001\left(1 - e^{-0.255t}\right)$. Then

$$0.8 = 1 - e^{-0.255t}$$
$$-0.2 = -e^{-0.255t}$$
$$\frac{\ln(0.2)}{-0.255} = t$$
$$t \approx 6.312 \text{ hours.}$$

6. A spherical raindrop evaporates at a rate proportional to its surface area. Note: you can do parts (e) and (f) WITHOUT doing parts (a)–(d).

   (a) If $V =$ volume of the raindrop and $S =$ surface area, write down a differential equation for $\frac{dV}{dt}$.
   (b) Your equation in (a) should include an unspecified constant $k$. What is the sign of $k$? Why?
   (c) Since $V = \frac{4}{3}\pi r^3$ for a sphere, write down an equation which relates $\frac{dV}{dt}$ for a sphere to $r$ and $\frac{dr}{dt}$.
   (d) Since $S = 4\pi r^2$ for a sphere, you can write $S$ in terms of $r$ and $\frac{dV}{dt}$ in terms of $r$ and $\frac{dr}{dt}$. Then the differential equation in part (a) becomes $\frac{dr}{dt} = k$. Show how this happens.
   (e) Solve the differential equation $\frac{dr}{dt} = k$, where $k$ is a constant.
   (f) If it takes 5 minutes for a spherical raindrop to evaporate to $\frac{1}{8}$ of its original volume, how long will it take to completely evaporate?

   ANSWER:

   (a) $\dfrac{dV}{dt} = kS$.
   (b) $k$ is negative because the raindrop evaporates and its volume decreases.
   (c) $\dfrac{dV}{dt} = 4\pi r^2 \dfrac{dr}{dt}$.
   (d) Since $\dfrac{dV}{dt} = kS$, we have $4\pi r^2 \dfrac{dr}{dt} = k(4\pi r^2)$, which gives $\dfrac{dr}{dt} = k$.
   (e) $dr = k\,dt$; $r = kt + r_0$.
   (f)

$$V(t) = \frac{4\pi}{3}(kt + r_0)^3,$$

$$\text{So} \quad V(5) = \frac{4}{3}\pi(5k + r_0)^3.$$

$$\text{On the other hand,} \quad V(5) = \frac{1}{8}V(0) = \frac{1}{8} \cdot \frac{4}{3}\pi r_0^3.$$

$$\text{Thus,} \quad \frac{4}{3}\pi(5k + r_0)^3 = \frac{1}{8} \cdot \frac{4}{3}\pi r_0^3$$

$$5k + r_0 = \sqrt[3]{\frac{1}{8}}r_0 = \frac{1}{2}r_0$$

$$k = \frac{\left(\frac{1}{2} - 1\right)r_0}{5} = -\frac{1}{10}r_0.$$

   Now, we want $V(t) = 0$ (i.e., the volume to be 0). Since $V(t) = \frac{4}{3}\pi(kt + r_0)^3$, we set $kt + r_0 = 0$. Then $t = -\dfrac{r_0}{k} = 10$ minutes.

7. A lake contains pollutants. A stream feeds clear mountain water into the lake at 2 gals/min. Polluted water is drained out of the lake at a rate of 2 gals/min by a second stream. If the volume of the lake if $V$ gals and time, $t$, is measured in minutes, and if it is assumed that the pollutants are spread evenly through the lake at all times, then the differential equation for $Q(t)$, the quantity of pollutant in the lake at time $t$ is (circle one):

   (a) $\dfrac{dQ}{dt} = -2Q$             (b) $\dfrac{dQ}{dt} = -2t$

   (c) $\dfrac{dQ}{dt} = -\dfrac{2Q}{V}$          (d) $\dfrac{dQ}{dt} = 2 - 2Q$

   (e) $\dfrac{dQ}{dt} = 2 - \dfrac{2Q}{V}$        (f) $\dfrac{dQ}{dt} = 2V - Qt$

   (g) $\dfrac{dQ}{dt} = 2Qt - V$         (h) $\dfrac{dQ}{dt} = Qe^{-2t}$

   (i) $\dfrac{dQ}{dt} = \dfrac{Q}{V}e^{-2t}$        (j) $\dfrac{dQ}{dt} = \dfrac{2Q - 2V}{V}$

   ANSWER:

   The pollutants are leaving the lake and no new pollutants are entering, so the net rate is just the rate out. The total volume out is 2 gals/min of which only $2 \cdot (Q/V)$ is the pollutant (Volume·Concentration), so

$$\frac{dQ}{dt} = -2\frac{Q}{V},$$

or choice (c).

## Problems and Solutions for Section 10.7

1. Suppose $y$ is a solution to the differential equation

$$\frac{dy}{dx} = f(y)$$

and that $f(y) \geq 0$ for all $y$. Which of the following could be a graph of $y$? (Circle one or more.)

(a)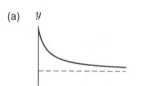

(b)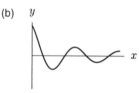

(c)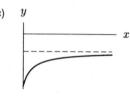

(d)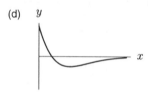

(e)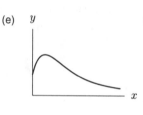

(f)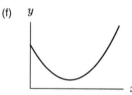

ANSWER:

Since $f(y) \geq 0$ for all $y$, we know that $dy/dx \geq 0$ for all $y$ so $y(x)$ is nondecreasing for all $y$. The only nondecreasing graph among the options given is choice (c).

2. Consider the differential equation $\dfrac{dy}{dt} = g(y)$. The graph of $g(y)$ is drawn below.

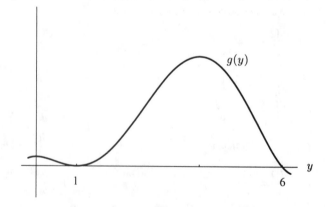

(a) What are the constant solutions to the differential equation $\dfrac{dy}{dt} = g(y)$? Which of them are stable?

(b) Sketch a graph of $y$ as a function of $t$ for representative initial values of $y$. You do not have to provide a scale for $t$.

ANSWER:

(a) The constant solutions to the differential equation $\dfrac{dy}{dt} = g(y)$ are $y = 1$ and $y = 6$ because for these values of $y$, $\dfrac{dy}{dt} = 0$, so $y$ is constant. The only stable solution is $y = 6$. Although solutions with $y(0) < 1$ approach 1 in the long run, it is best not to call $y = 1$ a stable equilibrium since solutions with $y(0)$ slightly greater than 1 tend to veer away.

(b)

3. The rates of change of the populations for four different species are given by the differential equations (i), (ii), (iii), and (iv) below. (These species do not interact, and so the differential equations are all independent of one another.) $P$ measures the population in thousands at time $t$ months. Each species starts with 1000 members ($P = 1$) at time $t = 0$. Assume that each of these differential equations holds indefinitely.

(i) $\dfrac{dP}{dt} = 0.05$    (ii) $\dfrac{dP}{dt} = -0.05P$    (iii) $\dfrac{dP}{dt} = 0.05(1000 - P)$    (iv) $\dfrac{dP}{dt} = 0.0005P(1000 - P)$

(a) For each of the four species, find the size of the population $P$ when the rate of change of the population is a maximum. (Remember $P(0) = 1$.)

(b) For each of the four species, find the size of the population $P$ when the rate of change of the population is a minimum. (Remember $P(0) = 1$.)

(c) For each of the four species, find *all* equilibrium values of the population, and state whether each equilibrium value is stable or unstable.

(d) For each of the four species, sketch a graph of the population as a function of time given the initial condition $P(0) = 1$.

ANSWER:

(a) We want to know when the rate of change, $\dfrac{dP}{dt}$, is a max. To approach this problem, let $f(P) = \dfrac{dP}{dt}$ (the rate of change is given as a function of $P$). To find the max of $f(P) = \dfrac{dP}{dt}$, set $f'(P) = 0$, confirm whether this is a max, and find the $P$ value for this max.

(i) $f(P) = 0.05$. The rate of change is constant ($f'(P) = 0$ for all $P$), so there is <u>no</u> maximum rate of change.

(ii) This equation describes exponential decay. Since we start with $P = 1$, $\frac{dP}{dt}$ will be negative for all time. No max.

(iii) $f(P) = 0.05(1000 - P) = 50 - 0.05P$    $f'(P) = -0.05$
$f'(P)$ can never equal zero, so we must check the (left) endpoint. The left endpoint is at $t = 0$, and $P(0) = 1$. Here $f(P) = \dfrac{dP}{dt} = 49.95$, and from there $\dfrac{dP}{dt}$ decreases to zero. This must be true, because $\dfrac{dP}{dt} > 0 \Rightarrow P$ is increasing $\Rightarrow \dfrac{dP}{dt}$ is decreasing. So $\dfrac{dP}{dt}$ has a

max (of 49.95) where $P = 1$.

   (iv)   $f(P) = 0.0005P(1000 - P) = 0.5P - 0.0005P^2$

$f'(P) = 0.5 - 0.001P = 0 \Rightarrow 0.5 = 0.001P \Rightarrow P = \dfrac{0.5}{0.001} \Rightarrow P = 500$.

Check that it's a max: $f''(P) = -0.001 < 0 \Rightarrow$ max.

**(b)**   (i)   Again, since the rate of change $\dfrac{dP}{dt}$ is constant (meaning $P(t)$ is linear) there is no min.

   (ii)   (See a.ii.) $f(P) = -0.05$. At the left endpoint, where $P = 1$, we have $\dfrac{dP}{dt} = -0.05$ is a min. (From there $\dfrac{dP}{dt}$ increases to zero.)

   (iii)   $f'(P) = -0.05$ (see a.iii). The left endpoint, where $P = 1$, is a max of $\dfrac{dP}{dt} = 49.95$. From there, $\dfrac{dP}{dt}$ decreases to zero.

It never attains the value zero, but in some sense zero is a "min" since $\dfrac{dP}{dt}$ cannot be less than zero. $\dfrac{dP}{dt}$ approaches zero as $P$ approaches 1000.

<u>Answer</u>: Either $\dfrac{dP}{dt}$ never attains a min, or it approaches a "min" of zero when $P = 1000$.

   (iv)   As seen in part (a), setting $f'(P) = 0$ yields a max of $\dfrac{dP}{dt}$, so we need to check endpoints. The (left) endpoint, where $p = 1$, is not a min. But $\dfrac{dP}{dt}$ decreases to zero as $P$ approaches 1000. So the answer, as in part b.iii, is either no min, or a "min" at $P = 1000$.

**(c)**   To find the equilibrium values, set $\dfrac{dP}{dt} = 0$. (No change in $P$.)

   (i)   No equilibrium, since $\dfrac{dP}{dt} = 0.05$.

   (ii)   $\dfrac{dP}{dt} = 0 = -0.05P \Rightarrow P = 0$. This is a stable equilibrium, because the population is dying off. Since $\dfrac{dP}{dt} < 0$, $P$ always will decrease to zero, no matter where it starts.

   (iii)   $\dfrac{dP}{dt} = 0 = 0.05(1000 - P) \Rightarrow P = 1000$

This is a stable equilibrium, meaning the population will always approach 1000, no matter what size it is at $t = 0$. If $P < 1000$ at $t = 0$, then $\dfrac{dP}{dt} > 0$, and $P$ increases until it levels off at 1000 as $\dfrac{dP}{dt}$ approaches 0. If $P(0) > 1000$, then $\dfrac{dP}{dt} < 0$, and $P$ decreases until it levels off at 1000 as $\dfrac{dP}{dt}$ approaches zero.

   (iv)   $\dfrac{dP}{dt} = 0 = 0.0005P(1000 - P) \Rightarrow P = 0$ or $P = 1000$. $P = 0$ is an unstable equilibrium, because if the population starts out at any value other than zero, it will grow larger and move away from the value zero. (If it starts out greater than 1000, it will never be less than 1000, so it will never approach zero.)

$P = 1000$ is a stable equilibrium, because the size of the population always approaches 1000. If $P$ starts out less than 1000, then $\dfrac{dP}{dt} > 0$, and $P$ approaches 1000 as $\dfrac{dP}{dt}$ approaches 0. If $P$ starts out greater than 1000, then $\dfrac{dP}{dt} < 0$, and $P$ decreases to 1000 as $\dfrac{dP}{dt}$ approaches 0.

(d)

(i)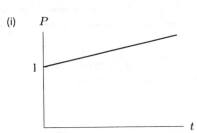

(ii)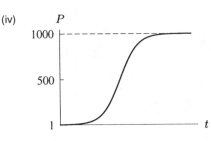

(iii) P

1000

t

(iv) P

1000

500

1

t

4. On January 1, 1879, records show that 500 of a fish called Atlantic striped bass were introduced into the San Francisco Bay. In 1899, the first year fishing for bass was allowed, 100,000 of these bass were caught, representing 10% of the population at the start of 1899. Owing to reproduction, at any time the bass population is growing at a rate proportional to the population at that moment.

(a) Write a differential equation satisfied by $B(t)$, the number of Atlantic striped bass a time $t$, where $t$ is in years since January 1, 1879 and $0 \leq t < 20$.

(b) Solve for $B(t)$, assuming $0 \leq t < 20$.

(c) Assume that when fishing starts in 1899, the rate at which bass are caught is proportional to the square of the population with constant of proportionality $10^{-7}$. Write a differential equation satisfied by $B(t)$, for $t > 20$.

(d) Assume that fishing practices from the start of 1899 are as described in part (c). What happens to the bass population in the long run?

ANSWER:

Let $B(t)$ be the bass population at time $t$.

(a) We are told that for $0 \leq t < 20$,

$$\frac{dB}{dt} = kB.$$

Also

$$B(0) = 500, \quad \text{and} \quad B(20) = 10^6.$$

(b) So $B(t) = Ae^{kt}$, where $A$ and $k$ are constants. Since $B(0) = A = 500$, we know $A = 500$ so $B(t) = 500e^{kt}$. Since $B(20) = 500e^{20k} = 10^6$, we have $e^{20k} = 2000$, so $20k = \ln 2000$ or $k = \dfrac{\ln 2000}{20} \approx 0.38$. So

$$B(t) = 500e^{0.38t}.$$

(c) We know that $\frac{dB}{dt}$ = Rate of growth − Rate of fishing, or

$$\frac{dB}{dt} = 0.38B - 10^{-7}B^2.$$

(d) The equilibria occur when $\frac{dB}{dt} = 0$, or at $B = 0$ and $B = \dfrac{0.38}{10^{-7}} = 3.8 \cdot 10^6$. The equilibrium at $B = 3.8 \cdot 10^6$ is stable since $\frac{dB}{dt} > 0$ for $0 < B < 3.8 \cdot 10^6$ and $\frac{dB}{dt} < 0$ for $B > 3.8 \cdot 10^6$. So in the long run $B = 3.8 \cdot 10^6$.

## Review Problems and Solutions for Chapter 10

1. Each graph below is a solution to at least one of the differential equations. Match them up in such a way that each graph is used only once. No work need be shown.

(A)

(B)

(C)

(D)

(a) $\dfrac{d^2y}{dt^2} = 2$ has solution graph _____

(b) $\dfrac{dy}{dt} = y - 2$ has solution graph _____

(c) $\dfrac{dy}{dt} = y(2 - y)$ has solution graph _____

(d) $\dfrac{dy}{dt} = -yt$ has solution graph _____

ANSWER:

(a) C. $y = t^2$.
(b) A. $y = -e^t + 1$, $y' < 0$ if $y < 2$.
(c) B. Zero solution, $y = 0$.
(d) D. $y = e^{-\frac{t^2}{2}}$

2. Discuss the solutions of the differential equation

$$\frac{dy}{dx} = y(1 - x - y).$$

Your discussion should include at least the following points:

- Are there any constant solutions?
- A sketch of several solution curves.

- Explain why the solution function $f$ for which $f(-1) = 1$ has a global maximum. What is the "long run" behavior of this function? (i.e., what can you say about $\lim_{x \to \infty} f(x)$?)
- Many solution functions have global maxima. Where do these maximum points appear on the graph?
- A discussion that includes other significant information may receive extra credit. Although you may use your calculator to get the picture, try to base your arguments on information taken directly from the differential equation.

Note: Solutions starting from negative values of $y$ are likely to grow so fast the the calculator will overflow, causing it to stop and give an error message.

ANSWER:

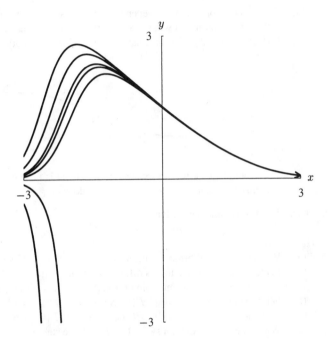

Solution Curves to $\frac{dy}{dx} = y(1 - x - y)$

The only constant solution is the curve $y = 0$. One can see this because if $y = c$,

$$\frac{dy}{dx} = c(1 - x - c) = 0.$$

But this holds for all $x$ only if $c = 0$.

Solutions will have global maxima when $\frac{dy}{dx} = 0$. This happens when $y = 0$ or when $1 - x - y = 0$. The first cannot happen, since solution curves do not intersect and $y = 0$ is a solution. Therefore, critical points can only occur on the line $x + y = 1$. If $y$ is positive, $\frac{dy}{dx}$ will be positive for $x > y - 1$ and negative for $x < y - 1$, so all critical points with positive $y$ will be maxima. Moreover, if $y(x) > 0$ for some $x$, then $y$ is decreasing for $x > 1$, so $y(x)$ approaches some limit greater than or equal to 0. Hence $y'(x) \to 0$ when $x \to \infty$. This means that

$$\frac{dy}{dx} = y(1 - x - y) \to 0$$

since $1 - x - y \to -\infty$, then $y \to 0$ (it's the other factor) as desired.

3. TRUE/FALSE questions. For each statement, write whether it is true or false and provide a short explanation or counterexample.

   (a) $y = x^2 + x$ is a solution to $\frac{dy}{dx} = 2(y - x^2) + 1$.

   (b) The solution of $\frac{dy}{dx} = x + 1$ passing through $(0, 1)$ is the same as the solution passing through $(0, 0)$, except it has been shifted one unit upward.

(c)   The solutions of $\frac{dP}{dt} = kP(L - P)$ are always concave down.

ANSWER:

(a)   TRUE. Substitute $y = x^2 + x$ in the left side of the equation $\dfrac{dy}{dx} = 2(y - x^2) + 1$.

$$\text{Left side} = 2x + 1.$$

Now substitute in the right side:

$$\text{Right side} = 2(x^2 + x - x^2) + 1$$
$$= 2x + 1.$$

(b)   TRUE. The slope field is independent of $y$, so solutions beginning at the same $x$-coordinate with different $y$-coordinates will be vertical translations of each other.

(c)   FALSE. This is the logistic equation, some of whose solutions look like:

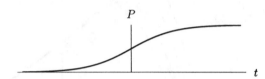

Note: A quick way to see that the statement is false is to note that when $k = 0$, $dP/dt = 0$, and thus $P = \text{const}$, which is not concave down.

4.   Consider the differential equation

$$\frac{dP}{dt} = \sin P$$

(a)   What are the equilibrium solutions with $-1 \le P \le 8$? Give exact answers.
(b)   Sketch solution curves to this differential equation for $-1 \le P \le 8$. Include all the equilibrium solutions and the solutions going through the points $(0, 1)$, $(0, 3)$, $(0, 5)$, $(0, 7)$.
(c)   What happens to the value of $P(t)$ as $t \to \infty$ if $P(0) = 1$?
(d)   What happens to the value of $P(t)$ as $t \to \infty$ if $P(0) = 6$?
(e)   What equilibrium solutions in $-1 \le P \le 8$ are stable and which are unstable?
(f)   Find $\dfrac{d^2 P}{dt^2}$ in terms of P.
(g)   Use your answer to part (f) to decide at which of the following points the solution curve is concave up. (Circle your answer(s). No reasons need be given.)

(1, 1)          (3, 3)          (5, 1)          (7, 3)

ANSWER:

(a)   $\frac{dP}{dt} = 0$ when $\sin P = 0$, i.e. if $P = k\pi$, so we have equilibria at $P = 0$, $P = \pi$, and $P = 2\pi$.
(b)   For $P$ in $(0, \pi)$, $\sin P$ is positive, so $\frac{dP}{dt}$ is positive, so $P$ is increasing; likewise $P$ is increasing for $P$ in $(2\pi, 3\pi)$. By a similar argument, $P$ is decreasing for $P$ in $(\pi, 2\pi)$. Thus the graph of $P$ will be as shown in Figure 10.7.17:

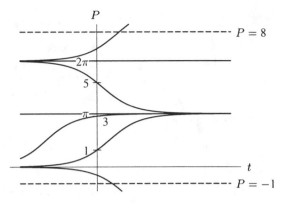

*Figure 10.7.17*

(c)   Looking at Figure 10.7.17, we note that $P = 1$ is in $(0, \pi)$, so $P(t) \to \pi$ as $t \to \infty$.

(d)   Looking at Figure 10.7.17, we note that $P = 6$ is in $(\pi, 2\pi)$ so $P(t) \to \pi$ as $t \to \infty$.

(e)   $P = \pi$ is stable; $P = 0$ and $P = 2\pi$ are unstable.

(f)   We differentiate the expression for $\frac{dP}{dt}$:

$$\frac{d^2P}{dt^2} = \frac{d}{dt}\left(\frac{dP}{dt}\right)$$
$$= \frac{d}{dt}(\sin P)$$
$$= \cos P \left(\frac{dP}{dt}\right)$$
$$= \cos P \sin P.$$

(g)   $(\cos P)(\sin P)$ is positive for $P = 1$ and negative for $P = 3$ so solution curves are concave up at $(1, 1)$ and $(5, 1)$.

## *Problems and Solutions for Focus on Modeling: Systems of Differential Equations* ▬▬▬

1.   Suppose the equations

$$\frac{dy}{dt} = -4y + 2xy, \qquad \frac{dx}{dt} = -x + xy$$

describe the rates of growth of two interacting species, where $x$ is the number of species $A$, measured in thousands, and $y$ is the number of species $B$, measured in thousands.

(a)   Describe what happens to each species in the absence of the other.

(b)   For each species, is the interaction with the other species favorable or unfavorable?

(c)   Summarize in words the nature of the interaction between these two species.

(d)   Determine all the equilibrium points in the $xy$-phase plane.

(e)   The slope field in the $xy$-phase plane is shown below. Sketch the trajectory for initial conditions of $x = 2.5$, $y = 0.5$. (In other words, there are initially 2500 of species $A$ and 500 of species $B$). Be sure to indicate with arrows which direction along the trajectory the populations will go in time, and show how you found this direction.

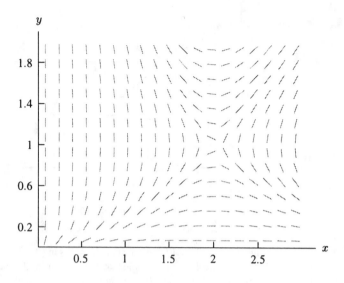

ANSWER:

(a) <u>Both die out</u>.

(b) <u>Favorable to both</u>.

(c) Each species would be lost without the other–symbiosis.

(d) $y' = -y(4 - 2x)$, $\quad x' = -x(1 - y)$ so Equilibrium points: $(0, 0)$, $(2, 1)$

(e) At $(2.5, 0.5)$:

$$\frac{dy}{dt} = -4(0.5) + 2(2.5)(0.5) = -2 + 2.5 = 0.5 \text{ (positive)}.$$

$$\frac{dx}{dt} = -2.5 + (2.5)(0.5) = -2.5 + 1.25 = -1.25 \text{ (negative)}.$$

Therefore if the initial conditions are $(2.5, 0.5)$, species A is decreasing while species B is increasing.

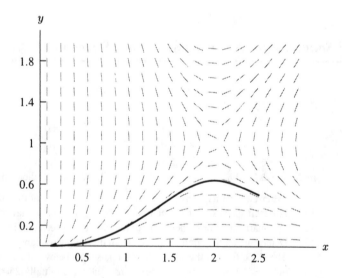

2. Suppose the equations $\dfrac{dy}{dt} = 2y - xy$ and $\dfrac{dx}{dt} = x - xy$ describe the rates of growth of two interacting species, where $x$ is the number of species $A$, measured in thousands, and $y$ is the number of species $B$, measured in thousands.

(a) In one sentence, summarize the nature of the interaction between these two species.

(b) The slope field in the $xy$-phase plane is shown below. Sketch the trajectory for the initial conditions $x = 1$, $y = 2$. (In other words, there are initially 1000 of species $A$ and 2000 of species $B$.) Be sure to indicate with arrows which direction along the trajectory the populations go in time, and show how you found this direction.

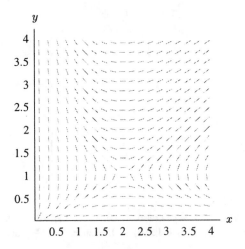

(c)    Describe the long-run behavior of the two populations with the initial conditions given in part (b).

ANSWER:

(a)    The two populations are competitors, since each would grow exponentially without the other; each suffers in the presence of the other.

(b)    At $(1,2)$ we have $\frac{dy}{dt} = 2 > 0$ and $\frac{dx}{dt} = -1 < 0$. This means $y$ is increasing and $x$ is decreasing, so the direction of the trajectory must be upwards and to the left.

(c)    From the trajectory we see that $y$ grows (in fact, exponentially) and $x$ dies out.

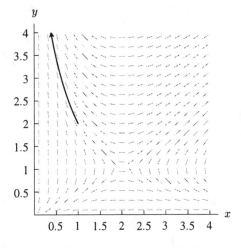

3.    On a fine spring day you stand in the Square and throw a bean bag high into the air and catch it. Sketch a trajectory which reflects the bean bag's trip. Label the points $A$, $B$ and $C$ on the trajectory where

$A =$ the point corresponding to the instant the bag is tossed;

$B =$ the bag reaches its highest altitude;

$C =$ the point corresponding to the instant you catch the bag;

$x =$ the altitude of the bean bag;

$v =$ the velocity of the bag.

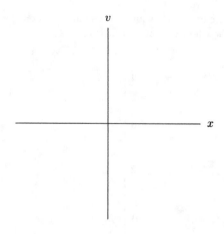

ANSWER:

We take the acceleration to be constant at $-32\text{ft}/\text{sec}^2$. Then $v = -32t + v_0$ and $x = -16t^2 + v_0t$ (we take $v(0) = v_0$ and $x(0) = 0$). Hence, $t = \frac{v_0 - v}{32}$ and

$$x = -16\left(\frac{v_0 - v}{32}\right)^2 + v_0\frac{v_0 - v}{32} = -\frac{1}{64}v^2 + \frac{1}{64}v_0^2.$$

(Remember that $v_0$, the initial velocity, is a constant.) The graph is shown below.

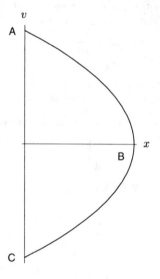

4.  Below is a graph of position versus time.

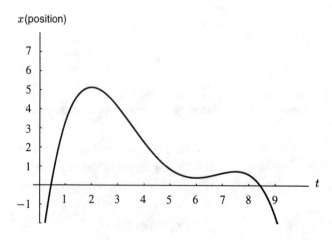

(a)   Sketch a rough graph of $v$ versus $t$.

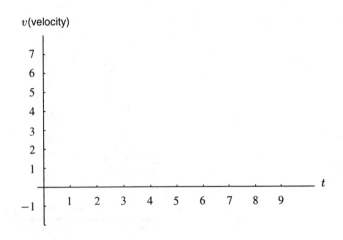

(b)   Graph the corresponding trajectory in the $xv$-plane.

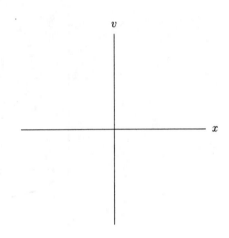

ANSWER:

(a)

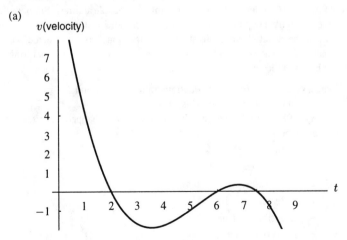

(b)   Taking values of $x$ and $v$ at the same time $t$, we get the following set of $(x, v)$ ordered pairs:

| $t = 1/2$ | $(0, 8)$ |
|---|---|
| $t = 1$ | $(3, 4)$ |
| $t = 2$ | $(5, 0)$ |
| $t = 3$ | $(4, -1.5)$ |
| $t = 4$ | $(2.5, -1.5)$ |
| $t = 5$ | $(1, -1)$ |
| $t = 5.5$ | $(1/2, -1/2)$ |
| $t = 6$ | $(1/3, 0)$ |
| $t = 6.5$ | $(1/2, 1/3)$ |
| $t = 7$ | $(2/3, 1/2)$ |
| $t = 7.5$ | $(4/3, 0)$ |
| $t = 8$ | $(1/2, -1)$ |
| $t = 8.5$ | $(0, -2)$ |

Plotting these gives the following picture:

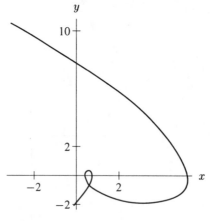

*Figure 10.7.18*

5. A fatal infectious disease is introduced into a growing population. Let $S$ denote the number of susceptible people at time $t$ and let $I$ denote the number of infected people at time $t$. Suppose that, in the absence of the disease, the susceptible population grows at a rate proportional to itself, with constant of proportionality 0.3. People in the infected group die at a rate proportional to the infected population with constant of proportionality 0.2. The rate at which people get infected is proportional to the product of the number of susceptibles and the number of infecteds, with constant of proportionality 0.001.

   (a) Write a system of differential equations satisfied by $S$ and $I$.
   (b) Find the equilibrium points for this system.
   (c) For each of the initial conditions below, cricle what happens as $t$ starts to increase. (No reasons need be given.)

   (i) $S = 400, I = 100$
   - $S$ increases, $I$ increases.
   - $S$ increases, $I$ decreases.
   - $S$ decreases, $I$ increases.
   - $S$ decreases, $I$ increases.
   - None of the above

   (ii) $S = 400, I = 400$
   - $S$ increases, $I$ increases.

- $S$ increases, $I$ decreases.
- $S$ decreases, $I$ increases.
- $S$ decreases, $I$ decreases.
- None of the above

(iii)  $S = 200, I = 300$
- $S$ increases, $I$ increases.
- $S$ increases, $I$ decreases.
- $S$ decreases, $I$ increases.
- $S$ decreases, $I$ decreases.
- None of the above

(iv)  $S = 100, I = 100$
- $S$ increases, $I$ increases.
- $S$ increases, $I$ decreases.
- $S$ decreases, $I$ increases.
- $S$ decreases, $I$ decreases.
- None of the above

ANSWER:

(a)  The system of differential equations is

$$\frac{dS}{dt} = 0.3S - 0.001SI,$$

$$\frac{dI}{dt} = 0.001SI - 0.2I.$$

(b)  In equilibrium, $\frac{dS}{dt} = \frac{dI}{dt} = 0$, i.e.

$$\frac{dS}{dt} = -0.001S(I - 300) = 0,$$

$$\frac{dI}{dt} = 0.001I(S - 200) = 0.$$

If we solve these two equations we find that the equilibria are at $(0,0)$ and $(200, 300)$.

(c)  Figure 10.7.19 shows how the nullclines around $(200, 300)$ divide first quadrant into four regions.

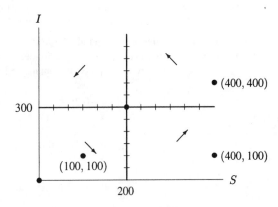

***Figure 10.7.19***

Figure 10.7.19 also shows the directions of arbitrary trajectories in each of these regions; for example, a trajectory in the upper-right region moves northwest. Using this figure, we can determine how $S$ and $I$ change in each of the four situations:

(i)   $S$ and $I$ both increase.

(ii)  $S$ decreases; $I$ increases.

(iii) None of the above.

(iv)  $S$ increases; $I$ decreases.

# Problems and Solutions for Focus on Modeling: Analyzing the Phase Plane

1. Which system of equations could have the phase plane diagram of Figure 10.7.20?

   (a) $\dfrac{dx}{dt} = -5x + y$ $\qquad$ $\dfrac{dy}{dt} = x - 5y$

   (b) $\dfrac{dx}{dt} = x - 5y$ $\qquad$ $\dfrac{dy}{dt} = 5x - y$

   (c) $\dfrac{dx}{dt} = -x + 5y$ $\qquad$ $\dfrac{dy}{dt} = -5x - y$

   (d) $\dfrac{dx}{dt} = x - 5y$ $\qquad$ $\dfrac{dy}{dt} = -5x - y$

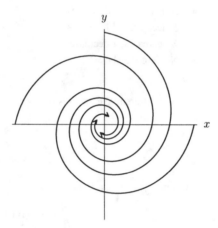

**Figure 10.7.20:** Phase Plane

ANSWER:

On the positive $x$ axis, all trajectories satisfy the conditions $\frac{dx}{dt} < 0$, $\frac{dy}{dt} < 0$. If we substitute $y = 0$ and some positive $x$-value into the equation, we see that only (c) can satisfy the above condition.

2. Let $x$ be the number of reptiles, $y$ be the number of mammals, and $z$ be the number of plants on the island of Komodo, all measured in thousands (e.g., $x = 50$ means 50,000 reptiles). The following differential equations give the rates of growth of reptiles, mammals, and plants on the island:

$$\frac{dx}{dt} = -0.2x - 0.04xy + 0.0008xz$$

$$\frac{dy}{dt} = -0.1y + 0.01xy$$

$$\frac{dz}{dt} = 2z - 0.002z^2 - 0.1xz$$

   (a) Describe what happens to each class if the other two were not present. Use the terms we learned in class, such as "exponential growth," to describe the type of population growth each class experiences in the absence of the other two.

   (i) Reptiles:

   (ii) Mammals:

   (iii) Plants:

   (b) Say that initially there are 100,000 plants (i.e., $z = 100$) on Komodo, and there are no reptiles or mammals.

   (i) Would the plant population increase or decrease initially?

(ii) Describe what would happen to the plant population in the long run. (If the plant population tends toward a particular value, then give that value.)

(iii) At what plant population would the number of plants be increasing the fastest?

(c) Who is eating whom on Komodo? Describe the nature of the interaction between each class.

(d) Find the equilibrium populations of reptiles, mammals, and plants (again assuming that none of the populations is zero).

Now assume that there are no plants ($z = 0$), but the reptile and mammal populations are non-zero.

(e) The slope field of the $xy$ phase plane is shown below. Sketch the trajectory starting from initial populations of 2000 reptiles and 2000 mammals ($x = 2$ and $y = 2$). Be sure to indicate with arrows in which direction the populations move in time along the trajectory. Finally, describe what happens to the reptile and mammal populations in the long run. Why does this make sense?

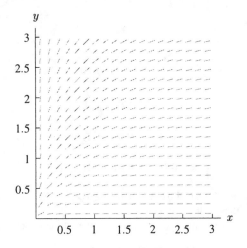

ANSWER:

(a) (i) Reptiles: $\dfrac{dx}{dt} = -0.2x \Rightarrow$ exponential decay

(ii) Mammals: $\dfrac{dy}{dt} = -0.1y \Rightarrow$ exponential decay

(iii) Plants: $\dfrac{dz}{dt} = 2(z - 0.001z^2) \Rightarrow$ logistic growth

(b) $\Rightarrow$ Logistic growth, carrying capacity $z = 1000 \left[ 2z(1 - 0.001z) \right] = 0 \Rightarrow z = 1000 \Big]$

(b) (i) Carrying capacity $= 1000 > P_0 = 100 \Rightarrow$ Plant population increases initially.

(ii) $\lim\limits_{t \to \infty} z(t) = 1000$ (Population tends toward carrying capacity.)

(iii) $\max\left(\dfrac{dz}{dt}\right) = \dfrac{1}{2}$ (carrying capacity)$= 500$; here the second derivative is zero.

(c) $\dfrac{dy}{dt} \propto +0.01xy \Rightarrow$ Mammals eat reptiles.

$\dfrac{dx}{dt} \propto +0.008xz \Rightarrow$ Reptiles eat plants.

(d) (i) $x(-0.2 - 0.04y + 0.008z) = 0$
Set $\frac{dy}{dt} = y(-0.1 + 0.01x) = 0$ to get $x = 10$.

and $\frac{dz}{dt} = z(2 - 0.002z - 0.1x) = z(2 - 0.002z - 1) = z(1 - 0.002z) = 0$ to get $z = 500$.

Then $\frac{dx}{dt} = -0.2 - 0.04y + 0.0008(500) = 0$ when $y = 5$
Equilibrium populations are:
$x = 10$, i.e., 10,000 reptiles

$y = 5$, i.e., 5,000 mammals

$z = 500$, i.e., 500,000 plants.

(e)

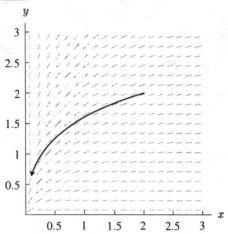

Plug in $x = 2$, $y = 2$:

$$\frac{dx}{dt} = -0.2(2) - 0.04(2)(2) < 0$$

$$\frac{dy}{dt} = -0.1(2) + 0.01(2)(2) < 0$$

So $x$ and $y$ are $\downarrow$. Arrows go $\swarrow$.

Reptile and mammal populations $\to 0$.

Makes sense because plants are the ultimate food source for both!

3.  The interaction of two populations $x(t)$ and $y(t)$ is modeled by the system

$$\frac{1}{x}\frac{dx}{dt} = 1 - x - ky, \qquad \frac{1}{y}\frac{dy}{dt} = 1 - y + kx,$$

where $k$ is a positive constant.

(a)  What type of interaction is modeled here (Symbiosis, Predator—Prey, Competition)?

(b)  Do the qualitative phase plane analysis for the case $k > 1$. For example, try $k = 2$. What happens in the long run?

(c)  Do the qualitative phase plane analysis for the case $k < 1$. For example, try $k = \frac{1}{2}$. What happens in the long run?

ANSWER:

(a)  We note that an increase in $y$ causes a decrease in $\frac{dx}{dt}$ (due to the $-ky$ term) and an increase in $x$ causes an increase in $y$ (due to the $+kx$ term). Thus, it is Predator-Prey model, with $y$ being the Predator and $x$ being the Prey.

(b)  For $k = 2$, we have $\frac{1}{x}\frac{dx}{dt} = 1 - x - 2y$ and $\frac{1}{y}\frac{dy}{dt} = 1 - y + 2x$. The phase plane diagram is below; one can see the trajectories spiraling toward $(0, 1)$. As for the equilibrium points, we have $x(1 - x - 2y) = 0$ and $y(1 - y + 2x) = 0$. Therefore, either $x = 0$, and then $y = 0$ or $y = 1$; or $y = 0$, and then $x = 0$ or $x = 1$; or $1 - x - 2y = 0$ and $1 - y + 2x = 0$, and then $x = \frac{1}{5}$, $y = \frac{3}{5}$. So we have $(0,0)$, $(1,0)$, $(0,1)$, and $(-\frac{1}{5}, \frac{3}{5})$ as our equilibrium points.

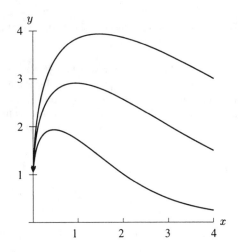

(c) For $k = \frac{1}{2}$, we have $\frac{1}{x}\frac{dx}{dt} = 1 - x - \frac{1}{2}y$ and $\frac{1}{y}\frac{dy}{dt} = 1 - y + \frac{1}{2}x$. The Phase Plane Diagram is below; one can see the trajectories spiraling toward $\left(\frac{2}{5}, \frac{6}{5}\right)$. As for the equilibrium points, we have $x(1 - x - \frac{1}{2}y) = 0$ and $y(1 - y + \frac{1}{2}x) = 0$. Therefore, either $x = 0$, and then $y = 0$ or $y = 1$; or $y = 0$, and then $x = 0$ or $x = 1$; or $1 - x - \frac{1}{2}y = 0$ and $1 - y + \frac{1}{2}x = 0$, and then $x = -\frac{2}{5}$, $y = \frac{6}{5}$. So we have $(0, 0)$, $(1, 0)$, $(0, 1)$, and $\left(\frac{2}{5}, \frac{6}{5}\right)$ as our equilibrium points.

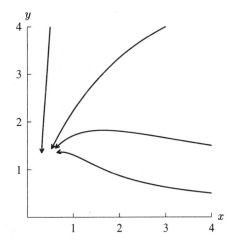

4. The acceleration of a moving object is given by

$$\frac{d^2 x}{dt^2} = x\left(\frac{dx}{dt} - 1\right)$$

where $x(t)$ is the position at time $t$.

(a) Set up a system of first order differential equations for position $x$ and velocity $v$.

(b) Do the qualitative phase plane analysis for this system, indicating clearly the null clines and constant solutions. (Consider positive and negative values for $x$ and $v$.)

(c) With the help of your graphing calculator, sketch two trajectories: one for initial values $x(0) = -3$, $v(0) = 3$ and the other for $x(0) = 3$, $v(0) = -2$.

(d) Consider the trajectory with initial values $x(0) = -3$ and $v(0) = 3$. Approximate the maximum and minimum values of $x$ (if such values exist). Approximate the maximum and minimum values of $v$ (if such values exist).

(e) Consider the trajectory with initial values $x(0) = 3$ and $v(0) = -2$. Approximate the maximum and minimum values of $x$ (if such values exist). Approximate the maximum and minimum values of $v$ (if such values exist).

(f)   Draw some general conclusions about what happens to $x(t)$ and $v(t)$ for different initial values.

ANSWER:

(a)   We have $v = \frac{dx}{dt}$ and $\frac{dv}{dt} = x(v-1)$.

(b)   To find points in the phase plane where slopes are vertical, we solve $\frac{dx}{dt} = 0$, to obtain $v = 0$. To find points with horizontal slopes, we solve $\frac{dv}{dt} = 0$, to obtain $x = 0$ or $v = 1$. Therefore, slopes are vertical along the $x$-axis and horizontal along the $v$-axis and the line $v = 1$. As for equilibrium points, we want both $\frac{dv}{dt}$ and $\frac{dx}{dt}$ equal to 0, which is only possible for $x = v = 0$. The slope field is shown below.

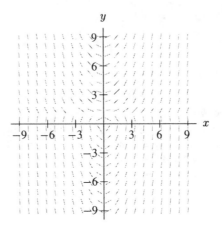

(c)

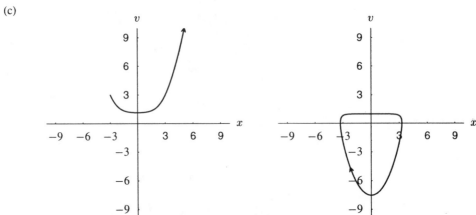

(d)   We see that the function continues indefinitely up and to the right. Thus, maximal values for $v$ and $x$ do not exist. We also see from the graph that the minimal value for $x$ is $x = -3$ (at the starting point) and the minimal value for $v$ is $v \approx 1.14$.

(e)   From the graph, we approximate the maximal value for $x$ to be $x \approx 3.24$, the maximal value for $v$ to be $v \approx 1.00$, the minimal value for $x$ to be $x \approx -3.24$, and the minimal value for $v$ to be $v \approx -7.60$

(f)   If initially the velocity is greater than one and the position is positive, the acceleration will be positive forcing the velocity and position to increase further. Thus, an object in this state will never fall, and does in fact climb without bound. If the velocity is greater than one, but position is negative, then the object will at first slow down (while moving in the positive direction) and then speed up again. If, however, the velocity is ever less than one, then a cycle will arise in which velocity decreases until the position is negative at which point the object begins to fall more slowly. The object eventually changes direction and the cycle recurs.

# Chapter 11 Exam Questions

*Problems and Solutions for Section 11.1* ━━━━━━━━━━━━━━

1. You are in a nicely heated cabin in the winter. Deciding that it's too warm, you open a small window. Let $T$ be the temperature in the room, $t$ minutes after the window was opened, $x$ feet from the window.

    (a) Is $T$ an increasing or decreasing function of $t$? Explain.

    (b) Is $T$ an increasing or decreasing function of $x$? Explain.

    ANSWER:

    (a) T is a decreasing function of $t$. When the small window is opened, the cold air comes in from the outside. As time goes on, the temperature of the cabin will decrease until it reaches a balance.

    (b) T is an increasing function of $x$. The further you are away from the window, the higher the temperature will be.

2. Consider Table 11.1.1 giving (in thousands) the number $f(x, y)$ of grape vines of age $x$ in year $y$.

**TABLE 11.1.1**

Age of Vine

| | | 0 | 1 | 2 | 3 | 4 | 5 | 6 | 7 | 8 | 9 | 10 | 11 | 12 | 13 | 14 | 15 | 16 |
|---|---|---|---|---|---|---|---|---|---|---|---|---|---|---|---|---|---|---|
| | 1980 | 3 | 3 | 3 | 3 | 3 | 2 | 2 | 0 | 0 | 2 | 2 | 2 | 1 | 0 | 0 | 0 | 0 |
| | 1981 | 4 | 3 | 3 | 3 | 3 | 3 | 2 | 2 | 0 | 0 | 2 | 2 | 2 | 1 | 0 | 0 | 0 |
| | 1982 | 4 | 4 | 3 | 3 | 3 | 1 | 1 | 1 | 1 | 0 | 0 | 1 | 1 | 1 | 0 | 0 | 0 |
| | 1983 | 0 | 0 | 0 | 1 | 1 | 3 | 1 | 1 | 1 | 1 | 0 | 0 | 1 | 1 | 1 | 0 | 0 |
| | 1984 | 7 | 0 | 0 | 0 | 1 | 1 | 3 | 1 | 1 | 1 | 1 | 0 | 0 | 1 | 1 | 1 | 0 |
| | 1985 | 4 | 7 | 0 | 0 | 0 | 1 | 1 | 3 | 1 | 1 | 1 | 1 | 0 | 0 | 1 | 1 | 1 |
| Year | 1986 | 4 | 4 | 7 | 0 | 0 | 0 | 1 | 1 | 3 | 1 | 1 | 1 | 1 | 0 | 0 | 1 | 1 |
| | 1987 | 7 | 4 | 4 | 7 | 0 | 0 | 0 | 1 | 1 | 3 | 1 | 1 | 1 | 1 | 0 | 0 | 1 |
| | 1988 | 12 | 7 | 4 | 4 | 7 | 0 | 0 | 0 | 1 | 1 | 3 | 1 | 1 | 1 | 1 | 0 | 0 |
| | 1989 | 12 | 12 | 7 | 4 | 4 | 7 | 0 | 0 | 0 | 1 | 1 | 3 | 1 | 1 | 1 | 1 | 0 |
| | 1990 | 9 | 12 | 12 | 7 | 4 | 4 | 7 | 0 | 0 | 0 | 1 | 1 | 3 | 1 | 1 | 1 | 1 |
| | 1991 | 8 | 9 | 12 | 12 | 7 | 4 | 4 | 7 | 0 | 0 | 0 | 1 | 1 | 3 | 1 | 1 | 1 |
| | 1992 | 8 | 8 | 9 | 12 | 12 | 7 | 4 | 4 | 7 | 0 | 0 | 0 | 1 | 1 | 3 | 1 | 1 |

(a) Describe in words the most striking pattern in the table.

(b) Explain why it is reasonable that usually the number in any box equals the number diagonally above (to the left). Write an equation to formally express this relation.

(c) In one year a fungal disease killed most of the older grapevines, and in the following year a long freeze killed most of the young vines. Which are these years?

(d) Why are there no ten year old vines in 1992?

(e) Fix the year $y = 1986$ and sketch the graph for the age distribution $g(x) = f(x, 1986)$ of grapevines in that year. Repeat for 1987. Describe and explain your observation.

(f) In 1986 a successful advertising campaign led to a dramatic increase in demand for premium wines. The growers followed by adding many more plants. Suppose a vine (the plant) produces the first harvestable grapes at age five, and is removed after sixteen years. How many (thousand) grape vines that bear fruit were there in the year 1986 and how many will be there in the year 1994?

ANSWER:

(a) Numbers seen in general to move diagonally downward to the right.

(b)    In any year you expect the number of vines of a given age to be the same as the number of vines that were a year younger the previous year. Thus,

$$f(x, y) = f(x - 1, y - 1).$$

(c)    1982 and 1983.
(d)    Because all one year old vines died in the 1983 freeze.
(e)    The distribution gets shifted one unit to the right from 1986 to 1987.
(f)    To get the number of vines that bear fruit, we add all entries in columns 5 to 16 for the year of interest. For 1986 we have

$$0 + 1 + 1 + 3 + 1 + 1 + 1 + 1 + 0 + 0 + 1 + 1 = 11.$$

11, 000 vines bore fruit in 1986. For 1994, columns 5 through 16 are the same as 3 through 14 in 1992, so we have

$$12 + 12 + 7 + 4 + 4 + 7 + 0 + 0 + 0 + 1 + 1 + 3 = 51.$$

51, 000 vines will bear fruit in 1994.

## *Problems and Solutions for Section 11.2*

1.    Describe the set of points in the 3-space:
    (a)    Whose $y$ coordinate is $-3$ and $z$ coordinate is 1.
    (b)    Whose $z$ coordinate is 4.
    (c)    Whose distance from the $y$-axis is 3.
    ANSWER:
    (a)    It is a line that passes through the point $(0, -3, 1)$ and parallel to the $x$-axis as shown in Figure 11.2.1
    (b)    It is a plane that passes through the point $(0, 0, 4)$ and parallel to the $xy$-plane as shown in Figure 11.2.2
    (c)    It is a cylinder centered at the $y$-axis with radius 3 as shown in Figure 11.2.3

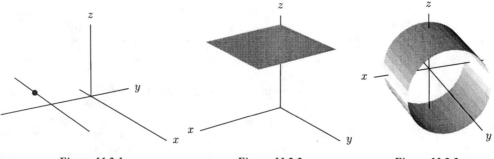

| *Figure 11.2.1* | *Figure 11.2.2* | *Figure 11.2.3* |

2.    You are at $(2, -1, 3)$ facing the $yz$-plane. You walk 2 units, turn right and walk for another 2 units. What are your coordinates now? Are you above or below the $xy$-plane?
    ANSWER:
    My coordinates are $(0, 1, 3)$ and I am above the $xy$-plane.

*Problems and Solutions for Section 11.3*

1.  Consider the following sets of points in space:

    A is the set of points $(x, y, z)$ whose distance from the $y$-axis is 2.

    B is the set of points $(x, y, z)$ whose distance from the $yz$-plane is 3.

    C is the set of points $(x, y, z)$ whose distance from the $z$-axis is equal to its distance to the $xy$-plane.

    Describe in words, write equations, and give a sketch for each of these sets of points.

    ANSWER:

    A is a cylinder of radius two centered around the $y$-axis (See Figure 11.3.4.) Its equation is

    $$x^2 + z^2 = 4.$$

    B consists of two planes parallel to the $yz$-plane at $x = 3$ and $x = -3$ (See Figure 11.3.5.) Its equation is

    $$x^2 = 9.$$

    C is two cones around the $z$-axis with vertex at the origin (See Figure 11.3.6.) Its equation is

    $$x^2 + y^2 = z^2.$$

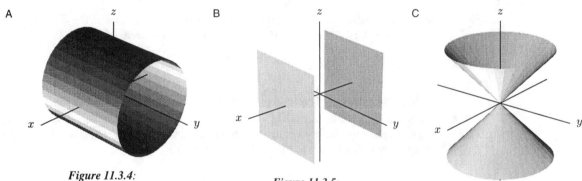

*Figure 11.3.4:*

*Figure 11.3.5:*

*Figure 11.3.6:*

2.  Draw a graph of $g(x, y) = \sqrt{x^2 - y^2}$ in the plane $x = 2$.

    ANSWER:

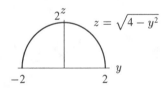

*Figure 11.3.7*

    When $x = 2$, $z = \sqrt{4 - y^2}$ which is the upper half of a circle of radius 2 centered at the origin.

3.  Describe in words the intersection of the surfaces $z = \sqrt{x^2 + y^2}$ and $z = 6 - x^2 - y^2$, sketch it, and give simplified equations for it.

    ANSWER:

    $z = \sqrt{x^2 + y^2}$ is a cone opening upwards, and $z = 6 - x^2 - y^2$ is is a parabola opening downwards. See Figure 11.3.8

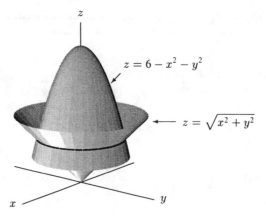

*Figure 11.3.8*

The level curves for both surfaces are circles, so we would expect the intersection to be a circle. Let's compute it: We have:

$$z = \sqrt{x^2 + y^2}$$
$$z = 6 - x^2 - y^2.$$

So $x^2 + y^2 = 6 - z$ and plugging this into the first equation, we get $z = \sqrt{6 - z}, z \geq 0$. This yields $z^2 + z - 6 = 0, z \geq 0$. So $z = 2$. Hence, the equations of the intersection are:

$$x^2 + y^2 = 4$$
$$z = 2.$$

So, it is indeed a circle (of radius 2) in the plane $z = 2$.

4. A spherical ball of radius one unit is in a corner touching both walls and floor. What is the radius of the largest spherical ball that can be fitted into the corner behind the given ball? (Hint: The smaller ball will not touch the corner point where the walls meet the floor.)

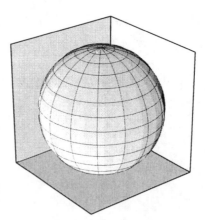

*Figure 11.3.9*

ANSWER:

Let the intersection of the walls represent the origin. Then the first sphere has equation

$$(x - 1)^2 + (y - 1)^2 + (z - 1)^2 = 1.$$

Then the second has equation

$$(x - r)^2 + (y - r)^2 + (z - r)^2 = r^2.$$

Since the second sphere is behind the given ball, its radius $r$ is between 0 and 1. The distance between the points $(r, r, r)$ and $(1, 1, 1)$ can be found two ways. From the distance formula it is $\sqrt{3(1-r)^2}$. It is also $1 + r$ so

$$\sqrt{3(1-r)^2} = 1 + r.$$

Since $1 - r \geq 0$, we have $\sqrt{(1-r)^2} = 1 - r$, and our equation becomes

$$\sqrt{3}(1-r) = 1 + r.$$

Solving for $r$ gives

$$\sqrt{3}r + r = \sqrt{3} - 1$$
$$r = \frac{\sqrt{3} - 1}{\sqrt{3} + 1}.$$

5.  Each of the graphs in Figure 11.3.10 shows the quantity $q$ that can be sold of a certain product (Product 1), as a function of its price $p_1$ and the price $p_2$ of another product (Product 2).

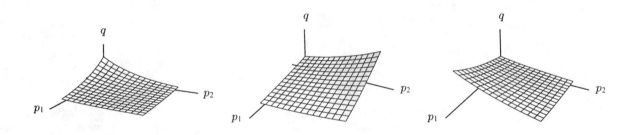

      (a)                                  (b)                                (c)

*Figure 11.3.10*

Choose which graph fits best and explain why if:

(a)  Product 1 is flashlights and Product 2 is batteries.
(b)  Product 1 is domestic cars and Product 2 is imported cars.

ANSWER:

(a)  The increasing of the price of either flashlights or batteries will decrease the quantity of the flashlights sold. So, (a) fits best.
(b)  The increasing of the price of domestic cars will decrease the quantity of domestic cars sold whereas increasing the price of imported cars will increase the quantity of domestic cars sold. So, (b) fits best.

6.  Match the graphs (A-E) to their functions.

(a)  $z = \sin y$
(b)  $z = -\sin x \sin y$
(c)  $z = (1/2)x^2 + \sin^2 y$
(d)  $z = -(1/9)x^3 \sin y$
(e)  $z = 3(\sin y)e^{(-x/5)}$

(A)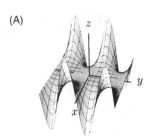

*Figure 11.3.11*

(B)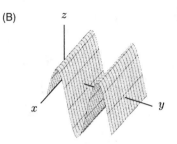

*Figure 11.3.12*

(C)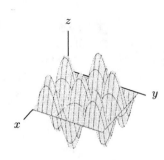

*Figure 11.3.13*

(D)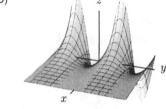

*Figure 11.3.14*

(E)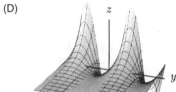

*Figure 11.3.15*

ANSWER:

(a)   B

(b)   C

(c)   E

(d)   A

(e)   D

7.   Match each of the following functions in (a)-(f), given by a formula, to the corresponding table of numerical values, graph and/or contour maps (i)-(xi). Some formulas may match NONE or MORE THAN ONE of the representations (i)-(ix).

(a)   $f(x, y) = x^2 - y^2$

(b)   $f(x, y) = 6 - 2x + 3y$

(c)   $f(x, y) = \sqrt{1 - x^2 - y^2}$

(d)   $f(x, y) = \dfrac{1}{1 + x^2 + y^2}$

(e)   $f(x, y) = 6 - 2x - 3y$

(f)   $f(x, y) = \sqrt{x^2 + y^2}$

(i)   **TABLE 11.3.2**

|  |  | | $x$ | | |
|---|---|---|---|---|---|
|  |  | −2 | −1 | 0 | 1 | 2 |
|  | 2 | 2.828 | 2.236 | 2.000 | 2.236 | 2.828 |
|  | 1 | 2.236 | 1.414 | 1.000 | 1.414 | 2.236 |
| $y$ | 0 | 2.000 | 1.000 | 0.000 | 1.000 | 2.000 |
|  | −1 | 2.236 | 1.414 | 1.000 | 1.414 | 2.236 |
|  | −2 | 2.828 | 2.236 | 2.000 | 2.236 | 2.828 |

(ii)   **TABLE 11.3.3**

|  |  | | $x$ | | |
|---|---|---|---|---|---|
|  |  | −2 | −1 | 0 | 1 | 2 |
|  | 2 | 0.111 | 0.167 | 0.200 | 0.167 | 0.111 |
|  | 1 | 0.167 | 0.333 | 0.500 | 0.333 | 0.167 |
| $y$ | 0 | 0.200 | 0.500 | 1.000 | 0.500 | 0.200 |
|  | −1 | 0.167 | 0.333 | 0.500 | 0.333 | 0.167 |
|  | −2 | 0.111 | 0.167 | 0.200 | 0.167 | 0.111 |

(iii)          **TABLE 11.3.4**

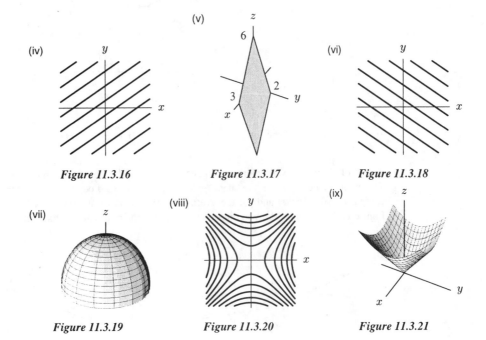

| | | $x$ | | | |
|---|---|---|---|---|---|
| | | $-2$ | $-1$ | $0$ | $1$ | $2$ |
| | $2$ | 0.00 | $-3.00$ | $-4.00$ | $-3.00$ | 0.00 |
| | $1$ | 3.00 | 0.00 | $-1.00$ | 0.00 | 3.00 |
| $y$ | $0$ | 4.00 | 1.00 | 0.00 | 1.00 | 4.00 |
| | $-1$ | 3.00 | 0.00 | $-1.00$ | 0.00 | 3.00 |
| | $-2$ | 0.00 | $-3.00$ | $-4.00$ | $-3.00$ | 0.00 |

(v)

(iv)

*Figure 11.3.16*      *Figure 11.3.17*      *Figure 11.3.18*

(vii)      (viii)      (ix)

*Figure 11.3.19*      *Figure 11.3.20*      *Figure 11.3.21*

ANSWER:

(a)   iii, viii
(b)   iv
(c)   vii
(d)   ii
(e)   v, vi
(f)   i, ix

8.   (a)   For the surface shown in Figure 11.3.22 sketch the cross-sections parallel to the $x$-axis with $y = 0$, $y = 1$, and $y = 2$.

(ix)

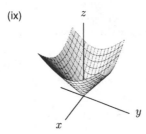

*Figure 11.3.22:*

(b)   What is the slope of the contour lines of the function $f(x, y) = 6 - 2x + 3y$? Why?
ANSWER:

(a)

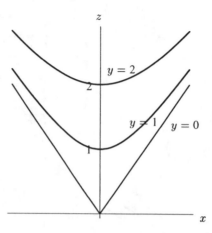

*Figure 11.3.23:*

(b)   Contours are of the form $f(x, y) = c$, or $6 - 2x + 3y = c$, hence $y = \frac{2x-6+c}{3}$. Therefore the slope is $\frac{2}{3}$.

9.   A soft drink company is interested in seeing how the demand for its products is affected by price. The company believes that the quantity, $q$, of soft drinks sold depends on $p_1$, the average price of the company's soft drinks, and $p_2$, the average price of competing soft drinks. Which of the graphs in Figure 11.3.24 is most likely to represent $p$ as a function of $q_1$ and $q_2$? Explain your answer.

(I) 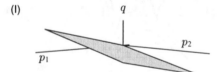   (II)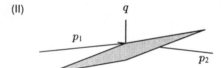

(III) 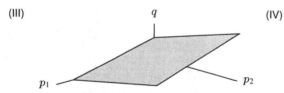   (IV)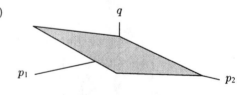

*Figure 11.3.24*

ANSWER:

If the average price, $p_1$, of the company's soft drinks increases, then the quantity, $q$, of soft drinks it sells will decrease. But if $p_2$, the average price of competing soft drinks, increases with $p_1$ constant, people will buy more of the company's product and $q$ will increase. Notice that the quantity $q$ will never be negative, therefore (III) is most likely to represent $q$ as a function of $p_1$ and $p_2$.

10.   (a)   Describe the set of points in 3-space satisfying the equation $y = x$.
(b)   For what values of the constant $k$ is the intersection between the set in (a) and the graph of $f(x, y) = x^2 - ky^2$ a straight line?
ANSWER:

(a)   It is a plane perpendicular to the $xy$-plane which passes through the line $y = x$. See Figure 11.3.25.

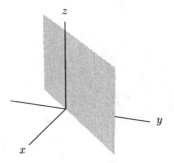

*Figure 11.3.25*

(b)    The intersection of the two surfaces must satisfy

$$y = x, \quad z = x^2 - ky^2.$$

So $z = x^2 - kx^2 = (1 - k)x^2$. In order for $z = (1 - k)x^2$ to be linear, the coefficient of the $x^2$ term must be zero. So, $1 - k = 0$. Thus, $k = 1$. Hence, we get the lines given by: $x = y$ and $z = 0$.

## Problems and Solutions for Section 11.4

1.    True or false? Two contours of the function $f(x, y)$ corresponding to different values of $f$ cannot ever cross.

    ANSWER:

    True. If they did cross, then at the point of intersection $f = a$ and $f = b$, so $a = b$. Therefore the contours cannot be for different values of $f$.

2.    True or false? The contours of the function $f(x, y) = 3x + 2y$ are all parallel lines with slope 3.

    ANSWER:

    False. The slope is $\dfrac{\Delta y}{\Delta x} = \dfrac{-3}{2}$.

3.    The contour diagram[1] in Figure 11.4.26 shows the level curves of the difference between July and January mean temperatures in $^\circ F$. Use it to answer the following questions.

    Does this graph support or contradict the claim that the largest annual temperature variations are found on the coasts of continents? Explain. (Please answer this question in complete sentences.)

---

[1] from Strahler and Strahler, *Modern Physical Geography* (New York: Wiley, 1992)

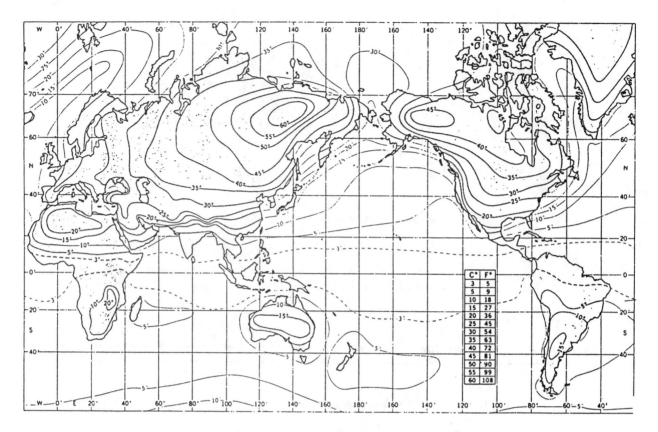

*Figure 11.4.26*

ANSWER:

This graph supports the claim that the largest annual temperature variations are found on the coasts of continents, as level curves are very close together near the coasts of continents.

4. Large earthquakes with centers near coastlines can generate *tsunami* waves which travel at speeds of up to 600 miles/hour in very deep water and are up to 90 feet high near shores. The curves in Figure 11.4.27[2] show the successive hourly positions of the tsunami wave front generated by the Alaskan earthquake of 1964. They are level curves of the function $T$, where $T(P)$ is the number of hours it takes for the wave front to reach a point $P$.

[2] from Strahler and Strahler, *Modern Physical Geography* (New York: Wiley, 1992)

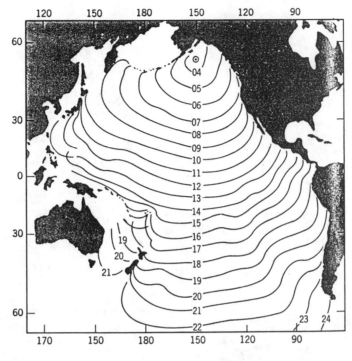

*Figure 11.4.27*

Does this graph support or contradict the claim that the tsunami waves travel with approximately equal speed in every direction? Explain. (Please answer this question in complete sentences.)

ANSWER:

This supports the claim that the tsunami waves travel with approximately equal speed in every direction as level curves are approximately circles.

5. Draw a possible contour diagram for the function whose graph is shown below. Label your contours with reasonable $z$-values.

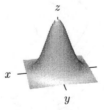

*Figure 11.4.28*

**616**

ANSWER:

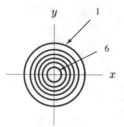

*Figure 11.4.29*

6. The contour diagram in Figure 11.4.30 (from *Geodynamics*, by Turcotte and Schubert) shows the magnitude (in micro-Teslas) of the present-day magnetic field of the earth. The present locations (longitude and latitude) of the magnetic poles are 73°N, 100°W and 68°S, 143°E.

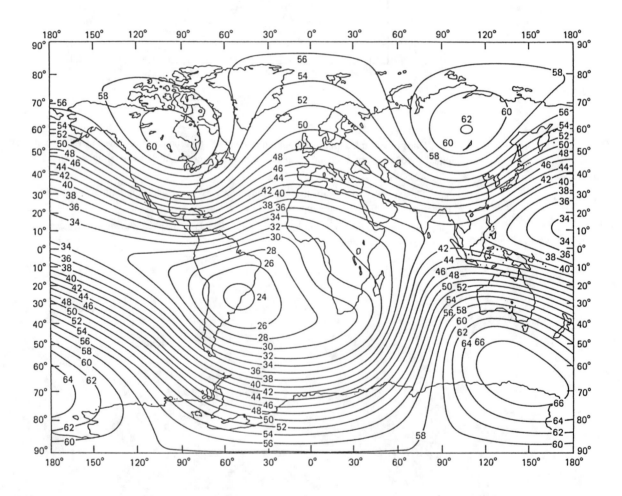

*Figure 11.4.30*

(a) Approximately what is the strength of the earth's magnetic field at the magnetic north and south poles, respectively.

(b) Generally speaking, the contour lines are more horizontal than vertical. Why do you think this is?

(c) Approximately what is the variation in the magnetic field across Australia? Across the same latitudes in South America? Can you propose an explanation for why your answers are so different?

ANSWER:

(a) About 58 micro-Teslas.

(b) The earth's magnetic field varies as you move away from or towards the poles, but not much as you move around them.

(c) Across Australia, the magnetic field varies from 44 to 60, or by 16 micro-Teslas. Across the same latitudes in South America, it varies from 26 to 24, or by about 2 micro-Teslas. South America contains a minimum for the magnetic field, so there is not much variation, whereas Australia is between a minimum and a maximum.

7. Consider the function $z = f(x, y) = y - x^2$.

(a) Plot the level curves of the function for $z = -2, -1, 0, 1, 2$. Label them clearly.

(b) Imagine the surface whose height above any point $(x, y)$ is given by $z = f(x, y)$. Suppose you are standing on the surface at the point where $x = 1, y = 2$.

    (i) What is your height?

    (ii) If you start to move on the surface parallel to the $y$-axis in the direction of increasing $y$, does your height increase or decrease? Justify your answer using your contour map.

    (iii) Does your height increase or decrease if you start to move on the surface parallel to the $x$-axis in the direction of increasing $x$? Justify your answer using your contour map.

ANSWER:

(a) In order to obtain equations describing the level curves of $f(x, y)$, we set $f(x, y)$ equal to each of the $z$ values given. this gives us the following equations describing five level curves of $f(x, y)$:

$$y = x^2 - 2$$
$$y = x^2 - 1$$
$$y = x^2$$
$$y = x^2 + 1 \qquad \text{and}$$
$$y = x^2 + 2.$$

These are equations of parabolas as shown by their graphs below:

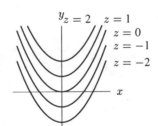

*Figure 11.4.31*

(b)  (i)  Since $f(x, y)$ gives the height above any point $(x, y)$, $f(1, 2)$ gives the value of your height, $h$. Thus, the height is,

$$h = f(1, 2) = 2 - (1)^2$$
$$= 1 \text{ unit}.$$

(ii)  Your height increases. This is because if we choose any $x$ value and keep it fixed, then as one moves parallel to the $y$-axis in the direction of increasing $y$, the value of $z$ on each successive contour encountered always increases. Say we let $x = 0$, then if one begins at the origin, according to the sketch, $z$ increases from 0 to 1 to 2 as $y$ increases. Similarly, for $x = 1$, as $y$ increases from 2, $z$ gets bigger and bigger so height increases. (See Figure 11.4.31)

(iii)  Your height decreases. For $x = 1$ and $y = 2$ we have $z = 1$. So you are initially on the $z = 1$ contour. Now with $y$ held at 2, as you move parallel to the $x$-axis in the direction of increasing $x$, you encounter contours with decreasing values of $z$; first $z = 0$, then $z = -1$ and then $z = -2$ (on the contour map in 7a). Since $z$ decreases as $x$ increases, your height decreases. (See Figure 11.4.31)

8.  The diagram in Figure 11.4.32 shows the contour map for a circular island. Sketch the vertical cross-section of the island through the center. Your sketch should show concavity clearly.

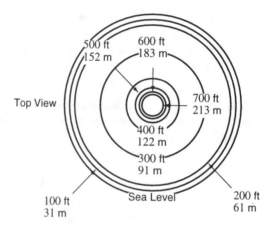

**Figure 11.4.32**

ANSWER:

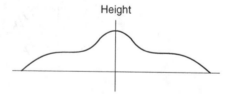

**Figure 11.4.33**

9.  Draw the level curves for $z = \ln(x) + \ln(y)$ at $z = -1, 0$, and 1. Show work and label.
    ANSWER:

$\ln x + \ln y$ is defined only if $x > 0$, $y > 0$. At $z = -1$, we have $-1 = \ln x + \ln y = \ln xy$. So $xy = e^{-1}$, $x > 0$.
At $z = 0$, we have $0 = \ln x + \ln y = \ln xy$. So $xy = e^0 = 1$, $x > 0$.
At $z = 1$ we have $1 = \ln x + \ln y = \ln xy$. So $xy = e$, $x > 0$.
Now we can draw the level curves for $z = \ln x + \ln y$ at $z = -1, 0, 1$ as shown in Figure 11.4.34.

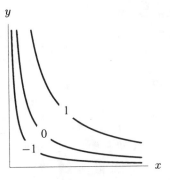

*Figure 11.4.34*

10. Figure 11.4.35 below shows the level curves[3] of the temperature $T$ in degrees Celsius as a function of $t$ hours and depth $h$ in centimeters beneath the surface of the ground at O'Neill, Nebraska from midnight ($t = 0$) one day to midnight ($t = 24$) the next.

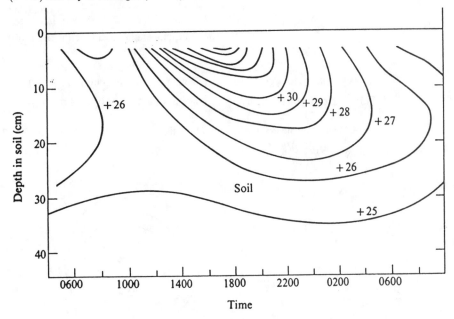

*Figure 11.4.35*

(a) Approximately what time did the sun rise? When do you think the sun is directly overhead? Explain your reasoning.

(b) Sketch graphs of the temperature as a function of time at 5 centimeters and at 20 centimeters below the surface.

(c) Sketch a graph of the temperature as a function of the distance at noon.

ANSWER:

(a) The sun rose at about 6 in the morning, because that is when the soil starts to heat up near the surface. The sun is directly overhead at around 11:30, because that is when the soil near the surface is heating up most rapidly (the contours are closest together).

---

[3]from S. J. Williamson, *Fundamentals of Air Pollution*, (Reading: Addison-Wesley, 1973)

(b)

Temperature
40
30
20
10
Time
6 10 14 18 22 2 6

*Figure 11.4.36:* The temperature as a function of time at 5cm

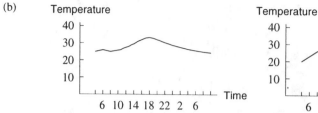

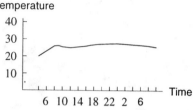

Temperature
40
30
20
10
Time
6 10 14 18 22 2 6

*Figure 11.4.37:* The temperature as a function of time at 20cm

(c)

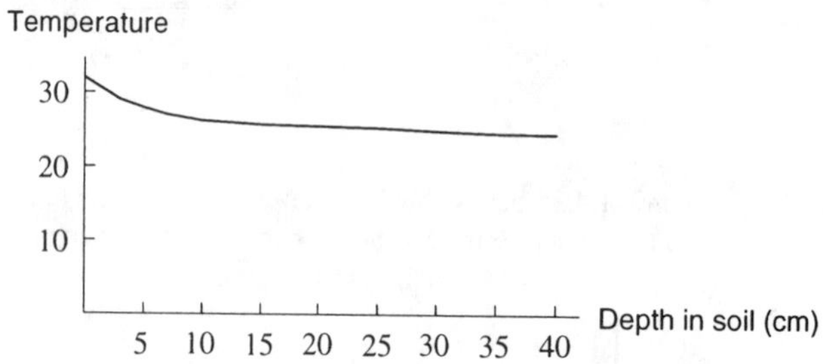

Temperature
30
20
10
Depth in soil (cm)
5 10 15 20 25 30 35 40

*Figure 11.4.38:* The temperature as a function of the distance at noon

11. Suppose that the temperature $T$ of any point $(x, y)$ is given by $T(x, y) = 100 - x^2 - y^2$.

    (a) Sketch isothermal curves (i.e. contours) for $T = 100$, $T = 75$, $T = 50$ and $T = 0$. Be sure to label each contour.

    (b) What does the graph of $T(x, y)$ look like if it is sliced by the plane $x = 1$? Draw it.

    ANSWER:

(a)

y
0
50
75
100
x
5
5√2
10

*Figure 11.4.39*

(b) The parabola $z = 99 - y^2$.

z
99
z = 99 − y²
y
√99
√99

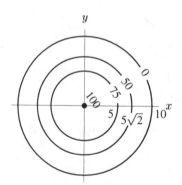

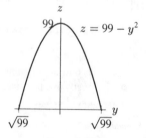

*Figure 11.4.40*

12.  Which of the following is a contour diagram for $f(x, y) = \sin x$?

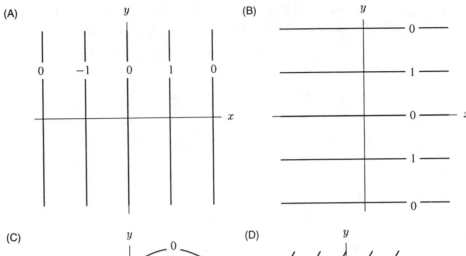

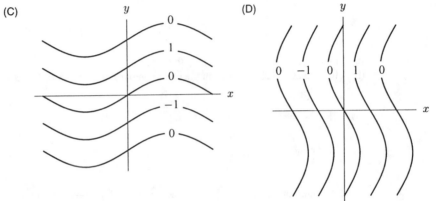

*Figure 11.4.41*

Justify your answer.

ANSWER:

(A), because $f(x, y) = c$ implies $\sin x = c$, which implies that $x$ is constant. So the contours are vertical lines.

## Problems and Solutions for Section 11.5

1.  True or False? If all of the contours of a function $f(x, y)$ are parallel lines, then the function must be linear. (If you think that the statement is true, explain why. If you think that it is false, present a counterexample.)

ANSWER:

False, for example take $f(x, y) = (x + y)^{1/3}$.

2.  True or false? If $f$ is a linear function, then $f(3, 5) - f(3, 4) = f(4, 5) - f(4, 4)$.

ANSWER:

True. $f(3, 5) - f(3, 4) =$ the slope of $f$ in the $y$-direction when $x = 3$. $f(4, 5) - f(4, 4) =$ the slope of $f$ in the $y$-direction when $x = 4$. Linear functions have the same slope in the $y$-direction anywhere.

3. True or false? If $f$ is any linear function of two variables, then $f(x, y + 1) = f(x + 1, y)$.

    ANSWER:

    False. Take $f(x, y) = x$. Then $f(x, y + 1) = x$ but $f(x + 1, y) = x + 1$.

4. Consider the (partial) contour diagram below for a linear function

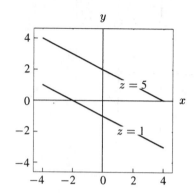

*Figure 11.5.42*

(a) Find an equation $z = f(x, y)$ for the function.

(b) In the diagram above, draw in the other contour lines for $z = 0, 1, 2, 3$ and $4$.

    ANSWER:

(a) The $x$-slope is $\frac{5-1}{4-(-2)} = \frac{2}{3}$

    The $y$-slope is $\frac{5-1}{2-(-1)} = \frac{4}{3}$

    So the equation is

$$z = c + \frac{2}{3}x + \frac{4}{3}y,$$

for some constant $c$. Since $z = 1$ when $x = 0$ and $y = -1$, we have $c = \frac{7}{3}$. so

$$z = \frac{7}{3} + \frac{2}{3}x + \frac{4}{3}y$$

5. The graph shows the level curve $z = 5$ of a plane. This plane passes through the point $(3, 1, 2)$. Determine the equation of this plane.

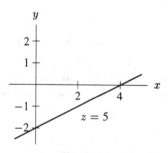

*Figure 11.5.43*

ANSWER:

From the graph we find that the level curve $z = 5$ passes through the points $(0, -2)$ and $(4, 0)$. So the points that the plane passes through are $(0, -2, 5)$, $(4, 0, 5)$ and $(3, 1, 2)$. The projections of these three points in the $xy$-plane are not colinear, so the plane cannot be parallel to the $z$-axis. Therefore, the equation of the plane might be taken of the form:

$$z = c + mx + ny.$$

Each of the three points must satisfy the equation:

$$5 = c - 2n$$
$$5 = c + 4m$$
$$2 = c + 3m + n.$$

This is a system of three linear equations and three unknowns; solving it, we get

$$c = 1, \quad m = 1, \quad n = -2.$$

Therefore, the equation of the plane is

$$z = 1 + x - 2y.$$

6. A plane passes through the points $(1, 3, -2)$, $(-1, -3, 4)$, and $(2, 1, -2)$.
   (a) Determine the equation of the plane.
   (b) If you were walking on this plane with no change in altitude, what would be the slope of your path in the $xy$-plane?

   ANSWER:

   (a) The projections of the three points in the $xy$-plane are not colinear. So, the plane cannot be parallel to the $z$-axis, and hence the equation of the plane might be taken of the form:

   $$z = c + mx + ny.$$

   Each of the three points must satisfy the equation:

   $$-2 = c + m + 3n$$
   $$4 = c - m - 3n$$
   $$-2 = c + 2m.$$

   This is a system of three linear equations and three unknowns, solving it we get

   $$c = 1, \quad m = -\frac{3}{2}, \quad n = -\frac{1}{2}.$$

   Therefore, the equation of the plane is

   $$z = 1 - \frac{3}{2}x - \frac{1}{2}y.$$

   (b) If you were walking on this plane with no change in altitude, then you walked along the contours of the plane. The slope of the contour $C = 1 - \frac{3}{2}x - \frac{1}{2}y$ is $-\frac{3}{2}/\frac{1}{2} = -3$ for some constant $C$. Therefore, the slope of your path in the $xy$-plane is $-3$.

7. Given the table of some values of a linear function:
   (a) Complete the table:

   **TABLE 11.5.5**

   | $y \backslash x$ | 2.5 | 3.0 | 3.5 |
   |---|---|---|---|
   | $-1$ | 6 |  | 8 |
   | 1 |  | 1 | 2 |
   | 3 | $-6$ |  |  |

   (b) Determine a formula for the function.

ANSWER:

(a)

**TABLE 11.5.6**

| $y\backslash x$ | 2.5 | 3.0 | 3.5 |
|---|---|---|---|
| $-1$ | 6 | 7 | 8 |
| 1 | 0 | 1 | 2 |
| 3 | $-6$ | $-5$ | $-4$ |

(b)    The linear function has the form

$$f(x,y) = ax + by + c$$

From the table we see that the slope in the $x$-direction is

$$\frac{7-6}{3-2.5} = 2,$$

and the slope in the $y$-direction is

$$\frac{0-6}{1-(-1)} = -3,$$

so $a = 2$, and $b = -3$. Also

$$8 = 3.5a - b + c.$$

Solving, we get

$$c = 8 - (3.5)2 - 3 = -2,$$

and the formula for the function is

$$f(x,y) = 2x - 3y - 2.$$

8.    Find an equation for the plane passing through $(1,2,3)$ and containing the $x$-axis. Explain what you are doing.

ANSWER:

Using the points $(0,0,0)$, $(1,0,0)$ and $(1,2,3)$, we see that the slope of the plane in the $y$ direction is $3/2$, the slope of the plane in the $x$ direction is $0$, and the $z$ intercept is $0$. Therefore, the equation for the plane is $z = 3/2y$.

9.    Find a formula for the linear function whose contours are as shown in Figure 11.5.44.

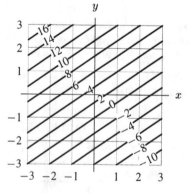

*Figure 11.5.44*

ANSWER:

$f(x,y) = Ax + By + C$ is a general linear function when $y$ changes from $-1$ to $1$, $f$ changes by 6 so $m_y = 3$. When $x$ changes from 1 to 2, $f$ changes by $-2$ so $m_x = -2$. It appears that $f(0,0) = 3$. So $f(x,y) = 3y - 2x + 3$.

10. A linear function $f(x, y)$ has the values $f(4, 2) = 1$, $f(1, 2) = 3$, and $f(4, 1) = 0$.
    (a) Find an equation for $f$.
    (b) Sketch the contour diagram of $f$.
    ANSWER:
    (a) A linear function $f(x, y)$ has the form:

    $$f(x, y) = ax + by + c.$$

    Since $f(4, 2) = 1$, $f(1, 2) = 3$ and $f(4, 1) = 0$, we have

    $$4a + 2b + c = 1$$
    $$a + 2b + c = 3$$
    $$4a + b + c = 0.$$

    Solving this system of three equations with three unknowns, we get:

    $$a = -\frac{2}{3}, \quad b = 1, \quad c = \frac{5}{3}.$$

    Thus,

    $$f(x, y) = -\frac{2}{3}x + y + \frac{5}{3}.$$

    (b) See Figure 11.5.45

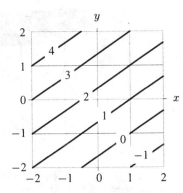

*Figure 11.5.45*

## Problems and Solutions for Section 11.6

1. Describe the set of points whose distance from the $y$-axis equals the distance from the $xz$-plane. Write an equation for this set in the form $G(x, y, z) = 0$. Can the set be described as the graph of a function of two variables?
    ANSWER:
    This is two cones centered around the $y$-axis with vertex at the origin (See Figure 11.6.46.) The equation is $x^2 + z^2 = y^2$. It can not be expressed as the graph of a function of two variables, because there are two values of $z$ for each value of $x$ and $y$ (except when $x = \pm y$): $z = \pm\sqrt{y^2 - x^2}$.

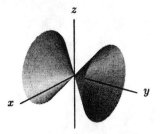

*Figure 11.6.46:*

2. Does the point $(-1, -1, 2)$ lie on any of the level surfaces of $f(x, y, z) = x^2 + 2y^2 + z^2$? If so, what is the equation of that level surface?

ANSWER:

Yes; $x^2 + 2y^2 + z^2 = (-1)^2 + 2(-1)^2 + 2^2 = 7$ so $x + 2y^2 + z^2 = 7$

3. What is the domain of $g(x, y, z) = \frac{x^2+y^2+z^2}{x^2+y^2+z^2-1}$? * Describe/draw the level surface $g = 4/3$.

ANSWER:

The domain of $g(x, y, z) = \frac{x^2+y^2+z^2}{x^2+y^2+z^2-1}$ is all the points in $xyz$-space except the points that satisfy $x^2 + y^2 + z^2 - 1 = 0$. The level surface $g = \frac{4}{3}$ is: $\frac{x^2+y^2+z^2}{x^2+y^2+z^2-1} = \frac{4}{3}$ which is a sphere $x^2 + y^2 + z^2 = 4$.

4. Sketch the level set of $f(x, y, z) = x^2 + z^2$ corresponding to $f = 1$ and describe it in words.

ANSWER:

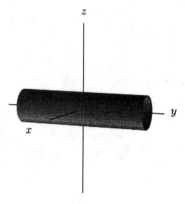

*Figure 11.6.47*

In the $xz$-plane, $1 = x^2 + z^2$ is a circle of radius 1 centered at the origin. Since there is no dependence on $y$, the graph will be a cylinder of radius 1, with its axis along the $y$-axis.

# Chapter 12 Exam Questions

*Problems and Solutions for Section 12.1*

1. True or false? Give a reason for your answer. $-\dfrac{\vec{a}}{\|\vec{a}\|}$ is a unit vector provided $\|\vec{a}\| \neq 0$.

   ANSWER:

   True. Dividing by length $\|\vec{a}\|$ gives the unit vector; $-\vec{a}/\|\vec{a}\|$ is a unit vector in opposite direction.

2. If $\vec{w} = \vec{i} - \vec{j} + 2\vec{k}$, $\vec{u} = 2\vec{i} + a\vec{j} + 3\vec{k}$, $\vec{v} = \vec{i} + \vec{j}$, find:

   (a) A unit vector parallel to $\vec{w}$.
   (b) The value of $a$ making $\vec{w}$ and $\vec{u}$ perpendicular.
   (c) A unit vector perpendicular to both $\vec{w}$ and $\vec{v}$.

   ANSWER:

   (a) A unit vector has length 1, so we divide $\vec{w}$ by its length to get a unit vector.

   $$\text{Length } \vec{w} = \|\vec{w}\| = \sqrt{1^2 + (-1)^2 + 2^2} = \sqrt{6}.$$

   So

   $$\text{Unit vector} = \frac{\vec{w}}{\|\vec{w}\|} = \left( \frac{1}{\sqrt{6}}\vec{i} + \frac{-1}{\sqrt{6}}\vec{j} + \frac{2}{\sqrt{6}}\vec{k} \right).$$

   (b) If $\vec{w}$ and $\vec{u}$ are perpendicular, $\vec{w} \cdot \vec{u} = 0$. $\vec{w} \cdot \vec{u} = (1, -1, 2) \cdot (2, a, 3) = 2 - a + 6 = 0$. Solving gives $a = 8$.

   (c) A unit vector perpendicular to $\vec{w}$ and $\vec{v}$ is $\dfrac{\vec{w} \times \vec{v}}{\|\vec{w} \times \vec{v}\|}$. As $\vec{w} \times \vec{v} = \begin{vmatrix} \vec{i} & \vec{j} & \vec{k} \\ 1 & -1 & 2 \\ 1 & 1 & 0 \end{vmatrix} = -2\vec{i} + 2\vec{j} + 2\vec{k}$

   and $\|\vec{w} \times \vec{v}\| = \sqrt{(2)^2 + (-2)^2 + (2)^2} = 2\sqrt{3}$,

   $$\frac{\vec{w} \times \vec{v}}{\|\vec{w} \times \vec{v}\|} = -\frac{1}{\sqrt{3}}\vec{i} + \frac{1}{\sqrt{3}}\vec{j} + \frac{1}{\sqrt{3}}\vec{k}.$$

3. Given the vectors $\vec{v}$ and $\vec{w}$ shown in the figure:

   (a) draw (and label) $\vec{v} + 3\vec{w}$
   (b) draw (and label) $\vec{v} - \vec{w}$

*Figure 12.1.48*

   (c) Is there some value of $t$ so that $\vec{w} + t\vec{v}$ is perpendicular to $\vec{w}$? If so, estimate (by eye) the value of $t$ (in terms of the lengths of $\vec{v}$ and $\vec{w}$). If not, explain why not.

ANSWER:

(a)

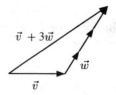

**Figure 12.1.49**

(b)

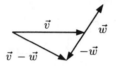

**Figure 12.1.50**

(c)   Yes

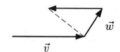

**Figure 12.1.51**

$t \approx -0.5$

4.  Three men are trying to hold a ferocious lion still for the veterinarian. The lion, in the center, is wearing a collar with three ropes attached to it and each man has hold of a rope. Charlie is pulling in the direction N62°W with a force of 350 pounds and Sam is pulling in the direction N43°E with a force of 400 pounds. What is the direction and magnitude of the force needed on the third rope to counterbalance Sam and Charlie? Draw a diagram—label and define variables.

ANSWER:

Let the $x$-axis be in the direction of $E$ and the $y$-axis be in the direction of $N$. Let $\vec{C}$ be the force of Charlie and let $\vec{S}$ be the force of Sam. Then

$$\vec{C}_x = -\|\vec{C}\|\sin 62°\vec{i} = -309.0\vec{i}$$
$$\vec{C}_y = \|\vec{C}\|\cos 62°\vec{j} = 164.3\vec{j}$$
$$\vec{S}_x = \|\vec{S}\|\sin 43°\vec{i} = 272.8\vec{i}$$
$$\vec{S}_y = \|\vec{S}\|\cos 43°\vec{j} = 292.5\vec{j}$$

So, the total force $\vec{T}$ of $\vec{C}$ and $\vec{S}$ is

$$\vec{T} = \vec{T}_x \vec{i} + \vec{T}_y \vec{j} = (\vec{S}_x + \vec{C}_x)\vec{i} + (\vec{S}_y + \vec{C}_y)\vec{j}$$
$$= -36.2\vec{i} + 456.8\vec{j}$$

Therefore, the counterbalance of $\vec{T}$ is

$$\vec{F} = -\vec{T} = 36.2\vec{i} - 456.8\vec{j}$$

We have $\theta = \arctan \frac{36.2}{456.8} = 4.5°$ and $\|\vec{F}\| = \sqrt{(36.2)^2 + (456.8)^2} = 458.23$. So, the magnitude of the third force is 458.23 and the direction is S 4.5° E.

5. Given the vectors $\vec{v}$ and $\vec{w}$ shown in Figure 12.1.52,

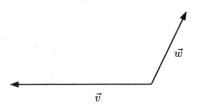

*Figure 12.1.52*

(a) draw (and label) $\vec{v} + 3\vec{w}$.

(b) Draw (and label) $\vec{v} - \vec{w}$.

(c) Is there some value of $t$ so that $\vec{w} + t\vec{v}$ is perpendicular to $\vec{w}$? If so, estimate (by eye) the value of $t$. If not, explain why not.

ANSWER:

(a)

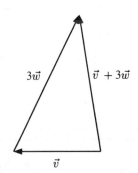

*Figure 12.1.53*

(b)

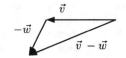

*Figure 12.1.54*

(c) For $t \approx 1.2$, $\vec{w} + t\vec{v}$ is perpendicular to $\vec{w}$.

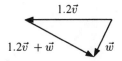

*Figure 12.1.55*

6.  Given the vectors $\vec{u}$ and $\vec{v}$ shown in Figure 12.1.56, draw the vectors $\vec{u} + \vec{v}$, $\vec{u} - \vec{v}$, and $\vec{u} + (-3)\vec{v}$.

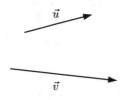

Figure 12.1.56

ANSWER:

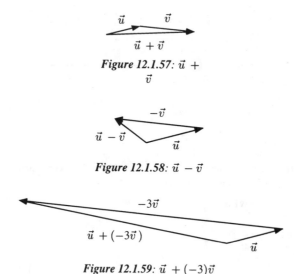

Figure 12.1.57: $\vec{u} + \vec{v}$

Figure 12.1.58: $\vec{u} - \vec{v}$

Figure 12.1.59: $\vec{u} + (-3)\vec{v}$

## Problems and Solutions for Section 12.2

1.  A bird is flying with velocity $\vec{v} = 10\vec{i} + 2\vec{j}$ (measured in m/sec) relative to the air. The wind is blowing at a speed of 5 m/sec parallel to the $x$-axis but opposing the bird's motion.

    (a)  Draw a picture showing the velocity of the bird relative to the air, $\vec{v}$, the velocity of the wind, $\vec{w}$, and the velocity of the bird relative to the ground, $\vec{u}$.
    (b)  Write the components of the vector $\vec{w}$.
    (c)  Find the components of the vector $\vec{u}$.
    (d)  Find the speed of the bird relative to the ground.

    ANSWER:

    (a)  The velocity relative to the ground is the velocity relative to the air plus the velocity of the air, so

    $$\vec{u} = \vec{v} + \vec{w}.$$

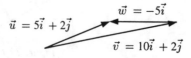

Figure 12.2.60

(b)  Since $\vec{w}$ has magnitude 5 m/s and is parallel to the $x$-axis but opposite to the bird's motion, $\vec{w}$ has just the component $-5\vec{i}$; negative because the bird's motion has a component $10\vec{i}$, 5 because $|\vec{w}| = 5$ and $\vec{i}$ because $\vec{w}$ is parallel to the $x$-axis.

(c)

$$\vec{u} = \vec{v} + \vec{w}$$
$$= 10\vec{i} + 2\vec{j} - 5\vec{i}$$
$$= 5\vec{i} + 2\vec{j}$$

(d)  The speed of the bird relative to the ground is the magnitude of the velocity of the bird relative to the ground $\vec{u}$. Thus we want

$$|\vec{u}| = \sqrt{(5)^2 + (2)^2}$$
$$= \sqrt{25 + 4}$$
$$= \sqrt{29} \text{ m/s.}$$

2.  A plane wants to go due Northeast, but a wind is blowing towards the North at 80 miles per hour. If the airspeed of the plane is 300 miles per hour, which direction should the plane head? What will be its groundspeed? Explain why your answers are reasonable.

ANSWER:

Let $\vec{i}, \vec{j}$ be the direction of east and north respectively. So the wind velocity is given as $80\vec{j}$. Let

$$\vec{v} = v_1\vec{i} + v_2\vec{j} \text{ be the air velocity of the plane.}$$
$$\vec{u} = u_1\vec{i} + u_2\vec{j} \text{ be the ground velocity of the plane.}$$

Since $\vec{u} = \vec{v} + 80\vec{j}$ then

$$u_1 = v_1$$
$$u_2 = v_2 + 80.$$

But,

$$\frac{u_2}{u_1} = \tan 45° = 1$$
$$(v_1)^2 + (v_2)^2 = 300^2.$$

We have

$$(v_2 + 80)^2 + (v_2)^2 = (300)^2$$
$$(v_2)^2 + 80v_2 - 41800 = 0$$
$$v_2 = -40 + 10\sqrt{434}$$
$$= 168.33 \text{ miles per hour.}$$
$$(v_1)^2 = (300)^2 - (v_2)^2$$
$$v_1 = 248.33 \text{ miles per hour.}$$

As

$$\tan\theta = \frac{v_2}{v_1}$$
$$= \frac{248.33}{168.33}$$
$$\theta = 55.87°.$$

Hence, the plane should head at N 55.87° E.

$$u_1 = v_1$$
$$= 248.33$$
$$u_2 = v_2 + 80$$
$$= 248.33.$$

Hence the groundspeed $u$ is

$$u = \sqrt{u_1^2 + u_2^2}$$
$$= \sqrt{(2)(248.33)^2}$$
$$= 351.20 \text{ miles per hour.}$$

3. An airplane wants to travel east, but there is a wind of 100 miles per hour blowing from the northwest. If the airspeed of the plane is 400 miles per hour, find the direction the plane should head (as an angle north of west) and its groundspeed.

ANSWER:

Let

$$\vec{v} = v_1\vec{i} + v_2\vec{j} \text{ be its air velocity.}$$
$$\vec{u} = u_1\vec{i} + u_2\vec{j} \text{ be its ground velocity.}$$
$$\vec{w} = w_1\vec{i} + w_2\vec{j} \text{ be the velocity of the wind.}$$

Let $\vec{i}$ and $\vec{j}$ be the direction of the East and North respectively. We have

$$\vec{w} = 100\cos\frac{\pi}{4}\vec{i} - 100\sin\frac{\pi}{4}\vec{j}$$
$$= 50\sqrt{2}\vec{i} - 50\sqrt{2}\vec{j}.$$

So,

$$\vec{v} = \vec{u} - \vec{w}$$
$$v_1 = u_1 - 50\sqrt{2}$$
$$v_2 = u_2 + 50\sqrt{2}.$$

With $u_2 = 0$ and $v_1^2 + v_2^2 = (400)^2$, we then have

$$(u_1 - 50\sqrt{2})^2 + (50\sqrt{2})^2 = (400)^2$$
$$u_1 = -323$$

and

$$v_1 = -323 - 50\sqrt{2}$$
$$= -393.7$$
$$v_2 = u_2 + 50\sqrt{2}$$
$$= 50\sqrt{2}.$$

Thus, its groundspeed is $u = \sqrt{u_1^2} = 323$ miles per hour and since

$$\theta = \tan^{-1}\left|\frac{v_2}{v_1}\right|$$
$$= \tan^{-1}\frac{50\sqrt{2}}{393.7}$$
$$= 10.19°$$

the plane should head at W $10.19°$ N.

## Problems and Solutions for Section 12.3

1. Say whether the following are true or false:

(a) The angle between $-\vec{i} + 2\vec{k}$ and $\vec{i} + \vec{j} + \vec{k}$ is less than $\pi/2$.

(b) The component of $\vec{u}$ in the direction of $\vec{v}$ is the same as the component of $\vec{v}$ in the direction of $\vec{u}$.

(c) The two planes $z = 3x - 2y + 5$ and $6x - 2y - 2z = 0$ are parallel.

(d) The triangle $ABC$ with vertices $A = 2\vec{i} + 4\vec{j}$, $B = 5\vec{i} - 2\vec{j}$, and $C = -3\vec{i} - \vec{j}$ is a right triangle.

(e) There are exactly 2 unit vectors perpendicular to the vector $\vec{i} + \vec{j} + \vec{k}$.

ANSWER:

(a) True. $(-\vec{i} + 2\vec{k}) \cdot (\vec{i} + \vec{j} + \vec{k}) = 1$ which is greater than 0, so $\theta < \pi/2$.

(b) False.

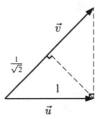

**Figure 12.3.61**

Let $\vec{u} = \vec{i}$ and $\vec{v} = \vec{i} + \vec{j}$. The component of $\vec{u}$ in the direction of $\vec{v} = \dfrac{\vec{u} \cdot \vec{v}}{\|\vec{v}\|} = \dfrac{1}{\sqrt{2}}$. The component of $\vec{v}$ in the direction of $\vec{u} = \dfrac{\vec{u} \cdot \vec{v}}{\|\vec{u}\|} = \dfrac{1}{1}$ and they are not equal.

(c) False. The first plane has normal $\vec{n}_1 = -3\vec{i} + 2\vec{j} + \vec{k}$ and the second plane has normal $\vec{n}_2 = 6\vec{i} - 2\vec{j} - 2\vec{k}$. Since these are not parallel (they are not scalar multiples) the planes must not be parallel.

(d) False.
$$\vec{AB} = (5\vec{i} - 2\vec{j}) - (2\vec{i} + 4\vec{j}) = 3\vec{i} - 6\vec{j}$$
$$\vec{AC} = (-3\vec{i} - \vec{j}) - (2\vec{i} + 4\vec{j}) = -5\vec{i} - 5\vec{j}$$
$$\vec{BC} = (-3\vec{i} - \vec{j}) - (5\vec{i} - 2\vec{j}) = -8\vec{i} + \vec{j}$$

None of the three pairs $\vec{AB} \cdot \vec{AC}$, $\vec{AB} \cdot \vec{BC}$, or $\vec{AC} \cdot \vec{BC}$ is 0 so no sides form a right angle.

(e) False. There are an infinite number.

2. Suppose $\vec{a}$ is a fixed vector of length 2, $\vec{b}$ is a vector which can rotate and has length 3, and $\theta$ is the angle between them. What is:

(a) The maximum value of $\vec{a} \cdot \vec{b}$, and for what value of $\theta$ does it occur?

(b) The minimum value of $\vec{a} \cdot \vec{b}$, and for what value of $\theta$ does it occur?

ANSWER:

(a) $\vec{a} \cdot \vec{b} = \|\vec{a}\|\|\vec{b}\|\cos\theta = 2 \cdot 3 \cdot \cos\theta = 6\cos\theta$. The maximum value is 6 when $\theta = 0$.

(b) The minimum value of $\vec{a} \cdot \vec{b}$ is $-6$ when $\theta = \pi$.

3. Suppose $\vec{u} = 4\vec{i} + b\vec{j} + 6\vec{k}$ and $\vec{v} = a\vec{i} + 2\vec{j} + 3\vec{k}$.

(a) Find value of $a$ and $b$ making $\vec{u}$ and $\vec{v}$ parallel.

(b) Find value of $a$ and $b$ making $\vec{u}$ and $\vec{v}$ perpendicular and $\vec{u}$ perpendicular to $\vec{j}$.

(c) Find value of $a$ and $b$ making $\vec{u}$ and $\vec{v}$ perpendicular and $\vec{v}$ parallel to the $yz-$plane.

ANSWER:

(a) If $\vec{u}$ and $\vec{v}$ are parallel, $\vec{u} = 2\vec{v}$ so $a = 2$ and $b = 4$.

(b) If $\vec{u}$ is perpendicular to $\vec{j}$, then $b = 0$. If $\vec{u}$ is perpendicular to $\vec{v}$ then $4a + 2b + 18 = 0$ So $a = -9/2$.

(c) If $\vec{v}$ is parallel to the $yz$-plane then $a = 0$ and since $2b + 18 = 0$, $b = -9$.

4. (a) Find the angle between the planes $5(x-1)+3(y+2)+2z = 0$ and $x+3(y-1)+2(z+4) = 0$.

   (b) Using vectors, prove that the two diagonals of a parallelogram with equal sides intersect perpendicularly.

   ANSWER:

   (a)

   $$\vec{n}_1 = 5\vec{i} + 3\vec{j} + 2\vec{k}$$
   $$\vec{n}_2 = \vec{i} + 3\vec{j} + 2\vec{k}$$
   $$\cos\theta = \frac{5+9+4}{\sqrt{38}\sqrt{14}} \simeq 0.7803$$
   $$\theta = 0.675 \quad \text{or} \quad 38.7°$$

   (b)

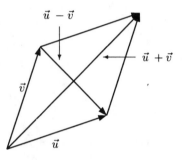

   **Figure 12.3.62**

   Two diagonals of parallelogram intersect perpendicularly if and only if

   $$(\vec{u} + \vec{v}) \cdot (\vec{u} - \vec{v}) = 0.$$

   Since the sides have equal length

   $$(\vec{u} + \vec{v}) \cdot (\vec{u} - \vec{v}) = \|\vec{u}\|^2 - \|\vec{v}\|^2 + \vec{u}\cdot\vec{v} - \vec{u}\cdot\vec{v} = 0.$$

5. Consider the plane $x + 2y + z = 0$.

   (a) Find a normal vector $\vec{n}$ to this plane.

   (b) Let $\vec{u} = \vec{i} + \vec{j} + \vec{k}$. Write $\vec{u}$ as the sum of a vector $\vec{v}$ which is parallel to $\vec{n}$ and a vector $\vec{w}$ which is parallel to the plane.

   (c) Using part (b) find the (shortest) distance from the point $P = (1,1,1)$ to the plane. Hint: Note that the point $Q = (0,0,0)$ is on the plane and that $\vec{u} = \vec{QP}$.

   ANSWER:

   (a) The coefficients of the variables $x$, $y$ and $z$ give us the $\vec{i}$, $\vec{j}$ and $\vec{k}$ components. We have $x+2y+z = 0$ so one normal is

   $$\vec{n} = \vec{i} + 2\vec{j} + \vec{k}.$$

   (b) $\vec{v}$ and $\vec{w}$ are the components of $\vec{u}$ in some directions. We know one of these directions to be that of the normal vector $\vec{n}$. We can therefore find the components of $\vec{u}$ in the direction of $\vec{n}$, $\vec{v}$.

   $$\vec{v} = \frac{\vec{u}\cdot\vec{n}}{\|\vec{n}\|}\frac{\vec{n}}{\|\vec{n}\|}$$
   $$= \frac{\vec{u}\cdot\vec{n}}{\|\vec{n}\|^2}\vec{n}$$
   $$= \frac{4}{6}\vec{n}$$
   $$= \frac{2}{3}\vec{i} + \frac{4}{3}\vec{j} + \frac{2}{3}\vec{k}$$

Hence,

$$\vec{w} = \vec{u} - \vec{v}$$

$$= \vec{i} + \vec{j} + \vec{k} - \left( \frac{2}{3}\vec{i} + \frac{4}{3}\vec{j} + \frac{2}{3}\vec{k} \right)$$

$$= \frac{1}{3}\vec{i} - \frac{1}{3}\vec{j} + \frac{1}{3}\vec{k}$$

which is the second component of $\vec{u}$. Since $\vec{w}$ should be parallel to the plane, we compute the dot product of $\vec{w}$ and $\vec{n}$,

$$\vec{w} \cdot \vec{n} = \left( \frac{1}{3} \right)(1) + \left( -\frac{1}{3} \right)(2) + \left( \frac{1}{3} \right)(1) = 0,$$

verifying that $\vec{w}$ is parallel to the plane $x + 2y = z = 0$.

(c) Since $Q(0,0,0)$ lies in the plane and $\vec{u} = \vec{QP}$, it implies $\vec{w}$ lies in the plane and $\vec{v}$ joins the head of $\vec{w}$ to $P$, as shown in the diagram below:

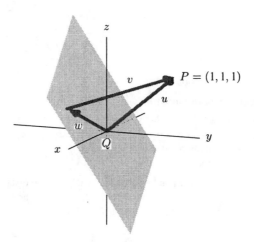

***Figure 12.3.63***

Since the shortest distance from a point to a plane is the perpendicular distance between them, the required distance is

$$\|\vec{v}\| = \sqrt{ \left( \frac{2}{3} \right)^2 + \left( \frac{4}{3} \right)^2 + \left( \frac{2}{3} \right)^2 }$$

$$= \sqrt{ \frac{8}{3} }$$

$$= \frac{2\sqrt{2}}{\sqrt{3}} \text{ units.}$$

6. One of the highlights of the Callaveras Fair besides the bullfrog jumping contest, is the watermelon seed spitting contest. The seed spitting is being done in the direction of $\vec{s} = 2\vec{i} + \vec{j}$. The wind velocity during the contest is $\vec{w} = \vec{i} + 5\vec{j}$ mph. The rules say that a legal wind in the direction of the seed spit must not exceed 3 mph. Mr. Samuel C. himself just spit for a record of 22 ft 1.4 inches. Will his record stand? Explain.

ANSWER:

See Figure 12.3.64

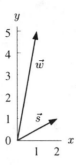

*Figure 12.3.64*

Since

$$\frac{\vec{s}}{|\vec{s}|} \cdot \vec{w} = \frac{2\vec{i} + \vec{j}}{\sqrt{2^2 + 1^2}} \cdot (\vec{i} + 5\vec{j})$$

$$= \frac{2}{\sqrt{5}} + \frac{5}{\sqrt{5}} = \frac{7}{\sqrt{5}} \approx 3.13 mph > 3mph$$

his record will not stand.

7. Determine the distance from:

(a) the point $(1, 3, -2)$ to the plane $2x + y - z = 1$.

(b) the plane $2x + y - z = 1$ to the plane $2x + y - z = 6$. (Hint: Although there are many approaches, projections come in handy.)

ANSWER:

(a) Let $P_1$ be the point on the plane such that the distance between $P_0$ and $P_1$ is the shortest. If $\vec{r}_0$ is the position vector of the point $P_0$ and $\vec{r}_1$ is the position vector of the point $P_1$, then $\vec{r}_0 - \vec{r}_1$ is parallel to the normal vector $\vec{n}$ of the plane. So,

$$|(\vec{r}_0 - \vec{r}_1) \cdot \vec{n}| = |\vec{r}_0 - \vec{r}_1| |\vec{n}|.$$

We have the distance, $d$, from the point $P_0$ to the plane,

$$d = |\vec{r}_0 - \vec{r}_1| = \frac{|(\vec{r}_0 - \vec{r}_1) \cdot \vec{n}|}{|\vec{n}|}.$$

Let $P_0 = (x_0, y_0, z_0), P_1 = (x_1, y_1, z_1)$ and $\vec{n} = 2\vec{i} + \vec{j} - \vec{k}$ then

$$(\vec{r}_0 - \vec{r}_1) \cdot \vec{n} = [(x_0 - x_1)\vec{i} + (y_0 - y_1)\vec{j} + (z_0 - z_1)\vec{k}] \cdot (2\vec{i} + \vec{j} - \vec{k})$$

$$= 2(x_0 - x_1) + (y_0 - y_1) - (z_0 - z_1)$$

$$= 2x_0 + y_0 - z_0 - (2x_1 + y_1 - z_1).$$

Since $P_1$ is on the plane, we have $2x_1 + y_1 - z_1 = 1$. Therefore

$$d = \frac{|(\vec{r}_0 - \vec{r}_1) \cdot \vec{n}|}{|\vec{n}|}$$

$$= \frac{|2(1) + 3 - (-2) - 1|}{\sqrt{2^2 + 1^2 + (-1)^2}}$$

$$= \sqrt{6}.$$

(b) Since a normal vector to the plane $2x + y - z = 1$ is $\vec{n}_0 = 2\vec{i} + \vec{j} - \vec{k}$, and a normal vector to the plane $2x + y - z = 6$ is $\vec{n}_1 = 2\vec{i} + \vec{j} - \vec{k}$. $\vec{n}_0 = \vec{n}_1$, the two planes are parallel. In order to find the distance between the two planes, we can choose whatever point $p_0$ on the plane

$2x + y - z = 1$ and then calculate the distance from $p_0$ to the plane $2x + y - z = 6$ by the formula derived in part (a). Let $P_0 = (0, 0, -1)$, then the distance, $d$, of the two planes is

$$d = \frac{|(\vec{r}_0 - \vec{r}_1) \cdot \vec{n}_1|}{|\vec{n}_1|}$$

$$= \frac{|2(0) + 1(0) + (-1)(-1) - 6|}{\sqrt{2^2 + 1^2 + (-1)^2}}$$

$$= \frac{5}{\sqrt{6}}.$$

8. Determine a formula for the distance between a point $(a, b, c)$ and the $y$-axis.

    ANSWER:

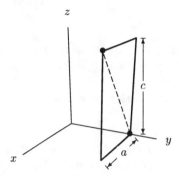

*Figure 12.3.65*

The point on the $y$-axis such that the distance from $(a, b, c)$ to the $y$-axis is the smallest is $(0, b, 0)$. Therefore the formula for the distance is

$$d = \sqrt{(a - 0)^2 + (b - b)^2 + (c - 0)^2}$$

$$= \sqrt{a^2 + c^2}$$

9. Determine two vectors of length 10 in the $xy$-plane that are normal to the parabola $y = x^2$ at $(1, 1)$.

    ANSWER:

    For $y = x^2$ at $(1, 1)$, $dy/dx = 2$. So, the tangent vector at $(1, 1)$ for $y = x^2$ is $\vec{T} = \vec{i} + 2\vec{j}$. Two vectors perpendicular to $\vec{T}$ are $\vec{n_1} = -2\vec{i} + \vec{j}$ and $\vec{n_2} = 2\vec{i} - \vec{j}$. Hence, the vectors of length 10 that are normal to $y = x^2$ are

$$10\frac{\vec{n_1}}{|\vec{n_1}|} = 10\frac{(-2\vec{i} + \vec{j})}{\sqrt{(-2)^2 + 1^2}} = 2\sqrt{5}(-2\vec{i} + \vec{j})$$

$$10\frac{\vec{n_2}}{|\vec{n_2}|} = 10\frac{(2\vec{i} - \vec{j})}{\sqrt{2^2 + (-1)^2}} = 2\sqrt{5}(2\vec{i} - \vec{j})$$

See Figure 12.3.66.

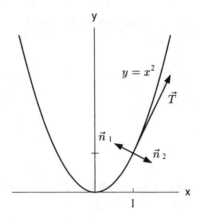

**Figure 12.3.66**

10. Determine the equation of the plane which contains the points $(1, 2, -1)$ and $(-2, 1, -3)$ and is perpendicular to the plane $x + 3y - 2z = 3$. Draw picture and explain!

   ANSWER:

   Suppose the equation of our plane is

   $$ax + by + cz + d = 0$$

   (where $a, b, c$ and $d$ are all real numbers). Then, a normal $\vec{n}_1$ to this plane is $\vec{n}_1 = a\vec{i} + b\vec{j} + c\vec{k}$, and the plane is perpendicular to $x + 3y - 2z = 3$ if and only if $\vec{n}_1$ is perpendicular to the normal $\vec{n}_2 = \vec{i} + 3\vec{j} - 2\vec{k}$ to $x + 3y - 2z = 3$ So, $\vec{n}_1 \cdot \vec{n}_2 = 0$ or $a + 3b - 2c = 0$. Now the points $(1, 2, -1)$ and $(-2, 1, -3)$ are on the plane so we get two more equations:

   $$a + 2b - c + d = 0$$
   $$-2a + b - 3c + d = 0.$$

   So, we now have to solve the system:

   $$a + 2b - c + d = 0$$
   $$-2a + b - 3c + d + 0$$
   $$a + 3b - 2c = 0$$

   We get the solution:

   $$a = -\lambda, \quad b = \lambda \quad c = \lambda \quad d = 0.$$

   where $\lambda$ is any real number. So the equation of our plane is:

   $$-x + y + z = 0.$$

11. Consider the triangle $ABC$ where $A$ is the point $(2, 5, -3)$, $B$ is the point $(0, 1, 2)$ and $C$ is the point $(4, 1, 0)$. Find the cosine of angle $BAC$.

   ANSWER:

   Let the angle $BAC$ be $\theta$. We have

   $$\vec{AC} = 2\vec{i} - 4\vec{j} + 3\vec{k}$$
   $$\vec{AB} = -2\vec{i} - 4\vec{j} + 5\vec{k}.$$

   So,

   $$\|\vec{AC}\| = \sqrt{2^2 + (-4)^2 + 3^2}$$
   $$= \sqrt{29}.$$

$$\|\vec{AB}\| = \sqrt{(-2)^2 + (-4)^2 + 5^2}$$
$$= \sqrt{45}.$$
$$\vec{AC} \cdot \vec{AB} = \|\vec{AC}\|\|\vec{AB}\|\cos\theta$$
$$\cos\theta = \frac{\vec{AC} \cdot \vec{AB}}{\|\vec{AC}\|\|\vec{AB}\|}$$
$$= \frac{(2\vec{i} - 4\vec{j} + 3\vec{k})(-2\vec{i} - 4\vec{j} + 5\vec{k})}{(\sqrt{29})(\sqrt{45})}$$
$$= \frac{27}{3\sqrt{145}}$$
$$= \frac{9}{\sqrt{145}}.$$

## Problems and Solutions for Section 12.4

1. True or false? Give a reason for your answer.

   (a) The vector $\vec{a} \times \vec{b}$ is parallel to the $z$-axis where $\vec{a}$ and $\vec{b}$ are shown in Figure 12.4.67 (both $\vec{a}$ and $\vec{b}$ are in the $xy$-plane).

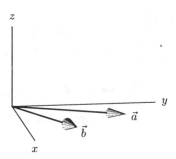

   *Figure 12.4.67*

   (b) The vector $\vec{a} \times \vec{b}$ has a positive $z$ component if $\vec{a}$ and $\vec{b}$ are as in part (a).

   ANSWER:

   (a) True. $\vec{a} \times \vec{b}$ is perpendicular to $\vec{a}$ and $\vec{b}$ and therefore to the $xy$-plane.
   (b) False. By the right-hand rule, $\vec{a} \times \vec{b}$ points in the negative $z$-direction.

2. Consider the statements A-E below and assume $\vec{v} \neq 0$ and $\vec{w} \neq 0$. For each of the situations (a)-(c), and for each statement, fill in the blank with

   **T** (meaning must be true), or
   **F** (meaning must be false), or
   **T or F** (meaning could be true, could be false).

   ### Statements

   A. $\vec{v}$ is perpendicular to $\vec{w}$.
   B. $\vec{v}$ is parallel to $\vec{w}$ (i.e., $\vec{v}$ and $\vec{w}$ are in the same or opposite directions).
   C. The angle $\theta$ between $\vec{v}$ and $\vec{w}$ satisfies $0 \leq \theta < \frac{\pi}{2}$
   D. The angle $\theta$ between $\vec{v}$ and $\vec{w}$ satisfies $\frac{\pi}{2} < \theta \leq \pi$.

    E.   At least one of $\|\vec{v}\,\|$ and $\|\vec{w}\,\|$ is greater than 1.

  (a)  Given that $\vec{v} \cdot \vec{w} = 2$, then
      Statement $A$ is
      Statement $B$ is
      Statement $C$ is
      Statement $D$ is
      Statement $E$ is

  (b)  Given that $(\vec{v} \times \vec{w}) \cdot \vec{u} = 0$ for all vectors $\vec{u}$, then
      Statement $A$ is
      Statement $B$ is
      Statement $C$ is
      Statement $D$ is
      Statement $E$ is

  (c)  Given that $\vec{v} \cdot \vec{w} = 0$ and $\vec{v} \times \vec{w} = \vec{i} + \vec{j} + \vec{k}$, then
      Statement $A$ is
      Statement $B$ is
      Statement $C$ is
      Statement $D$ is
      Statement $E$ is

    ANSWER:

  (a)  Given that $\vec{v} \cdot \vec{w} = 2$, then
      Statement $A$ is F, since if $\vec{v}$ and $\vec{w}$ are perpendicular, then $vecv \cdot \vec{w} = 0$.
      Statement $B$ is T or F, depending on the length of $\vec{v}$ and $\vec{w}$.
      Statement $C$ is T, since $\vec{v} \cdot \vec{w} > 0$.
      Statement $D$ is F, since $\vec{v} \cdot \vec{w} > 0$.
      Statement $E$ is T, since $2 = \vec{v} \cdot \vec{w} = \|\vec{v}\,\|\|\vec{w}\,\| \cos\theta$ and $\cos\theta \leq 1$

  (b)  Since $(\vec{v} \times \vec{w}) \cdot \vec{u} = 0$ for all vectors $\vec{u}$, we must have $\vec{v} \times \vec{w} = \vec{0}$. So
      Statement $A$ is F.
      Statement $B$ is T.
      Statement $C$ is T or F ($\theta = 0$ or $\pi$).
      Statement $D$ is T or F ($\theta = 0$ or $\pi$).
      Statement $E$ is T or F.

  (c)  Given that $\vec{v} \cdot \vec{w} = 0$ and $\vec{v} \times \vec{w} = \vec{i} + \vec{j} + \vec{k}$, then
      Statement $A$ is T.
      Statement $B$ is F.
      Statement $C$ is F.
      Statement $D$ is F.
      Statement $E$ is T, since $\|\vec{v} \times \vec{w}\,\| = \|\vec{v}\,\|\|\vec{w}\,\| \sin\theta = \|\vec{v}\,\|\|\vec{w}\,\| = \|\vec{i} + \vec{j} + \vec{k}\,\| = \sqrt{3}$

3.  Let $\vec{a}$ and $\vec{b}$ be any two nonzero vectors in 3-space, which are not parallel to one another. Write expressions for vectors representing the following:

  (a)  A unit vector parallel to $\vec{a}$.
  (b)  A vector perpendicular to $\vec{a}$ and $\vec{b}$.
  (c)  What is the value of $\vec{a} \cdot (\vec{a} \times \vec{b})$? Why?

    ANSWER:

  (a)  $\dfrac{\vec{a}}{\|\vec{a}\,\|}$

  (b)  $\vec{a} \times \vec{b}$

  (c)  Zero. Because $\vec{a} \times \vec{b}$ is perpendicular to $\vec{a}$.

4. For what value(s) of $a$ is the vector $\vec{v} = -6\vec{i} + a\vec{j} + 3\vec{k}$ :

    (a) Perpendicular to the plane $z = 2x - 5y + 7$?
    (b) In the same or opposite direction to the cross product $(\vec{i} + 2\vec{k}) \times ((\sqrt{2})\vec{j} + (\sqrt{2})\vec{k})$?

    ANSWER:

    (a)

    $$-6\vec{i} + a\vec{j} + 3\vec{k}$$
    $$2\vec{i} - 5\vec{j} - \vec{k}$$

    Thus, $a = 15$.

    (b) One way:

    $$(\vec{i} + 2\vec{k}) \times (\sqrt{2}\vec{j} + \sqrt{2}\vec{k}) = -2\sqrt{2}\vec{i} - \sqrt{2}\vec{j} + \sqrt{2}\vec{i}$$
    $$-2\sqrt{2}\vec{i} - \sqrt{2}\vec{j} + \sqrt{2}\vec{k}$$
    $$-6\vec{i} + a\vec{j} + 3\vec{k}.$$

    Thus, $a = -3$.
    Another way:

    $$(\vec{i} + 2\vec{k}) \cdot (-6\vec{i} + a\vec{j} + 3\vec{k}) = 0$$
    $$(\sqrt{2}\vec{i} + \sqrt{2}\vec{k}) \cdot (-6\vec{i} + a\vec{j} + 3\vec{k}) = 0.$$

    Thus, $a = -3$.

5. (a) Consider two vectors $\vec{v} = 2\vec{i} - \vec{j} + 3\vec{k}$ and $\vec{w} = a\vec{i} + a\vec{j} - \vec{k}$. For what values of $a$ are $\vec{v}$ and $\vec{w}$ perpendicular?
    (b) For what values of $a$ are $\vec{v}$ and $\vec{w}$ parallel?
    (c) Find the equation of the plane parallel to $2\vec{i} - \vec{j} + 3\vec{k}$ and to $3\vec{i} + 3\vec{j} - \vec{k}$ and containing the point $(1, 1, 1)$.

    ANSWER:

    (a) $\vec{v} \cdot \vec{w} = 2a - a - 3 = a - 3$. For $\vec{v}$ and $\vec{w}$ to be perpendicular we must have $\vec{v} \cdot \vec{w} = 0$, so $a = 3$.
    (b) $\vec{v} \times \vec{w} = (1 + 3a)\vec{i} + (3a - 2)\vec{j} + a\vec{k}$. For $\vec{v}$ and $\vec{w}$ to be parallel, $\vec{v} \times \vec{w} = \vec{0}$, so $1 + 3a = 0$, $3a - 2 = 0$, and $a = 0$. There is no value of $a$ satisfying all these equations, so $\vec{v}$ and $\vec{w}$ are never parallel.
    (c) The two vectors given are $\vec{v}$ and $\vec{w}$ with $a = 3$, so a normal vector is $\vec{v} \times \vec{w} = 10\vec{i} + 7\vec{j} + 3\vec{k}$. The equation of the plane is

    $$10x + 7y + 3z = c,$$

    for some constant $c$. Putting $(x, y, z) = (1, 1, 1)$, we get

    $$10 + 7 + 3 = c,$$

    $$20 = c.$$

    So the equation is

    $$10x + 7y + 3z = 20.$$

6. Given the points $P = (1, 2, 3)$, $Q = (3, 5, 7)$, and $R = (2, 5, 3)$, find:

    (a) The equation of the plane containing $P, Q,$ and $R$.
    (b) The area of the triangle $PQR$.
    (c) The (perpendicular) distance from the point $R$ to the line through $P$ and $Q$. (Hint: Use Part(b))

    ANSWER:

    (a) In order to find the equation of a plane containing the points $P$, $Q$, and $R$, we first find the displacement vectors $\overrightarrow{PQ}$, and $\overrightarrow{PR}$. So

    $$\overrightarrow{PQ} = (3 - 1)\vec{i} + (5 - 2)\vec{j} + (7 - 3)\vec{k} = 2\vec{i} + 3\vec{j} + 4\vec{k},$$

and

$$\overrightarrow{PR} = (2-1)\vec{i} + (5-2)\vec{j} + (3-3)\vec{k} = \vec{i} + 3\vec{j}.$$

Thus, a normal vector, $\vec{n}$, to the plane is given by

$$n = \overrightarrow{PQ} \times \overrightarrow{PR}$$
$$= (3(0) - 4(3))\vec{i} + (4(1) - 2(0))\vec{j} + (2(3) - 3(1))\vec{k}$$
$$= -12\vec{i} + 4\vec{j} + 3\vec{k}.$$

Since the point $P = (1, 2, 3)$ is on the plane, the equation of the plane is

$$-12(x-1) + 4(y-2) + 3(z-3) = 0,$$

which simplifies to

$$-12x + 4y + 3z = 5.$$

(b) In order to find the area of the triangle we again use the displacement vectors $\overrightarrow{PQ}$, and $\overrightarrow{PR}$ calculated in part (a). We know that the area of a parallelogram is $||\vec{n}|| = ||\overrightarrow{PQ} \times \overrightarrow{PR}||$. Thus the area of the triangle is

$$\frac{1}{2}||\vec{n}|| = \frac{1}{2}\sqrt{(-12)^2 + 4^2 + 3^2} = \frac{1}{2}\sqrt{169} = \frac{1}{2}(13) = 6.5.$$

(c) The formula for the area of the triangle is

$$\text{Area of triangle} = \frac{1}{2}(\text{Base} \cdot \text{Height}).$$

Let the base be $||\overrightarrow{PQ}||$, and the height is the perpendicular distance from the point $R$ to the line through $P$ and $Q$. Since we calculated $\overrightarrow{PQ}$ in part (a),

$$||\overrightarrow{PQ}|| = \sqrt{2^2 + 3^2 + 4^2} = \sqrt{29}$$

Solving for the height, and using the area of the triangle from part b

$$\text{Height} = \frac{2 \cdot \text{Area of Triangle}}{\text{Base}}$$
$$= \frac{2(6.5)}{\sqrt{29}} \approx 2.414$$

7. For what value(s) of $a$ is the vector $\vec{v} = -6\vec{i} + a\vec{j} + 3\vec{k}$:

   (a) Perpendicular to the plane $z = 2x - 5y + 7$?
   (b) Equal to the vector product $(\vec{i} + 2\vec{k}) \times (3\vec{j} + 3\vec{k})$?

   ANSWER:

   (a) For $\vec{v}$ to be perpendicular to the plane, $\vec{v}$ must be parallel to any vector normal to the plane. From the equation of the plane, $2x - 5y - z = -7$, we can obtain a normal vector from the coefficients of $x$, $y$ and $z$:
   $$\vec{n} = 2\vec{i} - 5\vec{j} - \vec{k}.$$
   If $\vec{v}$ is parallel to $\vec{n}$, then
   $$\vec{v} \cdot \vec{n} = 0.$$
   So

   $$(-6\vec{i} + a\vec{j} + 3\vec{k}) \cdot (2\vec{i} - 5\vec{j} - \vec{k}) = 0$$
   $$(-6)(2) + (a)(-5) + (3)(-1) = 0$$
   $$-12 - 5a - 3 = 0$$
   $$-5a = 15$$
   $$a = -3$$

   Thus $\vec{v}$ is perpendicular to the plane $z = 2x - 5y + 7$ when $a = -3$.

(b)  First we determine $(\vec{i} + 2\vec{k}) \times (3\vec{j} + 3\vec{k})$.

$$(\vec{i} + 2\vec{k}) \times (3\vec{j} + 3\vec{k}) = \begin{vmatrix} \vec{i} & \vec{j} & \vec{k} \\ 1 & 0 & 2 \\ 0 & 3 & 3 \end{vmatrix} = -6\vec{i} + -3\vec{j} + 3\vec{k}.$$

Setting the result equal to $\vec{v}$, we have

$$-6\vec{i} + a\vec{j} + 3\vec{k} = -6\vec{i}$$

so

$$a = -3.$$

8.  (a)  What is the geometric relation between $\vec{v}$ and $\vec{w}$ if $\vec{v} \cdot \vec{w} = \|\vec{v}\|\|\vec{w}\|$. Justify your answer.
    (b)  Compute the area of the triangle with vertices $A(0,0,0)$, $B(1,1,0)$, $C(1,2,1)$.
    (c)  Does the point $D(3,8,4)$ lie in the same plane as the triangle $ABC$? Explain why or why not.
    (d)  Use vectors and dot-products to prove Pythagoras' theorem: In a right triangle with sides $a$, $b$, $c$ (with $c$ the longest side) $c = a^2 + b^2$. (Hint: Let $\vec{u}$ and $\vec{v}$ be vectors along the short sides and compute $(\vec{v} - \vec{u}) \cdot (\vec{v} - \vec{u})$. Explain your reasoning!)

    ANSWER:

    (a)  Since always $\vec{v} \cdot \vec{w} = \|\vec{v}\|\|\vec{w}\|\cos\alpha$ (where $\alpha$ is the angle between $\vec{v}$ and $\vec{w}$), if $\vec{v} \cdot \vec{w} = \|\vec{v}\|\|\vec{w}\|$ then $\cos\alpha = 1$. This means that $\alpha = 0$, or $\vec{v}$ and $\vec{w}$ point in the same direction.
    (b)  Two sides of the triangle are $\vec{BA} = -\vec{i} - \vec{j}$ and $\vec{BC} = \vec{j} + \vec{k}$, hence $\vec{N} = \vec{BA} \times \vec{BC} = -\vec{i} + \vec{j} - \vec{k}$ is perpendicular to the triangle, and the area of the triangle is $\frac{1}{2}\|\vec{N}\| = \frac{1}{2}\sqrt{3} \approx 0.8660$.
    (c)  Since $\vec{AD} \cdot \vec{N} = -3 + 8 - 4 \neq 0$ the point $D$ does not lie in the plane. (Alternatively, the long way: The equation of the plane through $A, B, C$ is e.g. $\vec{N} \cdot \vec{R} = \vec{N} \cdot \vec{OA}$. In the long form this equation reads $x - y + z = 0$ (after multiplying by $(-1)$). The coordinates of $D$ clearly do not satisfy the equation.)
    (d)  Name the corners of the triangle $A$, $B$, $C$ with $C$ opposite to the longest side. Let $\vec{u} = \vec{CA}$ and $\vec{v} = \vec{CB}$. Then $\vec{v} - \vec{u} = \vec{AB}$, and $\|\vec{u}\| = b$, $\|\vec{v}\| = a$ and $\|\vec{v} - \vec{u}\| = c$. Taking the dot-product we get $c^2 = (\vec{v} - \vec{u}) \cdot (\vec{v} - \vec{u}) = \vec{v} \cdot \vec{v} - 2\vec{v} \cdot \vec{u} + \vec{v} \cdot \vec{u} = a^2 + b^2$, using that $\vec{v} \cdot \vec{u} = 0$ since $\vec{u}$ and $\vec{v}$ are perpendicular.

# Chapter 13 Exam Questions

*Problems and Solutions for Section 13.1*

1. True or false? Give a reason for your answer. If $\frac{\partial f}{\partial x} = \frac{\partial f}{\partial y}$ everywhere, then $f(x, y)$ is a constant.

   ANSWER:

   False. Take $f(x, y) = 2x + 2y$ for example.

2. The level curves of a function $z = f(x, y)$ are shown below. Assume that the scales along the $x$ and $y$ axes are the same. Arrange the following quantities in ascending order. Give a brief explanation for your reasoning.

   $$f_x(P), \quad f_y(Q), \quad f_y(R), \quad f_x(S), \quad \text{the number } 0$$

   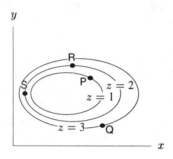

   *Figure 13.1.68*

   ANSWER:

   $f$ is decreasing sharply in the $x$-direction at $S$, and is decreasing gently in the $y$ direction at $Q$, so

   $$f_x(S) < f_y(Q) < 0.$$

   It is increasing gently in the $x$-direction at $P$ and sharply in the $y$-direction at $R$, so

   $$0 < f_x(P) < f_y(R).$$

3. Suppose that the price $P$ (in dollars) to purchase a used car is a function of $C$, its original cost (in dollars), and its age $A$ (in years). So $P = f(C, A)$. What is the sign of $\frac{\partial P}{\partial C}$? Explain.

   ANSWER:

   Positive. $\frac{\partial P}{\partial c}$ shows that if the age $A$ of the car is kept constant, the price $P$ increases when its original cost increases.

4. Answer the following questions using the contour diagram shown in Figure 13.1.69.

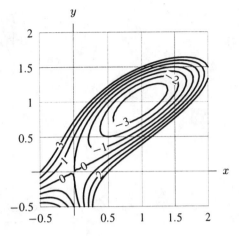

*Figure 13.1.69*

(a) Sketch a graph of $f(1, y)$.

(b) Sketch a graph of $f(x, 0)$.

(c) State whether each of $f_x(1, 0.5)$, $f_y(1.0, 5)$ is positive, negative, or nearly zero.

ANSWER:

(a)

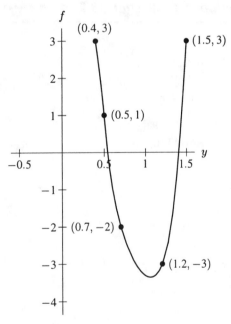

*Figure 13.1.70:* Graph of $f(1, y)$

646

(b)

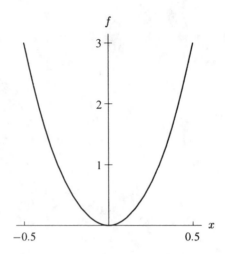

**Figure 13.1.71:** Graph of $f(x, 0)$

(c)   $f_x(1, 0.5)$ is positive, $f_y(1, 0.5)$ is negative.

## Problems and Solutions for Section 13.2

1.   True or false? There exists a function $f(x, y)$ with $f_x = 2y$ and $f_y = 2x$.
  ANSWER:
  True. $f(x, y) = 2xy$ works.

2.   Find $\dfrac{\partial}{\partial x}(\ln(x^2 y + 3))$
  ANSWER:

$$\frac{\partial}{\partial x}(\ln(x^2 y + 3)) = (\frac{1}{x^2 y + 3})(2xy)$$
$$= \frac{2xy}{x^2 y + 3}$$

3.   Find $f_H$ if $f(H, T) = \dfrac{2H + T}{(5 - H)^3}$
  ANSWER:

$$f_H = \frac{\partial}{\partial H}[\frac{2H + T}{(5 - H)^3}]$$
$$= \frac{(5 - H)^3(2) + (2H + T)(3)(5 - H)^2}{(5 - H)^6}$$
$$= \frac{4H + 3T + 10}{(5 - H)^4}$$

4.   Find $\dfrac{\partial H}{\partial w}\Big|_{(\pi/2, \pi/3)}$   if $H(w, t) = e^{\cos(2w + 3t)}$.
  ANSWER:

$$\frac{\partial H}{\partial w} = \frac{\partial}{\partial w}[e^{\cos(2w+3t)}]$$

$$= -e^{\cos(2w+3t)}(2)\sin(2w+3t)$$

$$= -2e^{\cos(2w+3t)}\sin(2w+3t)$$

Hence,

$$\left.\frac{\partial H}{\partial W}\right|_{(\pi/2,\pi/3)} = -2e^{\cos(2\pi)}\sin 2\pi$$

$$= 0.$$

5. If $\$P$ is invested in a bank account earning $r\%$ interest a year, compounded continuously, the balance, $\$B$, at the end of $t$ years is given by $B = f(P, r, t) = Pe^{rt/100}$.

   (a) Find $\partial B/\partial t$, $\partial B/\partial r$, and $\partial B/\partial P$.
   (b) What are the units of $\partial B/\partial t$? What is the practical interpretation (in terms of money) of $\partial B/\partial t$?

   ANSWER:

   (a)

$$\frac{\partial B}{\partial t} = \frac{\partial}{\partial t}Pe^{rt/100} = P(\frac{r}{100})e^{rt/100}$$

$$\frac{\partial B}{\partial r} = \frac{\partial}{\partial r}Pe^{rt/100} = P(\frac{t}{100})e^{rt/100}$$

$$\frac{\partial B}{\partial P} = \frac{\partial}{\partial P}Pe^{rt/100} = e^{rt/100}$$

   (b) The units of $\partial B/\partial t$ are dollars per year. $\frac{\partial B}{\partial t}$ is the rate at which $B$ is growing.

6. (a) Explain how you know that the function $U(x, t) = e^{-(x-ct)^2}$ satisfies the wave equation $U_{tt} = c^2 U_{xx}$.
   (b) Draw a graph of the shape of the wave at times $t = 0, 1, 2$.
   (c) What is the physical meaning of the parameter $c$?

   ANSWER:

   (a) As

$$U_t = 2c(x - ct)e^{-(x-ct)^2}$$

$$U_{tt} = -2c^2e^{-(x-ct)^2} + 4c^2(x - ct)^2e^{-(x+ct)^2}$$

   and

$$U_x = -2(x - ct)e^{-(x-ct)^2}$$

$$U_{xx} = -2e^{-(x-ct)^2} + 4(x - ct)^2e^{-(x-ct)^2}$$

   then

$$U_{tt} = -2c^2e^{-(x-ct)^2} + 4c^2(x - ct)^2e^{-(x-ct)^2}$$

$$= c^2[-2e^{-(x-ct)^2} + 4(x - ct)^2e^{-(x-ct)^2}]$$

$$= c^2 U_{xx}.$$

(b)

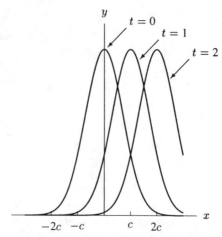

**Figure 13.2.72:** The graph of the wave at
$t = 0, 1, 2$

(c)   In one unit if time, the curve moves $c$ units to the right. So $c$ is the velocity of the wave.

7.   The ideal gas law states that

$$PV = RT$$

for a fixed amount of gas, called a *mole* of gas, where $P$ is the pressure (in atmospheres), $V$ is the volume (in cubic meters), $T$ is the temperature (in degrees Kelvin) and $R$ is a positive constant.

(a)   Find $\partial P/\partial T$ and $\partial P/\partial V$.

(b)   A mole of a certain gas is at a temperature of $300°\,K$, a pressure of 1 atmosphere, and a volume of $0.02\text{m}^3$. What is $\partial P/\partial V$ for this gas?

(c)   Explain the meaning of your answer to (b) in terms of temperature, pressure and volume.

ANSWER:

(a)

$$\frac{\partial P}{\partial T} = \frac{\partial}{\partial T}\left(\frac{RT}{V}\right),\ \text{since}\ P = \frac{RT}{V}$$
$$= \frac{R}{V}.$$
$$\frac{\partial P}{\partial V} = \frac{\partial}{\partial V}\left(\frac{RT}{V}\right)$$
$$= RT(-V^{-2})$$
$$= -\frac{RT}{V^2}.$$

(b)   We have

$$R = \frac{PV}{T} = \frac{1 \cdot (0.02)}{300}.$$

We substitute the given values into the expression obtained for $\partial P/\partial V$ in part (a).

$$\frac{\partial P}{\partial V} = -\frac{RT}{V^2}$$
$$= -\frac{\frac{(0.02)}{300}300}{(0.02)^2}$$
$$= -50\text{atm/m}^3$$

(c)   If a body of gas is at a temperature of $300°\,$K, a pressure of 1 atmosphere, and has volume $0.02\text{m}^3$, and if its temperature is held constant, then its pressure decreases as its volume increases, at a rate of $-50\text{atm/m}^3$.

The final estimate is

$$\frac{50.7 + 63.6}{2} = 57.15 \approx 57.$$

(c)    At $Q$, as $y$ increases for a fixed value of $x$, $z$ decreases so $z_y$ is $< 0$.

At $R$, the contour ($z = 2$) is approximately horizontal so as $x$ increases at a fixed value of $y$, for a small change in $x$, $z$ does not change so $z_x \approx 0$.

At $P$, as $y$ increases for a fixed value of $x$, $z$ increases so $z_y$ is positive. However, $z$ increases very gradually as shown by the wide spacing of the contours close to $P$ so $|z_y|$ is not very big.

At $S$, as $x$ increases at a fixed value of $y$, $z$ decreases so $z_x$ is negative. Thus $-z_x$ is positive. Since $z$ decreases very quickly as $x$ increases close to the point $S$, the contours being very close together near $S$, $|z_x|$ is very big.

We therefore have,

$$z_y(Q), \quad z_x(R) = 0, \quad z_y(P), \quad -z_x(S).$$

9.    Calculate the following derivatives:

(a)    $(\partial/\partial P)(P \ln(V^2 - P))$

(b)    If $f(\theta, \phi) = \sin^2(3\theta) \cdot \cos^3(4\phi)$, find $\partial f/\partial \theta$.

(c)    If $f(\theta, \phi)$ is as in part (b), find $\partial f/\partial \theta|_{\theta = \pi/12, \phi = \pi/16}$.

ANSWER:

(a)

$$\ln(V^2 - P) + P \cdot \frac{1}{V^2 - P}(-1) = \ln(V^2 - P) - \frac{P}{V^2 - P}$$

(b)    $2\sin(3\theta) \cdot \cos(3\theta) \cdot 3 \cdot \cos^3(4\phi) = 6\sin(3\theta) \cdot \cos(3\theta) \cos^3(4\phi)$

(c)

$$\left.\frac{\partial f}{\partial \theta}\right|_{\theta = \frac{\pi}{12}, \phi = \frac{\pi}{16}} = 6\sin(\frac{\pi}{4}) \cdot \cos(\frac{\pi}{4}) \cdot \cos^3(\frac{\pi}{4}) = \frac{6}{(\sqrt{2})^5} \approx 1.06$$

10.    In an electric circuit, two resistances, $R_1$ and $R_2$, are hooked up so that their combined resistance, $R$, is given by $1/R = 1/R_1 + 1/R_2$.

(a)    Find $\partial R/\partial R_1$.

(b)    Suppose $\partial R/\partial R_1 = 0.1$ for some values of $R_1$ and $R_2$. What does this tell you, in terms of resistances?

ANSWER:

(a)    Solve for $R$:

$$R = \frac{R_1 R_2}{R_1 + R_2}$$

so

$$\frac{\partial R}{\partial R_1} = \frac{R_2}{R_1 + R_2} - \frac{R_1 R_2}{(R_1 + R_2)^2}.$$

(b)    $\partial R/\partial R_1 = 0.1$ tells you that if $R_2$ is held constant, as $R_1$ is increased a small amount, the combined resistance $R$ increases at one tenth the amount.

11.    Let $V(x, y, z)$ and $S(x, y, z)$ represent the volume and surface area respectively of the rectangular solid shown in Figure 13.2.74.

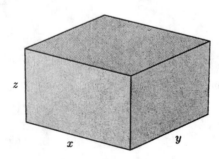

**Figure 13.2.74**

Determine:

(a) $\partial V/\partial x$ and $\partial S/\partial z$

(b) Explain $\partial V/\partial x$ in terms of how the solid changes geometrically with respect to $x$.

(c) Explain $\partial S/\partial z$ in terms of how the surface area of the solid changes geometrically with respect to $z$.

ANSWER:

(a) $V = xyz$ and $S = 2xy + 2yz + 2xz$, so

$$\frac{\partial V}{\partial x} = yz$$
$$\frac{\partial S}{\partial z} = 2(x + y).$$

(b) As $x$ increases by a small amount $\Delta x$, the solid gets longer, and its volume increases by $\Delta x$ times the area of the face perpendicular to the side of length $x$, that is, by $(yz)\Delta x$. So the rate of increase is $yz$.

(c) As $z$ increases by $\Delta z$, the solid gets taller, and each vertical face increases in area by $\Delta z$ times the horizontal length of the face. So the total area increases by $\Delta z(2x + 2y)$, so the rate of increase is $2x + 2y$.

12. If $g(x, y) = x^2 \cos(xy)$ find

(a) $\dfrac{\partial g}{\partial x}(1, \pi)$      (b) $\dfrac{\partial g}{\partial y}(1, \pi)$

ANSWER:

(a)

$$\frac{\partial g}{\partial x} = \frac{\partial}{\partial x}(x^2 \cos(xy))$$
$$= 2x \cos(xy) - x^2 y \sin(xy)$$

So,

$$\frac{\partial g}{\partial x}(1, \pi) = 2\cos \pi - \pi \sin \pi = -2.$$

(b)

$$\frac{\partial g}{\partial y} = \frac{\partial}{\partial y}[x^2 \cos(xy)]$$
$$= -x^3 \sin(xy)$$

Hence,

$$\frac{\partial g}{\partial y}(1, \pi) = -\sin \pi = 0.$$

## Problems and Solutions for Section 13.3

1. The volume $V = \pi r^2 h$ of a right circular cylinder is to be calculated from measured values of $r$ and $h$. Suppose $r$ is measured with an error of no more than 2% and $h$ with an error of no more than 0.5%. Using differentials, estimate the possible percentage error in the calculation of $V$. (In general, in measuring a quantity $Q$, the percentage error is $dQ/Q$.)

ANSWER:

$$V = \pi r^2 h$$
$$dV = 2\pi rh\, dr + \pi r^2 dh$$

so,

$$\frac{dV}{V} = \frac{2dr}{r} + \frac{dh}{h}$$

$$\left|\frac{dV}{V}\right| \le 2\left|\frac{dr}{r}\right| + \left|\frac{dh}{h}\right|$$

$$\le 2 \cdot 0.02 + 0.005$$

$$= 0.045$$

$$= 4.5\%.$$

2.  Consider the surface $z = x\sin(x/y)$, $y \ne 0$. Show that the tangent plane at any point of the surface passes through the origin.

    ANSWER:

    Tangent plane at $(X_0, Y_0, Z_0)$:

$$z = \frac{\partial z}{\partial x}(X_0, Y_0)(x - X_0) + \frac{\partial z}{\partial y}(X_0, Y_0)(y - Y_0) + Z_0$$

$$\frac{\partial z}{\partial x} = \sin\left(\frac{x}{y}\right) + \frac{x}{y}\cos\left(\frac{x}{y}\right)$$

$$\frac{\partial z}{\partial y} = -\frac{x^2}{y^2}\cos\left(\frac{x}{y}\right)$$

$$z = \left[\sin\left(\frac{X_0}{Y_0}\right) + \frac{X_0}{Y_0}\cos\left(\frac{X_0}{Y_0}\right)\right](x - X_0) + \left[-\frac{X_0^2}{Y_0^2}\cos\left(\frac{X_0}{Y_0}\right)\right](y - Y_0) + Z_0$$

$$z = \left[\sin\left(\frac{X_0}{Y_0}\right) + \frac{X_0}{Y_0}\cos\left(\frac{X_0}{Y_0}\right)\right]x + \left[-\frac{X_0^2}{Y_0^2}\cos\left(\frac{X_0}{Y_0}\right)\right]y$$

$$+ \left[\sin\left(\frac{X_0}{Y_0}\right) + \frac{X_0}{Y_0}\cos\left(\frac{X_0}{Y_0}\right)\right](-X_0) + \left[-\frac{X_0^2}{Y_0^2}\cos\left(\frac{X_0}{Y_0}\right)\right](-Y_0) + Z_0$$

$$= \left[\sin\left(\frac{X_0}{Y_0}\right) + \frac{X_0}{Y_0}\cos\left(\frac{X_0}{Y_0}\right)\right]x + \left[-\frac{X_0^2}{Y_0^2}\cos\left(\frac{X_0}{Y_0}\right)\right]y$$

$$+ \sin\left(\frac{X_0}{Y_0}\right)(-X_0) + X_0\sin\left(\frac{X_0}{Y_0}\right)$$

$$= \left[\sin\left(\frac{X_0}{Y_0}\right) + \frac{X_0}{Y_0}\cos\left(\frac{X_0}{Y_0}\right)\right]x + \left[-\frac{X_0^2}{Y_0^2}\cos\left(\frac{X_0}{Y_0}\right)\right]y.$$

    Because there is no constant term, $(x, y, z) = (0, 0, 0)$ is a point on the plane.

3.  A rectangular beam, supported at its two ends, will sag when subjected to a uniform load. The amount of sag is calculated from the formula:

$$S = Cpx^4/(wh^3),$$

    where

    $p = $ the load (newtons per meter of beam length),
    $x = $ the length between supports (meters),
    $w = $ the width of the beam (meters),
    $h = $ the height of the beam (meters), and
    $C = $ a constant that depends on units of measurement and on the material from which the beam is made.

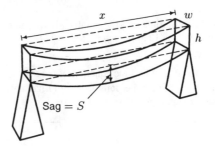

**Figure 13.3.75**

(a) Determine $dS$ for a beam 4 m long, 0.1 m wide, and 0.2 m high that is subjected to a load of 100 N/m.

(b) What conclusions can be drawn about the beam from the expression for $dS$? (i.e. which variables increase or decrease the sag?)

(c) For which variables is the sag most sensitive? For which variables is the sag the least sensitive? (Interpret in the context of the beam.)

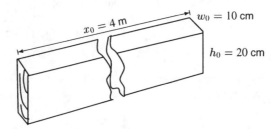

**Figure 13.3.76**

ANSWER:

(a) Since $S(x, w, h, p) = Cpx^4/(wh^3)$ then

$$S_x = \frac{4Cpx^3}{wh^3}$$

$$S_w = -\frac{Cpx^4}{w^2h^3}$$

$$S_h = -\frac{3Cpx^4}{wh^4}$$

$$S_p = \frac{Cx^4}{wh^3}$$

$$dS = S_x dx + S_w dw + S_h dh + S_p dp$$

$$= \frac{4Cpx^3}{wh^3} dx - \frac{Cpx^4}{w^2h^3} dw - \frac{3Cpx^4}{wh^4} dh + \frac{Cx^4}{wh^3} dp.$$

Hence,

$$dS \Big|_{(4, 0.1, 0.2, 100)} = \frac{4(100)(4)^3}{0.1(0.2)^3} C dx - \frac{100(4)^4}{(0.1)^2(0.2)^3} C dw - \frac{3(100)(4)^4}{(0.1)(0.2)^4} C dh + \frac{4^4}{(0.1)(0.2)^3} C dp$$

$$= 128,000,000 C dx - 1,280,000,000 C dw - 480,000,000 C dh + 320,000 C dp.$$

(b) The length $x$ and the load $p$ increase the sag; the width $w$ and the height $h$ decrease the sag.

(c) The sag is most sensitive to the width of the beam and least sensitive to the load.

4. What is the $z$-coordinate of the point $P(1,3,z)$ if $P$ lies on the plane which is tangent to the ellipsoid $4x^2 + y^2 + 9z^2 = 17$ at the point $(1,2,-1)$?

   ANSWER:

   First we need to find the equation of the tangent plane to the ellipsoid $4x^2 + y^2 + 9z^2 = 17$ at the point $(1,2,-1)$. Since the point $(1,2,-1)$ has negative $z$ value, we should write the equation of the lower half of the ellipsoid as

   $$z = f(x,y) = -\sqrt{\frac{17 - 4x^2 - y^2}{9}} = -\frac{1}{3}\sqrt{17 - 4x^2 - y^2}.$$

   We have $f_x(x,y) = \frac{4x}{3\sqrt{17-4x^2-y^2}}$, so $f_x(1,2) = \frac{4}{9}$ and $f_y(x,y) = \frac{y}{3\sqrt{17-4x^2-y^2}}$, so $f_y(1,2) = \frac{2}{9}$.
   Thus the equation of the tangent plane to the ellipsoid at $(1,2)$ is

   $$z = f(1,2) + f_x(1,2)(x-1) + f_y(1,2)(y-2)$$
   $$= -1 + \frac{4}{9}(x-1) + \frac{2}{9}(y-2)$$
   $$= \frac{1}{9}(2y + 4x - 17).$$

   Therefore, the $z$-coordinate of the point $P(1,3,z)$ is

   $$z = \frac{1}{9}((2)(3) + (4)(1) - 17) = -\frac{7}{9}.$$

5. Determine the tangent plane to $z = f(x,y) = 3e^{(x-y)}\ln x$ at $(x,y) = (1,1)$.

   ANSWER:

   We have

   $$f_x(x,y) = 3e^{(x-y)}\ln(x) + 3e^{(x-y)}\frac{1}{x}$$
   $$f_x(1,1) = 3e^{(1-1)}\ln(1) + 3e^{(1-1)}\frac{1}{1} = 3$$
   $$f_y(x,y) = -3\ln(x)e^{(x-y)}$$
   $$f_y(1,1) = -3\ln(1)e^{(1-1)} = 0$$
   $$f(1,1) = 3e^{(1-1)}\ln(1) = 0$$

   Therefore, the tangent plane at $(1,1)$ is

   $$z = f(1,1) + f_x(1,1)(x-1) + f_y(1,1)(y-1)$$
   $$= 3(x-1)$$

6. Find an equation for the tangent plane to the graph of $f(x,y) = e^{x\sin y}$ at the point $(1,\pi)$.

   ANSWER:

   $$f_x = e^{x\sin y}\sin y$$
   $$f_x(1,\pi) = e^0 \cdot 0 = 0$$
   $$f_y = e^{x\sin y}x\cos y$$
   $$f_y(1,\pi) = e^0 \cdot 1 \cdot -1 = -1$$

   So $z = 0x + -1y + c = -y + c$. We can find $c$ by noting that $f(1,\pi) = e^0 = 1$, so $z = 1$ on the plane at $(x,y) = (1,\pi)$. $1 = -1\cdot\pi + c$ so $c = 1 + \pi$. Therefore, $z = -y + (1+\pi)$.

7. A ball thrown from ground level (with initial speed $v$ and at an angle $\alpha$ with the horizontal) hits the ground at a distance $s = \frac{v^2 \sin(2\alpha)}{g}$ ($g \approx 10\frac{m}{s^2}$ is gravitational acceleration).

   (a) Find a reasonable domain for the values of $\alpha$ and $v$. (Hint: A football field is about $s = 100m$ long.)
   (b) Describe the shape of the graph, and/or sketch the graph of $s$ as a function of $(v, \alpha)$.
   (c) Calculate the differential $ds$. What does the sign of $\frac{ds}{d\alpha}(20, \frac{\pi}{3})$ tell you?
   (d) Use the linearization of $s$ about $(v, \alpha) = (20, \frac{\pi}{3})$ to estimate how $\alpha$ should change to get approximately the same distance $s$ when $v$ changes to $19m/s$.

   ANSWER:

   (a) We need $0 \le \alpha \le \frac{\pi}{2}$. At $\alpha = \frac{\pi}{4}$, we need $v = \sqrt{1000} \approx 32$ m/s to throw the ball the distance of a football field, so $0 \le v \le 50$ would seem a reasonable domain.
   (b) The graph looks like a valley that goes up and down along its length and whose cross-sections are parabolas.
   (c)
   $$ds = \frac{2v \sin(2\alpha)}{g}dv + \frac{2v^2 \cos(2\alpha)}{g}d\alpha.$$

   $$\frac{\partial s}{\partial \alpha} = \frac{2v^2 \cos(2\alpha)}{g}; \frac{\partial s}{\partial \alpha}(20, \frac{\pi}{3}) = \frac{2(20)^2 \cos(\frac{2\pi}{3})}{10} = 40 > 0$$

   indicates that as $\alpha$ increases and $v$ remains constant, $s$ increases.
   (d) At $(20, \frac{\pi}{3})$, $ds = 2\sqrt{3}dv + 40d\alpha$, so $\Delta s \approx 2\sqrt{3}\Delta v + 40\Delta\alpha$. To keep $\Delta s = 0$ when $\Delta v = -1$, we would need $\Delta\alpha = -\frac{2\sqrt{3}}{40}\Delta v \approx 0.086$; the angle would only need to be increased by 0.086 radians.

8. (a) Find the differential of $f(x, y) = x^2 + 3x \cos^2 y$.
   (b) Give a linear approximation of $f$ at the point $(1, \pi/4)$.
   (c) Give a contour diagram for the linear function in part (b).

   ANSWER:

   (a)
   $$df(x, y) = f_x(x, y)dx + f_y(x, y)\, dy$$
   $$= (2x + 3\cos^2 y)dx + 3x(2\cos y)(-\sin y)\, dy$$
   $$= (2x + 3\cos^2 y)dx - 6x \sin y \cos y\, dy$$

   (b) The linear approximation to $f$ at the point $(1, \pi/4)$ is

   $$f(x, y) \approx L(x, y) = f(1, \frac{\pi}{4}) + f_x(1, \frac{\pi}{4})(x - 1) + f_y(1, \frac{\pi}{4})(y - \frac{\pi}{4})$$
   $$= (1^2 + 3\cos^2 \frac{\pi}{4}) + (2 + 3\cos^2 \frac{\pi}{4})(x - 1) - 6\sin \frac{\pi}{4} \cos \frac{\pi}{4}(y - \frac{\pi}{4})$$
   $$= \frac{5}{2} + \frac{7}{2}(x - 1) - 3(y - \frac{\pi}{4})$$
   $$= \frac{7}{2}x - 3y + \frac{3\pi}{4} - 1.$$

(c)

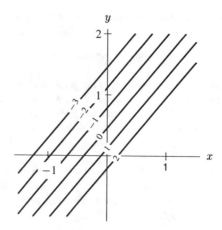

**Figure 13.3.77**

9.  If a function $z = g(x, y)$ has $g(1, 2) = 10$, $g_x(1, 2) = 7$ and $g_y(1, 2) = -5$, find the equation of the plane tangent to the surface $z = g(x, y)$ at the point where $x = 1$ and $y = 2$.

    ANSWER:

    The equation of the plane tangent to the surface $z = g(x, y)$ at the point where $x = 1$ and $y = 2$:

    $$z = g(1, 2) + g_x(1, 2)(x - 1) + g_y(1, 2)(y - 2)$$
    $$= 10 + 7(x - 1) - 5(y - 2)$$
    $$= 13 + 7x - 5y.$$

10. Let $r = f(x, y) = \sqrt{x^2 + y^2}$ and $\theta = \tan^{-1}(y/x)$ denote the change from rectangular to polar coordinates.

    (a)  Explicitly express the differential $dr$ in terms of $dx$, $dy$ and the partial derivatives of $f$.
    (b)  Describe/sketch the graph of $r = f(x, y)$.
    (c)  Find $r$ when $(x, y) = (6, 8)$. Suppose $x = 6$ and $y = 8$ have been measured within 1% and 2% relative errors. How large are the corresponding maximal absolute errors $\Delta x$ and $\Delta y$? Using differentials, estimate the resulting absolute and percentage errors for $r = \sqrt{x^2 + y^2}$.
    (d)  At time $t$ a vehicle is at $x = 3t - 1$, and $y = 1 + \frac{4}{t}$. Compute $\frac{dr}{dt}$ (first find $dx$, $dy$, then $dr$ in terms of $dt$).

    ANSWER:

    (a)

    $$dr = \frac{x}{\sqrt{x^2 + y^2}} dx + \frac{y}{\sqrt{x^2 + y^2}} dy.$$

    (b)  Inverted cone with 45° slant.
    (c)

    $$|\Delta x| \le 6 \cdot (1\%) = 0.06, \quad |\Delta y| \le 8 \cdot (2\%) = 0.16.$$

    Absolute error: $\Delta r \approx \frac{x}{\sqrt{x^2+y^2}} \Delta x + \frac{y}{\sqrt{x^2+y^2}} \Delta y$, so $|\Delta r| \le \frac{6}{10} 0.06 + \frac{8}{10} 0.16 = 0.164$. Relative error: $\left| \frac{\Delta r}{r} \right| \le \frac{0.164}{10} = 1.64\%$.

    (d)

    $$\frac{\partial r}{\partial t} = \frac{x}{\sqrt{x^2 + y^2}} \frac{\partial x}{\partial t} + \frac{y}{\sqrt{x^2 + y^2}} \frac{\partial y}{\partial t} = \frac{(3t - 1) \cdot 3 + (1 + \frac{4}{t})(-\frac{4}{t^2})}{\sqrt{(3t - 1)^2 + (1 + \frac{4}{t})^2}}.$$

## Problems and Solutions for Section 13.4

1.  True or false? Give a reason for your answer.

(a)   If $\vec{u}$ is a unit vector and the level curves of $f(x, y)$ are given in Figure 13.4.78, then at point $P$ we have $f_{\vec{u}} = \operatorname{grad} f$.

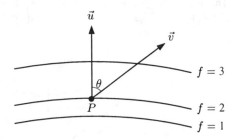

**Figure 13.4.78**

(b)   For the same $f$ as in part (a) and the unit vector $\vec{v}$ shown, $f_{\vec{v}} = \| \operatorname{grad} f \| \cos \theta$.

(c)   There is a function $z = f(x, y)$ and a point $P$ such that the maximum rate of change in $f$ as you move away from $P$ is 7 and the minimum rate of change in $f$ as you move away from $P$ is 5.

ANSWER:

(a)   False. $f_{\vec{u}}$ is a scalar; $\operatorname{grad} f$ is a vector.

(b)   True. $f_{\vec{v}} = (\operatorname{grad} f) \cdot \vec{v} = \| \operatorname{grad} f \| \| \vec{v} \| \cos \theta = \| \operatorname{grad} f \| \cos \theta$ since $\| \vec{v} \| = 1$.

(c)   False. If the maximum rate is 7, the minimum rate is $-7$.

2.   The depth of a pond at the point with coordinates $(x, y)$ is given by $h(x, y) = 2x^2 + 3y^2$ feet.

(a)   If a boat at the point $(-1, 2)$ is sailing in the direction of the vector $4\vec{i} + \vec{j}$, is the water getting deeper or shallower? At what rate? Assume that $x$ and $y$ are measured in feet.

(b)   In which direction should the boat at $(-1, 2)$ move for the depth to remain constant?

ANSWER:

(a)

$$\operatorname{grad} h = 4x\vec{i} + 6y\vec{j}$$

$$u = \frac{4\vec{i}}{\sqrt{17}} + \frac{\vec{j}}{\sqrt{17}}$$

$$h_u(-1, 2) = \operatorname{grad} h(-1, 2) \cdot u = (-4\vec{i} + 12\vec{j}) \cdot \left( \frac{4}{\sqrt{17}}\vec{i} + \frac{1}{\sqrt{17}}\vec{j} \right) = \frac{-4}{\sqrt{17}},$$

so $h$ is decreasing in direction of $\vec{u}$, i.e., water is getting shallower at rate of $4/\sqrt{17}$ ft/ft traveled.

(b)

$$\operatorname{grad} h(x, y) = 4x\vec{i} + 6y\vec{j}$$
$$\operatorname{grad} h(-1, 2) = -4\vec{i} + 12\vec{j} = -4(\vec{i} - 3\vec{j})$$

We want a vector perpendicular to this, so take, e.g., $3\vec{i} + \vec{j}$.

3.   Let $f(x, y) = 4x^2 - 9y^2$.

(a)   Sketch the level curves (contours) for this function which pass through the points $(2, 1)$, $(1, 2)$ and $(3, 2)$. Label the contours and the axes.

(b)   Indicate on your sketch (with an arrow) the direction of the gradient vector for this function at the point $(2, 1)$. What is the length of this gradient vector?

(c)   At what rate does $f(x, y)$ change if you move at unit speed away from the point $(2, 1)$ in the direction of the vector $\vec{v} = 4\vec{i} + 3\vec{j}$?

(d)   If $g(x, y) = 3x^2 + 2y^2$, at what angle do the contours of $f$ and $g$ intersect at the point $(2, 1)$?

(e)   What is the equation of the tangent plane to the graph of $z = f(x, y)$ at the point where $x = 2$ and $y = 1$?

ANSWER:

(a)  Through $(2, 1) : f(x, y) = 4x^2 - 9y^2 = 4(2)^2 - 9(1)^2 = 7.$
Through $(1, 2) : f(x, y) = 4x^2 - 9y^2 = 4(1)^2 - 9(2)^2 = -32.$
Through $(3, 2) : f(x, y) = 4x^2 - 9y^2 = 4(3)^2 - 9(2)^2 = 0.$

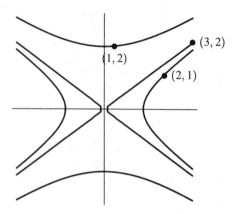

*Figure 13.4.79*

(b)

$$\text{grad } f = 8x\vec{i} - 18y\vec{j}$$
$$\text{At } (2, 1), \text{ grad } f \approx 16\vec{i} - 18\vec{j}$$
$$\| \text{grad } f \| = \sqrt{16^2 + 18^2} = 24.1$$

(c)

$$\text{unit vector } \vec{u} = 0.8\vec{i} + 0.6\vec{j}$$
$$f_{\vec{u}}(2, 1) = (16\vec{i} - 18\vec{j}) \cdot (0.8\vec{i} + 0.6\vec{j})$$
$$= 16(0.8) - 18(0.6) = 2.$$

(d)  grad $g = 6x\vec{i} + 4y\vec{j}$ At $(2, 1)$, grad $g = 12\vec{i} + 4\vec{j}$. The angle between gradients equals the angle between contours.

$$\cos \theta = \frac{(\text{grad } f) \cdot (\text{grad } g)}{\| \text{grad } f \| \| \text{grad } g \|} = \frac{(16\vec{i} - 18\vec{j}) \cdot (12\vec{i} + 4\vec{j})}{\sqrt{16^2 - 18^2}\sqrt{12^2 + 4^2}} = 0.3939.$$

So $\theta = 1.17$ radians.

(e)

$$z = f(2, 1) + f_x(2, 1)(x - 2) + f_y(2, 1)(y - 1) = 7 + 16(x - 2) - 18(y - 1).$$

4.  Suppose that the directional derivative of a function $f(x, y)$ at $(1, 1)$ in the direction $\vec{i}$ is $\sqrt{2}$, and in the direction $(1/\sqrt{2})\vec{i} + (1/\sqrt{2})\vec{j}$ is $-3$. Find the directional derivative of $f$ at $(1, 1)$ in the direction $\vec{u_3}$, where $\vec{u_3} = \frac{2}{\sqrt{13}}\vec{i} + \frac{3}{\sqrt{13}}\vec{j}$.
ANSWER:

$$\sqrt{2} = \text{grad } f \cdot \vec{u}$$
$$= (f_x, f_y) \cdot (1, 0)$$
$$= f_x$$

so $f_x(1,1) = \sqrt{2}$.

$$-3 = \operatorname{grad} f \cdot \vec{u_2}$$
$$= (f_x, f_y) \cdot (\frac{1}{\sqrt{2}}, \frac{1}{\sqrt{2}})$$
$$= \frac{f_x}{\sqrt{2}} + \frac{f_y}{\sqrt{2}}$$
$$= 1 + \frac{f_y}{\sqrt{2}}$$

since $f_x = \sqrt{2}$. So $-4\sqrt{2} = f_y(1,1)$. Finally,

$$f_{\vec{u_3}}(1,1) = \operatorname{grad} f \cdot \vec{u_3}$$
$$= (\sqrt{2}, -4\sqrt{2}) \cdot \frac{1}{\sqrt{13}}(2,3)$$
$$= \sqrt{\frac{2}{13}}(2 - 12)$$
$$= -10\sqrt{\frac{2}{13}}.$$

5.  Suppose that $f(x,y) = x^2 e^{xy}$.

(a)  Find an equation for the tangent plane to $f$ at the point $(1,0)$.

(b)  In what direction does $f$ increase the fastest at the point $(1,0)$? Give your answer as a unit vector.

ANSWER:

(a)

$$\frac{\partial f}{\partial x} = x^2 \cdot ye^{xy} + e^{xy} \cdot 2x \text{ at } (1,0) \qquad \frac{\partial f}{\partial x} = 2$$

$$\frac{\partial f}{\partial y} = x^2 \cdot xe^{xy} \text{ at } (1,0) \qquad \frac{\partial f}{\partial y} = 1$$

$$f(1,0) = 1$$

so the tangent plane is

$$z = 1 + 2(x-1) + 1(y-0) = 2x + y - 1$$

(b)  $f$ increases fastest in the direction of $\operatorname{grad} f(1,0) = 2\vec{i} + \vec{j}$. The unit vector is

$$\vec{u} = \frac{1}{\sqrt{5}}(2\vec{i} + \vec{j})$$
$$= \frac{2}{\sqrt{5}}\vec{i} + \frac{1}{\sqrt{5}}\vec{j}$$

6.  (a)  For the function $f(x,y) = x^2 y^3$ find the direction of the steepest increase at the point $(a,b) = (1,1)$.

(b)  Use the value of $f(1,1) = 1$ and the gradient to obtain a linear approximation for $1.05^2 \cdot 0.97^3$.

ANSWER:

(a)  If $f(x,y) = x^2 y^3$ then $\operatorname{grad} f(1,1) = 2\vec{i} + 3\vec{j}$ and the direction of the steepest increase is $\vec{u} = \frac{1}{\sqrt{13}}(2\vec{i} + 3\vec{j})$.

(b)  $f(1 + \Delta x, 1 + \Delta y) \approx f(1,1) + \operatorname{grad} f(1,1) \cdot \vec{v}$ where $\vec{v} = 0.05\vec{i} - 0.03\vec{j}$. Consequently, $f(1.05, 0.97) \approx 1 + 0.1 - 0.09 = 1.01$.

7.

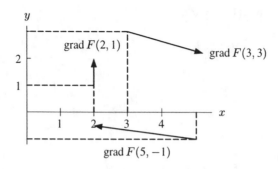

**Figure 13.4.80**

Figure 13.4.80 shows the gradient of $F(x, y)$ at $(2, 1)$, $(3, 3, )$, and $(5, -1)$. Give approximate values of the following:

(a) $F_x(5, -1)$
(b) $F_y(3, 3)$
(c) $F_x(2, 1)$
(d) $\vec{F}_{\vec{u}}(2, 1)$ with $\vec{u} = \dfrac{1}{\sqrt{2}}\vec{i} + \dfrac{1}{\sqrt{2}}\vec{j}$
(e) $\vec{F}_{\vec{u}}(3, 3)$ with $\vec{u} = \dfrac{1}{\sqrt{10}}\vec{i} - \dfrac{3}{\sqrt{10}}\vec{j}$

ANSWER:

(a) $F_x(5, -1) = -3$.
(b) $F_y(3, 3) = -1$.
(c) $F_x(2, 1) = 0$.
(d) $\vec{F}_{\vec{u}}(2, 1) = \operatorname{grad} f(2, 1) \cdot \vec{u} = (\vec{j}) \cdot (\frac{1}{\sqrt{2}}\vec{i} + \frac{1}{\sqrt{2}}\vec{j}) = \frac{\sqrt{2}}{2}$.
(e)

$$\vec{F}_{\vec{u}}(3, 3) = \operatorname{grad} f(3, 3) \cdot \vec{u} = (2\vec{i} - \vec{j}) \cdot (\frac{1}{\sqrt{10}}\vec{i} - \frac{3}{\sqrt{10}}\vec{j})$$

$$= \frac{2}{\sqrt{10}} + \frac{3}{\sqrt{10}} = \frac{5}{\sqrt{10}} = \frac{\sqrt{10}}{2}.$$

8. Suppose that $T(x, y) = x^2 + 2y^2 - x$ is the temperature at the point $(x, y)$. If you are standing at the point $(-2, 1)$ and decide to proceed in the direction of the point $(1, -3)$, will the temperature be increasing or decreasing at the moment you begin? At what rate?

ANSWER:

Find a unit vector, pointing from $(-2, 1)$ to $(1, -3)$:

$$\vec{u} = \frac{3\vec{i} - 4\vec{j}}{\sqrt{3^2 + (-4)^2}} = \frac{3}{5}\vec{i} - \frac{4}{5}\vec{j}.$$

The rate of change of $T$ in the direction $\vec{u}$, at $(-2, 1)$ is $T_{\vec{u}}(-2, 1) = (\operatorname{grad} T(-2, 1)) \cdot \vec{u}$.

$$\operatorname{grad} T(-2, 1) = \frac{\partial T}{\partial x}\bigg|_{x=-2, y=1} \vec{i} + \frac{\partial T}{\partial y}\bigg|_{x=-2, y=1} \vec{j} = -5\vec{i} + 4\vec{j}.$$

So, $T_{\vec{u}}(-2, 1) = (-5\vec{i} + 4\vec{j})(\frac{3}{5}\vec{i} - \frac{4}{5}\vec{j}) = -3 - \frac{16}{5} = -\frac{31}{5} < 0$. So, the moment you begin, the temperature decreases, at a rate $-\frac{31}{5}$, but it will increase eventually as the final temperature $T(1, -3) = 18$ is bigger than the initial one, $T(-2, 1) = 8$.

## Problems and Solutions for Section 13.5

1. True or False? If $f(x, y, z) = x^2 + y^2 + z^2$ then the highest point where $f = 1$ will have $\operatorname{grad} f = \vec{0}$.

ANSWER:

False. $\operatorname{grad} f$ is $\vec{0}$ at the highest point on the graph of $f$, not on a level set of $f$.

2. True or False?

   (a) If grad $f$ = grad $g$, then $f = g$.

   (b) If you know the directional derivative of $f(x, y)$ in two different directions at a point $P$ then you can find $\frac{\partial f}{\partial x}(P)$.

   (c) If $f(x, y) = x^2 + y^2$ then grad $f$ is perpendicular to the graph of $f$.

   ANSWER:

   (a) False. For example, $f = x$, $g = x + 2$. Then grad $f$ = grad $g = \vec{i}$ but $f \neq g$.

   (b) True, as with two different directional derivatives, we can find the derivative with respect to the $x$ and $y$ axes and thus we can determine the derivative at point $P$.

   (c) False. Gradients are perpendicular to contours of a function, not to the graph of the function itself.

3. Consider the surface given as the graph of a function $z = f(x, y)$. Let $\vec{u} = 1/\sqrt{17}(\vec{i} + 4\vec{j})$ and $\vec{v} = 1/5(-3\vec{i} + 4\vec{j})$. Suppose that

$$f_{\vec{u}}(1, 3) = 0, f_{\vec{v}}(1, 3) = 16, f(1, 3) = -7.$$

   Find the gradient of $f$ at $(1, 3)$, and the equation of the tangent plane to the surface at $(1, 3, 7)$.

   ANSWER:

$$\text{grad } f(1, 3) = a\vec{i} + b\vec{j}$$
$$0 = \text{grad } f(1, 3) \cdot \vec{u} = \frac{1}{\sqrt{17}}(a + 4b)$$
$$16 = \text{grad } f(1, 3) \cdot \vec{v} = \frac{1}{5}(-3a + 4b)$$

   So,

$$a + 4b = 0$$
$$-3a + 4b = 80$$
$$a = -20$$
$$b = 5$$
$$\text{grad } f(1, 3) = -20\vec{i} + 5\vec{j}.$$

   The equation of the tangent plane is

$$z = f(1, 3) + f_x(1, 3)(x - 1) + f_y(1, 3)(y - 3)$$
$$= -7 - 20(x - 1) + 5(y - 3)$$
$$= -2 - 20x + 5y$$

4. Suppose that as you move away from the point $(1, 2, 4)$, the function $f(x, y, z)$ increases most rapidly in the direction of the vector $0.6\vec{i} + 0.8\vec{k}$ and that the rate of increase of $f$ in this direction is 7. At what rate is $f$ increasing as you move away from the point $(1, 2, 4)$ in the direction of the vector $(1/\sqrt{3})\vec{i} + (1/\sqrt{3})\vec{j} + (1/\sqrt{3})\vec{k}$ ?

   ANSWER:

   We know $\| \text{grad } f \| = 7$ and that the direction of grad $f$ is $0.6\vec{i} + 0.8\vec{k}$. Since $0.6\vec{i} + 0.8\vec{k}$ is a unit vector, we must have grad $f = 7(0.6\vec{i} + 0.8\vec{k}) = 4.2\vec{i} + 5.6\vec{k}$. Now we want $f_{\vec{u}} = \text{grad } f \cdot \vec{u}$ where $\vec{u} = 1/\sqrt{3}\vec{i} + 1/\sqrt{3}\vec{j} + 1/\sqrt{3}\vec{k}$. So $f_{\vec{u}} = (4.2\vec{i} + 0.5\vec{j} + 6\vec{k}) \cdot ((1/\sqrt{3})\vec{i} + (1/\sqrt{3})\vec{j} + (1/\sqrt{3})\vec{k}) = 9.8/\sqrt{3} = 5.66$.

5. Write a paragraph explaining the meaning of and relationships between the partial derivative, the directional derivative and the gradient of a function $f$. Pay close attention to the meaning of these mathematical objects, as opposed to methods of computation. Do not simply list definitions: try to write as if you were explaining these objects to a friend who has had one year of one-variable calculus.

ANSWER:

The directional derivative is the rate of change of $f$ in a given direction; that is, it gives the change in $f$ per unit displacement in a given direction. The partial derivatives are special cases of the directional derivative in the direction of the coordinate axes. The gradient of $f$ is a vector whose direction is the direction in which $f$ increases fastest, and whose magnitude is the rate of change of $f$ in that direction. It has the property that its dot product with any unit vector gives the directional derivative of $f$ in the direction of that unit vector.

6. Consider the surface $xyz + x^2 - y^2 = 2$.

   (a) Find the equation of the tangent plane at $(3, 1, -2)$ in two different ways: first, by viewing the surface as the level surface of a function of 3 variables, $F(x, y, z)$; second, by viewing the surface as the graph of a function of two variables, $z = f(x, y)$. Explain what you are doing!

   (b) Find all points on the surface where a vector perpendicular to the surface is parallel to the $xy$-plane.

   ANSWER:

   (a) Let $F(x, y, z) = x^2 - y^2 + xyz - 2 = 0$. As grad $F = (2x + yz)\vec{i} + (-2y + xz)\vec{j} + (xy)\vec{k}$ and grad $F(3, 1, -2) = 4\vec{i} - 8\vec{j} + 3\vec{k}$, then the equation of the tangent plane is:

   $$[(x - 3)\vec{i} + (y - 1)\vec{j} + (z + 2)\vec{k}] \cdot [4\vec{i} - 8\vec{j} + 3\vec{k}] = 0$$
   $$(4x - 12) + (-8y + 8) + (3z + 6) = 0$$
   $$4x - 8y + 3z + 2 = 0.$$

   Alternate method:

   As $xyz + x^2 - y^2 = 2$, then $z = \dfrac{y^2 - x^2 + 2}{xy}$ for $xy \neq 0$. We are interested in $(x, y) = (3, 1)$. So, we are looking to see if we can define our function around this point.

   $$z = \frac{y}{x} - \frac{x}{y} + \frac{2}{xy}.$$

   Thus the equation of the tangent plane is

   $$z = -2 + \left.\frac{\partial z}{\partial x}\right|_{(3,1)} (x - 3) + \left.\frac{\partial z}{\partial y}\right|_{(3,1)} (y - 1).$$

   Since

   $$\frac{\partial z}{\partial x} = -\frac{y}{x^2} - \frac{1}{y} - \frac{2}{x^2 y} \quad \text{and} \quad \frac{\partial z}{\partial y} = \frac{1}{x} + \frac{x}{y^2} - \frac{2}{xy^2}$$

   we get

   $$z = -2 - \frac{4}{3}(x - 3) + \frac{8}{3}(y - 1).$$

   (b) Let $F(x, y, z) = x^2 - y^2 + xyz - 2 = 0$. We get grad $F = (2x + yz)\vec{i} + (-2y + xz)\vec{j} + (xy)\vec{k}$ and we want the point where grad $F \cdot \vec{k} = 0$. So,

   $$[(2x + yz)\vec{i} + (-2y + xz)\vec{j} + (xy)\vec{k}] \cdot \vec{k} = 0$$
   $$xy = 0.$$

   Thus, $x = 0$ or $y = 0$. If $x = 0$, then from the equation of the surface, we have:

   $$(0)^2 - y^2 + (0)yz - 2 = 0$$
   $$y^2 = -2.$$

   So there are no solutions. If $y = 0$ then

   $$x^2 - (0)^2 + x(0)z - 2 = 0$$
   $$x^2 = 2$$
   $$x = \pm 2.$$

   Hence the required points are: $(\sqrt{2}, 0, z)$ and $(-\sqrt{2}, 0, z)$ for all $z$. Geometrically, these points lie on two vertical lines.

7. Find the equation of the tangent plane to the surface $xyz + x^3 + y^3 + z^3 = 14$ at $(3, -2, 1)$.

    ANSWER:

    Let $F(x, y, z) = xyz + x^3 + y^3 + z^3 - 14$. The normal to this surface is:

$$\text{grad } F = (yz + 3x^2)\vec{i} + (xz + 3y^2)\vec{j} + (xy + 3z^2)\vec{k}.$$

Hence at $(3, -2, 1)$:

$$\text{grad } F = 25\vec{i} + 15\vec{j} - 3\vec{k}.$$

Let $(x, y, z)$ be any point on the tangent plane; then $(x - 3)\vec{i} + (y + 2)\vec{j} + (z - 1)\vec{k}$ should be in the plane. Hence,

$$[(x - 3)\vec{i} + (y + 2)\vec{j} + (z - 1)\vec{k}] \cdot \text{grad } F = 0$$
$$25(x - 3) + 15(y + 2) - 3(z - 1) = 0$$
$$25x + 15y - 3z = 42.$$

Thus the equation of the tangent plane is:

$$25x + 15y - 3z = 42.$$

8. Find an equation for the tangent plane to the ellipsoid $(x - 1)^2 + 4(y - 2)^2 + (z - 3)^2 = 17$ at the point $(3, 3, 6)$.

    ANSWER:

    Let $f(x, y, z) = (x - 1)^2 + 4(y - 2)^2 + (z - 3)^2 - 17$ be the function which gives the ellipsoid. In general, the equation of the tangent plane to the surface $f(x, y, z) = 0$ at the point $(x_0, y_0, z_0)$ is given by:

$$((x - x_0)\vec{i} + (y - y_0)\vec{j} + (z - z_0)\vec{k}) \cdot \text{grad } f(x_0, y_0, z_0) = 0.$$

In our case $(x_0, y_0, z_0) = (3, 3, 6)$, and $f(x, y, z) = x^2 - 2x + 4y^2 - 16y + z^2 - 6z + 9$, thus

$$\text{grad } f(3, 3, 6) = (2 \cdot 3 - 2)\vec{i} + (8 \cdot 3 - 16)\vec{j} + (2 \cdot 6 - 6)\vec{k} = 4\vec{i} + 8\vec{j} + 6\vec{k}.$$

Then, the equation of our tangent plane is given by:

$$((x - 3)\vec{i} + (y - 3)\vec{j} + (z - 6)\vec{k}) \cdot (4\vec{i} + 8\vec{j} + 6\vec{k}) = 0$$

equivalent to $2x + 4y + 3z = 36$.

9. Consider the function $g(x, y, z) = x^2 + y^2 + z^2$.

    (a) Describe the level set $g = 3$.

    (b) Find a vector perpendicular to the tangent plane to the level set $g = 3$ at the point $(1, 1, 1)$.

    ANSWER:

    (a) Sphere of radius $\sqrt{3}$ centered at the origin.

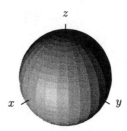

*Figure 13.5.81*

    (b) The gradient is perpendicular to the level set. $\text{grad } g = 2x\vec{i} + 2y\vec{j} + 2z\vec{k}$, $\text{grad } g(1, 1, 1) = 2\vec{i} + 2\vec{j} + 2\vec{k}$.

10. Consider the surface $z = xy$ and the point $P = (1, 2, 2)$.

   (a) Sketch the level curve for $z = 2$.
   (b) If a group of climbers at $P$ want to climb by way of the steepest route possible, in what direction should they begin?
   (c) Starting from $P$, sketch the vector found in part (b) on your sketch for part (a).
   (d) What is the slope that the climbers will encounter at $P$?
   (e) One of the climbers decides to move Southwest from $P$. (Assume the positive $y$-axis points North.)
      (i) Is this person ascending or descending?
      (ii) What is the slope of this person's path at $P$?
   (f) Determine a vector normal to the surface at $P$.
   (g) Determine an equation for the plane tangent to the surface at $P$.

   ANSWER:

   (a) See Figure 13.5.82.

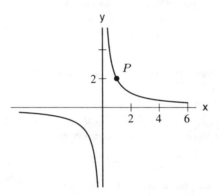

**Figure 13.5.82**

   (b) The tangent vector of the level curve for $z = 2$ at $P = (1, 2, 2)$ is $\vec{T} = \vec{i} - 2\vec{j}$. Then a vector normal to $\vec{T}$ is $\vec{n} = 2\vec{i} + \vec{j}$. Since the steepest route is in the direction perpendicular to the level curves, they should begin in the direction $2\vec{i} + \vec{j}$.

   (c) See Figure 13.5.83.

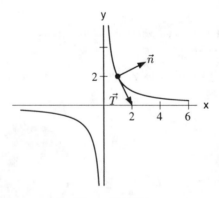

**Figure 13.5.83**

   (d) The slope that the climbers will encounter at $P$ is the directional derivative of $z$ in direction $\vec{u}$, where

$$\vec{u} = \frac{\vec{n}}{|\vec{n}|} = \frac{2\vec{i} + \vec{j}}{\sqrt{2^2 + 1^2}} = \frac{2}{\sqrt{5}}\vec{i} + \frac{1}{\sqrt{5}}\vec{j}.$$

$$f_{\vec{u}}\,(1,2) = \text{grad } f(1,2) \cdot \vec{u}$$
$$= (2\vec{i} + \vec{j}) \cdot (\frac{2}{\sqrt{5}}\vec{i} + \frac{1}{\sqrt{5}}\vec{j})$$
$$= \frac{4}{\sqrt{5}} + \frac{1}{\sqrt{5}}$$
$$= \sqrt{5}.$$

(e) (i) descending.

(ii) The direction of this person is $\vec{v} = -\vec{i} - \vec{j}$ then

$$\vec{u} = \frac{\vec{v}}{\|\vec{v}\|} = \frac{-\vec{i} - \vec{j}}{\sqrt{(-1)^2 + (-1)^2}} = -\frac{1}{\sqrt{2}}\vec{i} - \frac{1}{\sqrt{2}}\vec{j}.$$

So

$$f_{\vec{v}}\,(1,2) = \text{grad } f(1,2) \cdot \vec{u}$$
$$= (2\vec{i} + \vec{j}) \cdot (-\frac{1}{\sqrt{2}}\vec{i} - \frac{1}{\sqrt{2}}\vec{j})$$
$$= -\frac{3}{\sqrt{2}}.$$

(f) A vector normal to the surface at $P$ is

$$\vec{n} = 2\vec{i} + \vec{j} - \vec{k}.$$

(g) Tangent plane at $P$ is:

$$z = f(1,2) + f_x(1,2)(x-1) + f_y(1,2)(y-2)$$
$$= 2 + 2(x-1) + (y-2)$$
$$= 2x + y - 2.$$

## *Problems and Solutions for Section 13.6*

1. The quantity $z$ can be expressed as a function of $x$ and $y$ as follows: $z = f(x,y)$. Now $x$ and $y$ are themselves functions of $r$ and $\theta$, as follows: $x = g(r,\theta)$ and $y = h(r,\theta)$. Suppose you know that $g(1,\pi/2) = 0$, and $h(1,\pi/2) = 1$. In addition, you are told that $f_x(0,1) = 2$, $f_y(0,1) = 3$, $g_r(1,\pi/2) = 5$, $g_\theta(1,\pi/2) = 7$, $h_r(1,\pi/2) = 9$, $h_\theta(1,\pi/2) = 11$. Find $\frac{\partial z}{\partial r}|_{(1,\pi/2)}$.

   ANSWER:

   As $\frac{\partial z}{\partial r} = \frac{\partial f}{\partial x}\frac{\partial g}{\partial r} + \frac{\partial f}{\partial y}\frac{\partial h}{\partial r}$, then

   $$\frac{\partial z}{\partial r}\bigg|_{(1,\pi/2)} = (2)(5) + (3)(9)$$
   $$= 37.$$

2. People commuting to a city can choose to go either by bus or by train. The number of people who choose either method depends in part upon the price of each. Let $f(P_1, P_2)$ be the number of people who take the bus when $P_1$ is the price of a bus ride and $P_2$ is the price of a train ride.

   (a) What can you say about the signs of $\partial f/\partial P_1$ and $\partial f/\partial P_2$? Explain the reasons for your answers.

   (b) Suppose that the price of a bus ride, $P_1$, and the price of a train ride, $P_2$, each increases linearly over a period of time, with the price of a bus ride increasing at half the rate of the price of a train ride. Under what conditions will the number of people who ride the bus increase over that period? Explain.

ANSWER:

(a) $\partial f/\partial P_1 < 0$. If $P_2$ is fixed and $P_1$ increases, then the number of people riding the bus will decrease.

$\partial f/\partial P_2 > 0$. Likewise, if $P_1$ is fixed and $P_2$ increases, then the number of people riding the bus will increase.

(b) We are given that $dP_1/dt = 1/2\ dP_2/dt$.

$$\frac{df}{dt} = \frac{\partial f}{\partial P_1}\frac{dP_1}{dt} + \frac{\partial f}{\partial P_2}\frac{dP_2}{dt}$$

$$= \frac{\partial f}{\partial P_1}(\frac{1}{2}\frac{dP_2}{dt}) + \frac{\partial f}{\partial P_2}\frac{dP_2}{dt}$$

$$= \frac{dP_2}{dt}(\frac{1}{2}\frac{\partial f}{\partial P_1} + \frac{\partial f}{\partial P_2})$$

$dP_2/dt > 0$ and we want $df/dt > 0$ so,

$$\frac{1}{2}\frac{\partial f}{\partial P_1} + \frac{\partial f}{\partial P_2} > 0 \quad \text{or} \quad \frac{\partial f}{\partial P_2} > -\frac{1}{2}\frac{\partial f}{\partial P_2}.$$

Thus, the rate of which people switch from the train to the bus with respect to price increases in train fare should be more than half the rate of which they stop using the bus with respect to increases in bus fare.

3. Let $w = 3x\cos y$.

(a) If $x = u^2 + v^2, y = v/u$, find $\partial w/\partial u$ and $\partial w/\partial v$ at the point $(u, v) = (1, 1)$.

(b) If $x = e^{-t}$ and $y = \ln t$, find $\partial w/\partial t$ at the point $t = 1$.

ANSWER:

(a)

$$\frac{\partial w}{\partial u} = \frac{\partial w}{\partial x}\frac{\partial x}{\partial u} + \frac{\partial w}{\partial y}\frac{\partial y}{\partial u}$$

$$= (3\cos y)(2u) + (-3x\sin y)\left(-\frac{v}{u^2}\right)$$

$$= 6\cos\left(\frac{v}{u}\right)\cdot u + 3(u^2 + v^2)\sin\left(\frac{v}{u}\right)\cdot\left(\frac{v}{u^2}\right)$$

$$= 6\cos 1 + 6\sin 1$$

$$\simeq 8.29$$

$$\frac{\partial w}{\partial v} = \frac{\partial w}{\partial x}\frac{\partial x}{\partial v} + \frac{\partial w}{\partial y}\frac{\partial y}{\partial v}$$

$$= (3\cos y)(2v) + (-3x\sin y)\left(\frac{1}{u}\right)$$

$$= 6\cos\left(\frac{v}{u}\right)\cdot v - 3(u^2 + v^2)\sin\left(\frac{v}{u}\right)\cdot\frac{1}{u}$$

$$= 6\cos 1 - 6\sin 1$$

$$\simeq -1.81$$

(b)

$$\frac{\partial w}{\partial t} = \frac{\partial w}{\partial x}\frac{\partial x}{\partial t} + \frac{\partial w}{\partial y}\frac{\partial y}{\partial t}$$

$$= (3\cos y)(-e^{-t}) + (-3x\sin y)\left(\frac{1}{t}\right)$$

$$= -3\cos(\ln t)e^{-t} - 3e^{-t}\sin(\ln t)\cdot\frac{1}{t}$$

$$= -3\cos(\ln 1)e^{-1} - 3e^{-1}\sin(\ln 1)\cdot\frac{1}{1}$$

$$= -3\cos(0)e^{-1} - 3e^{-1}\sin(0)$$

$$= -3e^{-1}$$

$$\simeq -1.10$$

4. Suppose $f(x, y)$ is a function of $x$ and $y$ and define

$$g(u, v) = f(e^u + \cos v, e^u + \sin v).$$

Find $g_u(0, 0)$ given that

$$f(0, 0) = \pi, f_x(0, 0) = 1, f_x(1, 2) = 3, f_x(2, 1) = 5, f(2, 1) = e,$$

and

$$g(0, 0) = e, f_y(0, 0) = 2, f_y(1, 2) = 4, f_y(2, 1) = 6, f(1, 2) = \pi^2.$$

Show your work.

ANSWER:

When $u = 0$ and $v = 0$, we have

$$x = e^0 + \cos(0) = 2, \quad y = e^0 + \sin(0) = 1.$$

So

$$g_u(0, 0) = \frac{\partial f}{\partial x}\frac{\partial x}{\partial u} + \frac{\partial f}{\partial y}\frac{\partial y}{\partial u}$$

$$= \frac{\partial f}{\partial x}e^u + \frac{\partial f}{\partial y}e^u$$

$$= \frac{\partial f}{\partial x}(2, 1)e^0 + \frac{\partial f}{\partial y}(2, 1)e^0$$

$$= 5(1) + 6(1) = 11.$$

5. If $z = f(x, y)$ and $x = s + t, y = s - t$, show that $\left(\frac{\partial z}{\partial s}\right)\left(\frac{\partial z}{\partial t}\right) = (f_x)^2 - (f_y)^2$.

ANSWER:

Since $z = f(x, y)$ and $x = s + t, y = s - t$, we have, by the chain rule, that

$$f_s = \frac{\partial z}{\partial s} = \frac{\partial z}{\partial x}\frac{\partial x}{\partial s} + \frac{\partial z}{\partial y}\frac{\partial y}{\partial s} = f_x + f_y$$

$$f_t = \frac{\partial z}{\partial t} = \frac{\partial z}{\partial x}\frac{\partial x}{\partial t} + \frac{\partial z}{\partial y}\frac{\partial y}{\partial t} = f_x - f_y$$

$$f_s f_t = (\frac{\partial z}{\partial s})(\frac{\partial z}{\partial t}) = (f_x + f_y)(f_x - f_y) = (f_x)^2 - (f_y)^2$$

6. Sally is on a day hike at Mt. Baker. From 9 to 11:00 a.m. she zig-zags up $z = f(x, y)$ where $x$ is the number of miles due east of her starting position, $y$ is the number of miles due north of her starting position, and $z$ is her elevation in miles above sea level. Feeling tired, she decides to continue walking, but in such a way that her altitude remains constant from 11 a.m. to noon to settle her stomach for lunch. At 11:30 a.m., she will be passing through $(1, -2, 2)$ where $f_x(1, -2) = 3$ and $f_y(1, -2) = -2$. What is the slope of her "path" in the $x, y$ plane at this instant? That is, determine $dy/dx_{(1, -2)}$. (This "path" is among the level curves in the plane.)

ANSWER:

At $t = 11 : 30$ am, we know that her altitude remains constant, that is, $dz/dt = 0$. From the chain rule we have that

$$\frac{dz}{dt} = \frac{\partial z}{\partial x}\frac{dx}{dt} + \frac{\partial z}{\partial y}\frac{dy}{dt}$$

$$0 = 3\frac{dx}{dt} - 2\frac{dy}{dt}$$

Therefore,

$$\frac{dy}{dx}(1, 2) = \frac{3}{2}$$

7.  If $f(x, y) = x^3 + y^2$, and $x = e^u$, $y = ue^w$, find $f_w(1, 1)$ using the chain rule.

ANSWER:

When $(u, w) = (1, 1)$, $x = e$, $y = e$ so

$$\frac{\partial f}{\partial w}(-1, 1) = \frac{\partial f}{\partial x}(e, e) \cdot \frac{\partial x}{\partial w}(1, 1) + \frac{\partial f}{\partial y}(e, e) \cdot \frac{\partial y}{\partial w}(1, 1)$$

$$= 3e^2 \cdot 0 + 2e \cdot e$$

$$= 2e^2.$$

8.  If $f(x, y) = \sin(x) + y^2$, $x(u, v) = uv$ and $y(u, v) = u + v$

    (a)  If $H(u, v) = f(x(u, v), y(u, v))$, what is $H(0, 1)$?

    (b)  Use the chain rule to find $\dfrac{\partial H}{\partial v}(0, 1)$.

ANSWER:

(a)  $H(0, 1) = f(0 \cdot 1, 0 + 1) = f(0, 1) = \sin 0 + 1^2 = 1$

(b)

$$\frac{\partial H}{\partial v} = \frac{\partial f}{\partial x}\frac{\partial x}{\partial v} + \frac{\partial f}{\partial y}\frac{\partial y}{\partial v} = (\cos x)u + 2y \cdot 1 = u\cos(uv) + 2(u + v)$$

$$\left.\frac{\partial H}{\partial v}\right|_{(0,1)} = 0\cos 0 + 2(0 + 1) = 2.$$

## Problems and Solutions  for Section 13.7

1.  Find the following partial derivatives:

    (a)  $H_P(1, 2)$ if $H(P, T) = \dfrac{3P}{2P + T}$,

    (b)  $f_{xy}$ if $f(x, y) = (xy)^7$.

    ANSWER:

    (a)

    $$\frac{\partial H}{\partial P} = \frac{3(2P + T) - 3P(2)}{(2P + T)^2}$$

    so

    $$H_P(1, 2) = \frac{3(2)}{(2(1) + 2)^2} = \frac{3}{8}.$$

    (b)  $f(x, y) = x^7 y^7$ so

    $$f_{xy} = \frac{\partial}{\partial y}(7x^6 y^7) = 49x^6 y^6.$$

2.  Consider the level curves shown for the function $z = f(x, y)$.

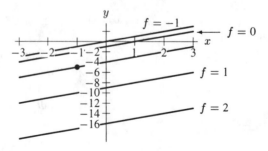

Figure 13.7.84

Determine the sign of the following:

(a) $f_x(-1, -5)$    (b) $f_y(-1, -5)$    (c) $f_{xx}(-1, -5)$

(d) $f_{yy}(-1, -5)$    (e) $f_{yx}(-1, -5)$

ANSWER:

(a) $f_x(-1, -5)$ positive    (b) $f_y(-1, -5)$ negative    (c) $f_{xx}(-1, -5)$ negative

(d) $f_{yy}(-1, -5)$ negative    (e) $f_{yx}(-1, -5)$ positive

## Problems and Solutions for Section 13.8

1. Find the quadratic approximation to the function $f(x, y) = \cos x \cos y$ valid near the origin. Show your work.

ANSWER:

As

$$f(x, y) \approx f(0, 0) + f_x(0, 0)x + f_y(0, 0)y + \frac{1}{2}f_{xx}(0, 0)x^2 + f_{xy}(0, 0)xy + \frac{1}{2}f_{yy}(0, 0)y^2$$

and

$$f_x = -\sin x \cos y$$
$$f_y = -\cos x \sin y$$
$$f_{xx} = -\cos x \cos y$$
$$f_{yy} = -\cos x \cos y$$
$$f_{xy} = \sin x \sin y$$

then,

$$f(x, y) \approx 1 - \frac{1}{2}x^2 - \frac{1}{2}y^2.$$

## Problems and Solutions to Review Problems for Chapter 13

1. (a) Find $\dfrac{\partial}{\partial P}\left(\dfrac{Pe^T}{T - e^P}\right)$. Do not simplify your answer.

(b) Find the directional derivative of $f(x, y) = x^3y + xy^2$ at the point $(1, 2)$ in the direction of $3\vec{i} - 4\vec{j}$.

(c) Find a unit vector perpendicular to both $\vec{i} - \vec{j} - \vec{k}$ and $2\vec{i} + \vec{k}$.

(d) The ideal gas law states that $PV = nRT$ where $n$ and $R$ are constants. Find the rate of change of pressure with respect to volume in an experiment where the temperature remains constant.

(e)   Find the angle between the vector $\vec{c} = 2\vec{i} + 3\vec{j} + \vec{k}$ and the positive $z$-axis.
ANSWER:

(a)

$$\frac{\partial}{\partial P}\left(\frac{Pe^T}{T - e^P}\right) = \frac{e^T}{T - e^P} + Pe^T \frac{\partial}{\partial P}\left(\frac{1}{T - e^P}\right)$$

$$= \frac{e^T}{T - e^P} + Pe^T \cdot (-1) \cdot (T - e^P)^{-2} \cdot (-e^P)$$

$$= \frac{e^T(T - e^P) + e^T \cdot e^P \cdot P}{(T - e^P)^2}$$

$$= e^T \cdot \frac{e^P(P - 1) + T}{(T - e^P)^2}.$$

(b)

$$\vec{v} = 3\vec{i} - 4\vec{j}.$$

$$\vec{u} = \frac{\vec{v}}{\|v\|} = \frac{3\vec{i} - 4\vec{j}}{5} = \frac{3}{5}\vec{i} - \frac{4}{5}\vec{j}.$$

$$\text{grad } f(x, y) = f_x\vec{i} + f_y\vec{j}$$
$$= (3x^2y + y^2)\vec{i} + (x^3 + 2xy)\vec{j}.$$

So

$$f_{\vec{v}}(1, 2) = \text{grad } f(1, 2) \cdot \vec{j}$$
$$= [(3 \cdot 1 \cdot 2 + 4)\vec{i} + (1 + 2 \cdot 1 \cdot 2 \cdot)\vec{j}] \cdot [\frac{3}{5}\vec{i} - \frac{4}{5}\vec{j}]$$
$$= 6 - 4$$
$$= 2.$$

(c)   $\vec{u} = \vec{i} - \vec{j} - \vec{k}$ and $\vec{v} = 2\vec{i} + \vec{k}$, so

$$\vec{u} \times \vec{v} = \begin{vmatrix} \vec{i} & \vec{j} & \vec{k} \\ 1 & -1 & -1 \\ 2 & 0 & 1 \end{vmatrix} = -\vec{i} - 3\vec{j} + 2\vec{k} = \vec{w}.$$

(d)   $P = \frac{nRT}{V}$ and $n$, $R$ and $T$ are fixed. So $\frac{\partial P}{\partial V} = -\frac{nRT}{V^2}$ is the desired rate of change

(e)   Let $\theta$ be that angle:

$$\cos\theta = \frac{\vec{c} \cdot \vec{k}}{\|\vec{c}\|\|\vec{k}\|}$$

$$= \frac{1}{\sqrt{4 + 9 + 1} \cdot 1}$$

$$= \frac{\sqrt{14}}{14}.$$

So,

$$\theta = \arccos\frac{\sqrt{14}}{14} = 1.30 rads.$$

2.   Consider the planes:

I.     $3x - 5y - z = 2$
II.    $5x = y + 3$
III.   $5x + 3y = 2$

IV.  $3x + 5y = 2$

V.  $3x + 5y + z = 2$

VI.  $y + 1 = 0$

Without giving reasons, list all of the planes which:

(a)  Are parallel to the $z$-axis.

(b)  Are parallel to $3x = 5y + z + 7$.

(c)  Contain the point$(1, -1, 6)$.

(d)  Are normal to the cross product of the vectors $\vec{a} = 2\vec{i} + 3\vec{k}$ and $\vec{b} = 3\vec{i} - \vec{k}$.

(e)  Could be the tangent plane to a surface $z = f(x, y)$, where $f$ is some function which has finite partial derivatives everywhere.

ANSWER:

(a)  II, III, IV, VI

(b)  I

(c)  I, III, VI

(d)  VI

(e)  I, II, V

**3.**

TABLE 13.10.7

|   |     | $y$ |     |     |
|---|-----|-----|-----|-----|
|   |     | 1.5 | 2.0 | 2.5 |
|   | 0.0 | 36  | 35  | 34  |
| $x$ | 1.0 | 38  | 37  | 35  |
|   | 2.0 | 44  | 42  | 38  |

Table 13.10.8 gives values of a function $f(x, y)$ near $x = 1$, $y = 2$.

(a)  Estimate $f_x(1, 2)$ and $f_y(1, 2)$. Use your answer in parts (b)-(f).

(b)  Use local linearity to give a "close-up" table of values of $f(x, y)$ for $x = .9, 1.0, 1.1$, and $y = 1.9, 2.0, 2.1$.

(c)  Give the equation of the tangent plane to the graph $z = f(x, y)$ at $x = 1$, $y = 2$.

(d)  Suppose $f(x, y)$ represents the temperature at $(x, y)$. If you are standing at $(1, 2)$, which direction should you head to heat up as rapidly as possible? If you moved in that direction a distance of .06, how much would you heat up?

(e)  Suppose you are standing at $(1, 2)$ and you start walking at unit speed towards the point $(5, 5)$. What will be the instantaneous rate of change of $f$?

(f)  The level curve for $f$ going through $(1, 2)$ will look like a straight line up close. What is the equation of this straight line? Explain your answer.

(g)  Estimate $f_{xx}(1, 2)$ and $f_{yy}(1, 2)$.

(h)  Is $f_{xy}(1, 2) > 0$? Explain.

(i)  Suppose the table of values given at the beginning of this problem is actually temperatures near $x = 1, y = 2$ at time $t = 0$ and that the temperatures satisfy the heat equation $u_t = k(u_{xx} + u_{yy})$. An instant later will the temperature at $x = 1, y = 2$ be warmer? Explain your answer.

ANSWER:

(a)

$$f_x(1, 2) \approx \frac{f(2, 2) - f(1, 2)}{2 - 1}$$

$$\approx \frac{42 - 37}{1}$$

$$\approx 5.$$

$$f_y(1, 2) \approx \frac{f(1, 2.5) - f(1, 2)}{2.5 - 2}$$

$$\approx \frac{35 - 37}{0.5}$$
$$\approx -4.$$

(other estimates are possible)

(b)

**TABLE 13.10.8**

|   |     | $y$ | | |
|---|-----|------|-----|-----|
|   |     | 1.9 | 2.0 | 2.1 |
| $x$ | 0.9 | 36.9 | 36.5 | 36.1 |
|   | 1.0 | 37.4 | 37 | 36.6 |
|   | 1.1 | 37.9 | 37.5 | 37.1 |

(c)   The equation of the tangent plane is:

$$z = f(1,2) + \frac{\partial z}{\partial x}\bigg|_{(1,2)} (x-1) + \frac{\partial z}{\partial y}\bigg|_{(1,2)} (y-2)$$
$$= 37 + 5(x-1) - 4(y-2)$$
$$= 40 + 5x - 4y.$$

(d)

$$\text{grad } f(1,2) = f_x(1,2)\vec{i} + f_y(1,2)\vec{j}$$
$$= 5\vec{i} - 4\vec{j}.$$

So in order to heat up as rapidly as possible, you should head in the direction of $5\vec{i} - 4\vec{j}$. Since $\| \text{grad } f \|$ is the rate of change in that direction,

$$\Delta f \approx \| \text{grad } f \|(0.06)$$
$$= (\sqrt{41})(0.06)$$
$$\approx 0.384.$$

(e)   Let $\vec{n}$ be the unit vector pointing from $(1,2)$ to $(5,5)$. Hence,

$$\vec{n} = \frac{(5-1)\vec{i} + (5-2)\vec{j}}{\sqrt{4^2 + 3^2}}$$
$$= \frac{4}{5}\vec{i} + \frac{3}{5}\vec{j}.$$

Then

$$f_{\vec{n}} = \text{grad } f \cdot \vec{n}$$
$$= (5\vec{i} - 4\vec{j}) \cdot (\frac{4}{5}\vec{i} + \frac{3}{5}\vec{j})$$
$$= \frac{8}{5}.$$

(f)   Since $f_x(1,2) = 5$ and $f_y(1,2) = -4$, the slope of the level curve is

$$\frac{f_y}{f_x} = \frac{-4}{5}.$$

So the equation is

$$y = \frac{4}{5}x + \frac{14}{5}.$$

(g)

$$f_x(0.5, 2) \approx \frac{f(1,2) - f(0,2)}{1} = \frac{37 - 35}{1} = 2$$

$$f_x(1.5, 2) \approx \frac{f(2,2) - f(1,2)}{1} = 5$$

So,

$$f_{xx}(1, 2) \approx \frac{f_x(1.5, 2) - f_x(0.5, 2)}{1} = 3.$$

$$f_y(1, 1.75) \approx \frac{f(1,2) - f(0,1.5)}{0.5} = \frac{37 - 38}{0.5} = -2$$

$$f_y(1, 2.25) \approx \frac{f(1,2.5) - f(1,2)}{0.5} = \frac{35 - 37}{0.5} = -4$$

So,

$$f_{yy}(1, 2) \approx \frac{f_y(1, 2.25) - f_y(1, 1.75)}{0.5} = -4.$$

(h)

$$f_x(1, 1.5) \approx \frac{44 - 36}{2} = 4$$

$$f_x(1, 2.5) \approx \frac{38 - 34}{2} = 2$$

Thus, $f_x$ seems to decrease as $y$ increases, so $f_{xy}(1, 2)$ is negative.

(i)  As $f_{xx} = 3$ and $f_{yy} = -4$, $f_t = k(f_{xx} + f_{yy}) = -k < 0$. So an instant later the temperature will be cooler.

# Chapter 14 Exam Questions

*Problems and Solutions for Section 14.1*

1.  (a)  Find all the critical points of the function

$$f(x,y) = xy + \frac{8}{x^2} + \frac{8}{y^2}.$$

(b)  Classify these critical points as local maxima, local minima, or saddle points.
ANSWER:

(a)  As

$$f_x = y - \frac{16}{x^3} = 0$$

$$f_y = x - \frac{16}{y^3} = 0$$

$$y = \frac{16}{x^3}$$

$$x = \frac{16}{y^3}$$

then

$$yx^3 = 16$$

$$(y)(\frac{16}{y^3})^3 = 16$$

$$y^8 = 2^8.$$

Hence, $y = 2$ or $y = -2$ and

$$x = \frac{16}{y^3}$$

$$= \frac{16}{(\pm 2)^3}$$

$$= \pm 2.$$

Thus, the critical points are $(2, 2)$ or $(-2, -2)$.

(b)  As

$$f_{xx} = 48x^{-4}$$

$$f_{yy} = 48y^{-4}$$

$$f_{xy} = 1$$

and at $(2, 2)$ or $(-2, -2)$ :

$$(f_{xy})^2 - (f_{xx})(f_{yy}) = 1 - (48)^2(\pm 2)^{-4}(\pm 2)^{-4}$$

$$= 1 - 9$$

$$= -8 < 0.$$

Moreover, $f_{xx} = (48)(\pm 2)^{-4} = 3 > 0$. Hence, $(2, 2)$ and $(-2, -2)$ are local minima.

2.  Is $(0, 0)$ a critical point of each of the following functions? (Circle yes or no.) If yes, circle the type of critical point. (No work need be shown.)

    (a)  $f(x, y) = \cos x \cos y$ yes no If yes: max min saddle
    (b)  $f(x, y) = \sin x \cos y$ yes no If yes: max min saddle
    (c)  $f(x, y) = 5x^4 + y^2$ yes no If yes: max min saddle
    (d)  $f(x, y) = -6x^2 + 3y^4$ yes no If yes: max min saddle
    (e)  $f(x, y) = -7x^4 - 3y^4$ yes no If yes: max min saddle
    (f)  $f(x, y) = 4 + \sqrt{x^2 + y^2}$ yes no If yes: max min saddle

    ANSWER:

    (a)  $-1 \le \cos x \le 1$ and $-1 \le \cos y \le 1$, so $-1 \le \cos x \cos y \le 1$ (for any $x, y$) But $\rho(0, 0) = 1$, therefore $(0, 0)$ is a (global) maximum.
    (b)  $\rho_x = \cos x \cos y$, so $\rho_x(0, 0) = 1$ and $\rho_y = -\sin x \sin y$, so $\rho_y(0, 0) = 0$ Therefore, $(0, 0)$ is not a critical point.
    (c)  Clearly, $\rho(x, y) = 5x^4 + y^2 \ge 0$ (for any $x, y$) and $\rho(x, y) = 0$, so $(0, 0)$ is a critical point and a local minimum.
    (d)  $\rho_x = -12x$, so $\rho_x(0, 0) = 0$, and $\rho_y = 12y^3$, so $\rho_y(0, 0) = 0$ Therefore, $(0, 0)$ is a critical point. Nevertheless, close to $(0, 0)$, we have $\rho(\varepsilon, 0) = -6\varepsilon^2 \le 0$ ($\varepsilon \ne 0$) and $\rho(0, \varepsilon) = 3\varepsilon^4 \ge 0$ ($\varepsilon \ne 0$), so $\rho(0, 0) = 0$, $(0, 0)$ is not max/min, $(0, 0)$ is saddle point.
    (e)  Clearly, $\rho(x, y) = -7x^4 - 3y^4 \le 0$ (for any $x, y$) and $\rho(0, 0) = 0$, so $(0, 0)$ is a (global) maximum.
    (f)  Clearly, $\rho(x, y) = \sqrt{x^2 + y^2} + 4 \ge 4$ (for any $x, y$) and $\rho(0, 0) = 4$, so $(0, 0)$ is a (global) minimum.

3.  Let $h(x, y) = x^3 + y^3 + 3xy + \frac{1}{8}$.

    (a)  Determine all local maxima, minima, and saddle points. Are the local extrema also global extrema?
    (b)  Match the function $h(x, y)$ in Part (a) to the plot of its level curves. Explain.

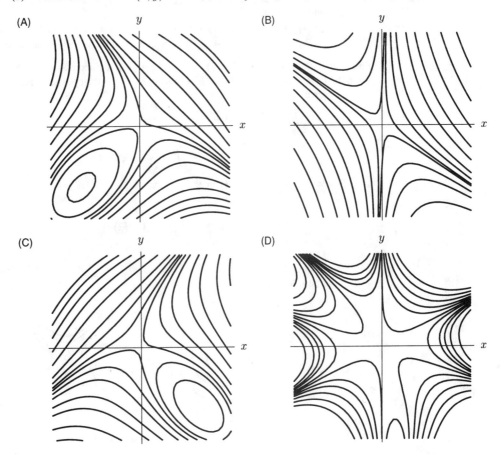

(A)

(B)

(C)

(D)

ANSWER:

(a) Solve:

$$\frac{\partial h}{\partial x} = 3x^2 + 3y = 0$$

$$\frac{\partial h}{\partial y} = 3y^2 + 3x = 0$$

Gives critical points $(0,0)$, $(-1,-1)$
disc. $D = 36xy - 9$
So, $(0,0)$ saddle, $(-1,-1)$ local max. No global max.

(b) plot (A) is the answer.

4. Suppose that $f(x,y) = x^2 + xy + y^2$.

(a) Find the critical point of $f$.
(b) Classify the critical point you found in part (a): local maximum, local minimum, or saddle point?
(c) Find an equation of the tangent plane to the graph of $f$ at the point $(1,1)$.
(d) Find a normal vector to the tangent plane you found in part (c).

ANSWER:

(a)

$$f_x = 2x + y \qquad 2x + y = 0$$

$$f_y = 2y + x \qquad 2y + x = 0$$

so

$$(x,y) = (0,0)$$

(b) $f_{xx} = 2$, $f_{yy} = 2$, $f_{xy} = 1$. $D = f_{xx}f_{yy} - (f_{xy})^2 = 4 - 1 > 0$. Since $f_{xx} > 0$ this is a local minimum.

(c) $z = f(1,1) + f_x(1,1)(x-1) + f_y(1,1)(y-1) = 3 + 3(x-1) + 3(y-1)$ or $z = 3x + 3y - 3$.

(d) $-3x - 3y + z = -3$ so $-3\vec{i} - 3\vec{j} + \vec{k}$ is normal to the tangent plane or any scalar multiple.

5. Find all the critical points of $f(x,y) = x^3 - 3x + y^2 - 6y$ and classify each as maximum, minimum, or saddle. Give a rough sketch of the level curves of $f$ near the critical points.

ANSWER:

(a) With $f(x,y) = x^3 - 3x + y^2 - 6y$ we find:

$$f_x = 3x^2 - 3 = 0 \quad \text{and}$$

$$f_y = 2y - 6 = 0.$$

So $x = -1, 1$ and $y = 3$. Hence the critical points are $(1,3)$ and $(-1,3)$. Let,

$$D = f_{xx}f_{yy} - (f_{xy})^2$$
$$= (6x)(2) - 0$$
$$= 12x.$$

Since at point $(1,3)$, $D = 12x = 12 > 0$ and $f_{xx}(1,3) = 6 > 0$ then point $(1,3)$ is a relative minimum. Also at point $(-1,3)$, $D = 12(-1) = -12 < 0$. Thus, point $(-1,3)$ is a saddle point.

(b)

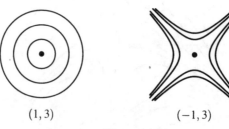

$(1,3)$ $\qquad\qquad\qquad$ $(-1,3)$

*Figure 14.1.1*

6. Find the critical points of $f(x, y) = x^3 - 3xy + y^2$ and classify each as maximum, minimum or saddle.

   ANSWER:

   From $f(x, y) = x^3 - 3xy + y^2$ we find

   $$f_x = 3x^2 - 3y = 0$$
   $$f_y = 2y - 3x = 0$$

   or

   $$y = x^2$$
   $$y = \frac{3}{2}x.$$

   Hence, $x = 0$ or $x = \frac{3}{2}$. When $x = 0$, $y = 0$, and when $x = \frac{3}{2}$, $y = \frac{9}{4}$. Thus the critical points are $(0, 0)$ and $\left(\frac{3}{2}, \frac{9}{4}\right)$.

   Let,

   $$\text{grad} = f_{xx}f_{yy} - (f_{xy})^2$$
   $$= (6x)(2) - 9$$
   $$= 12x - 9.$$

   So at the point $(0, 0)$, $\text{grad} = -9 < 0$. Hence, the point $(0, 0)$ is a saddle point. At the point $\left(\frac{3}{2}, \frac{9}{4}\right)$, $\text{grad} = 12\left(\frac{3}{2}\right) - 9 = 9 > 0$ and $f_{xx}\left(\frac{3}{2}, \frac{9}{4}\right) = 9 > 0$. Hence, $\left(\frac{3}{2}, \frac{9}{4}\right)$ is a minimum point.

## Problems and Solutions for Section 14.2

1. The temperature at each point $(x, y)$ in the first quadrant is $T(x, y) = \ln(xy) - x - y$. Determine the hottest point and its temperature or explain why it doesn't exist. Determine the coldest point and its temperature or explain why it doesn't exist.

   ANSWER:

   The partial derivatives are $T_x = \frac{y}{xy} - 1 = \frac{1}{x} - 1$ and $T_y = \frac{x}{xy} - 1 = \frac{1}{y} - 1$ Setting $T_x = 0$ gives $x = 1$, and setting $T_y = 0$ gives $y = 1$. Therefore, the critical point is $(1, 1)$ in the first quadrant. The discriminant is

   $$D(x, y) = T_{xx}T_{yy} - T_{xy}^2 = -\frac{1}{x^2}\left(-\frac{1}{y^2}\right) - 0 = \frac{1}{x^2y^2}.$$

   Since $D(1, 1) = \frac{1}{1^2 1^2} = 1 > 0$, and $T_{xx}(1, 1) = -\frac{1}{1^2} = -1 < 0$ then $(1, 1)$ is a local maximum and $T(1, 1) = -2$. The coldest temperature doesn't exist because in the first quadrant, as $x$ or $y$ gets bigger, the rate that $\ln(xy)$ increases is a lot slower than that of $x$ or $y$. That is to say

   $$\lim_{x, y \to \infty} T(x, y) = \lim_{x, y \to \infty} (\ln(xy) - x - y) = \lim_{x, y \to \infty} ((\ln x - x) + (\ln y - y)) = -\infty.$$

   Hence there is not a coldest point in the first quadrant.

2. (a) Describe the shape of the graph of $f(x, y) = 3x^2 + 3y^2 - 12x - 6y + 18$.
   (b) Sketch several contours of $f(x, y)$. (Hint: Complete squares!)
   (c) Find all maxima and minima (global or local) and all saddle points of $f(x, y)$.
   (d) What do the second derivatives tell you about the graph of $f(x, y) = 3x^2 + 1000xy + 3y^2 - 12x + 6y + 18$?

   ANSWER:

   (a) Paraboloid
   (b) By completing the squares, $f$ can be rewritten as

   $$f(x, y) = 3(x - 2)^2 + 3(y - 1)^2 + 3$$

   so the level curves are circles centered at $(2, 1)$.
   (c) From (b), it is clear that the only extremum is the minimum at $(2, 1)$, where $f = 3$.
   (d) For $f(x, y) = 3x^2 + 1000xy + 3y^2 - 12x + 6y + 18$, we have $f_{xx} = 6$, $f_{yy} = 6$, $f_{xy} = 1000$, so $D = f_{xx}f_{yy} - f_{xy}^2 = 36 - 1000^2 < 0$ at all points, so any critical point must be a saddle point, hence the function has no local extrema.

3. Let $f(x, y)$ be as in Problem 2 part (a) and let $T$ be the triangle with the corners $A(2, -1)$, $B(0, 1)$, and $C(-1, -2)$.

   (a) Sketch the triangle.
   (b) Find the minimum and the maximum value of $f(x, y)$ for $(x, y)$ inside the triangle (including its boundary).
   (c) Let $P$ be the parallelogram with corners $A$, $B$, $C$ as above together with the point $D(3, 2)$. Find the minimum value of $f(x, y)$ among all $(x, y)$ inside $P$ (including its boundary).

   ANSWER:

   (a)

   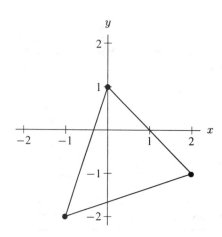

   *Figure 14.2.2:*

   (b) Since the only critical point of $f$ is $(2, 1)$, which falls outside the triangle, the extrema must be reached on the boundary. Since the level curves are circles, the minimum and maximum will occur at the closest and farthest points from $(2, 1)$, respectively. These can be found geometrically to be $(1, 0)$ and $(-1, -2)$, respectively, so the minimum of $f$ is $f(1, 0) = 9$, and the maximum is $f(-1, -2) = 57$.
   (c) Since the parallelogram contains the point $(2, 1)$, the minimum is $f(2, 1) = 3$.

## Problems and Solutions for Section 14.3

1. True or False? If $C$ is a circle in the plane, and if $f(x, y)$ is not constant when constrained to $C$, then there must be at least one point on $C$ where grad $f$ is perpendicular to $C$.

   ANSWER:

   True. Since $f$ is not constant on $C$, it must have a maximum (and minimum) so grad $f$ will be perpendicular to $C$ at these points.

2. (a) Find the critical point of $f(x, y) = x^2 y e^{-(x^2+y^2)}$. Do this by setting $t = -(x^2 + y^2)$ and optimizing $f(x, y, t) = x^2 y e^t$ subject to the constraint $t + x^2 + y^2 = 0$
   (b) What happens to the value of $f(x, y)$ as the distance from $(x, y)$ to the origin tends to infinity?
   (c) What are the global maxima and minima of $f$?

   ANSWER:

   (a) We have grad $f = \lambda$ grad $g$ so

   $$2xye^t = \lambda 2x$$
   $$x^2 e^t = \lambda 2y$$
   $$x^2 ye^t = \lambda.$$

This gives

$$\frac{2}{x} = 2x \quad \text{so } x = \pm 1$$

$$\frac{1}{y} = 2y \quad \text{so } y = \pm \frac{1}{\sqrt{2}}$$

Thus the critical points are $(1, \frac{1}{\sqrt{2}})$, $(1, -\frac{1}{\sqrt{2}})$, $(-1, \frac{1}{\sqrt{2}})$, $(-1, -\frac{1}{\sqrt{2}})$.

(b)  The value of $f(x, y)$ goes to 0.

(c)

$$f(1, \frac{1}{\sqrt{2}}) = f(-1, \frac{1}{\sqrt{2}})$$

$$= (1)(\frac{1}{\sqrt{2}})e^{-(1+1/2)}$$

$$= \frac{1}{\sqrt{2}}e^{-3/2} \text{ which is the global max.}$$

$$f(1, -\frac{1}{\sqrt{2}}) = f(-1, -\frac{1}{\sqrt{2}})$$

$$= -\frac{1}{\sqrt{2}}e^{-3/2} \text{ which is the global min.}$$

These critical points give the global max/min because $f(x, y)$ goes to zero as the distance from the origin goes to infinity.

3.  A zoo is designing a giant bird cage consisting of a cylinder of radius $r$ feet and height $h$ feet with a hemisphere on top (no bottom). The material for the hemisphere costs $\$20/ft^2$ and the material for the cylindrical sides costs $\$10/ft^2$; the zoo has a budget of $\$8000$. Find the values of $r$ and $h$ giving the birds the greatest space inside assuming the zoo stays within its budget.

ANSWER:

Total volume: $V = V_1 + V_2 = \frac{2}{3}\pi r^3 + \pi r^2 h$

Total cost: $C = C_1 + C_2 = 20 \cdot 2\pi r^2 + 10 \cdot (2\pi r \cdot h)$

Problem:

Maximize: $V(r, h) = \frac{2\pi}{3}r^3 + \pi r^2 h$

Subject to: $C(r, h) = 40\pi r^2 + 20\pi r h \leq 8000$ (and $r, h \geq 0$)

We assume $C(r, h) = 8000$ and use Lagrange multipliers:

$\text{grad } V = (2\pi r^2 + 2\pi r h)\vec{i} + \pi r^2 \vec{j}$ and $\text{grad } C = (80\pi r + 20\pi h)\vec{i} + 20\pi r \vec{j}$,

so

$$\text{grad } V = \lambda \, \text{grad } C$$

$$\frac{2\pi r^2 + 2\pi r h}{80\pi r + 20\pi h} = \frac{\pi r^2}{20\pi r}$$

$$2r^2 + 2rh = (4r + h) \cdot r$$

$$2r^2 = rh$$

$$r = 0 \text{ or } h = 2r.$$

$r = 0$ is not a right answer, because it implies $V = 0$. Using the budget constraint:

$$C(r, 2r) = 40\pi r^2 + 20 \cdot \pi r \cdot 2r = 8000$$

$$80\pi r^2 = 8000$$

$$r = \frac{10}{\sqrt{\pi}} \text{ and } h = 2r = \frac{20}{\sqrt{\pi}}.$$

4. You have two electric generators that burn natural gas and whose efficiency declines with output. The energy output is an increasing function of fuel input. Specifically

  Output = $a \ln(1 + x)$ for generator 1 and

  Output = $b \ln(1 + y)$ for generator 2,

where $x$ is the amount of fuel burned in generator 1 and $y$ is the amount of fuel burned in generator 2. Given a bound $T$ on the total amount of natural gas available, how shall we use this fuel in order to maximize output? Your answer should be in terms of $a$, $b$, and $T$.

ANSWER:

Let $T$ be the total amount of natural gas available, $x$ be the amount of fuel burned in generator 1 and $y$ be the amount of fuel burned in generator 2, then the total output $f(x, y)$ is

$$f(x, y) = a \ln(1 + x) + b \ln(1 + y),$$

we need to maximize $f(x, y)$ subject to the constraint

$$T = x + y.$$

So we have the Lagrangian function

$$\mathcal{L}(x, y, \lambda) = a \ln(1 + x) + b \ln(1 + y) - \lambda(x + y - T)$$

$$\frac{\partial \mathcal{L}}{\partial x} = \frac{a}{1 + x} - \lambda = 0$$
$$\frac{\partial \mathcal{L}}{\partial y} = \frac{b}{1 + y} - \lambda = 0$$
$$\frac{\partial \mathcal{L}}{\partial \lambda} = -(x + y - T) = 0$$

Solve for $x$ and $y$ we have,

$$x = \frac{a(1 + T) - b}{a + b} \qquad y = \frac{b(1 + T) - a}{a + b}.$$

5. All parts of this problem concern the diagram shown in Figure 14.3.3, which shows gradient vectors of a function $f(x, y)$.

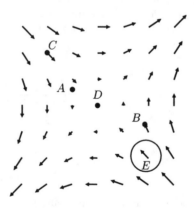

*Figure 14.3.3*

   (a) Sketch contours of $f$ that pass through the points $A$, $B$, and $C$.
   (b) Is the value of $f(C)$ greater than $f(A)$? Explain how you know.
   (c) Are there any critical points of $f$ shown in the diagram? If so, indicate whether they are local maxima, minima, or saddle points and explain why.
   (d) Mark the locations of the maximum and minimum values of $f$ when $(x, y)$ are constrained to lie on the circle.

(e) Explain how you know which is a maximum and which is a minimum.

ANSWER:

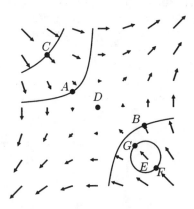

*Figure 14.3.4*

(a) See Figure 14.3.4
(b) No. $f(C) < f(A)$. Since the gradient at $C$ points towards $A$, $A$ must have greater value of $f$.
(c) $D$ is a critical point and looks like a saddle point since $f$ increases in some directions near $D$ and decreases in others.
(d) See Figure 14.3.4
(e) Point $F$ is a minimum since grad $f$ is perpendicular to the contour and the value of $f$ at $F$ is less than the value of $f$ at $G$. $G$ is a maximum.

6. A company has $250,000$ to spend on labor and raw materials. Let $L$ be the quantity of labor and $R$ be the quantity of raw materials. The production output $P$ of the company is $cRL$ (here $c$ is a positive constant). Suppose that each unit of labor costs $5000$ and the unit price of raw materials is $2500$.

(a) Draw a sketch of the contours of $P$ and the budget constraint; mark the place in your sketch where the constrained maximum occurs.
(b) Find the ratio of $R$ to $L$ that maximizes $P$.

ANSWER:

(a)

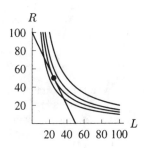

*Figure 14.3.5*

(b) Look for grad $f = \lambda$ grad $g$ with $g(R, L) = 5L + 2.5R$.

$$(cL, cR) = \lambda(2.5, 5),$$

$$cL = 2.5\lambda, \quad cR = 5\lambda,$$
$$R/L = 5\lambda/2.5\lambda = 2.$$

7.  (a)  Suppose that $f(x, y) = x^2 + 2y^2 - x$. Find and classify (as local maxima, minima, or saddle points) all critical points of $f$. If you find any local extrema, are they also global? Explain.

(b)  Find all extrema of the function $f$ when $(x, y)$ is constrained to lie on or inside the triangle with vertices $(0, -2), (0, 1), (1, -2)$.

ANSWER:

(a)

$$f(x, y) = x^2 + 2y^2 - x$$
$$\text{grad } f = (f_x \vec{i} + f_y \vec{j})$$
$$f_x = 2x - 1$$
$$f_y = 4y$$
$$(2x - 1)\vec{i} + 4y\vec{k} = 0$$
$$2x - 1 = 0$$
$$x = \frac{1}{2}$$
$$4y = 0$$
$$y = 0.$$
$$f_{xx} = 2$$
$$f_{yy} = 4$$
$$f_{xy} = 0$$
$$D = (2)(4) - 0^2 = 8 > 0$$
$$f_{xx} = 2 > 0$$
$$f(1/2, 0) = -\frac{1}{4}.$$

Thus the min is at $(1/2, 0)$ and it is global, $f$ can be rewritten as

$$f(x, y) = (x^2 - x + \frac{1}{4}) + 2y^2 - \frac{1}{4} = (x - \frac{1}{2})^2 + 2y^2 - \frac{1}{4}.$$

(b)  Since $(\frac{1}{2}, 0)$ is outside the triangle, there are no extrema in the interior of the triangle.

On the left side, we have $x = 0$, so $f = 2y^2$, $-2 \le y \le 1$. This has a local maximum of 8 at $y = -2$, a local minimum of 0 at $y = 0$, and a local maximum of 2 at $y = 1$.

On the bottom side, we have $y = -2$, so $f = x^2 + 8 - x$, $0 \le x \le 1$. This has a local maximum of 8 at $x = 0$ and $x = 1$, and local minimum of $\frac{31}{4}$ at $x = \frac{1}{2}$. On the side joining $(0, 1)$ and $(1, -2)$, we have $y = -3x + 1$, so we use the constraint $g(x, y) = 3x + y = 1$. Then

$$f_x = \lambda g_x \text{ which implies that } 2x - 1 = 3\lambda$$
$$f_y = \lambda g_y \text{ which implies that } 4y = \lambda$$

Together with the constraint, we get an extremum of $-\frac{17}{76}$ at $\left(\frac{13}{38}, -\frac{1}{38}\right)$. Since $f(0, 1) = 2$ and $f(1, -2) = 8$, this extremum is a minimum.

Thus $f$ has a global minimum of $-\frac{17}{76}$ at $\left(\frac{13}{38}, -\frac{1}{38}\right)$ and a global maximum of 8 at the points $(0, -2), (1, -2)$.

8.  Suppose that you want to find the maximum and minimum values of $f(x, y) = x^2 + y^2$ subject to the constraint $x + 2y = 4$.

(a)  Sketch the constraint equation and a few contours of $f$.

(b)  On your sketch, show the location (approximately, of course) of all maxima and minima of $f$ subject to the given constraint. How many are there?

(c)  Use the method of Lagrange multipliers to find the exact location(s) of the extrema that you found in part (b).

(d)  Are the point(s) you found in (c) maxima or minima?

ANSWER:

(a)

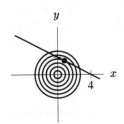

**Figure 14.3.6**

(b)  See Figure 14.3.6.

There is only one place where contours are tangent to the constraint.

(c)

$$g = x + 2y \quad f = x^2 + y^2 \qquad \text{grad } \vec{f} = \lambda \text{ grad } \vec{g} \quad \text{so } (2x, 2y) = \lambda(1, 2).$$

$$\text{Thus } 2x = \lambda \quad 2y = 2\lambda, \qquad \text{so } \frac{x}{y} = \frac{1}{2} \text{ and } x = \frac{y}{2}.$$

$$x + 2y = 4 \quad \frac{1}{2}y + 2y = 4 \quad \frac{5}{2}y = 4 \quad y = \frac{8}{5} \quad x = \frac{y}{2} = \frac{4}{5}$$

Thus the extremum is at $(\frac{4}{5}, \frac{8}{5})$.

(d)  Since the contours increase as they increase in radius, moving away from the point for tangency yields larger values of $f$. So the point is a minimum.

9.  Suppose the quantity, $q$, of a good produced depends on the number of workers, $w$, and the amount of capital, $k$, invested and is represented by the Cobb-Douglas function $q = 6w^{\frac{3}{4}}k^{\frac{1}{4}}$. In addition, labor costs are \$10 per worker and capital costs are \$20 per unit, and the budget is \$3000. Using Lagrange multipliers, find the optimum number of workers and the optimum number of units of capital.

ANSWER:

Let $c$ be the cost of producing the product where $c = 10w + 20k = 3000$. At optimum production, grad $q = \lambda$ grad $c$.

grad $q = (\frac{9}{2}w^{-\frac{1}{4}}k^{\frac{1}{4}}, \frac{3}{2}w^{\frac{3}{4}}k^{-\frac{3}{4}})$, and grad $c = (10, 20)$. Solving we get

$$\frac{9}{2}w^{-\frac{1}{4}}k^{\frac{1}{4}} = \lambda 10$$

and

$$\frac{3}{2}w^{\frac{3}{4}}k^{-\frac{3}{4}} = \lambda 20.$$

Solving yields $k = \frac{1}{6}w$, so substituting into $c$ gives

$$10w + 20(\frac{1}{6}w) = \frac{40}{3}w = 3000.$$

Thus, $w = 225$ and $k = 37.5$.

10.  Determine three positive numbers $x, y, z$ that maximize $x^3y^4z^5$ under the condition $x + y + z = 1$. How do you know whether you found a maximum?

ANSWER:

The objective function is

$$f(x, y, z) = x^3y^4z^5$$

and the constraint is

$$g(x, y, z) = x + y + z = 1.$$

Since grad $f = f_x\vec{i} + f_y\vec{j} + f_z\vec{k} = 3x^2y^4z^5\vec{i} + 4x^3y^3z^5\vec{j} + 5x^3y^4z^4\vec{k}$ and grad $g = g_x\vec{i} + g_y\vec{j} + g_z\vec{k} = \vec{i} + \vec{j} + \vec{k}$ . grad $f = \lambda$ grad $g$ gives

$$3x^2y^4z^5 = 1$$
$$4x^3y^3z^5 = 1$$
$$5x^3y^4z^4 = 1.$$

So, $x = \frac{3}{4}y$, $z = \frac{5}{4}y$. We also know $x + y + z = 1$ giving $y = \frac{1}{3}$, then $x = \frac{1}{4}$, $z = \frac{5}{12}$ and $f(\frac{1}{4}, \frac{1}{3}, \frac{5}{12}) = (\frac{1}{4})^3(\frac{1}{3})^4(\frac{5}{12})^5$. $(\frac{1}{4}, \frac{1}{3}, \frac{5}{12})$ maximize $x^3y^4z^5$ because point $(1, 0, 0)$ also satisfies $x + y + z = 1$ but $f(1, 0, 0) = 0 < f(\frac{1}{4}, \frac{1}{3}, \frac{5}{12})$.

# Chapter 15 Exam Questions

*Problems and Solutions for Section 15.1*

1. Felt Lake is a small reservoir that Stanford University uses as a supply for irrigation water. A contour map showing elevation is shown below. On the following page write down two sums, with six terms each, giving upper and lower bounds, respectively, for the volume of water within the grid. You need not evaluate the sums. Briefly explain your reasoning.

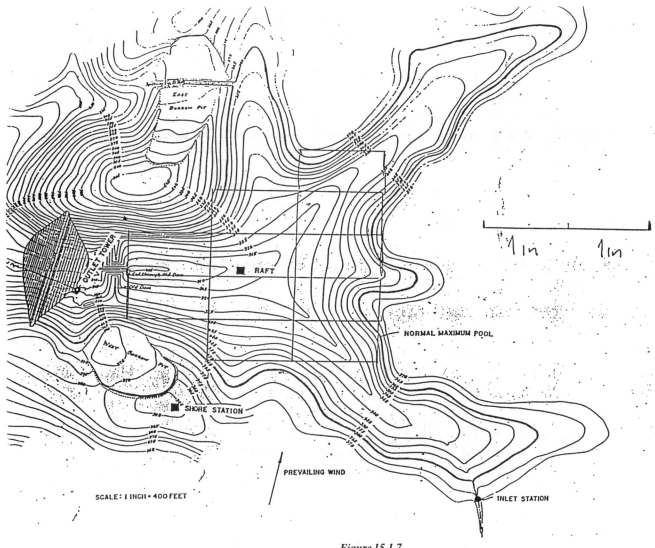

*Figure 15.1.7*

ANSWER:

The volume of water in the grid is the sum of the volumes of water in each 400 sq · ft section. This column in each section is thus 400 × depth of water in each square. Since the bottom of the lake is below the shoreline, the depth of the bottom is the elevation of that position of the lake relative to the shoreline. To compute upper and lower estimates for the volume of water in the grid, we need upper and lower estimates for the depth of the lake in each square, i.e,. the deepest and the shallowest the lake gets in each box. The shoreline has an elevation of 360 ft so this means the farthest and closest the depth gets is 360 ft, in each square.

Making use of the labels 1 through 6 in the boxes, let $l_i$ and $u_i$ denote the lower and upper limits, respectively, for the depth of water in box $i$. Then,

$$\text{Volume} \leq (400)^2(u_1 + u_2 + u_3 + u_4 + u_5 + u_6)$$
$$= (400)^2((360 - 305) + (360 - 310) + (360 - 315) + (360 - 325) + (360 - 315)$$
$$+ (360 - 325))$$
$$= (400)^2(55 + 50 + 45 + 35 + 45 + 35)$$

and,

$$\text{Volume} \geq (400)^2(l_1 + l_2 + l_3 + l_4 + l_5 + l_6)$$
$$= (400)^2((360 - 325) + (360 - 320) + (360 - 320) + (360 - 355) + (360 - 330)$$
$$+ (360 - 355))$$
$$= (400)^2(35 + 40 + 40 + 5 + 30 + 5).$$

## Problems and Solutions for Section 15.2

1. True or false? If $f$ is any two-variable function, then $\int_R f\, dA = 2 \cdot \int_S f\, dA$, where $R$ is the rectangle $0 \leq x \leq 2, 0 \leq y \leq 1$ and $S$ is the square $0 \leq x, y \leq 1$.

   ANSWER:

   False. $\int_R x\, dA = 2$ but $\int_S x\, dA = \frac{1}{2}$.

2. (a) Consider the average value of $e^{-(x+y)}$ on the square $R$ of side 2, centered at the origin. Write a double integral representing this average value (but do not evaluate it).

   (b) Without evaluating this average value, what can you say about its magnitude? Is it positive or negative? Give an upper bound and a lower bound. (These should differ by no more than 8.)

   (c) Evaluate exactly the average value of the function $e^{-(x+y)}$ on the square $-1 \leq x \leq 1, -1 \leq y \leq 1$.

   ANSWER:

   (a)
   $$\text{Average} = \left(\frac{1}{\text{area of } R}\right) \int_R e^{-(x+y)}\, dx\, dy = \frac{1}{4} \int_R e^{-(x+y)}\, dx\, dy$$

   (b) Average is positive because the function is positive everywhere. Since the maximum value of the function is $e^{-(-1-1)} = 7.39$ and the minimum value of the function is $e^{-(1+1)} = 0.135$ on the square, the average must be between these two: $0.135 < \text{Average} < 7.39$.

   (c)
   $$\frac{1}{4} \int_{-1}^{1} dx \int_{-1}^{1} e^{-(x+y)}\, dy = \frac{e - e^{-1}}{4} \int_{-1}^{1} e^{-x}\, dx$$
   $$= \left(\frac{e - e^{-1}}{4}\right)(e - e^{-1})$$
   $$= \frac{e^2 + e^{-2} - 2}{4}$$

3.  Let $R$ be the region in the first quadrant bounded by the $x$ and $y$-axes and the line $x + 2y = 6$. Write $\int_R \sqrt{x + 2y}\, dA$ as an iterated integral in two different ways and hence evaluate it. Your answer should contain a sketch of the region $R$.

ANSWER:

Solution 1: Integrating first over a horizontal strip, that is, with respect to $x$ from $x = 0$ (y-axis) to $x = 6 - 2y$ (the line) and then with respect to $y$ from $y = 0$ to $y = 3$.

$$\iint_R \sqrt{x + 2y}\, dA = \int_0^3 \int_0^{6-2y} \sqrt{x + 2y}\, dx\, dy$$

$$= \frac{2}{3} \int_0^3 \left[ (x + 2y)^{3/2} \Big|_{x=0}^{x=6-2y} \right] dy$$

$$= \frac{2}{3} \int_0^3 \left[ (6)^{3/2} - (2y)^{3/2} \right] dy$$

$$= \frac{2}{3} \left[ (6)^{3/2}(3) - \left( \frac{2}{5} \right)(2)^{3/2}(3)^{5/2} \right]$$

$$= \left( \frac{2}{3} \right)\left( \frac{3}{5} \right)(6)^{3/2}(3)$$

$$= \left( \frac{6}{5} \right)(6\sqrt{6})$$

$$= \frac{36\sqrt{6}}{5}.$$

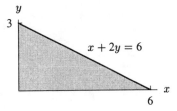

**Figure 15.2.8**

Solution 2: Integrating first over a vertical strip, that is, with respect to $y$ from $y = 0$ to $y = (6-x)/2$ (the line) and then with respect to $x$ from $x = 0$ to $x = 6$.

$$\iint_R \sqrt{x + 2y}\, dA = \int_0^6 \int_0^{(6-x)/2} \sqrt{x + 2y}\, dy\, dx$$

$$= \left( \frac{1}{2} \right)\left( \frac{2}{3} \right) \int_0^6 \left[ x + 2y \right]^{3/2} \Big|_{y=0}^{y=(6-x)/2}\, dx$$

$$= \frac{1}{3} \int_0^6 \left[ (x + 6 - x)^{3/2} - x^{3/2} \right] dx$$

$$= \frac{1}{3} \int_0^6 \left( 6^{3/2} - x^{3/2} \right) dx$$

$$= \frac{1}{3} \left[ 6^{3/2} x - \frac{2}{5} x^{5/2} \right] \Big|_0^6$$

$$= \frac{1}{3} \left[ 36\sqrt{6} - \left( \frac{2}{5} \right)(36)(\sqrt{6}) \right]$$

$$= 12\sqrt{6} \left[ 1 - \frac{2}{5} \right]$$

$$= \frac{36}{5}\sqrt{6}.$$

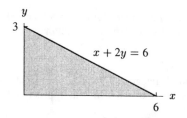

*Figure 15.2.9*

4. Consider the integral $\int_1^5 \int_{2x}^{10} f(x,y)\,dy\,dx$

(a) Sketch and label clearly the region over which the integration is being performed.

(b) Rewrite the integral with the integration performed in the opposite order.

ANSWER:

(a)

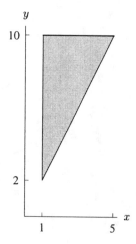

*Figure 15.2.10*

(b)

$$\int_2^{10} \int_1^{y/2} f(x,y)\,dx\,dy$$

5. (a) Let $R$ be the region in the first quadrant of the $xy$-plane lying between the curves $xy = 1$ and $xy = 8$ and the two straight lines $y = x$ and $y = 2x$. Sketch the region $R$ (finding the points where the curves and lines intersect) and set up, but do not evaluate, a double integral giving the area of $R$.

(b) Evaluate $\int_0^\pi \int_x^\pi \left( \frac{\sin y}{y} - \sin y \right) dy\,dx$ by first reversing the order of integration.

ANSWER:

(a)

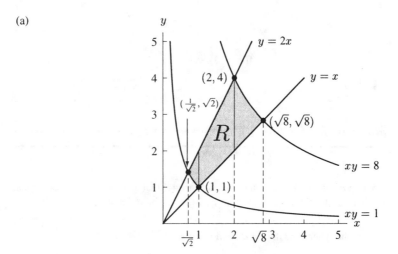

*Figure 15.2.11*

$$\text{Area of } R = \int_{1/\sqrt{2}}^{1} \int_{1/x}^{2x} dy\, dx + \int_{1}^{2} \int_{x}^{2x} dy\, dx + \int_{2}^{\sqrt{8}} \int_{x}^{8/x} dy\, dx$$

(b)

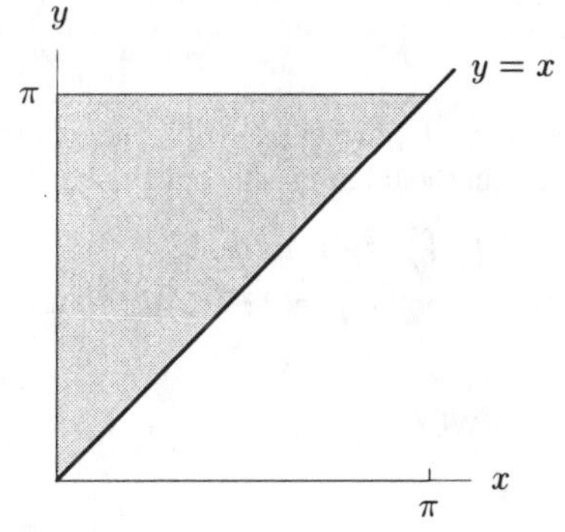

*Figure 15.2.12*

$$\int_{0}^{x} \int_{0}^{y} \left( \frac{\sin y}{y} - \sin y \right) dx\, dy = \int_{0}^{\pi} (\sin y - y \sin y)\, dy$$

$$= \int_{0}^{\pi} \sin y\, dy - \underbrace{\int_{0}^{\pi} y \sin y\, dy}_{\text{integration by parts}}$$

$$= (-\cos y) + (y \cos y - \sin y) \Big|_{0}^{\pi}$$

$$= 2 - \pi$$

6.  Find the volume under the graph of $f(x,y) = xe^{y}$ lying over the triangle with vertices $(0,0)$, $(2,2)$, $(4,0)$.

     ANSWER:

$$V = \int_{0}^{2} \int_{0}^{x} xe^{y}\, dy dx + \int_{2}^{4} \int_{0}^{4-x} xe^{y}\, dy dx$$

$$= \int_{0}^{2} (xe^{x} - x)\, dx + \int_{2}^{4} (xe^{4-x} - x)\, dx$$

$$= \left( xe^x - e^x - \frac{x^2}{2} \right) \Big|_0^2 + \left( -xe^{4-x} - e^{4-x} - \frac{x^2}{2} \right) \Big|_2^4$$

$$= 4(e^2 - 3).$$

## Problems and Solutions for Section 15.3

1. Set up *but do not evaluate* a (multiple) integral that gives the volume of the solid bounded above by the sphere $x^2 + y^2 + z^2 = 2$ and below by the paraboloid $z = x^2 + y^2$.

   ANSWER:

   The sphere and the paraboloid intersect at

   $$z^2 + (x^2 + y^2) = z^2 + z = 2$$
   $$z = 1$$
   $$x^2 + y^2 = 1$$
   $$\int_{-1}^{1} \int_{-\sqrt{1-x^2}}^{\sqrt{1-x^2}} \int_{x^2+y^2}^{\sqrt{2-x^2-y^2}} dz \, dy \, dx$$

2. Calculate the following integrals exactly. (Your answer should not be a decimal approximating the true answer, but should be exactly equal to the true answer. Your answer may contain $e$, $\pi$, $\sqrt{2}$, and so on.)

   (a) $\int_0^1 \int_0^z \int_0^y x^2 y^3 z^4 \, dx \, dy \, dz$
   (b) $\int_0^6 \int_0^3 (\cos 3y) \sin(2x + 5) \, dx \, dy$
   (c) $\int_3^4 \int_0^y y^2 e^{xy} \, dx \, dy$

   ANSWER:

   (a)

   $$\int_0^1 \int_0^z \frac{x^3 y^3 z^4}{3} \Big|_0^y dy \, dz = \int_0^1 \int_0^z \frac{y^6 z^4}{3} dy \, dz$$
   $$= \int_0^1 \frac{y^7 z^4}{21} \Big|_0^z dz$$
   $$= \int_0^1 \frac{z^{11}}{21} dz$$
   $$= \frac{1}{252}$$

   (b)

   $$\int_0^6 \int_0^3 (\cos 3y) \sin(2x + 5) \, dx \, dy = \int_0^6 \cos 3y \left( \frac{-\cos(2x+5)}{2} \right) \Big|_0^3 dy$$
   $$= \frac{1}{2} \int_0^6 \cos 3y (\cos 5 - \cos 11) \, dy$$
   $$= \frac{1}{6} (\cos 5 - \cos 11) \sin 3y \Big|_0^6$$
   $$= \frac{1}{6} (\cos 5 - \cos 11) \sin 18$$

(c)

$$\int_3^4 \int_0^y y^2 c^{xy} \, dx \, dy = \int_3^4 ye^{xy} \Big|_0^y \, dy$$

$$= \int_3^4 ye^{y^2} \, dy$$

$$= \frac{e^{y^2}}{2} \Big|_3^4$$

$$= \frac{1}{2}(e^{16} - e^9)$$

3.  Let $R$ be the pyramid with vertices $A(0,0,0)$, $B(0,0,1)$, $C(0,1,0)$, and $D(1,1,0)$.

(a)  Draw a picture of the pyramid in a coordinate system.

(b)  Find the equations of the four planes bounding the pyramid.

(c)  If $f(x, y, z)$ is a function defined on $R$, the volume integral $\int \int \int_R f(x, y, z) \, dV$ can be written as an iterated integral $\int_a^b \int_c^d \int_e^f f(x, y, z) \, dz \, dy \, dx$. Find the limits $a, b, c, d, e, f$ for this integral.

(d)  Evaluate the integral $\int \int \int_R xy \, dV$.

ANSWER:

(a)

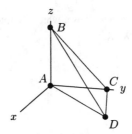

*Figure 15.3.13*

(b)   $z = 0, x = 0, x - y = 0, y + z = 1$

(c)   $\int \int \int_R f(x, y, z)\, dV = \int_0^1 \int_x^1 \int_0^{1-y} f(x, y, z)\, dz\, dy\, dx.$

(d)

$$\int \int \int_R xy\, dV = \int_0^1 \int_x^1 \int_0^{1-y} xy\, dz\, dy\, dx$$

$$= \int_0^1 \int_x^1 xy(1-y)\, dy\, dx = \int_0^1 x\left(\frac{y^2}{2} - \frac{y^3}{3}\right)\Bigg|_x^1 dx$$

$$= \int_0^1 x\left(\frac{1}{6} - \frac{x^2}{2} + \frac{x^3}{3}\right)dx = \left(\frac{x^2}{12} - \frac{x^4}{8} + \frac{x^5}{15}\right)\Bigg|_0^1$$

$$= \frac{1}{40}$$

## Problems and Solutions for Section 15.5

1.   Convert the integral $\displaystyle\int_{-2}^{2} \int_0^{\sqrt{4-x^2}} e^{-(x^2+y^2)}\, dy\, dx$ to polar coordinates and hence evaluate it exactly.
Sketch the region $R$ over which the integration is being performed.

ANSWER:

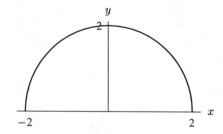

**Figure 15.5.14**

$$\int_{-2}^{2} \int_0^{\sqrt{4-x^2}} e^{-(x^2+y^2)}\, dy\, dx = \int_0^{\pi} \int_0^2 e^{-r^2} r\, dr\, d\theta$$

$$= \int_0^{\pi} -\frac{e^{-r^2}}{2}\Bigg|_0^2 d\theta$$

$$= \int_0^{\pi} -\frac{e^{-4}}{2} - \left(-\frac{e^{-0}}{2}\right) d\theta$$

$$= \int_0^{\pi} \left(\frac{1}{2} - \frac{e^{-4}}{2}\right) d\theta$$

$$= \left(\frac{1}{2} - \frac{e^{-4}}{2}\right) \int_0^{\pi} d\theta$$

$$= \frac{(1 - e^{-4})\pi}{2}$$

2.  Consider the two integrals

$$I_1 = \int_0^{\pi/3} \int_0^{1/\cos\theta} r\,dr\,d\theta, \qquad I_2 = \int_{\pi/3}^{\pi/2} \int_0^{\sqrt{3}/\sin\theta} r\,dr\,d\theta.$$

(a)  Sketch the region of integration for $I_1$.
(b)  Sketch the region of integration for $I_2$.
(c)  What is the relation between the values of $I_1$ and $I_2$? (Circle one.)

$$I_1 < I_2 \qquad I_1 = I_2 \qquad I_1 > I_2$$

Explain briefly how you can predict this relationship from your answers to parts (a) and (b) without evaluating the integral.

ANSWER:

(a)  We are given that $r$ goes from $r = 0$, the origin, to $r = 1/\cos\theta$. Rearranging $r = 1/\cos\theta$ gives

$$r\cos\theta = 1$$

which is $x = 1$ since $x = r\cos\theta$ so $r$ goes from the origin to the line $x = 1$. $\theta$ goes from $\theta = 0$, the $x$-axis, to $\theta = \pi/3$, a line making an angle of $\pi/3$ with the $x$-axis. Thus the sketch of $I_1$ looks like Figure 15.5.15.

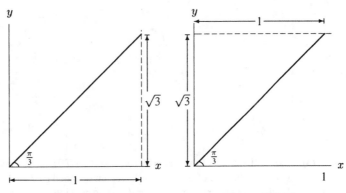

Figure 15.5.15          Figure 15.5.16

(b)  We are given that $r$ goes from $r = 0$, the origin, to $r = \sqrt{3}/\sin\theta$. Rearranging $r = \sqrt{3}/\sin\theta$ gives
$$r\sin\theta = \sqrt{3}$$
which is $y = \sqrt{3}$ since $y = r\sin\theta$ so $r$ goes from the origin to the line $y = \sqrt{3}$. $\theta$ goes from $\theta = \pi/3$, a line which makes an angle of $\pi/3$ with the $x$-axis, to $\theta = \pi/2$, the $y$-axis. So we get the sketch for $I_2$ as shown in Figure 15.5.16.

(c)  $I_1 = I_2$. This is because the regions of integration for $I_1$ and $I_2$, being congruent triangles, have equal areas. Thus since $I_1$ and $I_2$ are area integrals, $I_1 = I_2$.

3.  Calculate the following integrals:

(a)  $\displaystyle\int_0^2 \int_0^y x^5 y^7\,dx\,dy,$

(b)  $\displaystyle\int_R r\cos\theta\,dA$ where $R$ is the shaded region shown in Figure 15.5.17.

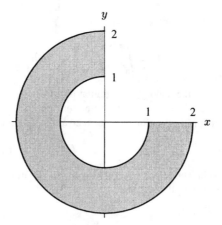

**Figure 15.5.17**

ANSWER:

(a)

$$\int_0^2 \left. \frac{x^6 y^7}{6} \right|_0^y dy = \int_0^2 \frac{y^{13}}{6} dy = \left. \frac{y^{14}}{84} \right|_0^2 = \frac{2^{14}}{84} = 195.05$$

(b)

$$\int_{\frac{\pi}{2}}^{2\pi} \int_1^2 r \cos\theta \, r \, dr \, d\theta = \int_{\frac{\pi}{2}}^{2\pi} \cos\theta \left. \frac{r^3}{3} \right|_1^2 d\theta$$

$$= \int_{\frac{\pi}{2}}^{2\pi} \frac{7}{3} \cos\theta \, d\theta$$

$$= \left. \frac{7}{3} \sin\theta \right|_{\frac{\pi}{2}}^{2\pi} = -\frac{7}{3}$$

4.  (a)  Sketch the graph of the equation $r = 3 + 2\cos(8\theta)$.
    (b)  Compute the area of the flower-like region bounded by $r = 3 + 2\cos(8\theta)$.
    (c)  Explain the presence of the $r$ in $r \, dr \, d\theta$ (in area integrals in polar coordinates).
        ANSWER:

    (a)

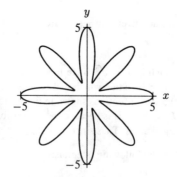

**Figure 15.5.18**

    (b)

$$A = \int_0^{2\pi} \int_0^{3+2\cos(8\theta)} r \, dr \, d\theta = \int_0^{2\pi} \left. \frac{r^2}{2} \right|_0^{3+2\cos(8\theta)} d\theta$$

$$= \frac{1}{2} \int_0^{2\pi} [9 + 12\cos(8\theta) + 4\cos^2(8\theta)] d\theta$$

$$= \frac{1}{2}\left[9\theta + \frac{12}{8}\sin(8\theta) + 4\left(\frac{\theta}{2} + \frac{\sin(16\theta)}{32}\right)\right]_0^{2\pi}$$

$$= 11\pi$$

(c)   In polar coordinates, the area element, $\Delta A \approx r\Delta\theta\Delta r$.

5.   A city by the ocean surrounds a bay, and has the semiannular shape shown in Figure 15.5.19.

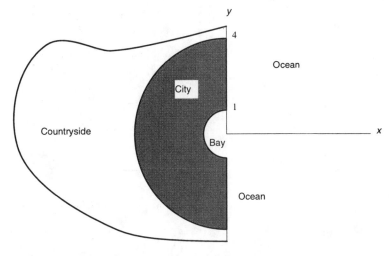

*Figure 15.5.19*

(a)   The population density of the city (in thousands of people per square mile) is given by the function $\delta(r,\theta)$, where $r$ and $\theta$ are the usual polar coordinates with respect the $x$ and $y$-axes indicated in Figure 15.5.19, and the distances indicated on the $y$-axis are in miles. Set up a double integral in polar coordinates that would give the total population of the city.

(b)   The population density decreases as you move away from the shoreline of the bay, and also decreases the further you have to drive to get to the ocean. Which of the following functions best describes this situation?

(a)   $\delta(r,\theta) = (4 - r)(2 + \cos\theta)$

(b)   $\delta(r,\theta) = (4 - r)(2 + \sin\theta)$

(c)   $\delta(r,\theta) = (r + 4)(2 + \cos\theta)$

(c)   Evaluate the integral you set up in (a) with the function you chose in (b), and give the resulting estimate for the population.

ANSWER:

(a)

$$\int_{\pi/2}^{(3\pi)/2}\int_1^4 \delta(r,\theta)r\,dr\,d\theta$$

(b)   We know that $\delta(r,\theta)$ decreases as $r$ increases, so that eliminates (c). We also know that $\delta(r,\theta)$ decreases as the $x$-coordinate decreases, but $x = r\cos\theta$. With a fixed $r$, $x$ is proportional to $\cos\theta$. So as the $x$-coordinate decreases, $\cos\theta$ decreases and (a) $\delta(r,\theta) = (4 - r)(2 + \cos\theta)$ best describes this situation.

(c)

$$\int_{\pi/2}^{3\pi/2}\int_1^4 (4 - r)(2 + \cos\theta)r\,dr\,d\theta = \int_{\pi/2}^{3\pi/2}\left.(2 + \cos\theta)\left(2r^2 - \frac{1}{3}r^3\right)\right|_1^4 d\theta$$

$$= 9\int_{\pi/2}^{3\pi/2}(2 + \cos\theta)\,d\theta$$

$$= 9[2\theta + \sin\theta]_{\pi/2}^{3\pi/2}$$

$$= 18(\pi - 1)$$

$$\approx 39.$$

Thus, the population is around $39,000$.

6. Evaluate exactly the integral $\int_R y\, dA$, where $R$ is each of the regions shown in Figure 15.5.20 and Figure 15.5.21.

(a)

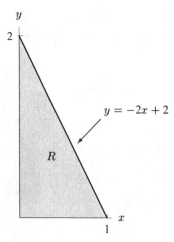

$$y = -2x + 2$$

$R$

*Figure 15.5.20*

(b)

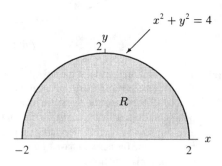

$$x^2 + y^2 = 4$$

$R$

*Figure 15.5.21*

ANSWER:

(a)

$$
\int_0^1 \int_0^{-2x+2} y\, dy = dx = \int_0^1 \left. \frac{y^2}{2} \right|_0^{-2x+2} dx
$$

$$
= \int_0^1 \frac{(-2x+2)^2}{2}\, dx
$$

$$
= \int_0^1 2(x-1)^2\, dx
$$

$$
= \left. \frac{2}{3}(x-1)^3 \right|_0^1
$$

$$
= \frac{2}{3}(0^3 - (-1)^3)
$$

$$
= \frac{2}{3}.
$$

(b)

$$
\int_0^\pi \int_0^2 r \sin\theta\, r\, dr\, d\theta = \int_0^\pi \sin\theta \left. \frac{r^3}{3} \right|_0^2 d\theta
$$

$$= \frac{8}{3} \int_0^\pi \sin \theta \, d\theta$$

$$= \frac{-8}{3} \cos \theta \Big|_0^\pi$$

$$= \frac{-8}{3}((-1) - (1))$$

$$= \frac{16}{3}.$$

## Problems and Solutions for Section 15.6

1. Consider the volume between a cone centered along the positive $z$-axis, with vertex at the origin and containing the point $(0, 1, 1)$, and a sphere of radius 3 centered at the origin.

   (a) Write a triple integral which represents this volume. Use spherical coordinates.
   (b) Evaluate the integral.

   ANSWER:

   (a) In spherical coordinates $(\rho, \theta, \phi)$, the equation of the cone is $\theta = \pi/4$ and the equation of the sphere is $\rho = 3$. Hence,

   $$V = \iiint_R dv$$

   $$= \int_0^{2\pi} \int_0^{\pi/4} \int_0^3 \rho^2 \sin \theta \, d\rho d\theta d\phi.$$

   (b)

   $$V = \int_0^{2\pi} \int_0^{\pi/4} \int_0^3 \rho^2 \sin \theta \, d\rho d\theta d\phi$$

   $$= 36 \int_0^{\pi/2} \int_0^{\pi/4} \sin \theta \, d\theta d\phi$$

   $$= (36)(\frac{2 - \sqrt{2}}{2})(\frac{\pi}{2})$$

   $$= 9(2 - \sqrt{2})\pi$$

2. We want to compute the volumes of the objects below. Give the integrand and the limits of integration in each case. (No reasons need be given. Note that $\rho, \phi, \theta$ are spherical coordinates and that $r, \theta, z$ are cylindrical coordinates.)

   (a) A wedge of cantaloupe, cut from a perfect sphere.

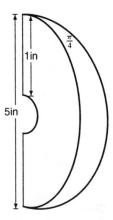

**Figure 15.6.22**

$$\text{Volume} = \int_a^b \int_c^d \int_e^f g(\rho, \phi, \theta)\, d\rho\, d\phi\, d\theta$$

$g(\rho, \phi, \theta) = \underline{\hspace{1cm}}$

$a = \underline{\hspace{1cm}}$   $b = \underline{\hspace{1cm}}$

$c = \underline{\hspace{1cm}}$   $d = \underline{\hspace{1cm}}$

$e = \underline{\hspace{1cm}}$   $f = \underline{\hspace{1cm}}$

(b)   A spherical bead with a cylindrical hole cut through the center.

$$\text{Volume} = \int_a^b \int_c^d \int_e^f g(r, \theta, z)\, dz\, dr\, d\theta$$

$g(r, \theta, z) = \underline{\hspace{1cm}}$

$a = \underline{\hspace{1cm}}$   $b = \underline{\hspace{1cm}}$

$c = \underline{\hspace{1cm}}$   $d = \underline{\hspace{1cm}}$

$e = \underline{\hspace{1cm}}$   $f = \underline{\hspace{1cm}}$

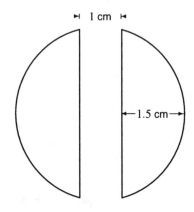

**Figure 15.6.23**

ANSWER:

(a)   To find the volume, we integrate the volume element which in spherical coordinates is $\rho^2 \sin\phi\, d\rho\, d\phi\, d\theta$. Thus, $g(\rho, \phi, \theta) = \rho^2 \sin\phi$.

The lower value for $\theta$ is $a = 0$ and the upper value is $b = \pi/4$ since the mid-section of the wedge spans an angle of $\pi/4$.

The lower value for $\phi$ is $c = 0$ and the upper value is $d = \pi$ since the wedge was cut from a perfect sphere so the angle through the arc along the outer boundary is $\pi$.

The lower value of $\rho$ is $e = 1.5$, that is, $(5/2 - 1)$, the radius of the smaller hollow sphere inside the cantaloupe, of whose boundary now serves as the inner boundary of the wedge. The upper value of $\rho$ is $f = 2.5$, that is, $(5/2)$ which is the radius of the sphere from which the wedge was cut.

(b) To find the volume of the bead, we integrate the volume element which, in cylindrical coordinates, is $r\,dz\,dr\,d\theta$. Thus, $g(r, \theta, z) = r$

The lower value for $\theta$ is $a = 0$ and the upper value is $b = 2\pi$ since the angle about the projection of the sphere into the $r\theta$-plane, a circle, is $2\pi$.

The lower value for $r$ is $c = 0.5$ and the upper value is $d = 2$. This is because the projection of the sphere into the $r\theta$-plane comprises two concentric circles so the lower value of $r$ is given by the radius of the smaller circle and the upper value by the radius of the bigger circle.

The lower value for $z$ is $e = -\sqrt{4 - r^2}$ and the upper value if $f = \sqrt{4 - r^2}$, i.e., the expressions which give the the lower and upper hemispheres of the sphere.

3.  A cylindrical tube of radius 2 cm and length 3 cm contains a gas. Since the tube is spinning around its axis, the density of the gas increases with its distance from the axis. The density, $D$, at a distance of $r$ cm from the axis is $D(r) = 1 + r$ gm/cc.

(a) Write a triple integral representing the total mass of the gas in the tube.
(b) Evaluate this integral.

ANSWER:

(a) $M = \displaystyle\int_0^{2\pi} \int_0^2 \int_0^3 (1 + r)r\,dz\,dr\,d\theta$

(b)

$$
\begin{aligned}
M &= \int_0^{2\pi} \int_0^2 \int_0^3 (1 + r)r\,dz\,dr\,d\theta \\
&= \int_0^{2\pi} \int_0^2 3r + 3r^2\,dr\,d\theta \\
&= \int_0^{2\pi} \frac{3r^2}{2} + r^3 \bigg|_0^2 \, d\theta \\
&= 14 \cdot 2\pi \\
&= 28\pi
\end{aligned}
$$

4.  (a) Set up the two-dimensional integral $\displaystyle\int_R xy\,dA$ where $R$ is the triangle in the $xy$-plane with vertices $(0, 1)$, $(-1, 0)$, and $(2, 0)$.

(b) Set up the three-dimensional integral $\int_R y\,dV$ where $R$ is the "ice-cream cone" enclosed by a sphere of radius 2 centered at the origin and the cone $z = \sqrt{3x^2 + 3y^2}$.
   (i) Use rectangular coordinates
   (ii) Use cylindrical coordinates
   (iii) Use spherical coordinates

ANSWER:

(a)

$$
\int_R xy\,dA = \int_0^1 \int_{y-1}^{2(1-y)} xy\,dx\,dy
$$

See Figure 15.6.24.

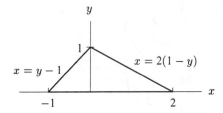

*Figure 15.6.24*

(b)

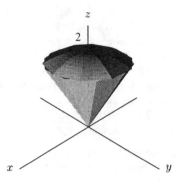

*Figure 15.6.25*

(i) Use rectangular coordinates $(x, y, z)$. Integrate first with respect to $z$ from $z = \sqrt{3x^2 + 3y^2}$ to $z = \sqrt{4 - x^2 - y^2}$ (the equation of the sphere with radius 2 and centered at the origin is $x^2 + y^2 + z^2 = 4$), then with respect to $y$ from $y = -\sqrt{1 - x^2}$ to $y = \sqrt{1 - x^2}$ (obtain $x^2 + y^2 = 1$ by eliminating $z$ between the equations of the two surfaces), and finally with respect to $x$ from $x = -1$ to $x = 1$ (obtained by setting $y = 0$ in $x^2 + y^2 = 1$). Thus,

$$\int_R y \, dV = \int_{-1}^{1} \int_{-\sqrt{1-x^2}}^{\sqrt{1-x^2}} \int_{\sqrt{3x^2+3y^2}}^{\sqrt{4-x^2-y^2}} y \, dz \, dy \, dx.$$

(ii) Use cylindrical coordinates, $(r, \theta, z)$.

$$\int_R y \, dV = \int_0^{2\pi} \int_0^1 \int_{\sqrt{3}r}^{\sqrt{4-r^2}} r^2 \sin\theta \, dz \, dr \, d\theta.$$

(iii) Use spherical coordinates $(\rho, \theta, \phi)$ for the cone, $z = \sqrt{3x^2 + 3y^2}$.

$$\rho \cos\phi = \sqrt{3}\rho \sin\phi$$
$$\tan\phi = \frac{1}{\sqrt{3}}$$
$$\phi = \frac{\pi}{6}.$$

Integrate first with respect to $\rho$ from $\rho = 0$ to $\rho = 2$, then with respect to $\phi$ from $\phi = 0$ to $\phi = \frac{\pi}{6}$, and finally with respect to $\theta$ from $\theta = 0$ to $\theta = 2\pi$. Then

$$\int_R y \, dV = \int_0^{2\pi} \int_0^{\pi/6} \int_0^2 \rho^3 \sin\theta \sin^2\phi \, d\rho \, d\phi \, d\theta.$$

5. Let $R$ be the ice-cream cone lying inside the sphere $x^2 + y^2 + z^2 = 4$ and inside the cone $z = \sqrt{3(x^2 + y^2)}$. Find the center of mass of $R$.

ANSWER:

In spherical coordinates the sphere has the equation $\rho = 2$, and the cone is given by $\sqrt{x^2 + y^2}/z = 1/\sqrt{3} = \tan\phi$, i.e., $\phi = \pi/6$. Using $z = \rho\cos\phi$, $x^2 + y^2 = \rho^2 \sin^2\phi$. Hence

$$V = \int_0^{2\pi} \int_0^2 \int_0^{\pi/6} 1 \cdot (\rho^2 \sin\phi) \, d\phi \, d\rho \, d\theta = 2\pi \cdot \frac{1}{3}\rho^3 \Big|_0^2 \cdot (-\cos\phi) \Big|_0^{\pi/6}$$

$$= \frac{16}{3}\left(1 - \frac{\sqrt{3}}{2}\right) \approx 2.244,$$

$$M_z = \int_0^{2\pi} \int_0^2 \int_0^{\pi/6} (\rho\cos\phi) \cdot (\rho^2 \sin\phi) \, d\phi \, d\rho \, d\theta$$

$$= 2\pi \cdot \frac{1}{4}\rho^4 \Big|_0^2 \cdot \frac{1}{2} \sin^2\phi \Big|_0^{\pi/6} = \pi.$$

Thus, $\bar{z} = M_z/V = 3\pi/8(2 - \sqrt{3}) \approx 1.400$. By symmetry the center of mass lies on the $z$-axis, i.e., $\bar{x} = \bar{y} = 0$. The corresponding integrals vanish, because of the occurence of $\int_0^{2\pi} \cos\theta \, d\theta$. (In rectangular coordinates, the integrand is odd, the $x$- and $y$-limits are symmetric about zero.)

6. Evaluate $\int_W z \, dV$ where $W$ is the first octant portion of the ball of radius 2 centered at the origin. Do this in two ways, using spherical and cylindrical coordinates.

ANSWER:

Spherical:

$$\int z \, dV = \int_0^{\pi/2} \int_0^{\pi/2} \int_0^2 \rho \cos\phi \rho^2 \sin\phi \, d\rho \, d\phi \, d\theta$$

$$= \left(\frac{\pi}{2}\right)\left(\frac{\rho^4}{4}\right)\Big|_0^2 \frac{\sin^2\phi}{2}\Big|_0^{\pi/2}$$

$$= \left(\frac{\pi}{2}\right)\left(\frac{16}{4}\right)\left(\frac{1}{2}\right) = \pi$$

Cylindrical:

$$\int z \, dV = \int_0^{\pi/2} \int_0^2 \int_0^{\sqrt{4-r^2}} zr \, dz \, dr \, d\theta$$

$$= \frac{\pi}{2} \int_0^2 r\left(\frac{z^2}{2}\right)\Big|_0^{\sqrt{4-r^2}} dr$$

$$= \frac{\pi}{2} \int_0^2 \frac{r}{2}(4 - r^2) \, dr$$

$$= \frac{\pi}{4}\left(2r^2 - \frac{r^4}{4}\right)\Big|_0^2 = \pi$$

# Chapter 16 Exam Questions

*Problems and Solutions for Section 16.1*

1.  True or false? Give a reason for your answer. The equations $x = \cos(t^3)$, $y = \sin(t^3)$ parameterize a circle.

    ANSWER:

    True. Since $x^2 + y^2 = (\cos t^3)^2 + (\sin t^3)^2 = 1$, all such points lie on a circle.

2.  Give parametrizations for the following:

    (a)  A circle of radius 3 in the plane, centered at origin, traversed clockwise.
    (b)  A circle of radius 2 in 3-space perpendicular to the $y$-axis.

    ANSWER:

    (a)

    $$x = 3\cos t$$
    $$y = -3\sin t$$

    for $0 \le t \le 2\pi$.

    (b)

    $$x = x_0 + 2\cos t$$
    $$y = y_0$$
    $$z = z_0 + 2\sin t$$

    for $0 \le t \le 2\pi$.

3.  Consider the plane $2x + y - 5z = 7$ and the line with parametric equation $\vec{r} = \vec{r}_0 + t\vec{u}$.

    (a)  Give a value of $\vec{u}$ which makes the line perpendicular to the plane.
    (b)  Give a value of $\vec{u}$ which makes the line parallel to the plane.
    (c)  Give values for $\vec{r}_0$ and $\vec{u}$ which make the line lie in the plane.

    ANSWER:

    (a)  Let
    $$F(x, y, z) = 2x + y - 5z - 7 = 0.$$
    The normal to the plane is grad $F = 2\vec{i} + \vec{j} - 5\vec{k}$. Thus we may take $\vec{u} = 2\vec{i} + \vec{j} - 5\vec{k}$.

    (b)  Let
    $$\vec{u} = u_1\vec{i} + u_2\vec{j} + u_3\vec{k}.$$

    As

    $$\vec{u} \cdot \text{grad } F = 0$$
    $$2u_1 + u_2 - 5u_3 = 0$$

    then we may take
    $$\vec{u} = 2\vec{i} + \vec{j} + \vec{k}.$$

    (c)  As points $(1, 0, -1), (2, 8, 1)$ lie in the plane, then the vector $(2-1)\vec{i} + (8-0)\vec{j} + (1+1)\vec{k} = \vec{i} + 8\vec{j} + 2\vec{k}$ should lie in the plane.
    Check: $(\vec{i} + 8\vec{j} + 2\vec{k}) \cdot \text{grad } F = 0$.
    So, we may take

    $$\vec{r}_0 = \vec{i} - \vec{k}$$
    $$\vec{u} = \vec{i} + 8\vec{j} + 2\vec{k}.$$

4. The equation $\vec{r} = \vec{i} + 5\vec{j} + 3\vec{k} + t(\vec{i} - \vec{j} + \vec{k})$ parameterizes a line through the points $(1, 5, 3)$, $(2, 4, 4)$, and $(0, 6, 2)$. What value of $t$ gives each of these three points?

   ANSWER:

$$\text{For point } (1, 5, 3), \ t = 0.$$
$$\text{For point } (2, 4, 4), \ t = 1.$$
$$\text{For point } (0, 6, 2), \ t = -1.$$

5. What curve, $C$, is traced out by the parameterization $\vec{r} = 2\vec{i} + \cos t\vec{j} + \sin t\vec{k}$ for $0 \le t \le 2\pi$? Either give a very complete verbal description or sketch the curve (or both).

   ANSWER:

   As $\vec{r} = 2\vec{i} + \cos t\vec{j} + \sin t\vec{k}$ or $x = 2$, $y = \cos t$, $z = \sin t$, then the curve $C$ is a circle of radius 1 centered at $(2, 0, 0)$ in the plane $x = 2$.

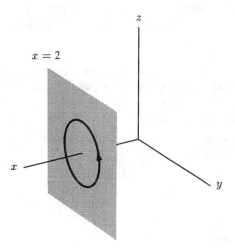

*Figure 16.1.26*

6. Which of the following diagrams represents the parametric curve $x = \sin t$, $y = \cos t$, $0 \le t \le \pi$?

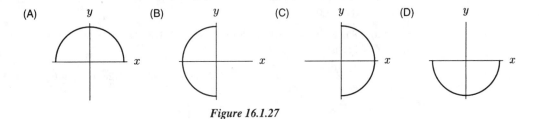

*Figure 16.1.27*

   Justify your answer.

   ANSWER:

   The curve starts at $(\sin 0, \cos 0) = (0, 1)$ and ends at $(\sin \pi, \cos \pi) = (0, -1)$, so it's either (B) or (C). Also, since $\sin t \ge 0$ for $0 \le t \le \pi$, $x \ge 0$ on the curve, so it must be (C).

1.  A child is sliding down a helical slide. Her position at time $t$ after the start is given in feet by $\vec{r} = \cos t\vec{i} + \sin t\vec{j} + (10 - t)\vec{k}$. The ground is the $xy$-plane.

    (a)  When is the child 6 feet from the ground?
    (b)  At time $t = 2\pi$, the child leaves the slide on the tangent to the slide at that point. What is the equation of the tangent line?

    ANSWER:

    (a)  When $10 - t = 6$, so $t = 4$.
    (b)  When $t = 2\pi$, the child is at the point $\vec{r}(\cos 2\pi\vec{i} + \sin 2\pi\vec{j} + (10 - 2\pi)\vec{k}) = \vec{i} + (10 - 2\pi)\vec{k}$. Tangent vector to slide is $\vec{r} = -\sin t\vec{i} + \cos t\vec{j} - \vec{k}$. At $t = 2\pi, \vec{r} = -\sin 2\pi\vec{i} + \cos 2\pi\vec{j} - \vec{k} = \vec{j} - \vec{k}$, so the equation is $\vec{r} = \vec{i} + (10 - 2\pi)\vec{k} + s(\vec{j} - \vec{k})$. Note: we use a different parameter ($s$ instead of $t$) because $s$ is measured from the time the child leaves the slide; thus $s = t - 2\pi$.

2.  Find parametric equations for the line through the point $(1, 1, 2)$ and parallel to the vector $2\vec{i} + \vec{j} - 2\vec{k}$ in which the particle is moving with speed 5 (the parameter $t$ represents time).

    ANSWER:

    We want an equation of the form $\vec{r} = \vec{r}_0 + t\vec{u}$ where $\vec{u}$ is parallel to the line and $\vec{r}_0$ is the position vector of the starting point. Thus, $\vec{u}$ is parallel to $2\vec{i} + \vec{j} - 2\vec{k}$ and $\vec{r}_0 = \vec{i} + \vec{j} + 2\vec{k}$. Since $\vec{u}$ also represents the displacement of the particle (the amount the particle moves) when $t$ increases by 1, we need $\|\vec{u}\| = 5$. Now $\vec{u} = c(2\vec{i} + \vec{j} - 2\vec{k})$, so $\|\vec{u}\| = c\sqrt{2^2 + 1^2 + (-2)^2} = 3c = 5$ so $c = 5/3$. Thus, $\vec{r} = \vec{i} + \vec{j} + 2\vec{k} + t(\frac{10}{3}\vec{i} + \frac{5}{3}\vec{j} - \frac{10}{3}\vec{k})$ or $x = 1 + (10t/3), y = 1 + (5t/3)$, and $z = 2 - (10t/3)$.

3.  Find parametric equations for a line through the points, $A = (1, 1, 1)$ and $B = (1, 2, 3)$ so that the point $A$ corresponds to $t = 0$ and the point $B$ to $t = 2$.

    ANSWER:

    $$x = 1$$
    $$y = \frac{t}{2} + 1$$
    $$z = t + 1$$

    for $-\infty < t < \infty$.

4.  (a)  Write down a parameterization of the line through the points $(2, 1, 3)$ and $(4, 5, 4)$.
    (b)  What value of $t$ (the parameter) gives the point $(2, 1, 3)$? What value of $t$ gives the point $(4, 5, 4)$?
    (c)  What part of the line is traced out as $t \to \infty$? As $t \to -\infty$?

    ANSWER:

    (a)  Since the vector which passes through $(2, 1, 3)$ and $(4, 5, 4)$ is $2\vec{i} + 4\vec{j} + \vec{k}$, the equation of the line is:

    $$\vec{r} = 2\vec{i} + \vec{j} + 3\vec{k} + t(2\vec{i} + 4\vec{j} + \vec{k})$$
    $$x = 2 + 2t$$
    $$y = 1 + 4t$$
    $$z = 3 + t.$$

    (b)

    $$t = 0 \text{ gives the point } (2, 1, 3),$$
    $$t = 1 \text{ gives the point } (4, 5, 4).$$

    (c)  As $t \to \infty$, the part from $(2, 1, 3)$ in the direction of $(4, 5, 4)$ is traced out. As $t \to -\infty$, the part from $(2, 1, 3)$ away from $(4, 5, 4)$ is traced out.

5. The path of an object moving in $xyz$-space is given by

$$(x(t), y(t), z(t)) = (t^2, t+1, t^3).$$

The temperature at a point $(x, y, z)$ in space is given by

$$f(x, y, z) = x^2 y - 2z.$$

(a) At time $t = 1$, what is the object's velocity, $\vec{v}$ ? What is its speed?

(b) Calculate the directional derivative of $f$ in the direction of $\vec{v}$ at the point $(1, 2, 1)$, where $\vec{v}$ is the velocity vector you found in part (a).

(c) Calculate $\dfrac{d}{dt} f(x(t), y(t), z(t))\Big|_{t=1}$ .

(d) Explain briefly how your answers to parts (a), (b) and (c) are related. Interpret them in terms of temperature.

ANSWER:

(a) $\vec{v} = 2t\vec{i} + \vec{j} + 3t^2\vec{k}$ . So at $t = 1$,

$$\vec{v} = 2\vec{i} + \vec{j} + 3\vec{k} .$$

Speed: $\|\vec{v}(1)\| = \sqrt{2^2 + 1^2 + 3^2}$. Thus

$$\text{Speed} = \sqrt{14}.$$

(b)

$$\text{grad } \vec{f} = 2xy\vec{i} + x^2\vec{j} - 2\vec{k} .$$

$$\vec{u} = \frac{\vec{v}}{\|\vec{v}\|} = \frac{2\vec{i} + \vec{j} + 3\vec{k}}{\sqrt{14}} \quad \text{(unit vector on } \vec{v} \text{ direction)}$$

Then

$$f_{\vec{u}}(1, 2, 1) = \text{grad } \vec{f} \cdot \vec{u} = \frac{(2)(1)(2)2 + 1 - (2)(3)}{\sqrt{14}}.$$

So,

$$f_{\vec{u}}(1, 2, 1) = \frac{3\sqrt{14}}{14}.$$

(c)

$$g(t) = f(x(t), y(t), z(t)) = t^4(t+1) - 2t^3$$
$$= t^5 + t^4 - 2t^3$$
$$\text{and} \quad \frac{d}{dt} g(t) = 5t^4 + 4t^3 - 6t^2$$
$$g'(1) = 5 + 4 - 6 = 3.$$

Thus,

$$\frac{d}{dt} f(x(t), y(t), z(t))\Big|_{t=1} = 3.$$

(d)

$$\frac{d}{dt} f(x(t), y(t), z(t))\Big|_{t=1} = f_{\vec{u}}(1, 2, 1) \cdot \text{speed}\Big|_{t=1} .$$

That is, the rate of change of temperature at the point where the object equals the directional derivative of the temperature on the direction the object is going times the speed of the object.

6. Let $f(x, y, z) = xy + yz + zx$. Then $f(1, 2, 3) = 11$.
   (a) Find grad $f(1, 2, 3)$.
   (b) Give an equation to the tangent plane to $xy + yz + zx = 11$.
   (c) Give a parametric equation for the normal line to $xy + yz + zx = 11$ at the point $(1, 2, 3)$.

   ANSWER:

   (a) grad $f(x, y, z) = (y + z)\vec{i} + (x + z)\vec{j} + (x + y)\vec{k}$. So, grad $f(1, 2, 3) = 5\vec{i} + 4\vec{j} + 3\vec{k}$.
   (b) The tangent plane must satisfy

   $$\text{grad } f(1, 2, 3) \cdot [(x - 1)\vec{i} + (y - 2)\vec{j} + (z - 3)\vec{k}] = 0$$
   $$(5\vec{i} + 4\vec{j} + 3\vec{k}) \cdot [(x - 1)\vec{i} + (y - 2)\vec{j} + (z - 3)\vec{k}] = 0$$
   $$5(x - 1) + 4(y - 2) + 3(z - 3) = 0.$$

   Thus, $5x + 4y + 3z - 22 = 0$.
   (c) The parametric equation for the normal line is

   $$x = 1 + 5t$$
   $$y = 2 + 4t$$
   $$z = 3 + 3t.$$

7. The equation $\vec{r} = x\vec{i} + y\vec{j} = 2\cos(2\pi t/360)\vec{i} + 2\sin(2\pi t/360)\vec{j}$ describes the motion of a particle moving on a circle. Assume $x$ and $y$ are in miles and $t$ is in days.

   (a) What is the radius of the circle?
   (b) What is the period of the circular motion?
   (c) What are the velocity and the speed of the particle when it passes through the point $(0, 2)$?

   ANSWER:

   (a)
   $$r = \sqrt{x^2 + y^2} = 2 \text{ miles}$$

   (b)
   $$\text{period } T = \frac{360}{2\pi}(2\pi) = 360 \text{ days}$$

   (c) As the velocity

   $$\vec{v} = \frac{d\vec{r}}{dt} = -\frac{\pi}{90}\sin(\frac{2\pi t}{360})\vec{i} + \frac{\pi}{90}\cos(\frac{2\pi t}{360})\vec{j}$$
   $$= -\frac{\pi}{180}y\vec{i} + \frac{\pi}{180}x\vec{j}$$

   then at point $(0, 2)$

   $$\vec{v} = -\frac{\pi}{180}(2)\vec{i} + \frac{\pi}{180}(0)\vec{j}$$
   $$= -\frac{\pi}{90}\vec{i}$$

   and the speed $\|\vec{v}\| = \frac{\pi}{90}$ miles per day.

## Problems and Solutions for Section 16.3

1. The following equations (i)-(viii) represent curves or surfaces. Match each of the equations with one of the geometric descriptions (a)-(g). Write your answers in the spaces to the right of the equations. If none of (a)-(g) applies, write "None." (Note: $\rho, \phi, \theta$ are spherical coordinates; $r, \theta, z$ are cylindrical coordinates.)

   (i)   $r = 2, 0 \le z \le 10$ _____

(ii) $x = t, y = 2t, z = 3t, 0 \le t \le 10$_____
(iii) $x = t^2, y = 2t^2, z = 3t^2, 0 \le t \le 10$_____
(iv) $z = 10, 0 \le r \le 10$_____
(v) $\rho = \frac{1}{\cos\phi}, 0 \le \phi \le \frac{\pi}{3}$_____
(vi) $\rho = \cos\phi, \theta = \frac{\pi}{4}, 0 \le \phi \le \frac{\pi}{3}$_____
(vii) $\phi = \frac{\pi}{4}, 0 \le \rho \le 10$_____
(viii) $z = r^2, \theta = \frac{\pi}{4}, 0 \le r \le 10$_____

(a) Part of a line through the origin.
(b) Part of a parabola through the origin.
(c) Line or curve through $(x, y, z) = (0, 0, 1)$ in a horizontal plane.
(d) Line or curve through $(x, y, z) = (0, 0, 1)$ in a vertical plane.
(e) Disc.
(f) Part of a cone.
(g) Part of a cylinder.

ANSWER:
(i) (g)
(ii) (a)
(iii) (a)
(iv) (e)
(v) (e)
(vi) (d)
(vii) (f)
(viii) (b)

2. Let $S$ be a circular cylinder of radius 0.2, such that the center of one end is at the origin and the center of the other end is at the point $(1, 0, 1)$.

(a) Find the $xyz$-equation of the plane, $P$, containing the base of the cylinder (i.e., the plane through the origin perpendicular to the axis of the cylinder).
(b) Find two unit vectors $\vec{u}$ and $\vec{v}$ in $P$ which are perpendicular to each other.
(c) Give parametrization for the following using $\vec{u}$ and $\vec{v}$ and one or more parameters. Specify the range of values your parameters must take on.
   (i) The circle in which the cylinder, $S$, cuts the plane, $P$.
   (ii) The surface of the cylinder $S$.

ANSWER:

(a) $\vec{n} = \vec{i} + \vec{k}$ is normal to $P$. $P : 1x + 0y + 1z = d$. But, $(0, 0, 0)$ is an element of $P$ so $d = 0$. Thus,

$$P : x + z = 0.$$

See Figure 16.3.28.

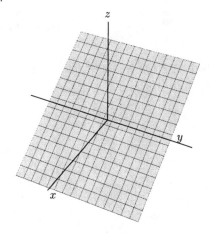

*Figure 16.3.28*

(b) Any vectors that are perpendicular to $\vec{n}$ belong to $P$. For example, $\vec{j}$ is a unit vector that works $(\vec{j} \cdot \vec{n} = 0$ and $\|\vec{j}\| = 1)$, so set $\vec{u} = \vec{j}$. For $\vec{v}$, take

$$\vec{v} = \frac{\vec{n} \times \vec{u}}{\|\vec{n} \times \vec{u}\|} = \frac{\begin{vmatrix} \vec{i} & \vec{j} & \vec{k} \\ 1 & 0 & 1 \\ 0 & 1 & 0 \end{vmatrix}}{\|\vec{n}\|(1)(1)} = \frac{-\vec{i} + \vec{k}}{\sqrt{2}}.$$

So,

$$\vec{u} = \vec{j}$$
$$\vec{v} = \frac{-\vec{i} + \vec{k}}{\sqrt{2}}.$$

(c) (i) $C$ is a circle of radius 0.2 on the plane determined by $\vec{u}$ and $\vec{v}$. Then we can take:

$$\vec{r}(\theta) = 0.2\cos\theta\vec{u} + 0.2\sin\theta\vec{v} \quad (0 \le \theta \le 2\pi)$$

or

$$x(\theta) = -0.2\sin\theta(\frac{\sqrt{2}}{2}) = -\frac{\sqrt{2}}{10}\sin\theta$$
$$y(\theta) = 0.2\cos\theta = 0.2\cos\theta$$
$$z(\theta) = 0.2\sin\theta(\frac{\sqrt{2}}{2}) = \frac{\sqrt{2}}{10}\sin\theta.$$

See Figure 16.3.29.

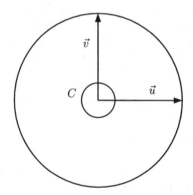

**Figure 16.3.29**

(ii) We just need to "sweep" the circle $C$ in Figure 16.3.29 in the direction $\vec{n} = \vec{i} + \vec{k}$, i.e.:

$$\vec{r}(\theta, t) = 0.2\cos\theta\vec{u} + 0.2\sin\theta\vec{v} + t\vec{n}$$

for $0 \le \theta \le 2\pi$ and $0 \le t \le 1$. Or:

$$x(\theta, t) = -\frac{\sqrt{2}}{10}\sin\theta + t$$
$$y(\theta, t) = \frac{2}{10}\cos\theta$$
$$z(\theta, t) = \frac{\sqrt{2}}{10}\sin\theta + t.$$

# Chapter 17 Exam Questions

*Problems and Solutions for Section 17.1*

1. Describe clearly what is meant by a vector field $\vec{v} = \vec{F}(\vec{r})$ where $\vec{r} = x\vec{i} + y\vec{j} + z\vec{k}$.

   ANSWER:

   A vector field assigns to every point $(x, y, z)$ in 3-space a vector $\vec{v}$ given by the function $\vec{v} = \vec{f}(x, y, z)$. In other words, a vector $\vec{v}$ (depending on the point) is "stuck on" to every point in space.

2. Sketch the vector fields $\vec{v} = y\vec{j}$ and $\vec{w} = y\vec{i}$.

   ANSWER:

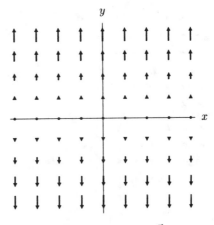

*Figure 17.1.30:* $\vec{v} = y\vec{j}$

$\vec{v}$ points vertically because the only component is the $y$ component. All vectors on a horizontal line are the same because $\vec{v}$ depends only on $y$.

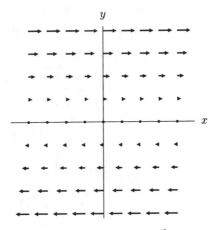

*Figure 17.1.31:* $\vec{w} = y\vec{i}$

The vectors are horizontal because the only component is the $x$ component. All vectors on a horizontal line are the same length because $\vec{v}$ depends only on $y$.

3. For each of the following vector fields, identify which one of the following figures could represent it. The scales in the $x$ and $y$ directions are the same. No reasons need be given. (a) $x\vec{i} + y\vec{j}$
(b) $x\vec{i} - y\vec{j}$  (c) $y\vec{i} + x\vec{j}$  (d) $y\vec{i}$  (e) $\vec{i} + x\vec{j}$  (f) $x^2\vec{i} + xy\vec{j}$

(I)

(II)

(III)

(IV)

(V)

(VI)

ANSWER:

(a) III  (b) V  (c) VI

(d) I  (e) II  (f) IV

4. Figure 17.1.32 shows the contour map of a function $z = f(x, y)$.

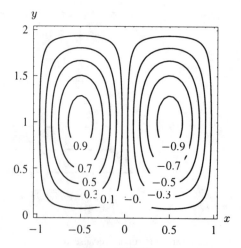

*Figure 17.1.32:*

(a)  Let

$$F(x) = \int_0^2 f(x, y) \, dy.$$

For what values of $x$ is $F(x)$ at a maximum? For what values of $x$ is it at a minimum? For what values of $x$ is $F(x) = 0$?

(b)  Let $\vec{F}$ be the gradient vector field of $f$, i.e., $\vec{F}$ = grad $f$. Which of the vector fields shown in Figure 17.1.33 is $\vec{F}$ ?

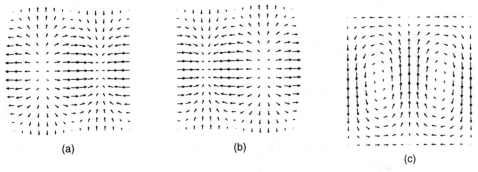

(a)                         (b)

(c)

*Figure 17.1.33:*

ANSWER:

(a)

$$x = -0.5, \quad F(x) \text{ is at a maximum.}$$
$$x = 0, \quad F(x) = 0.$$
$$x = 0.5, \quad F(x) \text{ is at a minimum.}$$

(b)  The vectors in (a) are perpendicular to the level curves, but point in the wrong direction. The vectors in (c) are not perpendicular to the level curves. So pick vector field (b).

# Chapter 18 Exam Questions

*Problems and Solutions for Section 18.1*

1. Explain clearly what is meant by a line integral $\int_C \vec{F} \cdot d\vec{r}$.

    ANSWER:

    $\vec{F}$ is a vector field, $C$ is an oriented curve. Divide the curve into small almost straight segments $\Delta\vec{r}$. Form the dot product of the $\vec{F}$ on one segment, $\vec{F} \cdot \Delta\vec{r}$. Sum over all segments and take the limit as $\|\Delta\vec{r}\| \to 0$. This gives the line integral.

2. True or False?

    (a)  $\int_C \vec{F} \cdot d\vec{r}$ is a number.
    (b)  $\int_C \vec{F} \cdot d\vec{r} = 0$ if $C$ is a closed curve.
    (c)  $\int_C \vec{F} \cdot d\vec{r}$ is a vector.
    (d)  $\int_{C_1} \vec{F} \cdot d\vec{r} = -\int_{C_2} \vec{F} \cdot d\vec{r}$ if $C_2$ is the curve $C_1$ traced out in the opposite direction.

    ANSWER:

    (a)  True. As $\vec{F} \cdot d\vec{r}$ is a scalar function.
    (b)  False. For example, if $C$ is a circle of radius 1 going clockwise around the origin and $\vec{F} = -y\vec{i} + x\vec{j}$, $\int_C \vec{F} \cdot d\vec{r} = 2\pi$.
    (c)  False. $\int_C \vec{F} \cdot d\vec{r}$ is a number because $\vec{F} \cdot d\vec{r}$ is a scalar function.
    (d)  True. Doing $\int_{C_2} \vec{F} \cdot d\vec{r}$ amounts to change the parameter from $t$ on $C_1$ to $-t$ on $C_2$.

3. (a)  Given the graph of the vector field, $\vec{F}$, shown in Figure 18.1.34, give a possible formula for such a field.

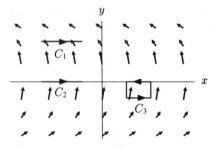

*Figure 18.1.34*

    (b)  List the following quantities in increasing order:

    (i)  $\int_{C_1} \vec{F} \cdot d\vec{r}$,

    (ii)  $\int_{C_2} \vec{F} \cdot d\vec{r}$,

    (iii)  $\int_{C_3} \vec{F} \cdot d\vec{r}$.

    ANSWER:

    (a)

$$\vec{F} = -y\vec{i} + \frac{1}{|y| + 1}\vec{j}$$

    (b)

$$\int_{C_1} \vec{F} \cdot d\vec{r} < \int_{C_2} \vec{F} \cdot d\vec{r} < \int_{C_3} \vec{F} \cdot d\vec{r}$$

**Problems and Solutions for Section 18.2**

1.  Calculate $\int_C \vec{F} \cdot d\vec{r}$ when $\vec{F} = (y+z)\vec{i} + (x+z)\vec{j} + \vec{k}$ and $C$ is the line from the origin to the point $(3,3,3)$.

    ANSWER:

    For $C$:

    $$\vec{r} = 3t(\vec{i} + \vec{j} + \vec{k}) \quad 0 \le t \le 1$$

    $$\int_C \vec{F} \cdot d\vec{r} = \int_0^1 \left((3t + 3t)\vec{i} + (3t + 3t)\vec{j} + \vec{k}\right) \cdot 3(\vec{i} + \vec{j} + \vec{k}) \, dt$$

    $$= \int_0^1 (18t + 18t + 3) \, dt$$

    $$= 3 \int_0^1 (12t + 1) \, dt = 3(6t^2 + t)\Big|_0^1$$

    $$= 3(6 + 1)$$

    $$= 21$$

2.  Find $\int_C \vec{F} \cdot d\vec{r}$ where $\vec{F} = (x+z)\vec{i} + z\vec{j} + y\vec{k}$ and $C$ is the line from the point $(2,4,4)$ to the point $(1,5,2)$.

    ANSWER:

    The straight line joining $(2,4,4)$ and $(1,5,2)$ is given in parametric form by:

    $$\begin{aligned} x &= 2 - t \\ y &= 4 + t \qquad 0 \le t \le 1 \\ z &= 4 - 2t \end{aligned}$$

    $$\int_C \vec{F} \cdot d\vec{r} = \int_0^1 \left((6 + 3t)\vec{i} + (4 - 2t)\vec{j} + (4 + t)\vec{k}\right) \cdot (-\vec{i} + \vec{j} - 2\vec{k}) \, dt$$

    $$= \int_0^1 \left(-6 + 3t + 4 - 2t - 2(4 + t)\right) \, dt$$

    $$= \int_0^1 (-t - 10) \, dt = \frac{21}{2}.$$

3.  Explain in words and symbols how to calculate the line integral $\int_C \vec{F} \cdot d\vec{r}$ given a parameterization, $\vec{r} = \vec{p}(t)$, of the curve $C$.

    ANSWER:

    Let

    $$\begin{aligned} \vec{F} &= F_1\vec{i} + F_2\vec{j} + F_3\vec{k} \\ d\vec{r} &= dx\vec{i} + dy\vec{j} + dz\vec{k} \\ \vec{r} &= \vec{p}(t) \\ &= p_1(t)\vec{i} + p_2(t)\vec{j} + p_3(t)\vec{k} \end{aligned}$$

    and let $C$ be a curve which connects points $A$ and $B$.

    $$\int_C \vec{F} \cdot d\vec{r} = \int_C (F_1 \, dx + F_2 \, dy + F_3 \, dz)$$

    $$= \int_{t_1}^{t_2} [F_1(p_1(t), p_2(t), p_3(t))p_1'(t)dt + F_2(p_1(t), p_2(t), p_3(t))p_2'(t)dt$$

    $$+ F_3(p_1(t), p_2(t), p_3(t))p_3'(t)dt]$$

**714**

where $t_1$ and $t_2$ denote the values of $t$ corresponding to points $A$ and $B$, respectively.

4. Let $\vec{F} = \sqrt{x^2 + y^2}\vec{i} + \sqrt{x^2 + y^2}\vec{j}$.

(a) Sketch $\vec{F}$ at each of the points on the axes below. Your sketch does not have to be to scale, but should show the correct direction for $\vec{F}$ at each point, and the relative magnitudes of $\vec{F}$ at different points should be roughly correct.

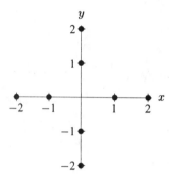

*Figure 18.2.35*

(b) Is the line integral of $\vec{F}$ around the unit circle traversed counterclockwise: positive, negative, or zero?

For any $\theta$, $0 \leq \theta \leq 2\pi$, let $C_\theta$ be the line segment from $(0,0)$ to the point $(\cos\theta, \sin\theta)$ on the unit circle.

(c) Give examples of angles $\theta$ for which $\int_{C_\theta} \vec{F} \cdot d\vec{r}$ is positive, zero, negative.

(d) For a fixed value of $\theta$, find a parametrization of $C_\theta$ and compute $\int_{C_\theta} \vec{F} \cdot d\vec{r}$. (Your answer will depend on $\theta$.)

ANSWER:

(a) $\vec{F}$ is of the form $c\vec{i} + c\vec{j}$ where $c > 0$, and all vectors on the same circle are of the same length. See Figure 18.2.36.

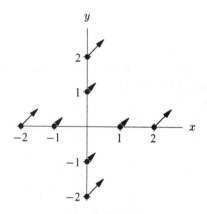

*Figure 18.2.36*

(b) Zero.
(c) (i) $\pi/4$.
    (ii) $-\pi/4$.
    (iii) $5\pi/4$.

(d) The line is $x = t\cos\theta, y = t\sin\theta$, for $0 \le t \le 1$. Then

$$\int_{c_\theta} \vec{F} \cdot d\vec{r} = \int_0^1 (t\vec{i} + t\vec{j}) \cdot (\cos\theta\vec{i} + \sin\theta\vec{j})\, dt$$

$$= \int_0^1 t(\cos\theta + \sin\theta)\, dt$$

$$= \frac{1}{2}(\cos\theta + \sin\theta)$$

## Problems and Solutions for Section 18.3

1. If $\vec{F} = x^2\vec{i} + z\sin(yz)\vec{j} + y\sin(yz)\vec{k}$, compute $\int_C \vec{F} \cdot d\vec{r}$ where C is the curve from $A(0, 0, 1)$ to $B(3, 1, 2)$ shown Figure 18.3.37in (messy computation can be avoided).

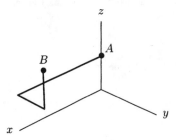

**Figure 18.3.37**

ANSWER:
$\vec{F} = \text{grad}(x^3/3 - \cos(yz))$ so

$$\int_C \vec{F} \cdot d\vec{r} = \left. \frac{x^3}{3} - \cos(yz) \right|_{(0,0,1)}^{(3,1,2)}$$

$$= 9 - \cos(2) + \cos(0)$$

$$= 10 - \cos 2$$

2. True or false? Give a reason for your answer.

   (a) There is a function $f(x, y)$ such that grad $f = x^2 + y^2$.
   (b) $\int_C \vec{F} \cdot d\vec{r} = 0$ for any closed curve $C$ and any vector field $\vec{F}$.

   ANSWER:

   (a) False. grad $f$ is a vector; $x^2 + y^2$ is a scalar.
   (b) This is true for a gradient vector field, but not all vector fields.

3. What does it mean to say that $\vec{F}$ is a gradient vector field?
   ANSWER:
   $\vec{F} = \text{grad}\,\phi$ where $\phi$ is a scalar function.

4. Explain what is meant by saying a vector field is conservative.
   ANSWER:
   A vector field $\vec{F}$ is called conservative if for any two points $P$ and $Q$, the line integral $\int_C \vec{F} \cdot d\vec{r}$ has the same value along any path $C$ from $P$ to $Q$ lying in the domain of $\vec{F}$.

5. (a) Given that $\vec{G}(x,y) = 3x\vec{i} + y^2\vec{j}$ find a function $g$ so that grad $g = \vec{G}$.

(b) Use the information from (a) to compute $\int_C \vec{G} \cdot d\vec{r}$ where $C$ is a curve beginning at the point $(1,4)$ and ending at the point $(0,5)$.

ANSWER:

(a) We find

$$\frac{\partial g}{\partial x} = 3x$$
$$\frac{\partial g}{\partial y} = y^2.$$

From the first equation we have

$$g = \frac{3x^2}{2} + f(y)$$

and we find $f(y)$ from the second equation to be

$$f(y) = \frac{y^3}{3} + C$$

where $C$ is an arbitrary constant. Hence,

$$g = \frac{3x^2}{2} + \frac{y^3}{3} + C.$$

(b) As $\vec{G} = \text{grad } g$ one has:

$$\int_C \vec{G} \cdot d\vec{r} = \int_{(1,4)}^{(0,5)} dg$$
$$= g(0,5) - g(1,4)$$
$$= \frac{5^3}{3} - \frac{3}{2} - \frac{4^3}{3}$$
$$= \frac{113}{6}.$$

6. Question (a)-(d) below refer to the two-dimensional vector field

$$\vec{F}(x,y) = -0.5y\vec{i} + 0.5x\vec{j}.$$

(a) Sketch the vector field $\vec{F}$ on the grid below at the gridpoints marked with dots, paying careful attention to the length and direction of the vectors.

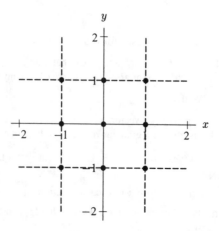

Figure 18.3.38

(b)   Write down parameterizations of the three line segments $C_1$, $C_2$, and $C_3$ shown in the figure below.

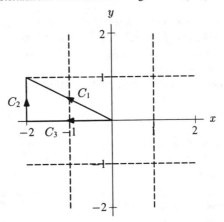

*Figure 18.3.39*

(c)   Use your parameterizations to compute the line integrals $\int_{C_1} \vec{F} \cdot d\vec{r}$, $\int_{C_2} \vec{F} \cdot d\vec{r}$, $\int_{C_3} \vec{F} \cdot d\vec{r}$.

(d)   Is $\vec{F}$ a conservative vector field? Justify your answer.

ANSWER:

(a)

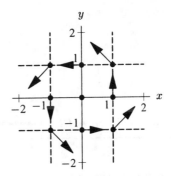

*Figure 18.3.40:*

(b)   The parameterizations of the three given line segments are:

$$C_1 : y = \frac{1}{2}t \quad x = -t \quad 0 \le t \le 2$$
$$C_2 : y = t \quad x = -2 \quad 0 \le t \le 1$$
$$C_3 : y = 0 \quad x = -t \quad 0 \le t \le 2$$

(c)

$$\int_{C_1} \vec{F} \cdot d\vec{r} = \int_{C_1} (-0.5 \cdot (\tfrac{1}{2}t)\vec{i} + 0.5 \cdot (-t)\vec{j}) \cdot (-\vec{i} + \tfrac{1}{2}\vec{j})dt$$

$$= \int_0^2 0\, dt = 0$$

$$\int_{C_2} \vec{F} \cdot d\vec{r} = \int_{C_2} (-0.5t\vec{i} + 0.5(-2)\vec{j}) \cdot (0\vec{i} + \vec{j})dt$$

$$= \int_0^1 -dt = -1$$

$$\int_{C_3} \vec{F} \cdot d\vec{r} = \int_{C_3} (-0.5 \cdot 0\vec{i} + 0.5 \cdot (-t)\vec{j}) \cdot (-\vec{i} + 0\vec{j})dt$$

$$= \int_0^2 0\, dt = 0$$

(d) $\vec{F}$ is not conservative, since $C = C_3 + C_2 - C_1$ is a closed curve, and $\int_C \vec{F} \cdot d\vec{r} = -1 \neq 0$.

7. (a) Is the following statement true or false? "If $\vec{F}(x, y) = P(x, y)\vec{i} + Q(x, y)\vec{j}$ is a gradient vector field, then $\frac{\partial P}{\partial y} = \frac{\partial Q}{\partial x}$". Explain your answer.

(b) Is there a function $f$ such that $\vec{F}(x, y) = (x^2 - y^2)\vec{i} + (-2xy)\vec{j} = \text{grad } f$? If so, find one, and if not, explain why not.

(c) Let $\vec{F}$ be the vector field defined in (b). Evaluate the line integral

$$\int_C \vec{F} \cdot d\vec{r},$$

where $C$ the path from $(0, 0)$ to $(1, 1)$ that goes along the $x$-axis to $(1, 0)$, and then vertically up to $(1, 1)$.

ANSWER:

(a) True if $P$ and $Q$ are differentiable with continuous partials. If $\vec{F} = P(x, y)\vec{i} + Q(x, y)\vec{j}$ is a gradient vector field, then there is a function $f$ such that $\frac{\partial f}{\partial x} = P(x, y)$ and $\frac{\partial f}{\partial y} = Q(x, y)$. From hypothesis, $f$ is twice differentiable with continuous second order partials, so $\frac{\partial f}{\partial x \partial y} = \frac{\partial f}{\partial y \partial x}$. We get $\frac{\partial P}{\partial y} = \frac{\partial Q}{\partial x}$.

(b) Suppose there exists such $f$ that $\frac{\partial f}{\partial x} = x^2 - y^2, \frac{\partial f}{\partial y} = -2xy$. From $\frac{\partial f}{\partial x} = x^2 - y^2$, we get $f = \frac{x^3}{3} - xy^2 + g(y)$ then $f_y = -2xy + g'(y) = -2xy$. So, $g'(y) = 0. g(y) =$constant. Take for example: $f(x, y) = \frac{x^3}{3} - xy^2$.

(c) Since $\vec{F} = \text{grad } f$,

$$\int_C \vec{F} \cdot d\vec{r} = f(1, 1) - f(0, 0)$$

$$= (\frac{1}{3} - 1) - 0 = -\frac{2}{3}.$$

## Problems and Solutions for Section 18.4

1. Which of the following vector fields is a gradient vector field? For any that is, find the potential function $f$ such that $\vec{F} = \text{grad } f$.

(a) $\vec{F} = x\vec{i} + y\vec{j}$
(b) $\vec{F} = y\vec{i} - x\vec{j}$

ANSWER:

(a) $\vec{F} = x\vec{i} + y\vec{j}$ is a gradient vector field as $\text{grad} \times \vec{F} = 0$. As

$$x = \frac{\partial f}{\partial x}$$

$$y = \frac{\partial f}{\partial y}$$

then

$$f = \frac{x^2}{2} + \frac{y^2}{2} + \text{constant}.$$

(b) As $\frac{\partial(y)}{\partial y} = 1$ and $\frac{\partial(-x)}{\partial x} = -1$, $\vec{F} = y\vec{i} - x\vec{j}$ is not a gradient vector field.

2. Let $\vec{F}$ and $\vec{G}$ be two 2-dimensional fields,

$$\vec{F} = 3x\vec{i} + 5y\vec{j} \text{ and } \vec{G} = 3y\vec{i} + 5x\vec{j}.$$

Let $C_1$ be the circle with center $(2, 2)$ and radius 1 oriented counterclockwise. Let $C_2$ be the path consisting of the straight line segments from $(0, 4)$ to $(0, 1)$ and from $(0, 1)$ to $(3, 1)$. Find the following line integrals. Explain your reasoning.

(a) $\int_{C_1} \vec{F} \cdot d\vec{r}$

(b)  $\int_{C_2} \vec{F} \cdot d\vec{r}$

(c)  $\int_{C_1} \vec{G} \cdot d\vec{r}$

(d)  $\int_{C_2} \vec{G} \cdot d\vec{r}$

ANSWER:

(a) Observe that $\vec{F}$ is a gradient field. In fact $\vec{F} = \text{grad} \, f$ for $f(x, y) = 3x^2/2 + 5y^2/2$. Also, $C_1$ is a closed curve. Therefore,

$$\int_{C_1} \vec{F} \cdot d\vec{r} = 0.$$

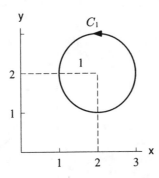

**Figure 18.4.41**

(b) Again, as $\vec{F} = \text{grad} \, f$, then

$$\int_{C_2} \vec{F} \cdot d\vec{r} = f(3, 1) - f(0, 4) = \frac{27}{2} + \frac{5}{2} - 0 - \frac{80}{2}.$$

Thus,

$$\int_{C_2} \vec{F} \cdot d\vec{r} = -24.$$

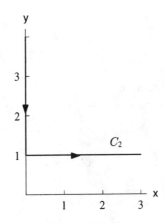

**Figure 18.4.42**

(c) We can use Green's Theorem:

$$\int_{C_1} \vec{G} \cdot d\vec{r} = \int_R \left(-\frac{\partial G_1}{\partial y} + \frac{\partial G_2}{\partial x}\right) dA$$

$$= \int_R (-3 + 5) \, dA$$

$$= +2(\text{Area(R)}) = 2(\pi)(1^2).$$

Thus,

$$\int_{C_1} \vec{G} \cdot d\vec{r} = 2\pi.$$

Or, $C_1 : (2 + \cos t)\vec{i} + (2 + \sin t)\vec{j}$ for $0 \leq t \leq 2\pi$. So,

$$\int_{C_1} \vec{G} \cdot d\vec{r} = \int_{C_1} (3y\vec{i} + 5x\vec{j}) \cdot (-\sin t\vec{i} + \cos t\vec{j}) \, dt$$

$$= \int_0^{2\pi} 3(2 + \sin t)(-\sin t) + 5(2 + \cos t)(\cos t) \, dt$$

$$= \int_0^{2\pi} (5\cos^2 t - 3\sin^2 t - 6\sin t + 10\cos t) \, dt$$

$$= 2\pi.$$

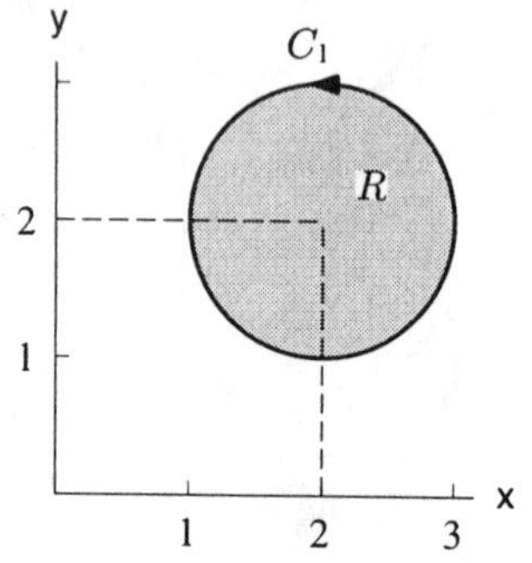

*Figure 18.4.43*

(d)

$$\int_A \vec{G} \cdot d\vec{r} = \int_A (3y\vec{i} + 5x\vec{j}) \cdot (\vec{j}) \, dt$$

$$= \int_4^1 (5)(0) \, dt = 0.$$

$$\int_B \vec{G} \cdot d\vec{r} = \int_B (3y\vec{i} + 5x\vec{j}) \cdot (\vec{i}) \, dt$$

$$= \int_0^3 (3)(1) \, dt = 9.$$

Adding them up:

$$\int_{C_2} \vec{G} \cdot d\vec{r} = 9.$$

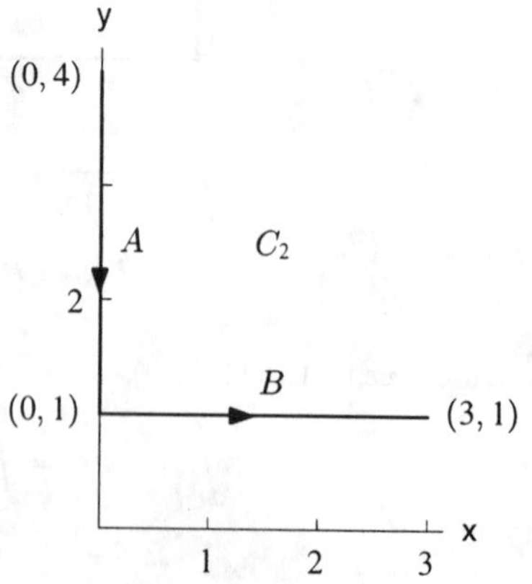

*Figure 18.4.44*

3. Let $\vec{F}(x,y)$ be the vector field $\vec{F}(x,y) = (x^2 + x)\vec{j}$. Let $C_1$ be the line from $(0,0)$ to $(1,1)$. Let $C_2$ be the unit circle traveled counterclockwise.

(a) Give a graph of this vector field.

(b) Give a parameterization of $C_1$ and $C_2$.

(c) Find $\int_{C_1} \vec{F} \cdot d\vec{r}$.

(d) Find $\int_{C_2} \vec{F} \cdot d\vec{r}$ using Green's theorem.

ANSWER:

(a)

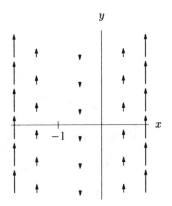

*Figure 18.4.45*

(b)  $C_1$:

$$x = t \quad 0 \le t \le 1$$
$$y = t.$$

$C_2$:

$$x = \cos\theta \quad 0 \le \theta \le 2\pi$$
$$y = \sin\theta.$$

(c)

$$\int_{C_1} \vec{F} \cdot d\vec{r} = \int_0^1 \vec{F}(x(t),y(t)) \cdot (x'(t)\vec{i} + y'(t)\vec{j})\, dt$$

$$= \int_0^1 (t^2 + t)\vec{j} \cdot (\vec{i} + \vec{j})\, dt$$

$$= \int_0^1 (t^2 + t)\, dt$$

$$= \left(\frac{t^3}{3} + \frac{t^2}{2}\right)\Big|_0^1$$

$$= \frac{1}{3} + \frac{1}{2} = \frac{5}{6}.$$

(d) By Green's theorem we have

$$\int_{C_2} \vec{F} \cdot d\vec{r} = \iint_S \left(\frac{\partial F_2}{\partial x} - \frac{\partial F_1}{\partial y}\right) dx\, dy$$

$$= \iint_S (2x + 1)\, dx\, dy$$

$$= \int_0^{2\pi} \int_0^1 (2r\cos\theta + 1) r\, dr\, d\theta$$

$$= \int_0^{2\pi} (\frac{2}{3}r^3 \cos\theta + \frac{r^2}{2}) \Big|_0^1 d\theta$$

$$= \int_0^{2\pi} (\frac{2}{3} \cos\theta + \frac{1}{2}) d\theta$$

$$= (\frac{2}{3} \sin\theta + \frac{1}{2}\theta) \Big|_0^{2\pi}$$

$$= \pi.$$

4.

(A)

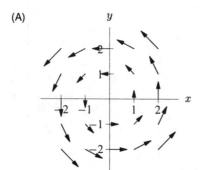

(B)

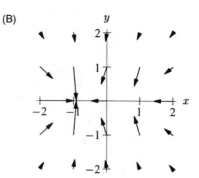

Figure 18.4.46:

Figure 18.4.47:

(a)  Which of the two vector fields shown is clearly not conservative? Explain why.

(b)  In the vector field you chose in (a) sketch a closed curve around which the circulation is nonzero.

   ANSWER:

(a)  (A) is clearly not conservative as it rotates around the origin, so its line integral around any circle centered at the origin will be non-zero.

(b)  Take $C : x^2 + y^2 = 1$ oriented counterclockwise.

# Chapter 19 Exam Questions

1. True or false? Give a reason for your answer. $\int_S \vec{F} \cdot d\vec{A}$ is a vector.

   ANSWER:

   $\vec{F} \cdot d\vec{A}$ is a scalar and so is the integral.

2. Consider four circular discs, $S_1, S_2, S_3, S_4$ each of radius 2 and centered on an axis, where:

   - $S_1$ is perpendicular to the $x$-axis at $x = 5$ with normal in the direction of increasing $x$.
   - $S_2$ is perpendicular to the $x$-axis at $x = 8$ with normal in the direction of decreasing $x$.
   - $S_3$ is perpendicular to the $y$-axis at $y = -6$ with normal in the direction of decreasing $y$.
   - $S_4$ is perpendicular to the $z$-axis at $z = 7$ with normal in the direction of increasing $z$.

   Consider the vector field $\vec{F} = x\vec{i} + y\vec{j} + (z + x)\vec{k}$.

   (a) Which of the flux integrals

       (i) $\int_{S_1} \vec{F} \cdot d\vec{A}$

       (ii) $\int_{S_2} \vec{F} \cdot d\vec{A}$

       (iii) $\int_{S_3} \vec{F} \cdot d\vec{A}$

       (iv) $\int_{S_4} \vec{F} \cdot d\vec{A}$

       are positive? negative? zero? How do you know?

   (b) Find $\int_{S_1} \vec{F} \cdot d\vec{A}$.

   ANSWER:

   (a) (i) $\int_{S_1} \vec{F} \cdot d\vec{A} > 0$ because $\vec{F} \cdot d\vec{A} = x\,dA = 5\,dA$.

       (ii) $\int_{S_2} \vec{F} \cdot d\vec{A} < 0$ because $\vec{F} \cdot d\vec{A} = -x\,dA = -8\,dA$.

       (iii) $\int_{S_3} \vec{F} \cdot d\vec{A} > 0$ because $\vec{F} \cdot d\vec{A} = -y\,dA = 6\,dA$.

       (iv) $\int_{S_4} \vec{F} \cdot d\vec{A} > 0$ because $\vec{F} \cdot d\vec{A} = (z+x)dA = (7+x)dA$. and $|x| \le 2$ so $7 + x > 0$

   (b)

   $$\int_{S_1} \vec{F} \cdot d\vec{A} = 5 \int dA$$
   $$= (5)(2)^2 \pi$$
   $$= 20\pi$$

3. Compute the flux integral of the vector field $\vec{G} = -y\vec{i} + x\vec{j} + xyz\vec{k}$ through the square $0 \le y \le 2$, $0 \le z \le 2$ in the $yz$-plane, oriented so that the normal vector points in the direction of the $x$-axis.

   ANSWER:

   At the square $S, x = 0$, then $\vec{G} = -y\vec{i}$. So,

   $$\int_S \vec{G} \cdot d\vec{A} = \int_0^2 \int_0^2 (-y)\,dy\,dz$$
   $$= \int_0^2 (-\frac{y^2}{2})\Big|_0^2 dt = -4.$$

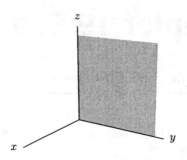

*Figure 19.1.48*

4. What is the flux of the vector field $\vec{F} = 2\vec{i} + 3\vec{j} + 5\vec{k}$ through a circle in the $xy$-plane of radius 3 oriented upward with center at the origin.

   ANSWER:

$$\begin{aligned}
\text{Flux} &= \int_A (2\vec{i} + 3\vec{j} + 5\vec{k}) \, d\vec{A} \\
&= \int_A (2\vec{i} + 3\vec{j} + 5\vec{k}) \cdot \vec{k} \, dA \\
&= 5 \int_A dA \\
&= (5)(3)^2 \pi \\
&= 45\pi
\end{aligned}$$

# Chapter 20 Exam Questions

*Problems and Solutions for Section 20.1*

1. Let $\vec{H} = 2x\vec{i} - 3xy\vec{j} + xz^2\vec{k}$,

   (a) What is div $\vec{H}$ $(x, y, z)$?

   (b) What is $\int_S \vec{H} \cdot d\vec{A}$, where $S$ is the cube with corners at $(0, 0, 0)$, $(1, 0, 0)$, $(0, 1, 0)$, $(0, 0, 1)$, $(1, 1, 0)$, and $(1, 1, 1)$?

   ANSWER:

   (a)

   $$\text{div } \vec{H} = \frac{\partial}{\partial x}(2x) + \frac{\partial}{\partial y}(-3xy) + \frac{\partial}{\partial z}(xz^2)$$
   $$= 2 - 3x + 2xz$$

   (b)

   $$\int_S \vec{H} \cdot d\vec{A} = \int_v \text{div} \cdot \vec{H} \, dV$$

   $$= \int_0^1 dx \int_0^1 dy \int_0^1 dz(2 - 3x + 2xz)$$

   $$= \int_0^1 dx \int_0^1 dy(2 - 2x)$$

   $$= \int_0^1 (2 - 2x)dx$$

   $$= (2x - x^2)\Big|_0^1$$

   $$= 1$$

2. Questions (a)-(c) refer to the two-dimensional fluid flow

   $$\vec{v}(x, y) = (x^2 + y^2)^a x\vec{i} + (x^2 + y^2)^a y\vec{j},$$

   where $a$ is a constant. (We allow $a$ to be negative, so $\vec{F}$ may or may not be defined at $(0, 0)$.)

   (a) Is the fluid flowing away from the origin, towards it, or neither?

   (b) Calculate the divergence of $\vec{F}$. Simplify your answer.

   (c) For what values of $a$ is div $\vec{F}$ positive? Zero? Negative?

   (d) What does your answer to (c) mean in terms of flow? How does this fit in with your answer to (a)?

   ANSWER:

   (a) The fluid is flowing from the orign.

   (b) The divergence of $\vec{F}$ is

   $$\text{div } \vec{F} = \frac{\partial v}{\partial x} + \frac{\partial v}{\partial y}$$
   $$= 2ax^2(x^2 + y^2)^{a-1} + (x^2 + y^2)^a + 2ay^2(x^2 + y^2)^{a-1} + (x^2 + y^2)^a$$
   $$= 2(x^2 + y^2)^a(1 + a)$$

   (c) Since div $\vec{F} = 2(x^2 + y^2)^a(1 + a)$, and we always have $2(x^2 + y^2)^a \geq 0$ for any $a$, so if $a > -1$ then div $\vec{F} > 0$, if $a = -1$, then div $\vec{F} = 0$, if $a < -1$, then div $\vec{F} < 0$.

   (d) If div $\vec{F} > 0$, it means that the flow rate is increasing as it is away from origin, i.e. the vectors in the vector field will be longer and longer when we move away from origin. If div $\vec{F} = 0$, it means that the flow is constant everywhere. If div $\vec{F} < 0$, then the flow rate is decreasing when we move away from origin. There is no contradiction between (c) and (a), no matter what div $\vec{F}$ is, the flow is always from origin.

3.  (a)  If $\vec{F}$ is a vector field, what is meant by div $\vec{F}$ at a point $P$? Your answer should say whether div $\vec{F}$ is a vector or a scalar, and explain what div $\vec{F}$ tells you if $\vec{F}$ represents the velocity of a moving fluid.

(b)  How is div $\vec{F}$ defined?

(c)  If $\vec{F} = ye^{x^2}\vec{i} + xye^{y}\vec{j} + z\cos(xy)\vec{k}$, find div $\vec{F}$.

ANSWER:

(a)  div $\vec{F}$ is a scalar and if $\vec{F}$ represents the velocity of a moving fluid, then the gain of fluid per unit volume per unit time in a small parallelepiped having center at $P(x, y, z)$ and edges parallel to the coordinate axes and having magnitude $\Delta x, \Delta y, \Delta z$, respectively, is given approximately by div $\vec{F}$.

(b)

$$\text{div } \vec{F} = \lim_{\Delta V \to 0}\left[\frac{1}{\Delta V}\int_{s}\vec{F}\cdot d\vec{s}\right] \text{ or } \frac{\partial F_1}{\partial x} + \frac{\partial F_2}{\partial y} + \frac{\partial F_3}{\partial z} \text{ where } \vec{F} = F_1\vec{i} + F_2\vec{j} + F_3\vec{k}.$$

(c)

$$\text{div } \vec{F} = \frac{\partial}{\partial x}(ye^{x^2}) + \frac{\partial}{\partial y}(xye^{y}) + \frac{\partial}{\partial z}(z\cos(xy))$$

$$= 2xye^{x^2} + xe^{y} + xye^{y} + \cos xy$$

## Problems and Solutions for Section 20.2

1.  True or false? Give a reason for your answer. If div $\vec{F} = 7$ for all $x$, $y$, $z$ and if $S$ is a surface enclosing a volume $V$, then $\int_{S}\vec{F}\cdot d\vec{A} = 7V$.

ANSWER:

True. By the divergence theorem.

2.  An oceanographic vessel suspends a paraboloid-shaped net below the ocean at depth of 1000 feet, held open at the top by a circular metal ring of radius 20 feet, with bottom 100 feet below the ring and just touching the ocean floor. Set up coordinates with the origin at the point where the net touches the ocean floor and with $z$ measured upward.

Figure 20.2.49

Suppose water is flowing with velocity:
$$\vec{F} = 2xz\vec{i} - (1100 + xe^{-x^2})\vec{j} + z(1100 - z)\vec{k}.$$

(a)  Write down an iterated integral $I_1$ for the flux of water through the net (oriented from inside to outside). Include the limits of integration but do not evaluate.

(b)   Use the Divergence Theorem to compare this integral with the flux $I_2$ across the circular disk which is the open top of the paraboloid-shaped net. In this way evaluate $I_1$.

ANSWER:

(a)   The net is $z = k(x^2 + y^2)$. Since $x^2 + y^2 = 20^2 = 400$ when $z = 100$, we have $k = 1/4$. So $z = 1/4(x^2 + y^2)$ and

$$I_1 = \int_{-20}^{20} \int_{-\sqrt{400-x^2}}^{\sqrt{400-y^2}} (2x(\frac{1}{4}(x^2 + y^2))\vec{i} - (1100 + xe^{-x^2})\vec{j}$$
$$+ \frac{1}{4}(x^2 + y^2)(1100 - \frac{1}{4}(x^2 + y^2))\vec{k}) \cdot (\frac{x}{2}\vec{i} + \frac{y}{2}\vec{j} - \vec{k})\, dx\, dy.$$

(b)   $\operatorname{div} \vec{F} = 2z + 1100 - 2z = 1100$. If the circular disk is oriented upward, the the Divergence theorem tells us

$$I_1 + I_2 = \int_W \operatorname{div} \vec{F}\, dW = \int_W 1100\, dW = 1100 \int_0^{2\pi} \int_0^{20} \int_{r^2/4}^{100} r\, dz\, dr\, dt$$

$$= 2\pi \int_0^{20} rz \Big|_{r^2/4}^{100}\, dr = 2\pi \int_0^{20} (100 - \frac{r^2}{4})\, dr$$

$$= \frac{2\pi(100)r^2}{2} - \frac{r^4}{16} \Big|_0^{20} = 20{,}000\pi.$$

Now,

$$I_2 = \int_{z=100} \vec{F} \cdot dA = \int 100(1000)\vec{k} \cdot d\vec{A} = 10^5 (\text{ area}) = 10{,}000\pi.$$

Thus $I_1 = \int \operatorname{div} -I_2 = 10{,}000\pi.$

## Problems and Solutions for Section 20.3

1.   Calculate curl $\vec{H}$ , where $\vec{H} = 2x\vec{i} - 3xy\vec{j} + xz^2\vec{k}$ .
ANSWER:

$$\operatorname{curl} \vec{H} = \begin{vmatrix} \vec{i} & \vec{j} & \vec{k} \\ \frac{\partial}{\partial x} & \frac{\partial}{\partial y} & \frac{\partial}{\partial z} \\ 2x & -3xy & xz^2 \end{vmatrix} = -z^2\vec{j} - 3y\vec{k}$$

2.   (a)   What is meant by curl $\vec{F}$ where $\vec{F}$ is a vector field? Is curl $\vec{F}$ a vector or a scalar?
(b)   How is curl $\vec{F}$ defined?
(c)   Find $\operatorname{curl}(-y\vec{i} + x\vec{j} + (z^2 + y^2 + x^2)\vec{k})$.
ANSWER:

(a)   curl $\vec{F}$ is a vector which tells you how a vector field is rotating. Its direction gives the axis of rotation; its magnitude gives the strength of rotation about the axis.
(b)   curl $\vec{F}$ can be defined geometrically the vector field with the following properties
- The direction of curl $\vec{F}$ $(x, y, z)$ is the direction $\vec{n}$ for which $\operatorname{circ}_{\vec{n}} (x, y, z)$ is the greatest.
- The magnitude of curl $\vec{F}$ $(x, y, z)$ is the circulation density of $\vec{F}$ around that direction.

If the circulation density is zero around every direction, then we define the curl to be $\vec{0}$.
   curl $\vec{F}$ is also defined by the following formula: If $\vec{F} = F_1\vec{i} + F_2\vec{j} + F_3\vec{k}$ , then

$$\operatorname{curl} \vec{F} = \left( \frac{\partial F_3}{\partial y} - \frac{\partial F_2}{\partial z} \right)\vec{i} + \left( \frac{\partial F_1}{\partial z} - \frac{\partial F_3}{\partial x} \right)\vec{j} + \left( \frac{\partial F_2}{\partial x} - \frac{\partial F_1}{\partial y} \right)\vec{k} .$$

728

(c)

$$\operatorname{curl}(-y\vec{i} + x\vec{j} + (z^2 + y^2 + x^2)\vec{k}) = \begin{vmatrix} \vec{i} & \vec{j} & \vec{k} \\ \frac{\partial}{\partial x} & \frac{\partial}{\partial y} & \frac{\partial}{\partial z} \\ -y & x & z^2 + y^2 + x^2 \end{vmatrix} = 2y\vec{i} - 2x\vec{j} + 2\vec{k}$$

3. The vector fields in Figures 20.3.50–20.3.52 each show a vector field of the form $\vec{F} = F_1\vec{i} + F_2\vec{j}$. Assume $F_1$ and $F_2$ depend only on $x$ and $y$ and not on $z$. For each vector field, circle the best answers. No reasons need be given.

(a)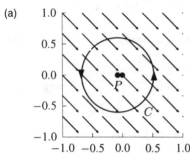

Figure 20.3.50:

(b)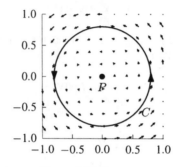

Figure 20.3.51:

(c)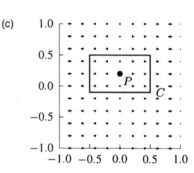

Figure 20.3.52:

(i)  $\int_C \vec{F} \cdot d\vec{r}$ is
    positive             negative             zero

(ii) div $\vec{F}$ at $P$ is
    positive             negative             zero

(iii) curl $\vec{F}$ at $P$ has a
    positive $z$ component     negative $z$ component     zero $z$ component

(iv) $\vec{F}$
    could be a gradient field         could not be a gradient field

ANSWER:

(a)  (i)   Zero
    (ii)  Zero
    (iii)  Zero
    (iv)  Could

(b)  (i)   Positive
    (ii)  Zero
    (iii)  Positive
    (iv)  Could not

(c)  (i)   Zero
    (ii)  Positive
    (iii)  Zero
    (iv)  Could

4. (a) Describe the vector field in 2-space

$$\vec{F}(x,y) = -y\vec{i} + x\vec{j}.$$

Your description should include a diagram.

(b) Now let's consider the vector field in 3-space

$$\vec{G}(x,y,z) = -y\vec{i} + x\vec{j} + xyz\vec{k}.$$

Note that on the $xy$-plane, i.e., when $z = 0$, this vector field looks like $\vec{F}$, since $\vec{G}(x,y,0) = -y\vec{i} + x\vec{j}$. Does knowing this tell you anything about curl $\vec{G}(x,y,0)$? If so, what? If not, why not?

(c)   Same question for div $\vec{G}(x, y, 0)$; does knowing that on the $xy$-plane $\vec{G}$ looks like $\vec{F}$ tell you anything about div $\vec{G}(x, y, 0)$? If so, what? If not, why not?

(d)   Compute curl $\vec{G}$ and div $\vec{G}$. Does your answer agree with what you said in (b) and (c)?

ANSWER:

(a)   The vector $\vec{V} = -y\vec{i} + x\vec{j}$ in the field has magnitude of $\sqrt{x^2 + y^2}$ and points perpendicularly to the position vector $\vec{r}$, i.e. it points in the direction of a circle around the origin counterclockwise. See Figure 20.3.53.

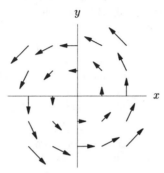

*Figure 20.3.53:*

(b)   The vector field of $\vec{F}$ definitely looks like it is swirling, so we expect a non-zero curl for curl $\vec{G}(x, y, 0)$. By the right hand rule, the direction of the curl will be along the positive $y$-axis, so the $y$-component of the curl will be positive.

(c)   For $\vec{F} = -y\vec{i} + x\vec{j}$. div $\vec{F} = \frac{\partial F_1}{\partial x} + \frac{\partial F_2}{\partial y} = 0$. But there is not enough information to know about div $\vec{G}(x, y, 0)$.

(d)

$$\text{curl}\,\vec{G} = \begin{vmatrix} \vec{i} & \vec{j} & \vec{k} \\ \frac{\partial}{\partial x} & \frac{\partial}{\partial y} & \frac{\partial}{\partial z} \\ -y & x & xyz \end{vmatrix} = xz\vec{i} - yz\vec{j} + 2\vec{k}.$$

So curl $\vec{G}(x, y, 0) = 2\vec{k}$, agrees with (b). div $\vec{G} = \frac{\partial F_1}{\partial x} + \frac{\partial F_2}{\partial y} + \frac{\partial F_3}{\partial z} = xy$. So, div $\vec{G}(x, y, 0) = xy \neq$ div $\vec{F}$, agrees with (c).

## Problems and Solutions for Section 20.4

1.   If curl $\vec{F}$ is parallel to the $x$-axis for all $x$, $y$, and $z$ and if $C$ is a circle in the $xy$-plane, then the circulation of $\vec{F}$ around $C$ is zero. True or false?

ANSWER:

True, because by Stoke's Theorem $\int_C \vec{F}\, dr = \int_S \text{curl}\,\vec{F} \cdot d\vec{A}$, where $S$ is the disc in the $x - y$ plane bounded by $C$. Since curl $\vec{F}$ is parallel to this disc, $\int_S \text{curl}\,\vec{F} \cdot d\vec{A} = 0$.

2.   Suppose $W$ is the object consisting of two solid cylinders meeting at right angles at the origin. One cylinder is centered on the $y-$axis, between $y = -5$ and $y = 5$ with radius 2 and the other is centered on the $x-$axis between $x = -5$ and $x = 5$ with radius 2. Let $S$ be the whole surface of $W$ except for the circular end of the cylinder centered at $(0, 5, 0)$. The boundary of $S$ is a circle, $C$; the surface $S$ is oriented outward. Let $\vec{F} = (3x^2 + 3z^2)\vec{j}$. You are also told that $\vec{F} = \text{curl}(z^3\vec{i} + y^3\vec{j} - x^3\vec{k})$.

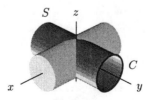

*Figure 20.4.54*

(a) Suppose you want to calculate $\int_S \vec{F} \cdot d\vec{A}$. Write down two other integrals which have the same value as $\int_S \vec{F} \cdot d\vec{A}$. Justify your answer.

(b) Find $\int_S \vec{F} \cdot d\vec{A}$ whatever by method is easiest.

ANSWER:

(a) Since $\vec{F}$ is a curl field, its divergence is zero. Thus its flux out of the boundary of $W$ is zero, by the Divergence Theorem. The boundary of $W$ consists of $S$ and the flat disk perpendicular to the $y$-axis through $(0, 5, 0)$ with radius of 2, oriented in the direction of the positive $y$-axis. Call this disk $D$. Then

$$\int_S \vec{F} \cdot d\vec{A} = -\int_D \vec{F} \cdot d\vec{A}.$$

We can also evaluate the integral using Stokes' Theorem: Since $\vec{F} = \text{curl}(z^3\vec{i} + y^3\vec{j} - x^3\vec{k})$,

$$\int_S \vec{F} \cdot d\vec{A} = \int_C (z^3\vec{i} + y^3\vec{j} - x^3\vec{k}) \cdot d\vec{r}$$

where $C$ is the boundary of $S$, which is the circle of radius 2, centered at $(0, 5, 0)$, lying in the plane perpendicular to the $y$-axis, and oriented clockwise when viewed from far out on the positive $y$-axis.

(b)

$$\int_D \vec{F} \cdot d\vec{A} = \int (3x^2 + 3z^2)\vec{j} \cdot (-\vec{j}\, dxdz)$$

$$= -3 \int_0^{2\pi} \int_0^2 r^2 r\, drd\theta$$

$$= (-3)(2)\pi \frac{r^4}{4}\Big|_0^2$$

$$= -24\pi.$$

# PART VII

# SAMPLE
# GATEWAY TESTS

**Differentiation Gateway Test I**

Name: _____

Instructor: _____

**Differentiate, assuming $a$ is a constant.**

1. $f(x) = (1 + 2x + x^3)^{1/2}$        _____

2. $y = \dfrac{2t}{1 + t^2}$        _____

3. $g(t) = at(a + t)^4$        _____

4. $\sin(2\theta + 5)$        _____

5. $\left(y + \frac{1}{y}\right)^5$        _____

6. $e^{z^2 + z}$        _____

7. $\ln(x \cos x)$        _____

8. $\tan(5 - t^2)$        _____

9. $\dfrac{y - 5}{5 - y^2}$        _____

10. Find $y'$: $e^{x+y} + x - y^2 = 3$        _____

## Solutions to Differentiation Gateway Test I

1. $f'(x) = \dfrac{1}{2}(1 + 2x + x^3)^{-1/2} \cdot (2 + 3x^2) = \dfrac{2 + 3x^2}{2\sqrt{1 + 2x + x^3}}$

2. $y' = \dfrac{(1 + t^2)(2) - (2t)(2t)}{(1 + t^2)^2} = \dfrac{2(1 - t^2)}{(1 + t^2)^2}$

3. $g'(t) = at \cdot (4(a + t)^3) + a(a + t)^4 = 4at(a + t)^3 + a(a + t)^4 = (a^2 + 5at)(a + t)^3$

4. $\dfrac{d(\sin(2\theta + 5))}{d\theta} = \cos(2\theta + 5) \cdot 2 = 2\cos(2\theta + 5)$

5. $5\left(y + \dfrac{1}{y}\right)^4 \cdot \left(1 - \dfrac{1}{y^2}\right)$

6. $e^{z^2 + z} \cdot (2z + 1)$

7. $\dfrac{1}{x\cos x} \cdot (1 \cdot \cos x - x \cdot \sin x) = \dfrac{\cos x - x\sin x}{x\cos x}$

8. $\dfrac{1}{\cos^2(5 - t^2)} \cdot (-2t) = \dfrac{-2t}{\cos^2(5 - t^2)}$

9. $\dfrac{(5 - y^2)(1) - (y - 5)(-2y)}{(5 - y^2)^2} = \dfrac{y^2 - 10y + 5}{(5 - y^2)^2}$

10.

$$e^{x+y} + x - y^2 = 3$$
$$e^{x+y} \cdot (1 + y') + 1 - 2y \cdot y' = 0$$
$$y' \cdot (e^{x+y} - 2y) = -e^{x+y} - 1$$
$$y' = \dfrac{-e^{x+y} - 1}{e^{x+y} - 2y} = \dfrac{e^{x+y} + 1}{2y - e^{x+y}}$$

**Differentiation Gateway Test II**

Name: _____

Instructor: _____

**Differentiate, assuming $a$ is constant.**

1.  $y = \tan(t^2)$                                 _____

2.  $f(x) = \dfrac{1}{\sqrt{x^2 + a^2}}$            _____

3.  $g(t) = t^2 e^{t^3}$                             _____

4.  $\sqrt{t}\cos t$                                _____

5.  $\ln(\sqrt{t})$                                 _____

6.  $\dfrac{x + \sin x}{x - 1}$                     _____

7.  $e^{\sin(2t)}$                                  _____

8.  $\sqrt{5 - t^7}$                                _____

9.  $\dfrac{x^2 + 5ax + a^2}{x}$                    _____

10. Find $y'$ : $\sin(xy) + y^2 x = 5$              _____

## Solutions to Differentiation Gateway Test II

1. $y' = \dfrac{1}{\cos^2(t^2)} \cdot (2t) = \dfrac{2t}{\cos^2(t^2)}$

2. $f'(x) = -\dfrac{1}{2}\left(x^2 + a^2\right)^{-3/2} \cdot (2x) = \dfrac{-x}{(x^2 + a^2)^{3/2}}$

3. $g'(t) = t^2(3t^2 e^{t^3}) + 2te^{t^3} = (3t^4 + 2t)e^{t^3}$

4. $\sqrt{t}(-\sin t) + \dfrac{1}{2\sqrt{t}}(\cos t) = \dfrac{\cos t}{2\sqrt{t}} - \sqrt{t}\sin t$

5. $\dfrac{1}{\sqrt{t}} \cdot \dfrac{1}{2\sqrt{t}} = \dfrac{1}{2t}$

6. $\dfrac{(x-1)(1+\cos x) - (x+\sin x)(1)}{(x-1)^2} = \dfrac{x\cos x - \cos x - \sin x - 1}{(x-1)^2}$

7. $e^{\sin(2t)} \cdot (\cos(2t)(2)) = 2\cos(2t)e^{\sin(2t)}$

8. $\dfrac{1}{2}(5 - t^7)^{-1/2} \cdot (-7t^6) = \dfrac{-7t^6}{2\sqrt{5 - t^7}}$

9. $1 + \dfrac{-1 \cdot a^2}{x^2} = 1 - \dfrac{a^2}{x^2}$

10.

$$\sin(xy) + y^2 x = 5$$
$$\cos(xy) \cdot (y + x \cdot y') + (y^2 + 2xy \cdot y') = 0$$
$$y\cos(xy) + x\cos(xy) \cdot y' + y^2 + 2xy \cdot y' = 0$$
$$y' \cdot (x\cos(xy) + 2xy) = -y^2 - y\cos(xy)$$
$$y' = -\dfrac{y^2 + y\cos(xy)}{x\cos(xy) + 2xy}$$

**Differentiation Gateway Test III**

Name: _____

Instructor: _____

**Differentiate, assuming $a$ is a constant.**

1.  $\cos^2 t$        _____

2.  $x\sqrt{1 - 5x^2}$        _____

3.  $\dfrac{y + 5}{y + 8}$        _____

4.  $e^x + x^e$        _____

5.  $x \sin(x + 5)$        _____

6.  $\dfrac{x}{\sqrt{x + a}}$        _____

7.  $\ln(5t^2 + 3t)$        _____

8.  $e^{-(x-20)^2/(2a^2)}$        _____

9.  $\sin(\sin(\theta + 5))$        _____

10.  Find $y'$ : $x^3 + 3xy^2 + y^3 = a^3$        _____

## Solutions to Differentiation Gateway Test III

1. $2\cos t \cdot (-\sin t) = -2\cos t \sin t$

2. $x \cdot \dfrac{1}{2}(1 - 5x^2)^{-1/2}(-10x) + \sqrt{1 - 5x^2} = \dfrac{-5x^2}{\sqrt{1 - 5x^2}} + \sqrt{1 - 5x^2}$

3. $\dfrac{(y + 8)(1) - (y + 5)(1)}{(y + 8)^2} = \dfrac{3}{(y + 8)^2}$

4. $e^x + exe^{-1}$

5. $x(\cos(x + 5)) + \sin(x + 5)$

6. $\dfrac{\sqrt{x + a} - x(1/2)(x + a)^{-1/2}}{(\sqrt{x + a})^2} = \dfrac{\frac{2x + 2a - x}{\sqrt{x+a}}}{x + a} = \dfrac{x + 2a}{(x + a)^{3/2}}$

7. $\dfrac{1}{5t^2 + 3t} \cdot (10t + 3) = \dfrac{10t + 3}{5t^2 + 3t}$

8. $e^{-(x-20)^2/(2a^2)} \cdot \left(\dfrac{-2}{2a^2}(x - 20)\right) = e^{-(x-20)^2/(2a^2)} \cdot -\dfrac{(x - 20)}{a^2}$

9. $\cos(\sin(\theta + 5)) \cdot \cos(\theta + 5)$

10. 

$$x^3 + 3xy^2 + y^3 = a^3$$
$$3x^2 + 3y^2 + 6xy \cdot y' + 3y^2 \cdot y' = 0$$
$$y' \cdot (6xy + 3y^2) = -3x^2 - 3y^2$$
$$y' = -\dfrac{x^2 + y^2}{2xy + y^2}$$

**Differentiation Gateway Test IV**

Name: _____

Instructor: _____

**Differentiate, assuming $a$ is a constant.**

1. $\sin(x + a\cos x)$ _____

2. $x(5 + x^2)^5$ _____

3. $\dfrac{\sin\theta + \cos\theta}{(\theta + 1)^2}$ _____

4. $\ln(\ln(2 - y))$ _____

5. $\sqrt{t + e^{\sin t}}$ _____

6. $\sqrt{x + 1}\left(5 - \dfrac{1}{\sqrt{x + 1}}\right)$ _____

7. $(\pi x)^e$ _____

8. $\dfrac{(x - 1)^{-1}}{\sqrt{x - 1}}$ _____

9. $\ln(\tan x)$ _____

10. Find $dy/dx$: $\quad a^{xy} + \ln(xy) = xy$ _____

## Solutions to Differentiation Gateway Test IV

1. $\cos(x + a\cos x) \cdot (1 - a\sin x)$

2. $(5 + x^2)^5 + 5x(5 + x^2)^4 \cdot (2x)$

3. $\dfrac{(\theta + 1)^2 \cdot (\cos\theta - \sin\theta) - (\sin\theta + \cos\theta)(2)(\theta + 1)}{(\theta + 1)^4}$

4. $\dfrac{1}{\ln(2 - y)} \cdot \dfrac{1}{2 - y} \cdot (-1) = -\dfrac{1}{(2 - y)\ln(2 - y)}$

5. $\dfrac{1}{2\sqrt{t + e^{\sin t}}} \cdot (1 + \cos t\, e^{\sin t}) = \dfrac{1 + (\cos t)e^{\sin t}}{2\sqrt{t + e^{\sin t}}}$

6. $\dfrac{5}{2\sqrt{x + 1}}$

7. $e\pi(\pi x)^{e - 1}$

8. $\dfrac{(x - 1)^{-1}}{\sqrt{x - 1}} = (x - 1)^{-\frac{3}{2}}$. Hence,

$$\frac{d}{dx}\left((x - 1)^{-\frac{3}{2}}\right) = -\frac{3}{2}(x - 1)^{-\frac{5}{2}}$$

9. $\dfrac{1}{\tan x} \cdot \dfrac{1}{\cos^2 x} = \dfrac{1}{\sin x \cos x}$

10.

$$a^{xy} + \ln(xy) = xy$$

$$a^{xy}\ln a \cdot \left(y + x\frac{dy}{dx}\right) + \frac{1}{xy} \cdot \left(y + x\frac{dy}{dx}\right) = y + x\frac{dy}{dx}$$

$$\left(y + x\frac{dy}{dx}\right) \cdot \left(a^{xy}\ln a + \frac{1}{xy} - 1\right) = 0$$

$$x\frac{dy}{dx} \cdot \left(a^{xy}\ln a + \frac{1}{xy} - 1\right) = -y \cdot \left(a^{xy}\ln a + \frac{1}{xy} - 1\right)$$

$$x\frac{dy}{dx} = -y$$

$$\frac{dy}{dx} = -\frac{y}{x}$$

**Differentiation Gateway Test V**

Name: _____

Instructor: _____

**Differentiate, assuming $a$ is a constant.**

1. $y = 5x - \dfrac{1}{2\sqrt{x}} + x^2\sqrt{x}$      _____

2. $f(t) = t\sin(5 - t)$      _____

3. $y = e^{-(a+x^2)}$      _____

4. $f(\theta) = \sqrt{\tan(a\theta + 5)}$      _____

5. $f(t) = \dfrac{t^2 + 5ta + a^2}{\sqrt{t}}$      _____

6. $y = \cos(z\sin z)$      _____

7. $g(y) = \big(\ln(2y)\big)^2$      _____

8. Find $\dfrac{dy}{dx}$ if $\dfrac{\sin(xy)}{2x - 3y} = y$.      _____

9. $g(x) = \dfrac{1}{\cos^2(x^2)}$      _____

10. $p(t) = et^{0.9} + e^2 t^{0.2} + e^3 t^{\sqrt{2}}$      _____

## Solutions to Differentiation Gateway Test V

1. $y' = 5 + \dfrac{1}{4}x^{-3/2} + \dfrac{5}{2}x^{3/2}$

2. $f'(t) = t\cos(5 - t)(-1) + \sin(5 - t) = \sin(5 - t) - t\cos(5 - t)$

3. $y' = -2xe^{-(a+x^2)}$

4. $f'(\theta) = \dfrac{1}{2\sqrt{\tan(a\theta + 5)}} \cdot \dfrac{1}{\cos^2(a\theta + 5)} \cdot (a)$

5. Dividing through by $\sqrt{t}$ yields $f'(t) = \dfrac{3}{2}t^{1/2}\dfrac{5a}{2}t^{-1/2} - \dfrac{a^2}{2}t^{-3/2}$

6. $y' = -\sin(z\sin z) \cdot (\sin z + z\cos z)$

7. $g'(y) = 2(\ln(2y))\left(\dfrac{1}{2y}\right)(2) = \dfrac{2\ln(2y)}{y}$

8. Multiplying by $2x - 3y$ gives

$$\frac{\sin(xy)}{2x - 3y} = y$$
$$\sin(xy) = 2xy - 3y^2.$$

Differentiating yields

$$\cos(xy)\left(y + x\frac{dy}{dx}\right) = 2y + 2x\frac{dy}{dx} - 6y\frac{dy}{dx}$$

$$y\cos(xy) - 2y = \left(2x - 6y - x\cos(xy)\right)\left(\frac{dy}{dx}\right)$$

$$\frac{dy}{dx} = \frac{y\cos(xy) - 2y}{2x - 6y - x\cos(xy)} = \frac{2y - y\cos(xy)}{x\cos(xy) + 6y - 2x}$$

9. $g'(x) = -2\dfrac{1}{\cos^3(x^2)} \cdot - \sin(x^2)(2x) = 4x\sec^2(x^2)\tan(x^2)$

10. $p'(t) = 0.9et^{-0.1} + 0.2e^2t^{-0.8} + \sqrt{2}e^3t^{\sqrt{2}-1}$

**Differentiation Gateway Test VI**

Name: _____

Instructor: _____

**Differentiate, assuming $a$ and $b$ are constants.**

1. $g(x) = \dfrac{x^2 - 1}{(x - 1)^2}$  _____

2. $h(x) = (2x - 1)\sqrt{1 - 5x^2}$  _____

3. $l(\theta) = \ln(\sin^2 \theta)$  _____

4. $h(y) = 2^{y^2 - 1}$  _____

5. $f(x) = xe^{1/x}$  _____

6. $p(t) = \ln(\sin t^2)$  _____

7. $i(x) = \dfrac{a + bx}{a - bx}$  _____

8. $e(x) = 1 + x + \dfrac{x^2}{2} + \dfrac{x^3}{6} + \dfrac{x^4}{24} + \dfrac{x^5}{120} + \dfrac{x^6}{720}$  _____

9. $p(q) = q^\pi + q^e + q^{\sqrt{2}} + \dfrac{q}{q + 1}$  _____

10. Find $dy/dx$:  $x^2 y^2 + xy = e^{xy}$  _____

## Solutions to Differentiation Gateway Test VI

1. $g(x) = \dfrac{x^2 - 1}{(x-1)^2} = \dfrac{x+1}{x-1}$, so $g'(x) = -\dfrac{2}{(x-1)^2}$

2. $h'(x) = (2)\left(\sqrt{1-5x^2}\right) + (2x-1)\left(\dfrac{1}{2\sqrt{1-5x^2}} \cdot (-10x)\right) = 2\sqrt{1-5x^2} + \dfrac{5x - 10x^2}{\sqrt{1-5x^2}}.$

3. $l'(\theta) = \dfrac{1}{\sin^2\theta}(2\sin\theta\cos\theta) = \dfrac{2\cos\theta}{\sin\theta}$

4. $h'(y) = (\ln 2)2^{y^2-1}(2y) = (2y\ln 2)2^{y^2-1}$

5. $f'(x) = x\left(-\dfrac{1}{x^2}e^{1/x}\right) + e^{1/x} = e^{1/x} - \dfrac{e^{1/x}}{x}$

6. $p'(t) = \dfrac{1}{\sin t^2}(\cos t^2)(2t) = 2t\dfrac{\cos t^2}{\sin t^2}$

7. $i'(x) = \dfrac{b(a-bx) - (-b)(a+bx)}{(a-bx)^2} = \dfrac{2ab}{(a-bx)^2}$

8. $e'(x) = 1 + x + \dfrac{x^2}{2} + \dfrac{x^3}{6} + \dfrac{x^4}{24} + \dfrac{x^5}{120}$

9. $p'(q) = \pi q^{\pi-1} + eq^{e-1} + \sqrt{2}q^{\sqrt{2}-1} + \dfrac{1}{(q+1)^2}$

10. Differentiating implicitly gives

$$x^2y^2 + xy = e^{xy}$$

$$x^2(2y)\dfrac{dy}{dx} + 2xy^2 + x\dfrac{dy}{dx} + y = e^{xy}\left(x\dfrac{dy}{dx} + y\right)$$

$$\dfrac{dy}{dx}\left(2x^2y + x - xe^{xy}\right) = -2xy^2 - y + ye^{xy}$$

$$\dfrac{dy}{dx} = \dfrac{ye^{xy} - 2xy^2 - y}{-xe^{xy} + 2x^2y + x}$$

**Integration Gateway Test I**

Name: _____

Instructor: _____

**Find the following integrals. Assume $a$ is a constant.**

1. $\displaystyle \int \left( x^2 + \frac{1}{x^2} - \frac{1}{\sqrt{x}} \right) dx$ _____

2. $\displaystyle \int \left( \sin t - \frac{\cos t}{2} \right) dt$ _____

3. $\displaystyle \int \left( e^x - \frac{1}{x} \right) dx$ _____

4. $\displaystyle \int 3(x+1)^2 \, dx$ _____

5. $\displaystyle \int \sqrt{x}(x+a) \, dx$ _____

6. $\displaystyle \int \frac{y^2 + 1/y}{y} \, dy$ _____

7. $\displaystyle \int \sin(\theta + 2) \, d\theta$ _____

8. $\displaystyle \int a e^{(x+1)} \, dx$ _____

9. $\displaystyle \int \frac{dx}{x^2 + 1}$ _____

10. $\displaystyle \int \frac{dt}{\sqrt{1 - t^2}}$ _____